PARTICLE SIZE MEASUREMENT

POWDER TECHNOLOGY
SERIES

Edited by
B. SCARLETT
Department of Chemical Engineering
Loughborough University of Technology

Particle Size Measurement

TERENCE ALLEN Ph.D.

Senior Lecturer in Powder Technology
University of Bradford

LONDON
CHAPMAN AND HALL

First published 1968
Second edition 1975
published by Chapman and Hall Ltd
11 *New Fetter Lane, London EC4P 4EE*
Typeset by E.W.C. Wilkins Ltd., London and Northampton
and printed in Great Britain by
Lowe & Brydone Printers Limited,
Thetford, Norfolk

Reprinted 1977

ISBN 0 412 13490 X

Library of Congress Catalog Card Number 74-13830

Distributed in the U.S.A. by Halsted Press, a Division
of John Wiley & Sons, Inc., New York

Contents

			Page	
Foreword to the First Edition			*Page*	xiv
Preface to the First Edition				xv
Preface to the Second Edition				xvii
Acknowledgments				xviii

1 Sampling of powders   1

1.1 Introduction   1
1.2 Golden rules of sampling   1
1.3 Bulk sampling   2
1.4 Sampling from a moving stream of powder   2
1.5 Sampling from a conveyer belt or chute   10
1.6 Sampling from a bucket conveyor   10
1.7 Sampling from wagons and containers   12
1.8 Sampling from heaps   12
1.9 Sample dividing   13
    1.9.1 *Coning and quartering*   15
    1.9.2 *Table sampling*   15
    1.9.3 *Chute splitting*   16
    1.9.4 *Spinning riffling*   18
    1.9.5 *Scoop sampling*   18
    1.9.6 *Miscellaneous devices*   19
1.10 Reduction from laboratory sample to analysis sample   22
1.11 Reduction from analysis sample to measurement sample   25
1.12 Testing sampling devices   25
    1.12.1 *Experimental tests of laboratory sample-splitting techniques*   27

2 Sampling of dusty gases in gas streams   31

2.1 Introduction   31
2.2 Basic procedure   32
    2.2.1 *Sampling positions*   33
    2.2.2 *Temperature and velocity survey*   34
    2.2.3 *Sampling points*   35

2.3 Sampling equipment   37
  2.3.1 *Nozzles*   37
  2.3.2 *Dust sampling collector*   37
  2.3.3 *Ancillary apparatus*   42
  2.3.4 *On-line dust extractions*   42
  2.3.5 *The Anderson stack sampler*   44
2.4 Corrections for anisokinetic sampling   45
  2.4.1 *Theory*   47
2.5 Other techniques   50

3 **Sampling and sizing from the atmosphere**   55
3.1 Introduction   55
3.2 Inertial techniques   56
3.3 Filtration   61
3.4 Electrostatic precipitation   61
3.5 Thermal precipitation   62
3.6 Light scattering   66
3.7 Miscellaneous techniques   67

4 **Particle size, shape and distribution**   74
4.1 Particle size   74
4.2 Particle shape   76
  4.2.1 *Shape factors*   77
4.3 Average diameters   85
4.4 Methods of presenting size analysis data   90
4.5 Devices for representing the cumulative distribution curve as a
    straight line   93
  4.5.1 *Arithmetic normal distributions*   93
  4.5.2 *The log-normal distributions*   95
  4.5.3 *The Rosin-Rammler distribution*   98
  4.5.4 *Mean particle sizes and specific surface evaluation for*
        Rosin-Rammler distributions   98
  4.5.5 *Evaluation of non-linear distributions on log-normal paper* 99
  4.5.6 *Evaluation of shape factors from parallel log-normal curves* 106
4.6 The law of compensating errors   106
Appendix   107
4.7 Manipulation of log-probability equation   107
4.8 Phi-notations   110

5 **Sieving**   113
5.1 Introduction   113
5.2 Types of sieves   113
5.3 British standard specifications   113
5.4 Methods for the use of fine mesh sieves   115

5.5 Sieving errors   115
5.6 Electroformed micromesh sieves   120
5.7 Wet sieving   121
5.8 Air-jet sieving   122
5.9 Felvation   123
5.10 The sonic sifter   124
5.11 Calibration of sieves   124
5.12 Conclusion   125

6 **Microscopy**   128
6.1 Introduction   128
6.2 Optical microscopy   128
6.2.1 *Preparation of slides*   129
6.3 Particle size   131
6.4 Transmission electron microscopy   132
6.4.1 *Specimen preparation*   132
6.4.2 *Replica and shadowing techniques*   135
6.4.3 *Chemical analysis*   135
6.5 Scanning electron microscopy   136
6.6 Manual methods of sizing particles   136
6.6.1 *Graticules*   137
6.6.2 *Training of operators*   139
6.7 Semi-automatic aids to microscopy   140
6.8 Automatic counting and sizing   146
6.9 Quantitative image analysers   148
6.10 Specimen improvement techniques   148
6.11 Statistical considerations governing the determination of size
       distributions by microscope count   148
6.12 Conclusion   150

7 **Interaction between particles and fluids in a gravitational field**   154
7.1 Introduction   154
7.2 Relationship between drag coefficient and Reynolds' number
       for a sphere settling in a liquid   155
7.3 The laminar flow region   157
7.4 Critical diameter for laminar flow settling   157
7.5 Particle acceleration   158
7.6 Errors due to the finite extent of the fluid   159
7.7 Errors due to the discontinuity of the fluid   160
7.8 Brownian motion   162
7.9 Viscosity of a suspension   163
7.10 Calculation of terminal velocities in the transition region   163
7.11 Turbulent flow region   167
7.12 Non-rigid spheres   168

7.13 Non-spherical particles   168
    7.13.1 *Stokes' region*   168
    7.13.2 *Transition region*   171
7.14 Concentration effects   172
7.15 Hindered settling   176

8 Dispersion of powders   178
8.1 Discussion   178
8.2 Density determination   183
8.3 Viscosity   183
8.4 Sedimentation systems   184
    Table 8.1 *List of wetting and dispersing agents*   184
    Table 8.2 *Dispersing solutions for powders*   185
8.5 Densities and viscosities of some aqueous solutions   189

9 Incremental methods of sedimentation size analysis   191
9.1 Basic theory   191
    9.1.1 *Variation in concentration within a settling suspension*   191
    9.1.2 *Relationship between density gradient and concentration*   192
9.2 Resolution for incremental methods   193
9.3 The pipette method   193
    9.3.1 *Experimental errors*   197
9.4 The photosedimentation technique   200
    9.4.1 *Introduction*   200
    9.4.2 *Theory*   201
    9.4.3 *The extinction coefficient*   202
    9.4.4 *Photosedimentometers*   203
    9.4.5 *Discussion*   206
9.5 X-ray sedimentation   206
9.6 Hydrometers   210
9.7 Divers   212
9.8 The specific gravity balance   214
9.9 Appendix: worked examples   214
    9.9.1 *Wide-angle scanning photosedimentometer*   214
    9.9.2 *Conversion from surface distribution to weight distribution*   216
    9.9.3 *The Ladal X-ray sedimentometer*   218

10 Cumulative methods of sedimentation size analysis   221
10.1 Introduction   221
10.2 Two-layer methods   221
10.3 Homogeneous suspensions (theory)   222
10.4 Sedimentation balances   223
    10.4.1 *The micromerograph*   230
10.5 Sedimentation columns   232

10.6 Manometric methods   235
10.7 Pressure on the walls of the sedimentation tube   235
10.8 Decanting   236
10.9 The β-back scattering method   237
10.10 Discussion   240
10.11 Appendix   241

11 **Fluid classification**   247
11.1 Introduction   247
11.2 Assessment of classification efficiency   247
11.3 Systems   250
11.4 Counterflow equilibrium classifiers in the gravitational field —
        elutriators   250
    11.4.1 *Water elutriators*   254
    11.4.2 *Air elutriators*   256
11.5 Counterflow equilibrium classifiers in the centrifugal field 260

12 **Centrifugal methods**   265
12.1 Introduction   265
12.2 Stokes' diameter determination   266
12.3 Two-layer technique   266
    12.3.1 *Theory*   266
    12.3.2 *Two-layer technique using a photometric method of
            analysis*   267
    12.3.3 *Early instruments: the Marshall centrifuge and the M.S.A.
            particle size analyser*   268
    12.3.4 *The photocentrifuge*   270
    12.3.5 *The Joyce-Loebl disc centrifuge*   273
12.4 Homogeneous suspension   273
    12.4.1 *Sedimentation height small compared with distance from
            centrifuge axis*   273
12.5 Cumulative sedimentation theory for a homogeneous suspension 274
12.6 Variable time method (variation of P with t)   275
12.7 Variable inner radius (variation of P with S)   275
12.8 Shape of centrifuge tubes   276
12.9 Alternative theory (variation of P with S)   277
12.10 Variable outer radius (variation of P with S)   278
12.11 Incremental analysis with a homogeneous suspension   279
    12.11.1 *The Simcar centrifuge*   279
    12.11.2 *General theory*   279
    12.11.3 *The Ladal X-ray centrifuge*   283
    12.11.4 *The modified pipette withdrawal centrifuge*   286
    12.11.5 *Theory for the modified pipette withdrawal centrifuge* 286

12.12 The Super centrifuge 289
12.13 The Ultracentrifuge 290
12.14 Conclusion 291
12.15 **Appendix** Worked example 293
    (1) *Simcar centrifuge* 293
    (2) *X-ray centrifuge* 295
    (3) *Modified pipette centrifuge* 296

13 **The electrical sensing zone method of particle size distribution determinative (the Coulter principle)** 301
    13.1 Introduction 301
    13.2 Operation 301
    13.3 Calibration 302
    13.4 Evaluation of results 304
    13.5 Theory 305
    13.6 Effect of particle shape and orientation 306
    13.7 Coincidence correction 307
    13.8 Pulse shape 309
    13.9 End-point determination 310
    13.10 Commercial equipment 311
    13.11 Conclusion 312

14 **Radiation scattering methods of particle size determination** 314
    14.1 Introduction 314
    14.2 Scattered Radiation 318
    14.14.2.1 *The Rayleigh region* $(D \ll \lambda)$ 318
      14.2.2 *The Rayleigh-Gans region* $(D < \lambda)$ 318
    14.3 State of polarization of the scattered radiation 320
    14.4 Turbidity measurement 321
    14.5 High-order Tyndall spectra (HOTS) 323
    14.6 Light-scattering equipment 324

15 **Permeametry and gas diffusion** 328
    15.1 Flow of a viscous fluid through a packed bed of powder 328
    15.2 The aspect factor, k 330
    15.3 Alternative derivation of Kozeny's equation using equivalent capillaries 331
    15.4 Other flow equations 332
    15.5 Experimental applications 333
    15.6 Preparation of powder bed 333
    15.7 Constant pressure permeameters 333
    15.8 Constant volume permeameter 337
    15.9 Fine particles 340

15.10 Types of flow 341
15.11 Transitional region between viscous and molecular flow 342
15.12 Experimental techniques for determining Z_1 343
15.13 Calculation of permeability surface 344
15.14 Diffusional flow for surface area measurement 344
15.15 The relationship between diffusion constant and specific
    surface 345
15.16 Transient-state flow 346
15.17 Steady-state flow 348
15.18 The liquid phase permeameter 350
15.19 Application to hindered settling 353

16 Gas adsorption 355
16.1 Introduction 355
16.2 Theories of adsorption 356
    16.2.1 *Langmuir's isotherm for ideal localized monolayers* 356
    16.2.2 *BET isotherm for multilayer adsorption* 358
    16.2.3 *The three-parameter BET equation* 361
    16.2.4 *Discussion of the BET theory* 362
    16.2.5 *Shape of isotherms* 364
    16.2.6 *Modification of the BET equation* 364
    16.2.7 *The relative method of Harkins and Jura* 365
    16.2.8 *Comparison between BET and Harkins and Jura methods* 366
    16.2.9 *The t-curve method* 366
    16.2.10 *Kiselev's equation* 369
16.3 Experimental techniques — factors affecting adsorption 370
    16.3.1 *Degassing* 370
    16.3.2 *Pressure* 371
    16.3.3 *Temperature and time* 371
    16.3.4 *Adsorbate gas and surface area* 371
16.4 Experimental techniques — volumetric methods 372
    16.4.1 *Principle* 372
    16.4.2 *Volumetric apparatus for high surface areas* 372
    16.4.3 *Volumetric apparatus for low surface areas* 373
16.5 Experimental technique — gravimetric methods 375
    16.5.1 *Principle* 375
    16.5.2 *Single — spring balances* 375
    16.5.3 *Multiple -spring balances* 376
    16.5.4 *Beam balances* 376
16.6 Continuous-flow gas chromatographic methods 377
    16.6.1 *Commercially available continuous-flow-type apparatus* 382
16.7 Standard volumetric gas adsorption apparatus 383
    16.7.1 *Worked example* 384
16.8 Commercially available volumetric and gravimetric-type
    apparatus 386

17 Other methods for determining surface area 394
17.1 Introduction 394
17.2 Calculation from size distribution data 395
17.3 Adsorption from solution 396
    17.3.1 *Orientation of molecules at the solid – liquid interface* 396
    17.3.2 *Polarity of organic liquids and adsorbents* 397
    17.3.3 *Drying of organic liquids and adsorbents* 399
17.4 Methods of analysis of amount of solute adsorbed on solid
    surfaces 399
    17.4.1 *Langmuir trough* 399
    17.4.2 *Gravimetric method* 400
    17.4.3 *Volumetric method* 400
    17.4.4 *The Rayleigh interferometer* 400
    17.4.5 *The precolumn method* 401
17.5 Theory for adsorption from solution 401
17.6 Quantitative methods for adsorption from a solution 402
    17.6.1 *Adsorption of non-electrolytes* 402
    17.6.2 *Fatty acid adsorption* 402
    17.6.3 *Adsorption of polymers* 402
    17.6.4 *Adsorption of dyes* 403
    17.6.5 *Adsorption of electrolytes* 403
17.7 Theory for heat of adsorption from a liquid phase 403
    17.7.1 *Surface free energy of a fluid* 403
    17.7.2 *Surface entropy and energy* 404
    17.7.3 *Heat of immersion* 405
17.8 Static calorimetry 406
17.9 Flow microcalorimetry 406
    17.9.1 *Experimental procedures – liquids* 407
        (a) *pulse adsorption* 407
        (b) *equilibrium adsorption* 408
        (c) *successive adsorption* 409
    17.9.2 *Calibration* 409
    17.9.3 *Determination of the amount of solute adsorbed – the*
        precolumn method 410
    17.9.4 *Gases* 410
    17.9.5 *Application to the determination of surface area* 411

18 Determination of pore size distribution 414
18.1 Miscellaneous techniques 414
18.2 Gas adsorption methods 414
18.3 The hysteresis loop 416
18.4 Pore size distribution by gas adsorption 418
18.5 The *t*-curve method for intermediate pores 419
18.6 The modellers method for pore structure analysis 423

18.7 Analysis of micropores; the MP method 424
18.8 Mercury porosimetry 425

Appendix 1. Equipment and suppliers 433

Appendix 2. Manufacturers' and suppliers' addresses 438

Author Index 442

Subject Index 452

Foreword to the First Edition

The study of the properties and behaviour of systems made up of particulate solids has in the past received much less attention than the study of fluids. It is, however, becoming increasingly necessary to understand industrial processes involving the production, handling and processing of solid particles, in order to increase the efficiency of such systems and to permit their control. During the past few years this has led to an increase in the amount of study and research into the properties of solid particle systems. The results of this effort are widely dispersed in the literature and at the moment much of the information is not available in a form in which it is likely to influence the education of students, particularly in chemical engineering, who may later be employed in industrial organizations where they will be faced with the problems of solids handling. It is also difficult for the engineer responsible for the design or selection of solids handling equipment to make use of existing knowledge, with the result that industrial practice is not always the best that is achievable. It is hoped that the publication of a series of monographs on Powder Technology, of which this is the first, will help by providing accounts of existing knowledge of various aspects of the subject in a readily available form.

It is appropriate that the first monograph in this series should deal with the measurement of the size of small particles since this is the basic technique underlying all other work in powder technology. The reliability of research results, for example, on the size reduction of solid particles, cannot be better than the reliability of the particle size measurement techniques employed. Too often the difficulties and limitations of size measurement are ignored in such work, so that any conclusions become suspect. The importance of a thorough understanding of the problems involved in measuring the size of small particles for anyone working in any aspect of powder technology is therefore difficult to overestimate. It is hoped that this monograph, written by an experienced size analyst who has studied critically most of the methods described, will be of value in encouraging an informed and critical approach to the subject and that it will help in the selection of equipment and in realistic assessment of the value of particle size measurements.

J. C. WILLIAMS

Postgraduate School of Powder Technology,
University of Bradford

xiv

Preface to the First Edition

Although man's environment, from the interstellar dust to the earth beneath his feet, is composed to a large extent of finely divided material, his knowledge of the properties of such materials is surprisingly slight. For many years the scientist has accepted that matter may exist as solids, liquids or gases although the dividing line between the states may often be rather blurred; this classification has been upset by powders, which at rest are solids, when aerated may behave as liquids, and when suspended in gases take on some of the properties of gases.

It is now widely recognized that powder technology is a field of study in its own right. The industrial applications of this new science are far reaching. The size of fine particles affects the properties of a powder in many important ways. For example, it determines the setting time of cement, the hiding power of pigments and the activity of chemical catalysts; the taste of food, the potency of drugs and the sintering shrinkage of metallurgical powders are also strongly affected by the size of the particles of which the powder is made up. Particle size measurement is to powder technology as thermometry is to the study of heat and is in the same state of flux as thermometry was in its early days.

Only in the case of a sphere can the size of a particle be completely described by one number. Unfortunately, the particles that the analyst has to measure are rarely spherical and the size range of the particles in any one system may be too wide to be measured with any one measuring device. V.T. Morgan tells us of the Martians who has the task of determining the size of human abodes. Martian homes are spherical and so the Martian who landed in the Arctic has no difficulty in classifying the igloos as hemispherical with measurable diameters. The Martian who landed in North America classified the wigwams as conical with measurable heights and base diameters. The Martian who landed in New York classified the buildings as cuboid with three dimensions mutually perpendicular. The one who landed in London gazed about him despairingly before committing suicide. One of the purposes of this book is to reduce the possibility of further similar tragedies. The above story illustrates the problems involved in attempting to define the size of particles by one dimension. The only method of measuring more than one dimension is microscopy. However, the mean ratio of significant dimensions for a particulate system may be determined by using two methods of analysis and finding the ratio of the two mean sizes. The proliferation of measuring techniques is due to the wide range of sizes and size dependent properties that have to be measured;

a twelve-inch ruler is not a satisfactory tool for measuring mileage or thousandths of an inch and is of limited use for measuring particle volume or surface area. In making a decision on which technique to use, the analyst must first consider the purpose of the analysis. What is generally required is not the size dependent. In such circumstances it is important whenever possible to measure the desired property, rather than to measure the 'size' by some other method and then deduce the required property. For example, in determining the 'size' of boiler ash with a view to predicting atmospheric pollution, the terminal velocity of the particle should be measured; in measuring the 'size' of catalyst particles, the surface area should be determined, since this is the property that determines its reactivity. The cost of the apparatus as well as the ease and the speed with which the analysis can be carried out have then to be considered. The final criteria are that the method shall measure the appropriate property of the particles, with an accuracy sufficient for the particular application at an acceptable cost, in a time that will allow the result to be used.

It is hoped that this book will help the reader to make the best choice of methods. The author aims to present an account of the present state of the methods of measuring particle size; it must be emphasized that there is a considerable amount of research and development in progress and the subject needs to be kept in constant review. The interest in this field in this country is evidenced by the growth of committees set up to examine particle size measurement techniques. The author is Chairman of the Particle Size Analysis Group of the Society for Analytical Chemistry. Other committees have been set up by The Pharmaceutical Society and by British Standards Institution and particle size analysis is within the terms of reference of many other bodies. International Symposia were set up at London, Loughborough and Bradford Universities and it is with the last-named that the author is connected. The book grew from the need for a standard textbook for the Postgraduate School of Powder Technology and is published in the belief that it will be of interest to a far wider audience.

TERENCE ALLEN

Postgraduate School of Powder Technology,
University of Bradford

Preface to the Second Edition

The science of particle size measurement has developed rapidly since the first edition of *Particle Size Measurement*. This second edition is, therefore, a complete rewrite of the book. The chapter on sampling has been expanded to three chapters and similar expansion has taken place elsewhere. Chapter 4 is built around the work of Harold Heywood whose death has impoverished those who knew him from both a personal and professional viewpoint.

The revised chapter on microscopy owes much to the lecture notes of Dr V. Timbrell as presented at the Harold Heywood Memorial Symposium held at Loughborough in 1973. My thanks are due to Dr Timbrell for his permission to use these notes.

The sedimentation chapters reflect my preference for incremental over cumulative sedimentation. The design of many sedimentation columns renders them unsuitable for accurate analysis, although some can give reproducible results; many sedimentation balances leave a lot to be desired and these faults have obviously tempered my judgment.

Disc centrifuges are now supreme for sub-micrometre analyses and a great deal of pioneer work in this field has been carried out at Bradford. The Coulter principle is now widely accepted and its imperfections tolerated because of its overall attractiveness. Permeametry is largely unchanged although a wider use of gas diffusion techniques may be expected because of its greater accuracy with comparable simplicity. Although gas adsorption techniques have been standardized, differences of opinion do exist on the interpretation of results, particularly with porous solids.

This book is a byproduct of the Courses on Particle Size Measurement which are directed by the author and take place at regular intervals at both the University of Bradford and at the Center for Professional Advancement, P.O. Box 997, 29 Division Street, Somerville, New Jersey 08876, U.S.A.

T. A.

Postgraduate School of Powder Technology,
University of Bradford

Acknowledgments

I would like to express my grateful thanks to Dr Brian H. Kaye for introducing me to the fascinating study of particle size analysis. My thanks are also due to numerous workers in this field for the helpful discussions we have had. Bradford Universsity has provided me with a well-equipped laboratory in which, in teaching others, I have learnt some of the secrets of this science. One of my students was Mr T.S. Krishnamoorthy and the chapter on gas adsorption is taken from his M.Sc. thesis. At Bradford, Mr John C. Williams has always had the time to offer helpful advice and criticism. I make no apology for taking up so much of his time since his advice was invariably good and whatever virtue this book possesses is due, in part, to him.

My thanks are also due to holders of copyright for permission to publish and to many manufacturers who have given me full details of their products.

Finally, I would like to thank my wife for her forbearance while the writing of this book has been in progress.

T. A.

1 Sampling of Powders

1.1 Introduction

The powders awaiting analysis in a laboratory are frequently of unknown origin. The first question that the analyst must resolve is the accuracy required of the analysis and the answer depends to a great extent on how faithfully the sample represents the bulk.

Although a great deal of effort has been directed to obtaining accurate size analyses of given samples of powder, many analysts seem unaware of the difficulty of obtaining a representative sample from any given batch. It is necessary that the selected samples for measurement should be representative of the bulk in grain size distribution and the relative fractions of its various constituents, irrespective of whether a physical or chemical assay is to be carried out, since these characteristics are frequently interdependent. The magnitude of the problem may be realized when one considers that the characteristics of many tons of material are assumed on the basis of analyses carried out on grams or even milligrams.

Several methods of sampling prior to analysis are available, but there is a scarcity of information as to the merits of the various techniques. Since no analysis can be more accurate than the sampling procedure preceding it, the analyst should know the expected accuracy of the sample.

The reduction from bulk to measurement sample may be conveniently divided into the four stages illustrated below:

Process or delivery of materials	Gross sample	Laboratory sample	Measurement sample
$(10^n$ kg)	(kg)	(g)	(mg)

1.2 Golden rules of sampling

There are many possible situations in which a sample has to be obtained and conditions often necessitate the use of inferior techniques. Some principles can however be laid down, and they should be adhered to whenever possible:

Rule 1. A powder should be sampled when in motion.

Rule 2. The whole of the stream of powder should be taken for many short increments of time in preference to part of the stream being taken for the whole of the time.

Observance of these rules coupled with an understanding of the manner in which segragation may have occurred during the previous treatment of the powder will lead to the best sampling procedure. Any sampling method which does not follow these rules should be regarded as a second-best method liable to lead to errors.

1.3 Bulk sampling

There are a very large number of possible systems from which the gross sample has to be abstracted, so it is impossible to lay down instructions which will meet all situations. The problem may be to obtain a sample from continuous streams, batches, packets, heaps or trucks. The difficulty is that when a particulate material is handled, segregation may take place. The most important segregation-causing property is particle size and the problem is enhanced with free-flowing material. When poured into a heap, the fines tend to collect at the centre of the heap. In vibrating containers a layer of coarse material tends to collect near the surface; even if a large particle is more dense than the smaller particles in which it is immersed, it can be made to rise towards the surface. This can be demonstrated by placing a one-inch-diameter steel ball in a beaker which is then filled with sand to a depth of about two inches. By stroking the base of the beaker gently with one hand, the steel ball can be made to rise to the surface of the sand. Since the surface region is always rich in coarse particles, samples should never be removed from the surface region. An understanding of these tendencies to segregation prevents careless practice in obtaining samples.

When sampling is undertaken from a continuous stream, the sampling may be continuous of intermittent. In continuous sampling a portion of the flowing stream is split off and frequently further subdivided subsequently. In intermittent sampling the whole stream is taken for small increments of time at fixed time intervals. These increments are usually compounded and samples for analysis taken from this gross sample. Consignment sampling is carried out on a single consignment (e.g. a truck-load or wagon-load).

A general rule in all sampling is that whenever possible the sample should be taken when the powder is in motion. This is usually easy with continuous processes; with consignment sampling it may be possible during the filling or emptying of storage containers.

1.4 Sampling from a moving stream of powder

In collecting from a moving stream, care should be taken to offset the effects of segregation. For example, if the powder may be sampled as it falls from the end of a conveyor; this is one of the best methods of sampling and should be adopted whenever possible. The powder on the conveyor will probably show two forms of segregation. If the powder was charged on to the conveyor belt from a centrally placed feeder or hopper outlet, the fines will tend to concentrate at the centre of the

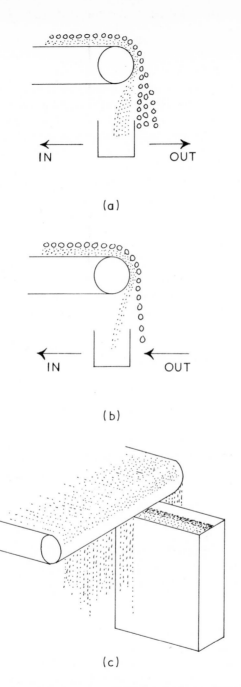

IN OUT

(a)

IN OUT

(b)

(c)

Fig. 1.1. Sampling from moving streams. (a) Bad sampling technique (b) Good sampling technique (c) Sampling procedure to be adopted for mass flow rate.

belt and the coarse particles will roll to the outer edges. If there has been any vibration of the belt, larger particles will tend to rise to the top of the bed of powder.

Each increment should be obtained by collecting the whole of the stream for a short time. Care must be taken in putting the sampler in and out of the stream. Figure 1.1 shows correct and incorrect methods of doing this.

Unless the time during which the sample receiver is stationary in its receiving position is long compared with the time taken to insert and withdraw the sampler, the method shown in figure 1.1(a) will lead to an excess of coarse particles as the surface region of the stream, usually rich in coarse particles, is sampled for a longer time than the rest of the stream. The method shown in figure 1.1(b) is not subject to this objection. If the method shown in the figure (b) is not possible due to some obstruction, the ratio of stationary time to moving time for the receiver should be made as large as possible.

In many cases it is not possible to collect the whole of the stream as this would give too large an amount to be handled. The best procedure is to pass through the stream a sample collector of the form shown in figure 1.1(c).

The width of the receiver, b, will be chosen to give an acceptable weight of sample but must not be made so small that the biggest particles have any difficulty

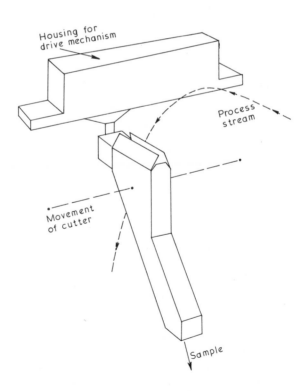

Fig. 1.2.(A)full-stream (GECO) sampler.

in entering the receiver. Particles that strike the edges of the receiver are likely to bounce out and not be collected so that the effective width is $(b\text{-}d)$, where d is the diameter of the particles. The effective width is therefore greater for small particles than for large particles. To reduce this error to a reasonable level, the ratio of box width to the diameter of the largest particle should be made as large as possible with a minimum value of 20:1. The depth a of the receiver must be great enough to ensure that it is never full of powder. If the receiver fills up before it finishes its traverse through the powder, a wedge-shaped heap will form a size selective particle collector. As more material falls on the top of the heap the fine particles will percolate through the surface of the heap and be retained, whereas coarse particles will roll down the sloping surface and be lost. The length of the receiver c should be sufficient to ensure the full depth of the stream is collected.

A proprietary example of this type of sampler is the GECO manufactured by John Smith & Co. Ltd, Horsham, Sussex, a diagram of which is shown in figure 1.2.

This equipment is satisfactory for many applications but it has limitations which restrict its use [16]. These are:

(1)   Although comparatively readily designed into a new plant, it is frequently difficult and expensive to add to an existing plant.

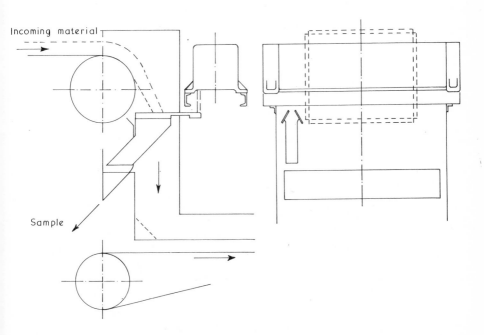

Fig. 1.2.(b) Traversing-type sampler in a chute.

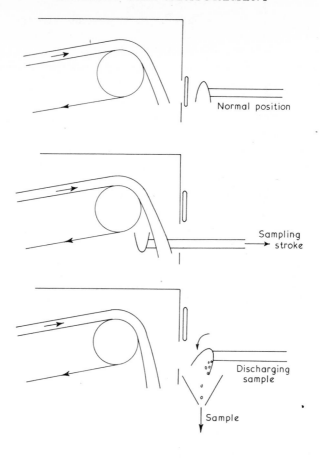

Normal position

Sampling stroke

Discharging sample

Sample

Fig. 1.3. Full stream trough sampler.

(2)   The quantity of sample obtained is given by the product of slit width and
       plant rate divided by the cutter speed and is independent of stream shape
       or area. This proportionality to the plant rate can be inconvenient when
       the plant rate is subject to wide variations and a fixed sample is required.
       On the other hand, where a plant daily average is required, this is a
       necessary requirement of the sampler. Also the quantity of sample may
       be inconveniently large.

(3)   It is difficult to enclose the sampler to the extent required to prevent the
       escape of dust and fume when handling a dusty product.

       Figure 1.3 shows a sampler designed by I.C.I. [16] to sample a dusty material,
sampling taking place only on the return stroke. This is suitable provided the
trough does not overfill. For this reason the constant volume sampler, the action of

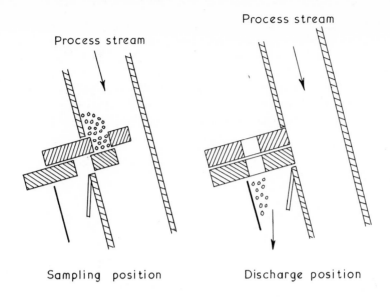

Fig. 1.4. Constant volume sampler.

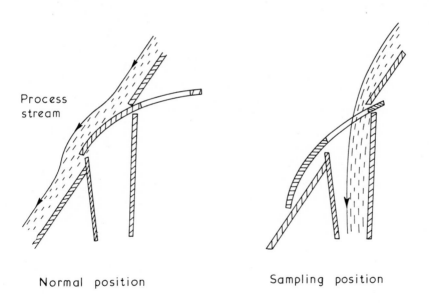

Fig. 1.5. Slide valve sampler.

which can be readily understood from figure 1.4, cannot be recommended. The slide valve sampler (figure 1.5) and the sample conditioner (figure 1.6), developed by the same company, also have defects which render then unsuitable for collecting size-representative samples.

A variant of this problem is encountered in sampling from preweighed batches. Such an automatic sampling system is shown in figure 1.7 [17]. From a consideration of this diagram, it can be seen that the device is liable to be highly size selective.

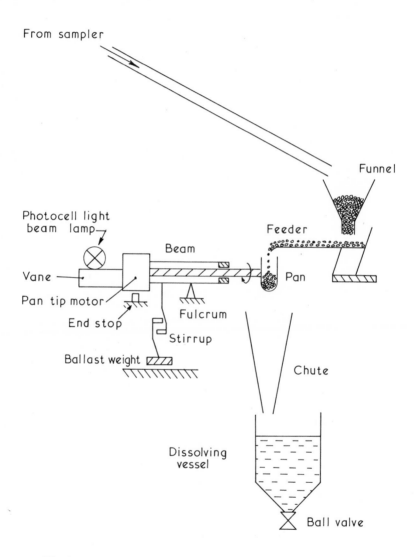

Fig. 1.6. Schematic diagram of system for sample conditioning.

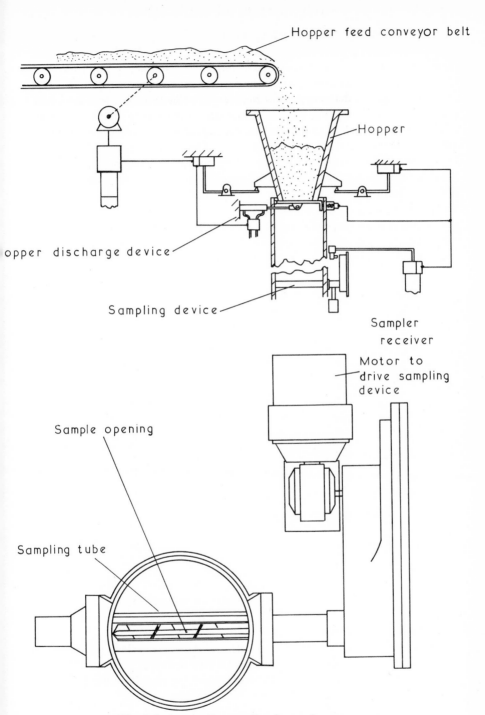

Fig. 1.7. Automatic sampling from a hopper.

1.5 Sampling from a conveyor belt or chute

When a sample is to be collected from a conveyor belt, the best position for collecting the increments is where the material falls in a stream from the end of the belt. If access at such a point is not possible, the sample must be collected from the belt. The whole of the powder on a short length of the belt must be collected, and again it must be borne in mind that the particles at the edge of the belt may not be the same size as those at the centre, and particles at the top of the bed may not be the same as those at the bottom. If the belt can be stopped, the sample can be collected by inserting into the stream a frame consisting of two parallel plates shaped to fit the belt; the whole of the material between the belts is then swept out. With the belt in motion, the same procedure could be adopted but it is difficult to do this by hand. Some mechanical samplers are available for collecting a sampie from a moving conveyor belt (figure 1.8); before using such a device its action should be carefully examined to ensure that it collects the whole of the stream and does not, for example, leave a thin layer on the belt.

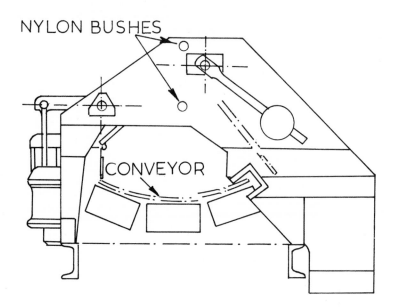

Fig. 1.8. Automatic sampler for belt conveyor.

1.6 Sampling from a bucket conveyor

In sampling from a bucket conveyor no attempt should be made to collect part of the material from a bucket. Each increment should consist of the whole of the contents of a bucket. If this is too large an amount for convenient handling, it should be reduced in size by one of the methods described later.

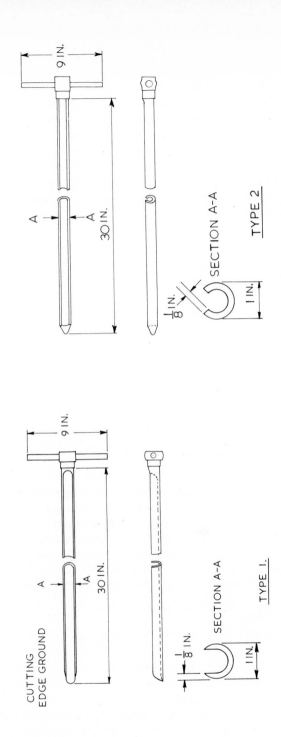

Fig. 1.9. Sampling spears.

1.7 Sampling from wagons and containers

It is very difficult, in fact practically impossible, to obtain a satisfactory sample from a wagon or container, because of the severe segregation that would almost certainly occur in filling the wagon and in its subsequent motion. A method for removing samples that avoids some of the worst errors is described in [6]. No increments are to be collected at less than 12 inches below the surface; this avoids the surface layer in which extreme segregation will probably have occurred due to vibration. In removing the samples there must be no surfaces down which particles can slide; this is achieved either by pushing in a sampling probe which extracts the sample (figure 1.9), or by removing particles by hand in such a way that no sliding occurs; when the sample region is exposed the sample can be extracted.

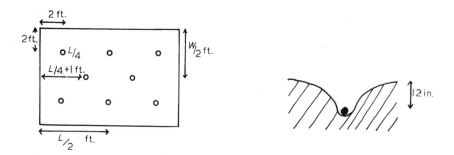

Fig. 1.10. Sampling points for a wagon or truck
(sampling from bottom of granular excavation).

Increments should be extracted at 8 points as shown in figure 1.10. This method of obtaining a sample is mentioned here because it is possible that there may be circumstances in which there is no alternative but to use it, but this must not be taken to imply that such methods will give satisfactory sampling. Every effort should be made to avoid this method and to use one that satisfies the two 'golden rules'. If a powdered material is in a container, the container has been filled and presumably is going to be emptied. At both these times, the powder will be in motion, and a more satisfactory sampling procedure can then be used.

1.8 Sampling from heaps

There is only one sound piece of advice to give regarding sampling from a heap. 'Don't! Never!' Examination of the cross section of a heap of powder containing particles of different sizes shows that there is a very marked segregation, the fine particles being concentrated in a region near the axis of the heap, with the coarse particles in the outer part of the heap.

The photograph (figure 1.11) of the cross section of a heap of granules of two sizes shows the segregation of powder when it is poured into a heap. Although

Fig. 1.11. Cross section of a binary powder showing how powders 'unmix' when poured into a heap, the finer particles tending to remain in the centre. Sizes: coarse (black) approximately 1 mm diameter; fine (white) approximately 0·2 mm diameter.

segregation does not occur on such a scale with sub-sieve granules, it indicates the care that must be taken when sampling from a heap. Sometimes a sample has to be obtained from a powder at rest, an indication that the sampling is taking place at the wrong time, since it must at some time have been in motion. In this case, the sample should be compounded from incremental samples and a lower sampling efficiency is to be expected. Figure 1.12 shows a pneumatic probe for extracting such samples.

In one case a binary mixture of equal weights of particles of two sizes, having a diameter ratio of 2·8, was poured into a heap and the concentration of fine particles in different parts of the heap was found to vary between 1 and 70%. Any attempt to find the composition of the whole heap from measurements based on sampling from a heap has, therefore, little chance of giving an accurate answer.

The solution to the problem of sampling from a heap lies in the fact that the powder must have been poured to form the heap, and this is the time when the sample should be collected; increments can be withdrawn from the falling stream by one of the recommended methods.

1.9 Sample dividing

The gross sample is frequently too large to be handled easily, and before sending it to the laboratory for testing, it may have to be reduced to a more convenient weight. Obviously this must be done in such a way that the laboratory sample has the same size grading as the gross sample. The principles involved here are the same as those already discussed when considering the collection of the gross sample. The first step is to realize the difficulties involved, and to understand the ways in which size segregation of the powder is likely to occur. The sampling procedure must then

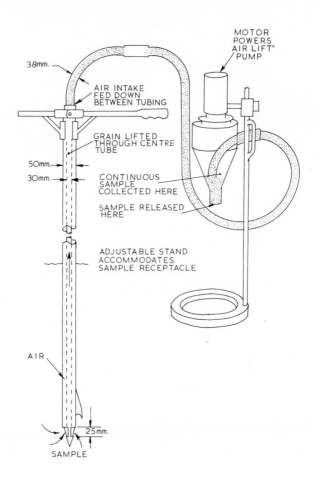

Fig. 1.12. Pneumatic probe sampler for sampling from heaps.

be designed so as to minimize the effects of segregation. The two 'golden rules' of sampling mentioned earlier apply equally here. The best method of sample dividing is:

(1)   Get the powder into motion in a stream.
(2)   Each increment should be obtained by collecting the whole of the stream for a short time.

Increments are collected at equal time intervals and put together to form the laboratory sample. To obtain the best results, the stream should be made as homogeneous as possible. If complete homogeneity of the stream is achieved, then clearly every increment will have the same size grading as the whole of the material and, in such an imaginary case, it would be enough to collect one increment. If there are considerable changes in the size grading of the material from one part of the stream to another, the probability of getting increments with the same size grading as the whole is reduced. Everything must be done to make the process of sample dividing easier and, by giving thought to the handling of the powder fed to a sample divider, more accurate results can be obtained. For example, if the sample divider is fed from a hopper, this hopper should have steep sides (at least 70°) so that mass flow is likely to occur when it is emptied, and the hopper should be filled in such a way that size segregation does not occur; this can best be done by moving the pour point about so that the surface of the powder in the sample divider is always more or less horizontal and no conical heap is formed. Several sample-dividing devices have been recommended and some of these are in wide use. Each method will be described briefly and its action discussed.

1.9.1 Coning and quartering

This method of sample dividing consists of pouring the material into a conical heap and relying on its radial symmetry to give four identical samples when the heap is flattened and divided by a cross-shaped metal cutter [figure 1.13(a)]. This method would give reliable results if the heap were symmetrical about a vertical axis and if the line common to the two cutting planes coincided with this axis. In practice the heap is unlikely to be symmetrical, and the second condition, symmetry of cutting, would be very difficult to achieve without precision equipment. Since severe size segregation will certainly occur in forming the heap, departure from symmetry in the cutting will lead to differences in the size of the four portions into which the heap is cut. The method is very dependent on the skill of the operator, and should not be used. If coning and quartering can be used, this implies that the quantity of material to be divided is such that it can easily be moved by hand; it is just as easy to feed it into the hopper of a device such as a rotary sample divider in which increments are collected from a stream in an acceptable manner.

1.9.2 Table sampling

In a sampling table [figure 1.13(b)] the material is fed to the top of an inclined plane in which there are series of holes. Prisms placed in the path of the stream break it into fractions. Some powder falls through the holes and is discarded, while the powder remaining on the plane passes on to the next row of prisms and holes, and more is removed, and so on. The powder reaching the bottom of the plane is the sample. The objection to this device is that it depends on the initial feed being uniformly distributed, and complete mixing after each separation, a condition not in general achieved. As it relies on the removal of part of the stream sequentially, errors are compounded at each separation, hence its accuracy is low.

1.9.3 Chute splitting (figure 1.13(c))

The chute splitter consists of a V-shaped trough along the bottom of which is a series of chutes alternately feeding two trays placed on either side of the trough. The laboratory sample is poured into the chute and repeatedly halved until a sample of the desired size is obtained.

When carried out with great care on a laboratory scale this method can give satisfactory sample division, but if the trough is filled in such a way that segregation occurs the results are liable to be misleading. The method is particularly prone to operator bias, which is frequently detectable by unequal splitting of the sample.

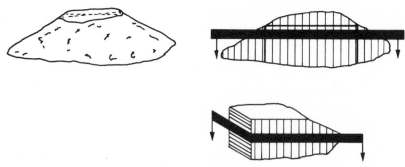

Fig. 1.13.(*a*) cone and quartering.

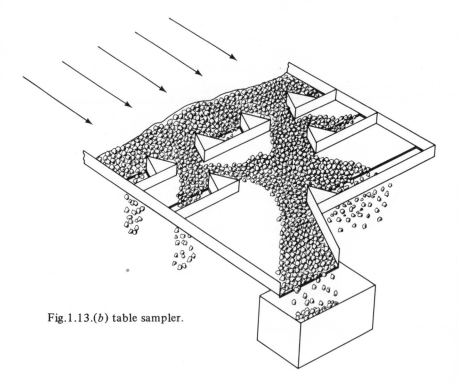

Fig.1.13.(*b*) table sampler.

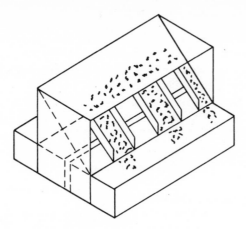

Fig. 1.13.(c) chute splitter.

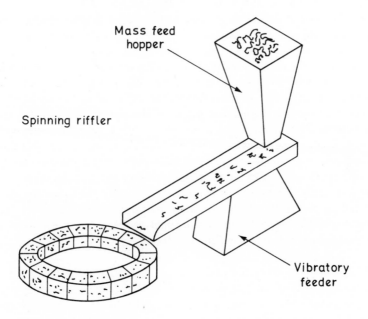

Mass feed hopper

Spinning riffler

Vibratory feeder

Fig. 1.13.(d) spinning riffler.

Scoop sampling

Fig. 1.13.(*e*) scoop sampling.

1.9.4 Spinning riffling (figure 1.13(*d*))

The best methods consist of setting the powder in motion in a stream and collecting increments from the stream. In the spinning riffler divider the powder flows from a feed into a series of segmented boxes placed on a rotating table as shown in figure 1.13(*d*).

The best method of using this device is first to fill the hopper in such a way that little segregation occurs, by avoiding the formation of a heap. The table is then set in motion and the hopper outlet opened so that the powder flows into the collecting boxes. The rate of flow of the powder and the speed of rotation of the table should be adjusted so that the table rotates at least thirty times during the time the powder is flowing. The powder in alternate boxes (say, box nos 1, 3, 5, ... etc.) is put together as the required material, of half the mass of the original powder, and the powder from the other boxes is rejected. The process is repeated with the retained half of the powder to give a further reduction and this is continued until the sample is reduced to the required weight. If this process is too lengthy and the sample must be divided more quickly, it is permissible to take the contents of one of the sample collecting boxes as the retained portion of the powder, but this introduces greater possibility of error and much more careful attention must be paid to the avoidance of segregation in the feed hopper so that the stream of powder is as nearly as possible homogeneous; as a further precaution the number of table rotations during the sampling dividing process should be increased to 100. The spinning riffler is probably the best method available. The effect of operator skill is less important than in most other methods.

1.9.5 Scoop sampling (figure 1.13 (*e*))

The method consists of plunging a scoop into the batch and withdrawing a sample. This is particularly prone to error since the whole of the sample does not pass through the sampling device, and since the sample is taken from the surface, where it may not be typical of the mass. In an attempt to eliminate segregation produced in previous handling, it is usual to shake the sample vigorously in a container before sampling.

Figure 1.14 shows five modes of shaking which were investigated by Kaye [13], using six operators in order that both operator and technique bias could be

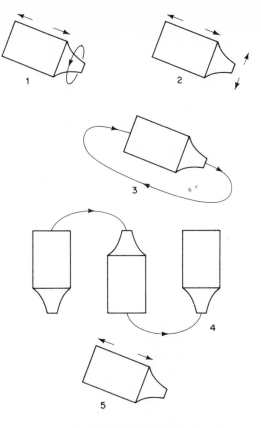

Fig. 1.14. Five modes of shaking a container prior to
removing a sample for analysis.

evaluated. The samples consisted of coarse and fine particles mixed in known
proportions. Of the methods investigated, the first was preferred since, with this
method, the bias was random, though it varied with the operator. The other techniques introduced a decided bias into the sample, which was difficult to eliminate,
thus demonstrating that the efficiency of a sampling technique depends on the
previous history of the powder.

Kaye also tested a standard laboratory shaker, 'the microid pipette flask shaker'
(Griffin and George Ltd), and found that its efficiency depended on its speed but
even at peak efficiency it was no better than manual shaking.

1.9.6 Miscellaneous devices
A number of devices are commercially available which are similar in principle to the
spinning riffler. In the oscillating hopper sample divider the feed hopper is pivoted
about a horizontal axis so that it can oscillate during emptying. Two collectors are

placed under the hopper outlet so that the powder flows into them alternately. The contents of one box are retained; at each stop the weight of the sample is thus halved.

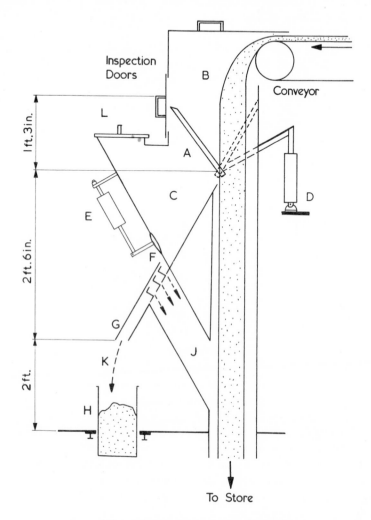

Fig. 1.15. Moving-flap sample divider.

The moving-flap sample divider (figure 1.15) consists essentially of a flap which is pivoted about a horizontal axis so that it can rest in either of two positions. The stream of powder to be divided falls on to the flap and is deflected into one of two containers according to the position of the flap. The movement of the flap is controlled electronically so that a fraction of the stream is collected in one container and retained; the rest of the material falls into the other container and is rejected.

All the above methods, the rotating table, the oscillating hopper and the moving flap, satisfy the criterion that they collect the whole of the stream of powder for a short time, such increments being collected at equal time intervals. All are capable of giving satisfactory sample division. There are other methods of sample dividing described in the literature and sometimes used which do not satisfy the requirement laid down here.

The rotary sample divider (figure 1.16) is very similar in principle to the spinning riffler. The powder falls through a hopper outlet on to a cone whose position may be varied to very the outlet aperture. The powder slides down the cone into containers on a revolving table.

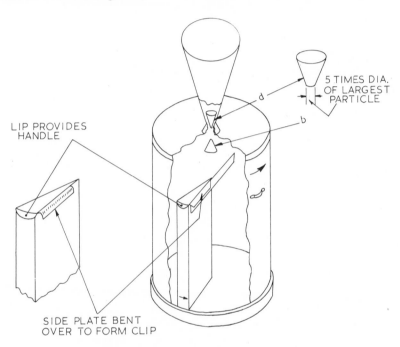

Fig. 1.16. Rotary sample divider.

A splitter described by Fooks [15] (figure 1.17), consists of a feeder funnel through which the sample is fed. It passes on to the apex of two resting cones, the lower fixed, the upper adjustable by means of a spindle. Segments are cut from both cones and by rotating the upper cone the effective area of these slits may be varied to vary the sampling proportion. Material which falls through the segmental slots is passed to a sample pot. The residue passes over the cone and out of the base of the unit.

A similar unit may be installed in a feedpipe down which particulate material is flowing. In this unit the splitter cones are mounted within the feedpipe and the sample falling through the segmental slots passes out of a side pipe, while the remainder flows over the cone and continues down the feedpipe.

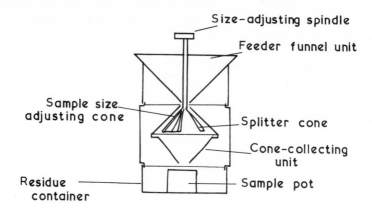

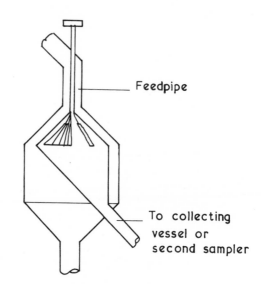

Fig. 1.17. Fooks's sample splitter.

1.10 Reduction from laboratory sample to analysis sample

The methods described so far are suitable for the reduction of a gross sample collected from a process to a weight that can conveniently be sent to the size analysis laboratory, normally of the order of one pound. To obtain the amount required for the actual measurement a further reduction is necessary, and again careful consideration must be given to the problem of obtaining an analysis sample with the same size grading as the laboratory sample. The amount of material required as an analysis sample depends on the size measurement technique being used.

For sieving it would normally be 25 to 50 g, for sedimentation it would depend on whether the technique was cumulative (0·5 g) or incremental (8–12 g), for elutriation 0·5 g.

It is sometimes suggested that a satisfactory sample division can be made by shaking the bottle containing the laboratory sample in order to mix it, then extracting the analytical sample with a scoop [13]. For accurate work this method should not be used for the following reasons:

(1)   Shaking a bottle containing a powder is not an effective method of mixing particles of different sizes. Anyone who doubts this should try the experiment of putting into a glass bottle equal volumes of two powders of different sizes and colours and examining the mixture after shaking. Pockets of segregated material form and cannot be broken up by further shaking. In particular the surface will be made up predominantly of the larger particles. A sample removed by a scoop must include part of the surface, where the composition is very likely to be different from that of the whole of the sample.

(2)   A further objection to the use of a scoop is that it is liable to be size-selective, favouring the collection of fine particles. The reason for this is that, when the scoop is removed from the material, some particles will flow down the sloping surface of the powder retained in the scoop; the finer particles tend to be captured in the surface craters and retained, whereas coarse particles are more likely to travel to the bottom of the slope and be lost. This effect is particularly important if a flat blade (such as a spatula) is used for the removal of the sample. Such methods should never be used

The spinning riffler is the equipment recommended for subdivision down to a gram, but the powder needs to be free-flowing. Coning and quartering a paste [18] has been used for preparing samples down to about 20 mg in weight but the efficiency of the method is operator-dependent. Sampling a stirred suspension with a syringe is quite a good method for fine powder suspensions, but with suspensions of coarser powders, concentration gradients and segregation of particle sizes due to gravitational settling and the centrifugal motion of the liquid caused by the stirring action are more likely to arise. For these reasons Burt et al. [19] have developed a suspension sampler which is shown in figure 1.18. The sampler consists of a glass cylinder closed at either end by stainless-steel plates. Around the periphery of the base plate are ten equidistant holes leading to ten centrifuge tubes via stainless-steel capillary tubes. The cover plate has a central hole through which passes a stirrer; a sealable inlet for introduction of the powder suspension, and a gas orifice which enables the gas pressure to be increased or decreased. In operation 100 cm^3 of suspension is introduced, stirred, then blown into the test tubes under a small applied pressure. Burt analysed a mixture of barium sulphate (0·25 g) and calcium carbonate (0·25 g) in 100 ml of water. The percentage of barium sulphate in each of the ten tubes was then determined and found to give significantly better results than syringe withdrawal, i.e. approximately 1·0% standard deviation as opposed to 3·0%.

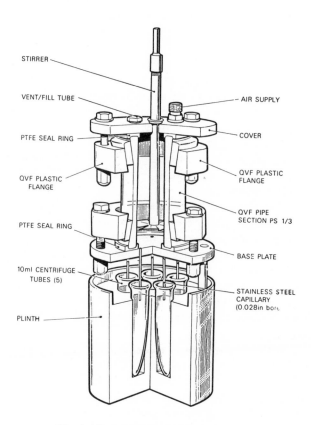

Fig. 1.18. Burt's suspension sampler.

(a) Suspension sampler, 10ml to 2ml

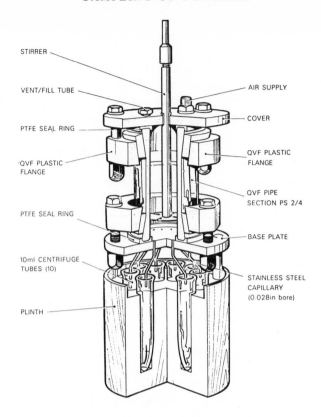

STIRRER

VENT/FILL TUBE

PTFE SEAL RING

QVF PLASTIC
FLANGE

PTFE SEAL RING

10ml CENTRIFUGE
TUBES (10)

PLINTH

AIR SUPPLY

COVER

QVF PLASTIC
FLANGE

QVF PIPE
SECTION PS 2/4

BASE PLATE

STAINLESS STEEL
CAPILLARY
(0.028in bore)

Fig. 1.18. Burt's suspension sampler.
(b) Suspension sampler, 100ml to 10ml

1.11 Reduction from analysis sample to measurement sample

In microscopy the required sample consists of a few milligrams of material. This may be extracted from the analysis sample by incorporating it in a viscous liquid in which it is known to disperse completely. The measurement sample may then be extracted with a measuring rod [12]. An alternative technique is to disperse the analysis sample in a liquid of low viscosity with the addition of a dispersing agent if necessary. The measurement sample may be withdrawn using a pipette or, preferably, a sample divider as illustrated in [11].

1.12 Testing sampling devices

A powder to be assayed may be considered as a mixture of components A and B. For an ideal sample the probability that the number fraction of the bulk p in terms of A shall be represented by the corresponding composition p_i of a perfect sample can be computed from the number of particles of A and B in the sample n and in the bulk N.

$$\mathrm{Var}(p_i) = \frac{p(1-p)}{n}\left[1 - \frac{n}{N}\right] \tag{1.1}$$

n/N in many practical cases tending to zero. The standard deviation of the bulk σ equals the square root of the variation (Var p_i).

Instead of the number fraction it is more convenient to assess sample and bulk composition in terms of weight fractions P and P_i, giving:

$$\mathrm{Var}(P_i) = \frac{P(1-P)}{w}\left[PW_B + (1-P)W_A\right]\left(1 - \frac{w}{W}\right) \tag{1.2}$$

where W and w are the bulk and sample weights respectively and W_A and W_B are the average weights of individual grains of components A and B.

This function may be used to assess the efficiency of a real, non-ideal sampling device. In this case the variance of the sample assay P_n will be greater than $\mathrm{Var}(P_i)$ due to sampling errors. The experimental variance is given by:

$$\mathrm{Var}(P_n) = \sum \frac{(x - \bar{x})^2}{n} \tag{1.3}$$

where $\bar{x}$ is the true fraction by weight of component A or B, x the fraction obtained after sampling and n the number of observations. The standard deviation σ_n of the samples is given by the square root of the experimental variance.

The efficiency of a non-ideal sampler can be defined as:

$$C = \frac{\mathrm{Var}(P_i)}{\mathrm{Var}(P_n)} \tag{1.4}$$

and should approximate to unity when sampling errors are low. The maximum error will be:

$$E = \pm 100 \frac{2\sigma_n}{P}. \tag{1.5}$$

Numerical example

Any powder can be considered as being made up of two components, the fraction above and below a certain size. For a reduction of 16 to 1 during sampling with $W_A = 0\cdot10$ g, $W_B = 0\cdot05$ g and $w = 50$ g, equation (1.2) becomes:

$$\mathrm{Var}(P_i) = \frac{3}{16} W_B (P^3 - 3P^2 + 2P).$$

The maximum value of the variance, derived by differentiation and equating the differential to zero, occurs for $P = (1 + 1/\sqrt{3})$ giving $\mathrm{Var}(P_i) = 0\cdot000361$ and $\sigma = 1\cdot90\%$.

This means that, if a gross sample is broken down to 16 laboratory samples, 68% of them would attribute $50 \pm 1\cdot90\%$ to the known mean size, 95% would attribute $50 \pm 3\cdot80\%$ to the known mean size and substantially all the samples would give 50 ± 5·70% to the mean size, provided no sampling bias existed.

This deviation is similar to what one would expect if one took samples of balls from a well-mixed bag containing half red balls and half white balls. If 100 balls were removed (n/N very small) from equation (1.1), $\sigma = 5\%$. That is, the maximum number of red balls one would expect to have would be 65, i.e. the mean + 3 standard deviations. If 10 000 balls were removed the standard deviation would fall to 0·5%. If the experimental errors exceeded these values one would suspect either a non-random mix or selective sampling.

It is obvious that the larger the sample, the smaller will be the deviations. The size of a practicable laboratory sample is usually minute in relation to the whole of the material being examined. Thus the laboratory sample itself is subject to a degree of variation which is unrealistically large. There are two ways of reducing this variation; one is to make up a bulk sample from many increments and divide them down to produce laboratory samples, and the second is to take a number of replicate samples and mix them.

1.12.1 Experimental tests of laboratory sample-splitting techniques

One approach [20] has been to make up a binary mixture of sand, having all particles of the one component and none of the other being able to pass through a designated sieve. The preparation of this mixture is not as straightforward as it might appear at first sight, due to the wide tolerances in sieve aperture. The exercise was repeated using a sugar−sand mixture. The mixture was divided into sixteen samples which were then separated into the original components and the relative percentages compared with the original.

Experimental data

Coarse sand and sugar	30 − 36 mesh, 347−286 μm
Fine sand	60−100 mesh, 173−104 μm

     36-mesh tolerance, 66 μm
     60-mesh tolerance, 51 μm

The smallest size present in the coarse grade was 220 μm and the largest in the fine grade 224 μm. Since sieve tolerances have been found to be much better than standard specifications it may be accepted that no overlap exists between these grades. This hypothesis was tested and found to be correct, repeated sieving of mixtures of the two grades effected total separation:

Density of sugar and sand (g ml^{-1}) respectively 1·635 and 2·650
Weight of bulk (800 g)
Weight percentage coarse or sand (60)
Average weight of individual particles (g)
Coarse sand, $2 \cdot 84 \times 10^{-4}$; fine sand, $0 \cdot 233 \times 10^{-4}$; sugar, $1 \cdot 23 \times 10^{-4}$
From equation (1.2)

for sugar−sand mixture	$\mathrm{Var}(P_i) = 0 \cdot 0086\ (\%)^2$
for sand mixture	$\mathrm{Var}(P_i) = 0 \cdot 0058\ (\%)^2$

Experimental results

	Standard deviation (σ_n)		Estimated Max^m error (E)	
	Sugar– Sand %	Sand– sand %	Sugar– sand %	Sand– sand %
Cone quartering	5·76	6·81	19·2	
Scoop sampling	6·31	5·14	21·0	17·1
Table sampling	2·11	2·09	7·0	7·0
Chute splitter	1·10	1·01	3·7	3·4
Spinning riffler	0·27	0·13	0·9	0·4
Random error Var(P_i)	0·09	0·08	0·3	0·3

Very little confidence can be placed in any analysis where the sample has been obtained by one of the first three techniques. Further, the spinning riffler is so superior to all the other methods that whenever possible this should be used. Another conclusion that may be drawn from this table is that there is no significant difference between sampling different sizes and different densities except with the spinning riffler.

In other experiments it was established that the sampling accuracy with the spinning riffler was similar with both hand and vibratory feeding. Sampling efficiency does not depend on the percentage of fines in the powder, but when this is low powder losses become significant. Varying the weight of the bulk did not significantly affect the resulting analyses. A minimum of 35 presentations is required with the spinning riffler to obtain optimum results, increasing this does not markedly affect the results. It is more difficult to obtain representative samples with finer powders (sub-350 mesh replacing the coarse grade), but this may be due to measurement difficulties.

Tests on three of the devices were also carried out by six operators with the following results:

	Standard deviation of coarse percentage		
Operator	*Spinning riffler*	*Chute splitter*	*Cone and quartering*
1	0·54	0·34	1·48
2	0·60	1·34	1·80
3	0·40	0·52	0·61
4	0·68	0·72	1·00
5	0·69	1·28	0·93
6	0·85	1·18	1·09
Average	0·64	1·00	1·20

(1) Not only does the spinning riffler have the lowest average standard deviation, the standard deviations have less scatter, demonstrating less operator bias. With an experienced operator (3) all values of σ are low, but a significant difference exists between the three techniques.

(2) An alternative approach has been used in the critical examination of a spinning riffler to find how various factors influence its efficiency (2).

(3) The investigators used quartz and copper sulphate crystals of the same size and designed experiments to investigate the relative effect of the different factors. Their conclusions were that the efficiency:

- (a)   is dependent on the relative proportions of the mixture (it increased when the proportion of copper sulphate was raised from 1% to 5%).
- (b)   increases with increasing particle size.
- (c)   is reproducible under similar experimental conditions.
- (d)   is not affected by combination of variables.
- (e)   is not affected by the number of volume units (a volume unit consists of the single presentation of a sample container to the feed. Since the minimum number of such units was 100, this statement applies only to larger values than this).

The powders mixed in these experiments contained particles all of the same size, hence the main cause of segregation was not present, and the conclusions may not apply in the more usual case where size segregation occurs.

References

[1]   Pearce, M. (Sept. 1960), 'Solids sampling techniques', *Inst. Chem. Engrs*, Annual Symposium on Solids Handling.

[2]   Hawes, R.W.M., and Muller L.D. (1960), 'A small rotary sampler and preliminary study of its use' A.E.R.E.–R3051 (Harwell).

[3]   A.S.T.M. C.136–67 (1967), *Sieve or Screen Analysis of Fine and Coarse Aggregates.*

[4]   A.S.T.M. C.311–68 (1968), *Sampling and Testing Fly Ash for Use as an Admixture in Portland Cement.*

[5]   A.S.T.M. D.345–48, (1948), *Sampling and Testing Calcium Chloride for Roads and Structual Applications.*

[6]   A.S.T.M. D.451–63, (1963), *Sieve Analysis of Granular Mineral Surfacing for Asphalt Roofing and Shingles.*

[7]   A.S.T.M. D. 452–63, (1963), *Sieve Analysis of Non-granular Mineral Surfacing for Asphalt Roofing and Shingles.*

[8]   B.S. 1017: 1960:Part 1, *Sampling from Bulk (Coal)*; Part 2 (*Coke*).

[9]   B.S. 1796: 1952, *Methods for the Use of B.S. Fine-mesh Test Sieves.*

[10] B.S. 1377: 1961, *Methods of Testing Soils for Civil Engineering Purposes.*

[11] B.S. 616: 1963, *Methods for Sampling Coal Tar and its Products.*

[12] B.S. 3406: 1963, Part 1, *Sub-division of Gross Sample down to 2·0ml.*

[13] Kaye, B.H. (1961), London Univ., Ph.D. thesis.

[14] *Symposium on the Analysis of Calcerious Materials* (1965), Soc. for Chem. Ind.

[15] Fooks, J.C. (1970) 'Sample splitting devices', *Br. Chem. Engr.* 15, 6, 799.

[16] Hulley, B.J. (1970), 'Sampling and sample conditioning in on-line fertiliser analysis', *Chemical Engineer*, CE 410–CE 413.

[17] Cordell, R.E. (Oct. 1969), *Automatic Sampling System*, U.S. Patent 3, 472, 079.

[18] Burt, M.W.G. (1967), *Powder Technology*, 1, 103.

[19] Burt, M.W.G., Fewtrell, C.A., and Wharton, R.A. (1973), *Powder Technology*, 7, 6, 327–30.

[20] Allen, T., and Khan, A.A. (1970), *Chemical Engineering*, **238**, CE 108–112.

2 Sampling of Dusty Gases in Gas Streams

2.1 Introduction

Legislation requires that manufacturers carefully monitor and control their particulate gas discharge effluent. Pollution today is a very 'dirty' word and visible discharge from chimneys with deposition of soot and sulfurous compounds creates a barrier between the industrialist and an environment-conscious public. The industrialist who accepts his duty to society and the environment equips his factories with dust arresting plant such as filters, cyclones, electrostatic precipitators and scrubbers, balancing the cost against his profit margins. His less public spirited counterpart keeps this non-productive plant to the minimum required by law. In both cases regular sampling of the dusty gas streams must be carried out, in the former case to ensure that the plant is working efficiently and in the latter to ensure that the legal requirements are met. Procedures for sampling particulate matter suspended in a gas stream have been described [1–3, 38–41]. These all emphasize the need to obtain representative samples. The samples must be taken across the cross section of the duct to represent the total dust burden. The size distribution is usually required so that the deposition pattern of the discharge may be estimated, the larger particles falling more rapidly than the smaller ones. Since the particles are very fragile, the sampling device often incorporates size-grading sections. Representative samples are extremely difficult to obtain, a single series of tests may well take a week or more and a complete survey on a large plant may take several months.

Problems encountered are those of gaining access to the gas stream and then removing a representative sample from a distribution which is seldom uniform (figure 2.1).

There are then difficulties in removing a sample which is representative of the gas stream at this point, since a sample will be representative only if the velocity of aspiration into the nozzle is equal to the gas velocity at that point. This is known as *isokinetic sampling*. Under isokinetic conditions there is no disturbance of the gas streamlines and al the particles approaching the nozzle, and only those, will enter it [14–17]. As it is not possible to collect increments of the whole emission it is necessary to select suitable sampling positions across the cross-sectional area perpendicular to the direction of gas flow. Since the quantity of emission varies with time, results can only give an average for the time of tests. Tests should be duplicated and averages taken. With four points and an extraction time of 2 minutes per point, agreement should be better than 50% and the average taken [1]. Increasing the number of points to eight should improve the likely accuracy to 15% and an increase to 24 with a sampling time of 10 minutes should give an accuracy of 5% [2].

Greater discrepancies may indicate a faulty test or that plant conditions have varied, hence further tests are required. The plant cycle should also be observed to establish loading conditions. Averages do not normally include short periods of high dust emissions as during soot blowing. Attempts to include these could well render it impossible to get any measure of agreement.

2.2 Basic procedures

(1)   Select a suitable access position.
(2)   Conduct a temperature and velocity survey.
(3)   Assemble and test the sampling apparatus.
(4)   Carry out isokinetic sampling at preselected point for preselected times.
(5)   Remove the apparatus containing deposited solids.
(6)   Repeat the velocity and temperature survey.
(7)   Repeat steps (4), (5) and (6).
(8)   Determine the mass and size distribution of collected samples; make the necessary calculations and fill in report.

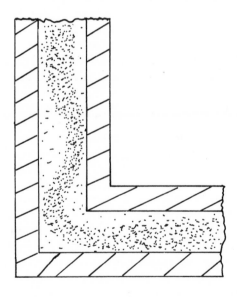

Fig. 2.1. (a) Pattern of flow of dusty gas round a bend.

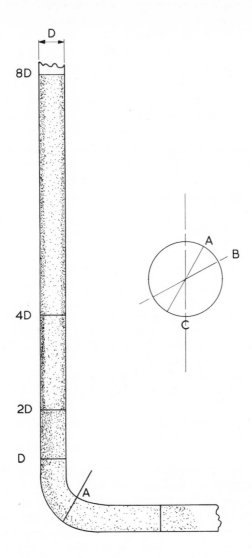

Fig. 2.1. (*b*) Pattern of flow round a gently sloping bend.

2.2.1 Sampling positions

The ideal sampling position is in the flue immediately prior to the discharge point in order to determine the actual emission. Since this is often impracticable, the position should be as near to the outlet as possible. Further, the dust burden is seldom distributed uniformly over the cross section of the flue and this non-uniformity is aggravated by gas turbulence. Disturbances are caused by inlets, outlets, bends, constrictions and dampers and, in order to minimize the effects of these, it is preferable to select a site eight to ten duct diameters downstream, three to five diameters upstream from a disturbance. Often this is physically impossible and compromises must be made. The sampling position should be downstream of any settling chamber, dust collecting plant or long horizontal duct where grit may collect, otherwise the amounts collected in the dust traps must be determined separately and subtracted from the amounts of collected dust.

Sansone [38] investigated the patterns of flow of solids downstream from a 90° bend. Particles were fed into an air stream in a horizontal duct and concentrations were determined in a vertical section using a twelve-point sampling pattern at the centre of annuli of equal areas. Some of his results are given in table 2.1.

Table 2.1 Mean values of relative particle concentrations (radius of bend, $2D$; gas velocity, 40 ft s^{-1}).

Number of diameters	*Sampling points*											
from bend	A1	A2	A3	A4	B1	B2	B3	B4	C1	C2	C3	C4
H	0·66	0·72	0·51	84	0·64	0·56	0·53	0·90	0·65	0·83	1·19	1·12
1	0·33	0·24	0·20	78	0·35	0·15	1·35	2·13	0·27	0·22	0·13	0·68
2	0·49	0·23	0·34	1·01	0·34	0·15	0·98	1·42	0·25	0·37	0·76	1·46
4	0·67	0·47	0·47	1·13	0·28	0·26	0·57	1·15	0·33	0·38	0·76	1·28
8	0·78	0·59	0·54	0·73	0·73	0·72	0·56	10·70	0·62	0·57	0·71	0·79
16	0·78	0·59	0·54	0·73	0·73	0·72	0·56	0·70	0·62	0·57	0·71	0·79

H indicates the horizontal cross section; *A* is a diameter through the elbow of the bend; *B* and *C* are at 30° to diameter *A*.

The data in the above table reveal that concentrations are generally higher immediately downstream of a bend along the duct wall farthest from the centre of curvature of the elbow. Similarly the concentrations are low along the duct wall nearest the centre of turning. In negotiating the bend, particles resist change of direction and are thrown to the outer wall. There is also a loss in concentration due to assuming that particle concentrations at centres of equal areas are representative of these areas. These effects are enhanced with a gas velocity of 80 ft s^{-1}.

2.2.2 Temperature and velocity survey

These should be carried out at ten equally spaced points along a sampling line, excluding the 50 mm nearest the flue walls. If temperature variations exceed 10%, a leak should be suspected and this should be plugged otherwise the position is unsuitable.

If the ratio of maximum to minimum velocity exceeds 2, the four-point method of sampling is unsuitable. Gas flow is rarely uniform across the cross section of a duct. For streamline flow (R_e less than 2000), the velocity on the axis is twice the mean velocity, and for fully turbulent flow (R_e greater than 2500), the axial velocity equals the mean velocity at $D/6$ from the walls, and it is claimed that a sample extracted at this point will be representative, but this is discounted by Stairmand [3], who states that the dust distribution rarely follows the gas distribution. Hawksley [4] also discusses variation of dust and gas flow across a duct.

2.2.3 Sampling points

In B.S. 893 the use of twenty-four sampling points, with at least three access holes, is recommended. The sampling lines should form the diameters of a hexagon with sampling access at alternate ends and sampling points at $0.07r$, $0.21r$, $0.39r$, $0.65r$, $1.35r$, $1.61r$, $1.79r$, $1.94r$ from the access point (r being the radius of the flue). These points are at the centres of annuli of equal area. Rectangular ducts should be divided up into twenty-four rectangles of equal area with sampling points at the centres of each rectangular element.

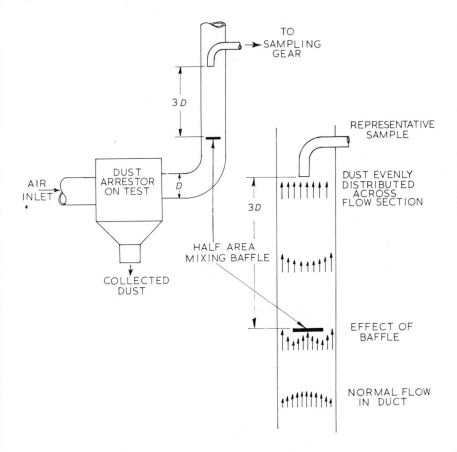

Fig. 2.2. Dust arrestor on test; laboratory rig.

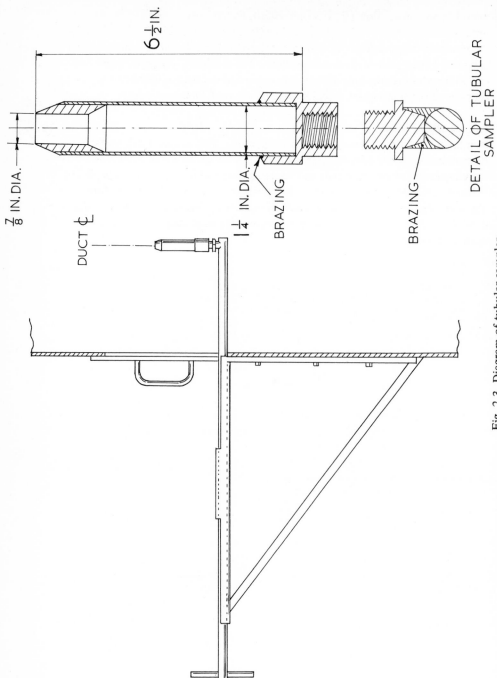

DETAIL OF TUBULAR SAMPLER

$6\frac{1}{2}$ IN.

$\frac{7}{8}$ IN. DIA.

$1\frac{1}{4}$ IN. DIA.

BRAZING

BRAZING

DUCT ₵

Fig. 2.3. Diagram of tubular sampler

In B.S. 3405 four or eight points are recommended, again at the centre of annuli of equal area. The four points lie on mutually perpendicular diameters at a distance $0.7r$ from the centre of the duct. With eight sampling points, four lie on mutually perpendicular diameters distance $0.5r$ from the centre of the duct and four on the same diameters $0.87r$ from the centre of the duct. A reduction to a single sampling point has been made by Stairmand (figure 2.2) [3; 5; 6, p. 583], who uses a half-area centrally located obstruction (a mixing baffle), three duct diameters upstream of the sampling probe, leaving at least two duct diameters of straight pipe downstream of the sampling probe. He claims that the sampling baffle makes the concentration of dust at the sampling position fairly uniform.

A device for routine sampling, for comparative purposes only, has also been developed [7] (figure 2.3). This consists of a suitable probe inserted into the flue duct. The open end faces the gas stream where it flows either horizontally or downwards so that the momentum of the grit carries it into the sampler. The device was used to detect failure of electrostatic precipitators and multicyclones installed on boilers earlier than would otherwise have been possible without expensive testing.

2.3 Sampling equipment

The accepted method of sampling flue gases in the U.K. is given in B.S. 893 [2]. The method is lengthy and complicated, but in spite of development and experience, more recently issued standards of other countries [8] differ only in detail. A more recently issued British Standard (B.S. 3405) [1] gives simplified procedures for quick investigations.

The basic equipment consists of a set of nozzles attached to a sampling tube; a miniature collector to retain the particles; means for determining the amount of gas sampled and the gas velocities in the ducts; means for withdrawing samples of gas through the system; thermometers, manometers, cooling coils, catchpots, connecting tubing and stopwatches.

2.3.1 Nozzles [2, 3]

The nozzles may vary in shape and construction but they should be of circular cross section, the open end having a thickness less than 1.3 mm and the internal and external surfaces having an inclination not greater than $45°$ to the axis of the nozzle (figures 2.4 and 2.5). With blunt-edged probes, a damming effect occurs upstream from the probe which deflects particles away from it [9–13]. The nozzle size must be chosen so that, with isokinetic sampling , the maximum flow rate will be within the capacity of the sampling equipment. Tables showing the correct nozzle size for the maximum Pitot differential are usually supplied with the dust-sampling apparatus.

2.3.2 Dust-sampling collector

The purpose of the sampling collector is to remove the particulate matter from the gas sample extracted from the main duct. Where it is only desired to determine concentration, the choice is fairly easy; where composition or size distribution has

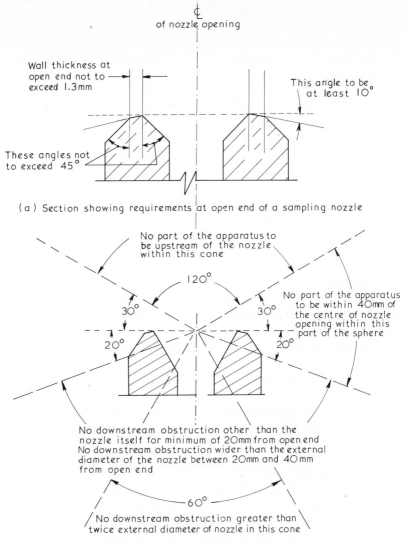

(a) Section showing requirements at open end of a sampling nozzle

(b) Diagram showing clearances necessary between open end of sampling nozzle and other parts of the apparatus

Fig. 2.4. Requirements for sampling nozzles (B.S. 3405). (a). Section showing requirements at open of a sampling nozzle. (b) Diagram showing clearances necessary between open end of sampling nozzle and other parts of apparatus.

to be determined, more precautions have to be taken. Stairmand describes a range of collectors in [3] and discusses their performance, other descriptions are to be found in [1].

The perfect collector would offer little resistance to gas flow even when it had collected a considerable amount of dust. Further, the dust should be easily

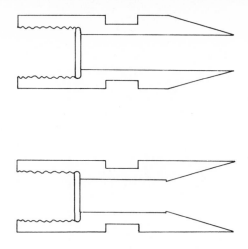

Fig. 2.5. Alternative designs for sampling nozzles.

separable from the collector without residual contamination. The only collector without these requirements is the electrostatic precipitator, but difficulties arise in the use of this equipment [5].

The range of collectors described by Stairmand consists of :

(a)   Cyclone separators;
(b)   Glass-wool filters;
(c)   Ferrule glass-wool filters;
(d)   Slag-wool filters;
(e)   Composite filters;
(f)   Terylene and superfine glass-wool filters;
(g)   Soluble filters;
(h)   Volatile filters;
(i)   Soxhlet filters;
(j)   Ceramic thimble filters;
(k)   Electrostatic filters;
(l)   Impingement filters.

A high efficiency cyclone (figures 2.6 and 2.7) forms a useful sample collector, since it can colleot large quantities of dust without increase of resistance. In many cases it will trap more than 95% of the suspended matter and may be used without a backing filter. When the dust is fine or complete removal is required, the cyclone may be backed by any of the range of filters annotated above.

A typical 'absolute' filter is shown in figure 2.8, an electrostatic filter in figure 2.9 and an impingement filter in figure 2.10.

The simplest equipment consists of a small cyclone without a series filter. Locating the cyclone near the nozzle end of the probe so that it is within the flue, is a

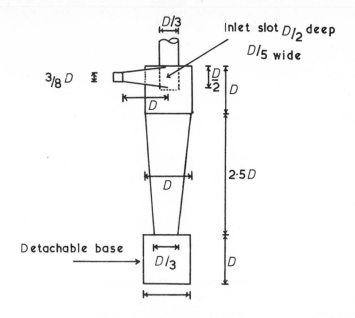

Fig. 2.6. Proportions of sampling cyclone.

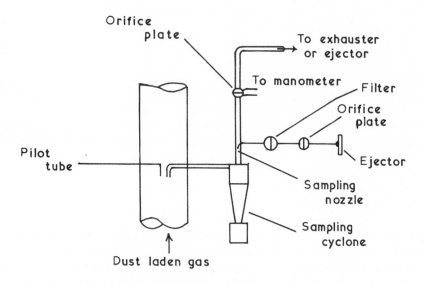

Fig. 2.7. Arrangement of sampling cyclones.

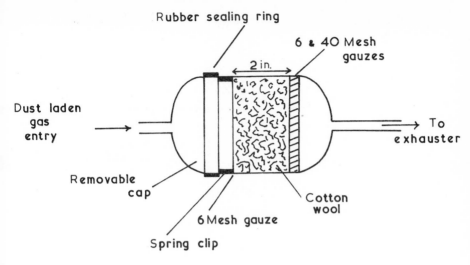

Fig. 2.8. Glass-wool filter.

further simplification, since the need to heat the cyclone and probe to prevent condensation is eliminated. The sampling rate and gas volume may be determined by measuring the pressure drop across the cyclone or by means of an orifice plate.

A refinement of the above apparatus is to pass the gas from the cyclone through a filter, usually of packed glass fibres, thus enabling the collection of particles that have escaped through the cyclone [30, 32].

Proprietary equipment based on the above design are used by B.C.U.R.A. [42], C.E.G.B., N.C.B. and others [6, p. 604].

Other equipment has heated filters on the outward end of the probe or unheated filters on the inward end of the probe, (see [10]). Equipment developed by BISRA for rapid sampling using filters is described by Granville and Jaffrey [30].

The I.C.I. sampler forms one of the most useful of the composite equipment [3, 10] (figure 2.11). It consists of a nozzle attached to a heated probe, glass-wool filter, cooling coil, catchpot, orifice plate flowmeter and an ejector. Appropriate manometers and thermometers are provided so that the necessary calculations for correct isokinetic sampling can be made.

With the C.E.G.B. mark II dust sampler the dust is collected in a glass fabric or paper thimble. Details of design and operation are given in [10, p. 605].

With the impingement-type filters, the dust is classified according to its aerodynamic properties. This is preferable to microscopic methods or sieving since these properties may more easily be related to particle behaviour on leaving the stack, the approximate area of deposition and the probable point of respiratory deposition. Further, the classification is carried out in situ which reduces the probable breakdown of flocculates.

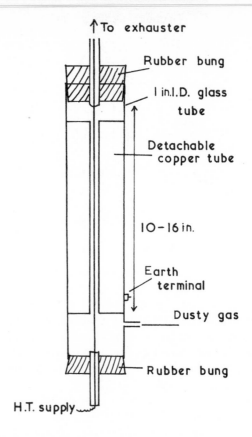

Fig. 2.9. Electrostatic precipitator for dusty gases.

2.3.3 Ancillary apparatus

(a) Pitot tube (B.S. 1042). This should face directly into the gas stream with a maximum deviation (angle of yaw) of 10°.

(b) Pressure measuring instrument (s). An inclined gauge reading 0·05 to 0·30 mbar to ± 0·01 mbar.

(c) A probe tube to which nozzle is attached maintained at a temperature sufficient to prevent condensation. If the dust collector is fitted immediately after the nozzle and before the probe, this requirement does not hold. In the former case the probe should be constructed of stainless steel.

(d) Flow and temperature-measuring device to measure V to 5% and T to 5° K.

(e) A control valve to regulate flow through the equipment.

(f) A method for withdrawing sample at required rate for isokinetic sampling.

2.3.4 On-line dust extractions

An on-line isokinetic particle sampler for continuously sampling finely divided

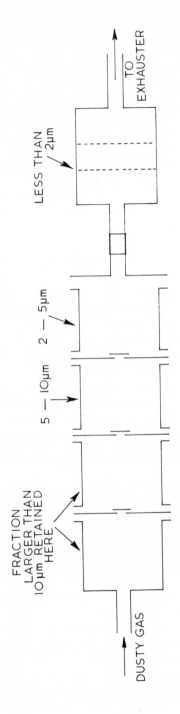

Fig. 2.10. Train of impingement samplers.

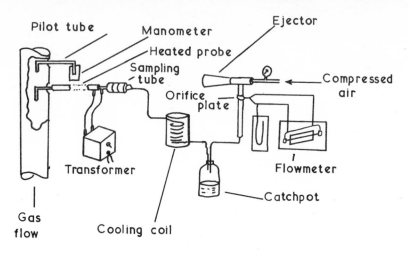

Fig. 2.11. Equipment for sampling dust from flowing gases.

material being transported in a flow system is the subject of a patent[34] (figure 2.12). The particulate material flows through conduit 1 and is sampled at nozzle 2, which is positioned high enough into the flow stream so that it is not affected by any disturbances in the flow due to housing 3.

An artificial atmosphere of dry nitrogen gas is maintained within sampling tube 4 to control the pressure within the tube as well as to transport particles out of it. The nitrogen exits at 5 creating a partial vacuum at the intersection with 2, thus drawing the particulates into the system isokinetically. The pressure is maintained at the pressure in conduit 1 by outlet 6, which is connected to the automatic differential pressure control 4. When a difference in pressure is noted, a signal is fed to the automatic valve which varies the valve position to maintain equal pressure.

2.3.5 The Anderson stack sampler

The Andersen stack sampler [43] has a cascade impactor type sampling head which, in operation, is mounted inside the flue (figure 2.13).

The sampler contains nine jet plates, each having a pattern of precision-drilled orifices. The nine plates, separated by 2·5 mm stainless-steel spacers, divide the sample into eight fractions of particle size ranges. The jets on each plate are arranged in concentric circles which are offset on each succeeding plate. The size of the orifices is the same on the given plate, but is smaller for each succeeding downstream plate. Therefore, as the sample is drawn through the sampler at a constant flow rate, the jets of air flowing through any particular plate direct the particulates toward the collection area on the downstream plate directly below the circles of jets on the plate above. Since the jet diameters decrease from plate to plate, the velocities increase such that whenever the velocity imparted to a particle is sufficiently great, its inertia will overcome the aerodynamic drag of the turning airstream and the

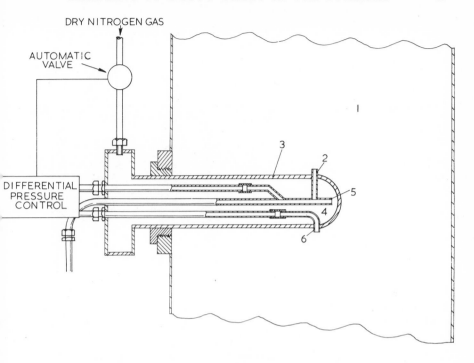

Fig. 2.12. Isokinetic particle sampler (Lynn).

particle will be impacted on the collection surface. Otherwise, the particle remains in the airstream and proceeds to the next plate. Since the particle deposit areas are directly below the jets, seven of the plates act as both a jet stage and a collection plate. Thus, no. 0 plate is only a jet stage and no. 8 plate is only a collection plate.

The Andersen stack sampler has been calibrated by several independent laboratories in order to arrive at the correct respective size cuts for each stage. The calibrators are referenced to unit density (1 g cm^{-3}), spherical particles, so that the aerodynamically equivalent-sized particles collected on each stage are always identical for any given flow rate. For this reason, a stack sample containing a mixture of shapes and densities is fractionated and collected according to its aerodynamic characteristics and is aerodynamically equivalent in size to the unit density spheres collected on each specific stage during calibration.

2.4 Corrections for anisokinetic sampling [11]
A measure of dust content can be expressed as:

(a)   The mass flow rate of dust. This is the mass of dust passing per unit time across an element of area of the gas stream. In isokinetic sampling, the quantity directly determined is the amount of dust passing, during the time of sampling, across an area in the gas stream equal to the area of the nozzle opening.

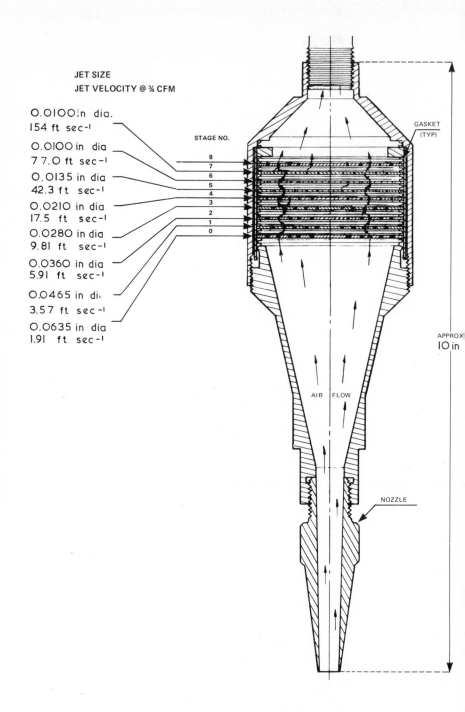

JET SIZE
JET VELOCITY @ ¾ CFM

STAGE NO.

0.0100 in dia.
154 ft sec⁻¹

0.0100 in dia
77.0 ft sec⁻¹

0.0135 in dia
42.3 ft sec⁻¹

0.0210 in dia
17.5 ft sec⁻¹

0.0280 in dia
9.81 ft sec⁻¹

0.0360 in dia
5.91 ft sec⁻¹

0.0465 in dia
3.57 ft sec⁻¹

0.0635 in dia
1.91 ft sec⁻¹

8
7
6
5
4
3
2
1
0

GASKET
(TYP)

APPROX
10 in

AIR FLOW

NOZZLE

Fig. 2.13. The Andersen stack sampler.

(b)   The concentration of dust. This is the mass of dust per unit volume of gas, and is usually calculated from the ratio of the mass of dust collected to the volume of gas sampled. When sampling is isokinetic, the concentration of dust in the sample is equal to the concentration in the gas stream at the point of sampling.

When the sampling velocity differs from that of the gas stream (anisokinetic sampling), the gas streamlines are disturbed, causing some particles to be deflected from their original direction of motion, so that the quantity of particles entering the probe per unit time will differ from that entering under isokinetic conditions (see figure 2.14). It will be less when the sampling velocity is less than that of the gas stream, because some of the gas that should enter the probe flows past it carrying some particles with it. Conversely, if the sampling velocity is higher the amount of particles entering the probe will be too high. It is easy to envisage what happens in the case of very fine or very coarse particles. When the particles are very fine, they follow closely the deflected gas streams and the amount entering is proportional to the sampling velocity. That is, the *concentration* of fine particles in the sample is equal to that of the gas stream, irrespective of the sampling velocity. When the particles are coarse, their inertia is so great that they persist in their original direction of motion, the amount entering the probe is independent of the sampling velocity. That is, the *mass flow rate* of coarse particles is measured correctly irrespective of the sampling velocity.

If the particles cover a range of sizes, anisokinetic sampling affects not only the mass of particles in the sample, but also their size distribution. During prolonged sampling the flow rate of the gas stream may vary throughout the test, and it may not be possible to vary the sampling rate to compensate for this. A method for correcting this is described later.

2.4.1 Theory

The mass of particles M_s entering the nozzle at a sampling velocity V_s is related to the mass M entering the nozzle when the sampling velocity V equals the gas velocity by the equation:

$$\frac{M_s}{M} = (1-\alpha)\frac{V_s}{V} + \alpha \qquad (2.1)$$

where α is a parameter depending on the inertia of the particles and the gas flow pattern at the sampling nozzle, and is constant for V_s/V between $\frac{1}{2}$ and 4.

$$\text{For fine particles} \qquad \alpha = 0 \quad \text{and} \quad \frac{M_s}{M} = \frac{V_s}{V} \qquad (2.2)$$

as stated above.

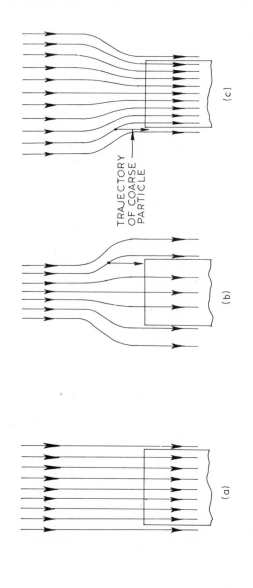

Fig. 2.14. (a) Isokinetic sampling; representative concentration and grading. (b) Sampling velocity too low; excess of coarse particles. (c) Sampling velocity too high; deficiency of coarse particles.

For coarse particles $\quad \alpha = 1 \quad$ and $\quad \dfrac{M_s}{M} = 1$ $\hfill (2.3)$

as stated earlier, i.e. the correct flow rate is obtained whatever the value of the ratio of sampling velocity to gas velocity [13].

Badzioch [14] shows that:

$$\alpha = 1 - \lambda/L \, \exp(-L/\lambda) \hfill (2.4)$$

where λ is the range of the particle, given by:

$$\lambda = \frac{vV}{g} \hfill (2.5)$$

v being the free-falling diameter of the particle, V being the velocity of the gas stream, and λ the distance a particle would travel before coming to rest if projected in a still gas with velocity V.

For particles obeying Stokes' law:

$$\lambda = \frac{(\rho_s - \rho_f) \, d^2 V}{18\eta} \hfill (2.6)$$

where d is the particle diameter,

$\qquad \rho_s, \rho_f$ are the densities of solid and fluid respectively,

$\qquad \eta$ is the viscosity of the fluid,

L is a length representative of the distance upstream of the nozzle over which there is a disturbance in the gas stream [12]:

Internal diameter of nozzle (in)	$\frac{3}{8}$	$\frac{1}{2}$	$\frac{5}{8}$	$\frac{3}{4}$	$\frac{7}{8}$	1
L (cm)	4·5	4·0	3·5	3·0	2·5	2·0 .

In the practice of dust sampling, it is difficult to achieve truly isokinetic conditions. The true dust concentration in the gas stream is given by:

$$c = \frac{M}{aV} \hfill (2.7)$$

where a is the area of the sampling nozzle.

It follows from equation (2.2) that, when sampling fine dusts, the observed concentration will be nearly correct whatever the sampling velocity, provided it is calculated from the rate of dust collection M_s divided by the volume rate of sampling aV_s.

When sampling coarse dusts anisokinetically, a correct value is obtained if M_s is divided by (aV) from equation (2.3).

When the fine dust method is used, the apparent dust concentration C_s is:

$$C_s = \frac{M_s}{aV_s} = M \left\{ (1-\alpha)\frac{V_s}{V} + \alpha \right\} /aV_s \hfill (2.8)$$

Substituting for M from equation (2.7) gives:

$$C_s = C\left\{\frac{\alpha V}{V_s} + (1-\alpha)\right\} \tag{2.9}$$

The percentage error E is given by:

$$E = 100\frac{C_s - C}{C} = -100\alpha\left\{\frac{V_s - V}{V_s}\right\} \tag{2.10}$$

Similarly, when the coarse dust method is used, the apparent dust concentration is given by:

$$C_s^1 = C\left\{(1-\alpha)\frac{V_s}{V} + \alpha\right\}. \tag{2.11}$$

The percentage error E^1 is given by:

$$E^1 = 100\frac{C_s^1 - C}{C} = 100(1-\alpha)\frac{V_s - V}{V}. \tag{2.12}$$

The latter method will give the more accurate result if E^1 is smaller than E, if:

$$\alpha > \frac{V_s}{V + V_s}. \tag{2.13}$$

True dust concentrations may be determined by two anisokinetic tests and α evaluated from equation (2.9). Other equations ((2.1) and (2.11)) may be used if the mass flow rate and the 'coarse dust' method is used. α may also be determined by comparing the measured size distribution of a sample with the known size distribution of a dust.

Sampling at a fixed velocity leads to some simplifications of the apparatus and procedure, and it can be used when the particles are known to be very fine or very coarse. Figure 2.15 shows errors in the *concentration* calculated by the fine dust method (equation (2.10). The particle density is taken as 1 g cm^{-2} and the viscosity $2 \cdot 5 \times 10^{-4}$ poise. For 5 μm particles , the error will not exceed 7% if the sampling velocity is kept constant at 25 ft s^{-1}, and the gas velocity varies from 15 to 60 ft s^{-1} It can also be seen that the error will be numerically smaller when the sampling velocity exceeds the gas velocity. The error in *mass flow rates* (equation (2.12)) is very much higher.

Figure 2.16 shows the errors in the *mass flow rates* of coarse particles under the above conditions. It also represents the errors in the concentration by the coarse dust method. It can be seen that errors in sampling grit particles with a fixed velocity is small, particularly when the sampling velocity is less than the gas velocity.

2.5 Other techniques (29)

For *in situ* measurements the absorption of visible light, gamma rays and accoustical energy have also been investigated. The most widely attempted techniques have

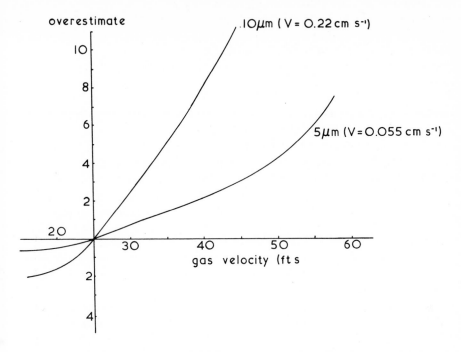

Fig. 2.15. Errors in concentration of particles sampled at a fixed velocity of 25 ft s^{-1} with a nozzle of 1-in diameter. Density of dust is 1 g cm^{-2}.

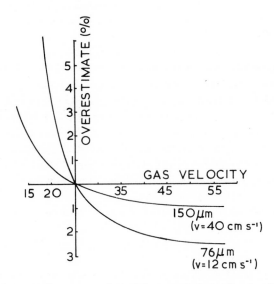

Fig. 2.16. Errors in mass flow rates of particles sampled at a fixed velocity.

used absorption of visible light [21–23]. The two problems associated with this type of device are that turbidity is a function of the projected surface area of particles within the light beam, whereas most requirements are for a mass-dependent technique, and that the light absorbed by a particle is not linearly related to size, i.e.:

$$\text{turbidity} = k \ c \ L \ S_w \ K$$

where k is a shape factor,
         c is concentration of particles in the beam,
         L is the length of the light path in the suspension,
         S_w is the weight specific surface of the particles in the beam,
         K, the extinction coefficient, is the ratio of the light cut off by the particles
            to the light which would be cut off if the laws of geometric optics held.
Despite these objections the technique is useful for continuous monitoring.

A similar approach utilized gamma radiation from a nuclear source and a Geiger-tube detector [24]. Absorption of the energy is again a function of path length, concentration and absorption factor, In this case the absorption factor is proportional to the atomic number, hence the mass of the particles, provided they are reasonably uniform in chemical composition.

A third technique is the absorption of accoustical energy [25]. The response is influenced by individual particle characteristics and gas density and gives very poor sensitivity to particle concentration.

Continuous analysis of extracted particulates has also been investigated. Several of these are a direct measurement of the mass collected and the primary problem is related to representative sampling. A system based on an electrobalance has been used as a direct measure of mass. The extracted particulate is deposited on a collection media, which is then automatically cut off, transferred to the balance and weighed. The approach is really semi-continuous and would have application primarily where high accuracy on variable particulate is required. A second technique for direct mass measurement is based on frequency of oscillation as a function of the mass of material deposited on the surface. The most widely investigated extraction approach is based on collection of the particulate on a filter media and detection of the mass through absorption of low-energy Beta-particles [26]. Absorption of the energy is a function of the total mass collected and chemical composition of the sample. Indirect measurements based on electrical, light absorbance and light reflectande have been employed. The electrical devices measure current transferred by the particles from a charging zone to discharge collection plates [27, 28]. Light absorbance and reflectance have also been used.

The application of continuous monitoring instrumentation presents fundamental difficulties. In particular the techniques do not satisfy usual requirements. They may be used as process monitors after complete characterization of the system using manual methods. However, the engineer should be fully aware of the complexities introduced by the interaction between particulate properties and potential measurement approaches.

References

[1] B.S. 3405: (1961), *Simplified Methods for Measurement of Grit and Dust Emission from Chimneys.*

[2] B.S. 893: (1940), *Methods of Testing Dust-extraction Plant and the Emission of Solids from Chimneys.*

[3] Stairmand, C.J. (1951), 'Sampling of dust-laden gases', *Trans. Inst. Chem. Engrs,* **29**, 31.

[4] Hawksley, P.G.W., Badzioch, S., and Blackett, J.H. (1961), *Measurement of Solids in Flue Gases,* British Coal Utilisation Res. Assoc., Leatherhead.

[5] Anon. (1941), 'Sampling of gas-borne particles', *Engineering,* **152**, 141, 181.

[6] Nonhebel, G. (ed.) (1964), *Gas Purification Processes,* Newnes.

[7] Lees, B., and Morley, M.C. (1960), 'A routine sampler for detecting variations in the emission of dust and grit', *J. Inst. Fuel,* **33**, 90Δ95.

[8] D2928. (1970), *Method for Sampling Stacks for Particulate Matter,* American Society for testing and materials.

[9] Walter, E., (1957), *Staub,* **53**, 880.

[10] Szabolcs, G. (1959), *Energia es atomtechnika,* **9**, 12.

[11] Badzioch, S. (1960), 'Correction for anisokinetic sampling of gas-borne dust particles', *J. Inst. Fuel,* **33**, 512, 106—10.

[12] Howells, T.J., Beer, J.M., and Fells, I. (1960), 'Sampling of gas-borne particles', *J. Inst. Fuel,* **33**, 512.

[13] Whiteley, A.B., and Reed, L.E. (1959), 'The effect of probe shape on the accuracy of sampling flue gases for dust content', *J. Inst. Fuel,* **32**, 316.

[14] Badzioch, S. (1957), *Members Information Circular,* No. 174, B.C.U.R.A., see 4.

[15] Davies, C.N., *Dust is Dangerous,* Faber and Faber.

[16] Watson, H.H. (1954), *Am. Ind. Hyg. Assoc., Quarterly,* **15**, 1.

[17] Haines, G.F., and Hemeon, W.C.L., *Information Circular,* No. 5, American Iron and Steel Institute.

[18] Hemeon, W.C.L., and Haines, G.F. (1954), 'The magnitude of errors in stack dust sampling', *Air Repair,* **4**, 159.

[19] Badzioch, S. (1959), 'Collection of gas-borne particles by means of an aspirated sampling nozzle, *J. Appl. Phys.,* **10**, 26.

[20] Thring, M.W. (1957), *Air Pollution,* Butterworths.

[21] Dorizin, V.G., and La Mer., V.K. (1959), *J. Colloid Sci.,* **14**, 74.

[22] Kerker, M., and Matijevic, E. (1958), *J. Air Poll. Control Assoc.,* **18**, 665.

[23] Wober, W.G. (1968), *Research and Developement,* **12**, 18.

[24] Molzhe, J., and Demmrich, H. (1969), *Neue Hue He,* **14**, 198.

[25] Mitchell, R.L., and Engdahl, R. B. (1968), *J. Air Poll. Control Assoc.,* **18**, 216.

[26] McShane, W.P., and Bulba, E., (1968), *J. Air Poll. Control Assoc.,* **18**, 216.

[27] Grindell, D.H. (1960), *Proc. Inst. Elec. Eng.,* **34**.

[28] Konig, W., and Rock, H. (1960), *Staub,* **20**, 212.

[29] Dorsey, J.A., and Burckle, J.O. (1971), 'Particulate emissions and process monitors', *Chem. Eng. Progress,* **67**, 8, 92—6.

[30] Granville, R.A., and Jaffrey, W.G. (Feb. 1959), 'Dust and grit in flue gases engineering', **187**, 4851, 285—8.

[31] Langejan, J.J.D. (1969), 'Description and operating instructions of the C.S.I.R. sampling equipment for isokinetic sampling of dust laden gas', *S. Africa*

Council for Scientific and Industrial Res. Sp. Rep. 123.

[32] Overbeck, E.M., and Thayer, K.B. (1970), 'Review on particulate sampling', A.S.M.E., Paper 70, P.E.T. -1.

[33] Bahco, A.B. (1969), *Particle detector,* Br. Pat. Spec. 1, 047, (Br. Pat. Abstr.), Dec. 12, 9 (49), D1.

[34] Lynn, L.G. (1969), *Isokinetic particle sampler*, U.S. patent, 3, 473, 388, 21.

[35] Granville, R.A., and Jaffrey, W.G. (1959), *Engineering,* **187**, 4851, 285–8.

[36] Granville, R.A., and Jaffrey, W.G. (1969), *J. Inst. Fuel,* **42**, 225.

[37] Granville, R.A., and Jaffrey, W.G. (1968), *Smokeless Air,* **147**, 59–61.

[38] Sansone, E.B. (Sept.–Oct., 1969), *Am. Ind. Hyg. Assoc. J.,* 487–93; also (1967),'Sampling airborne solids in ducts following a 90° bend', Univ. of Michigan, Ph. D. thesis.

[39] American Society for Mechanical Engineers, (1957), *Determining dust concentration in a gas stream,* Power test code No. 27.

[40] Wolfe, E.A. (1961), *Gas Flow Rate and Particulate Matter Determination of Gaseous Effluents*, Bay area air pollution control district 1480, Mission Street, San Fransisco, Calif., U.S.A.

[41] Los Angeles Air pollution control district (1963), *Source Testing Manual,* 434, San Pedro Street, Los Angeles 13, Calif., U.S.A.

[42] Airflow developments (1968),'New dust and smoke monitor', *Smokeless air,* **147**, 59–61.

[43] Andersen, A.A. (1958), *J. Bacterial,* 76, 471–84.

3 Sampling and Sizing from the Atmosphere

3.1 Introduction

Sampling from the atmosphere is carried out mainly to monitor health hazards. The Clean Air Act, 1956, requires the discharge of effluent into the atmosphere to be reduced to a minimum using 'the best practical means' and health inspectors have been appointed to enforce this nebulous legislation. Problems facing inspectors include identifying the source of collected particulate matter and determining whether it is liable to be injurious to health and whether it constitutes a 'nuisance'. Physical and chemical assay may help to resolve these problems.

Particle size determination of collected dust is also necessary for determining the grade efficiency curves for dust arresting plant. The techniques involved here are usually quite different to those used for sizing discharge from chimneys and flue gases, since the quantities of collected material are usually much greater and the individual particles are more robust.

Collecting and examining closed atmospheres, such as are found in factories and mines, is also of importance, since dusty atmospheres are often injurious to health and sometimes form explosion hazards. Examples of the former are asbestos giving rise to asbestosis; silica, silicosis and coal dust, pneumoconiosis.

Methods of sampling and measuring the size distribution of aerosols have been studied extensively [1—4], and a detailed survey of equipment available in the U.K. has been presented [5]. The broad objective is to obtain a representative sample, either in such a way that the health of nuisance hazard may be estimated immediately or in such a way that it may be examined further without altering the characteristics of interest. For these reasons some sampling devices have been developed which automatically size grade the collected particles and others which collect the particulate matter so that further examination may be carried out with the minimum of effort, e.g. gravimetric assay for concentration determination and microscopic analysis for size grading.

Many aerosol particles consist of flocs or aggregates and in collecting and redispersing them the identity of the original distribution is often lost. This may be of little importance if the toxic effect is being examined, but of fundamental importance when settling behaviour is being studied. The statistical accuracy accuracy of the collected samples is usually very low since small samples are collected from enormous inhomogeneous volumes of gases. For this reason the expense of sophisticated collecting devices cannot always be justified, and collecting devices which are expensive in terms of highly qualified operators may be similarly discarded. It is also found that particular industries have developed their own equipment. For these and other reasons a wide range of sampling devices are available. They tend, however, to fall into one of the following categories:

(1)   Inertial techniques, impingement, impaction and sedimentation;
(2)   Filtration;
(3)   Electrostatic precipitation;
(4)   Thermal precipitation;
(5)   Light scattering.

3.2 Inertial techniques

Simple sedimentation techniques are suitable for high particle concentrations. With low concentrations a deep cell is required to give a sufficiently dense deposit, but the time of sampling becomes impractically long. Sedimentation cells have the useful property that the particles are not altered physically in the course of collection; usually there is no size selection [6, 7].

Size distribution measurements may be made using the Casella settlement dust counter, in which a volume of air is enclosed in a cylinder at the base of which is an arrangement for exposing a number of microscope slides in sequence. By timing the exposures and counting the number of particles collected on each slide, a particle size distribution may be obtained.

The earliest methods of sampling gas-borne particles have incorporated impingement devices [13–15]. The principle is shown in figure 3.1. The large jet with low velocity will deposit the larger particles on the slide, while the small jet will deposit the smaller particles on a subsequent slide.

All impactors are designed to separate particles from gas streams by their inertia which causes them to impact against a collecting plate when the gas streams are made to abruptly change direction. Owens [16] and Ferry [17] used single jets and a dry glass slide to collect the samples which were then analysed by microscopy. A comprehensive review of early techniques used for air-pollution studies is to be found in [16].

Modern impactors both sample and classify in order to reduce the subsequent labour of the microscope examination. The most versatile and popular aerosol sampler and grader is the 'cascade impactor' developed by May [18], and many variations of the instrument exist (figure 3.2).

The May cascade impactor samples liquid or solid particles from 0·5 to 50 μm diameter and deposits them in four size fractions on separate glass discs. The intake velocity is kept deliberately low in order that delicate particles may be deposited without damage; for this reason it is particularly useful for establishing the efficacy of sprays for spreading insecticides, fine mists, atomized liquids, as well as pollen, spores, smokes and other delicate structures. The glass collecting discs are coated with a medium suitable for the material to be collected. For solid particles, a non-drying, sticky film is used. For liquid particles, dyes, etc., other media have been

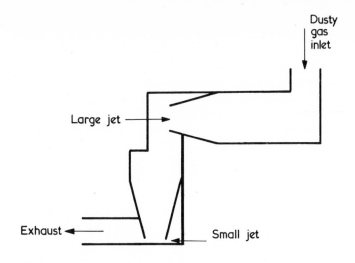

Fig. 3.1. Impingement device for collecting airborne particles.

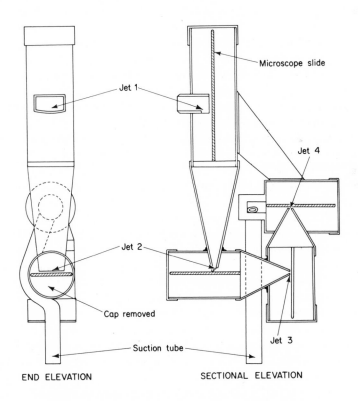

Fig. 3.2. The cascade impactor (after May [18]).

devised. The coated discs are loaded into each of the four stages; a filter paper, if required, is put into the fifth stage for the collection of fines and a source of suction is connected to the outlet pipe. After running for a given time, the discs are unloaded and mounted on glass slides. The slides are evaluated by strip counting or, for more accurate analysis, a Porton graticule (see chapter 6) is used in the microscope eyepiece. An alternative procedure is to calibrate the impactor [19].

The impaction process was examined theoretically by May and later by others [20, 21], all of whom showed that the impaction efficiency is related to a dimensionless parameter ψ given by:

$$\psi = \frac{V\rho d^2}{\eta L} \times \text{const.}$$

where ρ is material density, V is the air velocity across the impaction surface, d is the Stokes' diameter, η is the air viscosity and L is the jet width.

May's impactor has been used by Laskin [22] on heavy aerosol particles. Other writers have carried out extensive theoretical and experimental work with cascade impactors [20, 23, 24]. Characteristics and design of impactors have also been improved [25–27]. Davies and Aylward [20] in a theoretical study of rectangular jets, showed that the sharpness of the cut should improve if the jet-to-slide clearance is reduced to approximately $\frac{3}{8}$ of the jet width.

Einbinder [28] suggested this should also hold for circular jets, a suggestion that was investigated by Pilcher et al.,[25] who sized particles from 25 to 0·5 μm diameter and found that the ratio was not critical. A modified impactor extending into the sub-micron range is described by Sonkin [29]. Special duty impactors have also been developed, e.g. Brink's five-stage cascade impactor for sampling and grading acid mists in the size range 0·3 to 3·0 μm [30].

A multistage impactor was described by Anderson [31] for use primarily with biological material in which the gas stream passes through small circular holes in a plate and impinges on a prepared surface in a Petri dish. A calibration of this impactor has been reported [32] and a simplified application to the study of airborne fungus [38].

Buchholz [33, 34] describes a low-pressure cascade impactor and Burkholz uses one for droplet size determination in the 0·5 to 10 μm size range [35]. Jacobson et al. describe a new midget impactor [36]. The commercially available four-stage Cassella cascade impactor, samples at the rate of $17\frac{1}{2}$ l min^{-1} with a size range 0·5 to 50 μm. It has already been tested, with particular reference to calibration, by Soole [37]. The standard dust sampling equipment in the U.S.A. is the midget impinger [39] developed from the Greenburg-Smith impinger [13]. This employs a jet and plate immersed in a liquid of low volatility so that the arrested particles are retained in suspension in the liquid [40–46]. Gelman Hawksley manufacture one instrument which operates at 1 cfm and a midget impinger which operates at 0·1 cfm.

In the Konimeter [47], a measured volume of air is sucked through a narrow aperture at high velocity by means of a spring-loaded piston. The particles impinge on a slide coated with adhesive, so that the particles may be counted microscopic-ally. The collecting efficiency of this instrument is reported to be low, aggregation on the slide makes counting difficult, and the instrument cannot be recommended for size analysis [48]. Sizing may be speeded up with this instrument using a newly developed scanner.

In the Owens jet counter [16] and the Bausch & Lomb dust counter [49] the air passes through a humidifying chamber and then expands through a narrow slit. Moisture condenses on the particles, thus aiding the deposition. Such devices have a very variable efficiency depending on the type of aerosol being examined [48].

Cunningham *et al.* [50] report on a programme for classifying airborne particu-late material with respect to time and size using inertial impaction. The major chemical constituents were measured using infrared spectroscopy and showed vari-ations of the chemistry with size and time. This programme was initiated as a result of the Pasadena Smog Aerosol Study [51] and followed a similar study by Whitby *et al.* [52—54], who concluded that in a photochemical smog sub-micrometre particles arise from condensation and coagulation of photochemical reaction products, whereas larger particles arise from reflotation or other mechanical sources. Cunningham used a four-stage Lundgren impactor [55, 56] which uses rotating drums as the impaction surface in each stage. The impactor operates at a flow rate of 6·8 m^3 h^{-1} and collects samples with mass-median diameters of 12, 3, 1·2 and 0·3 μm. Using a continuous drive mechanism, it was operated for 21 continuous hours and later, using a stepwise mode of operation, for 3 days with 3 hours at each step. The particles were deposited on a Mylar film and the size distribution deter-mined by weighing. The Lundgren impactor has also been used in comparison studies with a light scattering counter [121] and to determine variation of particle size concentration and composition with time [122].

Leary [57] has used an autoradiographic technique in which radioactive particles are sized through their emission. A filter carrying a deposit of radioactive particles is placed in contact with a photographic plate for selected exposure times. The number of tracks is counted and an equation applied to calculate the size of each particle. The technique can only be applied to small particles (0·1 to 20 μm) and has the advantage that aggregates may be distinguished from single particles. Cowan [58] has reported on a simpler method which depends on the formation of a visible spot on the film.

In the Cascade Centripeter [128—130] air is sampled at 30 l min^{-1}. When the air stream passes through an orifice, the central flow lines pass right through, and the peripheral flow lines deflected sharply and particles separated from them by their inertia. A series of three orifices of diminishing diameter are used to give cuts at 14, 4 and 1·2 μm.

The Conifuge, which consists of a cone and shell rotating at 3000 rev min^{-1}, draws in 25 ml of dusty air per minute (see figure 3.3). The indrawn cloud is winn-owed by an internally circulating stream of clean air in such a way that the particles are classified according to their settling velocities and deposited on a glass slide in a continuously graded sample [59]. Unit density spheres in the size range 0·8 to 30 μm

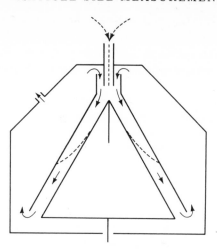

Fig. 3.3. The Conifuge (after Sawyer and Walton [59]). The solid arrows represent air flow, the broken arrows represent particle trajectories.

can be handled, the size grading being carried out by microscope count. Mathematical and graphical solutions relating deposition point and particle size are provided. A description of the application of this instrument for measuring the distribution and concentration of cigarette smoke is given by Keith [60]. The Goetz aerosol spectrometer [61, 62] consists of a centrifuge heliz which collects the airborne particles and a console to monitor and control the instrument. Particles are graded and deposited on aremovable strips from which they may be removed for analysis by titration, or a microscopic examination may be carried out. A conical aerosol centrifuge has also been developed by Stoeber [63].

In order to determine the concentration of respirable dust in a cloud it is necessary to remove large particles which do not reach the lung and efficiently collect the fines. In a study of collection through vertical and horizontal ducts (elutriator), Walton [63] showed that, with the former, the sampling efficiency is $1 - (f/v)$, where the sampling efficiency is defined as the fractional number of particles of falling speed f collected with an intake velocity v; with the latter, the sampling efficiency for a volume flow rate Q is $1 - fA/Q$, where A is the horizontally projected flow area of the duct. As a result of these studies, a horizontal elutriator was developed with a cut at a falling speed of 0·15 cm s^{-1} which is equivalent to a 7 μm sphere of density 1 g ml^{-1} falling in air; later instruments were constructed to give a cut at 5 μm [64]. The sample is collected on filter paper and may be examined gravimetrically or by using a microscope. In the discussion following Walton's paper [65] Dawes drew attention to field work carried out by Safety in Mines Research Establishment (SMRE) with a horizontal elutriator [66] in which it was found that the size selection characteristic was not stable with time, but that over an eight-hour period the cut size rose from 7 to 10 μm due, it was suggested, to redispersion of dust collected on the elutriator plates caused by the entrance of large particles. This effect was not noted by Wright of the Pneumoconiosis Research Unit of the Medical Research Council in Cardiff, who was working on an elutriator, now available as the Hexlet, which was similar to that of Walton. In this instrument, unit density spheres larger than 7 μm diameter are collected in a soxhlet thimble and the weight determined gravimetrically. The aspiration rate is 50 l min^{-1} compared to the 2·5 l min^{-1} of the gravimetric dust sampler.

The SMRE work resulted in the development of several instruments for sampling respirable dust in coal mines and these are marketed by Casella. The Simgard [8, 9, 10] is based on a parallel plate being collected on a membrane filter. Suction is effected by ejecting a stream of carbon dioxide gas from a small nozzle into the diffuser throat.

In the Simped [11, 12], the parallel plate elutriator are replaced by cyclones. The instrument weighs only 805 g and samples at the rate of 1·85 l min^{-1}, taking its power from the miner's cap lamp battery.

Other specialized sampling devices are: the plutonium dust sampler [64] for collecting particles larger than 1 μm at an aspiration rate of 1000 l min^{-1}; personal air samplers, for long period samples of respirable dust at an aspiration rate of 2 l min^{-1}; the Hirst spore trap for long period sampling of airborne spores and pollens and the airborne bacteria sampler for sampling bacteria for subsequent counting after incubation.

3.3 Filtration

Most filtration methods are unsuitable for collecting solid aerosol particles for microscopic analysis, since aggregation tends to occur on the filter if concentrated aerosols are sampled, while smaller particles tend to penetrate deeply between the fibres of the usual fibrous material used as filtering media so that they cannot be microscopically counted. Such filters are, however, useful for gravimetric assay.

Filtration is the simplest method of removing particles from the atmosphere for subsequent analysis; however, removal of particles from a filter and dispersion prior to size analysis will usually completely alter the size characteristics of the sample due to the breakdown of flocs. The most efficient filter mediums for this purpose are the membrane filters which can exhibit almost 100% collection efficiency for particle size above 0·01 μm with the bulk of the material deposited on or near the surface. These filters consist of cellulose esters which are soluble in acetone, so that it is possible to dissolve away the filter and transfer the deposited material to prepared surfaces for further examination (Kalmus [65]). The deposited particles may be examined *in situ*, using reflection microscopy, or the membrane can be made transparent by adding a few drops of cedar oil and examination carried out by transmission microscopy.

3.4 Electrostatic precipitation

When a charged particle passes between two electrodes carrying a high electric potential, it will move normally to the direction of flow under the force of the electric field.

The electrostatic precipitator, based on this principle, consists of an ionizing cathode at a high potential surrounded by a collecting anode; typically, these consist of concentric cylinders, the inner one often being a single wire. The dust passes between the cylinders, picks up a charge and travels to the anode where the charge is deposited. For extremely small particles, the charge consists of an excess or deficiency of one electron, and the transfer of electrons from one electrode to the other constitutes an electric current which may be measured with a microammeter. The magnitude of the current indicates the number of particles, and their size may be found by varying the flow rate or the applied potential [66–68]. Details of the design of an ion chamber is given by Hurd and Mullins [120]. This particular equipment has two flat circular plates parallel to each other and maintained at a fixed potential difference.

The trajectories of particles in an electrostatic field depend on their size and their electron charge. Since particles larger than about $0·01 \mu$ may have an excess or deficiency of more than one electron more than one size of particle may be deposited at the same point. An instrument that uses this technique with some success has been developed by Yoshikawa [69]. In order that a microscope count may be carried out the particles are collected on membrane filters.

Instruments based on this principle have been used for aerosols of bacteria [70, 71], and an improved instrument has been described by Morris *et al.* [72]. This instrument consists of a cylindrical glass tube 12 in long and 2 in diameter with a central electrode. The inner surface of the cylinder is coated with a suitable material to act as the other electrode and to collect the samples. With the central electrode at 10 kV and a flow rate of 10 to $20 \ 1 \ min^{-1}$, the collection efficiency was found to be 100%. In one version the cylinder is rotated and contains up to 10 ml of liquid, so that collection in liquid could be effected directly. The principle advantages of this type of instrument are high collection efficiency over a wide size range, low resistance and high flow-rate capacity [73]. It is not very suitable for number concentration measurements. Microscope analysis of the deposited particles may be simplified by placing electron microscope grids [74] or transparent plastic [48] over the anode. Several other studies of this technique have been carried out (see [75, 76]).

3.5 Thermal precipitation

Dust [77, 78] particles in suspension move away from hotter to colder regions. This effect was noted first by Tyndall and later by Lord Rayleigh, and Aitkin showed that the force that caused this movement was thermal in origin.

For particles of the same order of size or greater than the mean free path of the gas molecules, an equation may be developed using 'thermal creep' theory. This is based on the force set up at the gas–solid interface between a particle and the surrounding gas. When the gas temperature increases along the surface, the molecules leaving the surface will have a greater component of velocity in the direction of the temperature increase than when they arrived at the surface. The net result is a creeping flow of gas from the colder to the warmer regions along the surface of the particle giving a net force in the cold direction.

Epstein [79] developed the following equation for the thermal force:

$$F_t = \frac{9\pi\eta^2 D}{2\rho_f T \left(2 + \dfrac{x_g}{x_p}\right)} \frac{dT}{dx}.$$

where D is the particle diameter; η, the gas viscosity; ρ_f, the gas density; T, the gas temperature; dT/dx, the thermal gradient; and x_g and x_p are the thermal conductivities of the gas and particle respectively.

Equating with Stokes' resistance, including Cunningham's correction, gives the velocity in the thermal gradient as:

$$U_t = -\frac{3C\eta}{2\rho T \left(2 + \dfrac{x_g}{x_p}\right)} \frac{dT}{dx}$$

where $C = (1 + 2A\lambda/D)$, see equation (7.18). This equation is found to give good agreement with experimental results.

For very small particles, equations based on the kinetic theory of gases have been developed [80]. Waldmann's equation may be written:

$$U_t = -\frac{1}{\left(5 + \dfrac{\pi}{2}\right)} \cdot \frac{x_g}{P} \frac{dT}{dx}$$

where P is the gas pressure. For further details readers are reffered to [81, p. 417].

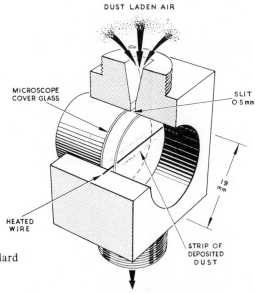

Fig. 3.4. Sampling head of standard thermal precipitator.

This principle is applied in thermal precipitation where the hot body is an electrically heated wire placed between two collecting plates. The thermal precipitator developed by Watson [82] (figure 3.4) consists of a channel 0·51 mm wide between two microscope cover glasses with an axially situated electrically heated wire heated to about 100°C above ambient.

A dust sample, about 9 mm long and 1 mm wide, is collected on each plate. The normal flow is 7 cm³ min⁻¹ and collection efficiency is high for sub-5 μm particles. Larger particles are collected elsewhere in the instrument. The collecting device may be modified so that the sample is collected directly on an electron microscope grid, although transfer of particles from the collecting plate to a suitable film and thence to a grid is a more usual procedure. This instrument is manufactured by C.F. Casella & Co., and also distributed by Mines Safety Appliances.

Direct measurement of collection efficiency indicates that this type of instrument collects virtually all particles from 5 to 0·01 μm in size [83–86].Sampling efficiency has been found to be unaffected by air speeds up to 6 ms⁻¹ [87].

Modifications to the traditional design [88] include a means of centring the wire in position [89], the substitution of a ribbon for the wire to give a more uniform deposit [90], the provision of an inlet elutriator to exclude coarse particles [91], the attachment of a rotating magazine containing six pairs of cover glasses to avoid the contamination arising when glasses have to be transferred from the sampling head to a slide box [92].

The instrument of Beadle and Kitto [93] deposits twelve dust strips on a slide and also employs an inlet elutriator and a bellows driven by clockwork. A reversible water aspirator, much smaller and more convenient than the standard form, has been developed by Wright [94] and is manufactured by Adams. Long running thermal precipitators may be operated for periods of hours rather than minutes. In that of Camber et al. [95] the sample slide rotates continuously; in Walton's [96] the slide oscillator and in that of Orr and Martin [97] the slide is replaced by a transparent tape.

Hamilton's long period (8 hours) dust sampler is the standard instrument for determining dust concentrations in British coal mines [98]. (Casella & Co.). The air enters through an inlet elutriator, then passes over a horizontal slide where particles down to 1 or 2 μm are deposited by gravity settlement, the fine particles are deposited at the far end of the slide by a hot ribbon. Aspiration at 2 cm³ min⁻¹ is by an electric pump energized by the battery that heats the wire.

Balashov et al. [99] have used a composite instrument to obtain samples at very low concentrations. Thermal precipitators sampling large volumes of air and providing dust deposits large enough for weighing have been developed [100]. Casella market one instrument for short period sampling in the size range up to 20 μm for evaluation of health hazards, such as pneumoconiosis and another for long period sampling of respirable dust.

The Thermopositor (figure 3.5) collects samples of dust, smoke, fog, bacteria, pollen and spores. Air at up to 1 l min⁻¹ is drawn into the space between two discs, the upper one being heated and the lower one cooled. The particulate matter is deposited on a substrate of glass, paper, metal foil or membrane.

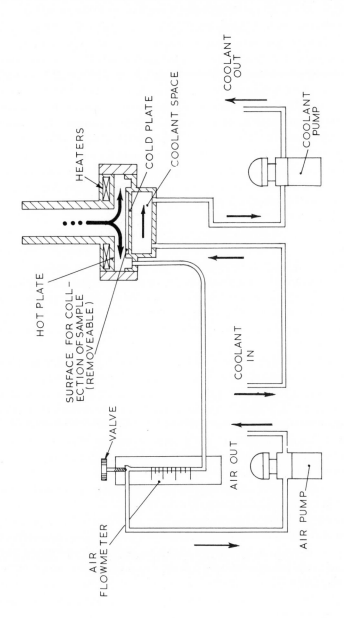

Fig. 3.5. The Thermopositor.

3.6 Light scattering

Aerosol particles scatter light in a manner which is determined by their size and shape and frequency of the scattered light. A number of investigators have applied this phenomenom in the developement of instruments for automatic particle sizing of aerosols. In the machine developed by Gucker *et al.* [101, 102], a stream of aerosol particles in a sheath of filtered air is passed through a light beam, and the light scattered in a forward direction between 1° and 20° by each particle in transit is collected by an optical system which incorporates a photocell. The resulting electrical pulses are amplified, sized and sorted using a multichannel pulse height selector. Very dilute aerosols must be used to avoid coincidence errors. In a later instrument [103] right angle scattering was used. Right angle scattering is also used in the Aerosoloscope [104] which draws in air at the rate of $1.8 \, l \, min^{-1}$ and dilutes it to give a maximum count rate of 2000 particles per minute. The resulting electrical pulses are graded into twelve size channels corresponding to sizes in the 1 to 60 μm range at initial concentrations of up to several thousand particles per cubic centimetre.

The modern theory of light scattering as developed by Mie is dealt with in detail by van de Hulst [106]. In particular, the radial distribution of scattered intensity is a function of particle size, wavelength of the incident light, and refractive index of the scattering medium. The changing intensity of forward scattered light with changing particle size is more sensitive than at any other angle. In later commercial equipment full-forward scattered radiation is detected in conjuction with light traps to eliminate the superimposed incident light which would otherwise swamp the scattered light.

The Bausch & Lomb dust counter 40-1 uses the near-forward light scattering principle [105] (figure 3.6). The direct light is captured by a light trap and completely absorbed, and light scattered through an angle of from 24° to 40° is reflected via a parabolic mirror to a photomultiplier (figure 3.6). The instrument is notable for its built-in calibration system and is designed to operate in the following size ranges: 0.3, 0.5, 1.0, 2.0, 5.0 and 10 μm in seven increments. Incorporated in the instrument is a dilution system which permits counting at dust concentrations of up to 10^6 particles per cubic foot.

The Royco airborne dust counter works for a similar size range and is available with or without a gas dilution system (figure 3.7).

These instruments have not been adopted for routine use in mines because of the stringent power and weight considerations imposed by practical considerations. For these reasons the above principles have been applied by the Centre for Air Environmental Studies in the construction of a battery driven portable counter [107]. The CAES portable instrument can handle 1500 particles per cubic centimetre at several size levels with instantaneous readout. Since no light trap is employed a compromise viewing angle of 135° to the incident radiation is used.

The HIAC automatic portable counter employs light blocking, the attenuation pulses being measured as particles are drawn through the measurement zone (figure 3.8). Five standard models are available with one to five size channels with a claimed

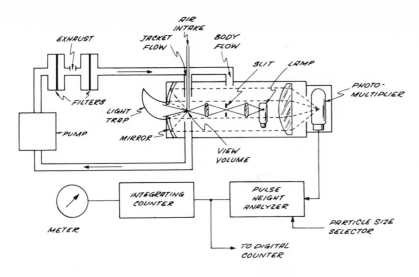

Fig. 3.6. Functional block diagram of the dust counter.

size range of from 2 to 9000 μm at flow rates from 20 to 225 000 cm^3 min^{-1} depending on the particle size range.

The errors with light scattering particle counters are discussed by Kratel [108] and instruments are compared by Rimberg and Keafer [109] who find little agreement between them.

3.7 Miscellaneous techniques

The Langer acoustical particle counter [110–113] samples particles through a narrow tube, and a sound pulse is generated as their speed is reduced due to projection into a wide exit cavity. In its present state of development, it responds to all + 30 μm particles, misses some of the − 30 μm particles and has a lower limit of sensitivity of 10 μm: Operating flow rates are 10 to 100 ms^{-1} and particle counts up to 10 000 min^{-1}.

In the hot wire anemometer [114], aerosol particles are drawn past a fine, short, hot filament, from which heat is extracted due to impingement on the filament and as a result of turbulence due to the presence of particles. The method is suggested for the sizing of particles greater than 2 or 3 μm in diameter.

A diffusion battery [115, 116] has also been described in which small particles in a gas are subjected to molecular bombardment, which causes them to move in an erratic manner. Airborne particles passing through a narrow capillary tend, therefore, to collide with the capillary walls, and this property may be used for size determination of sub-micrometre particles.

The amplitude of vibration of airborne particles in an intense sound field has been used for determining particle size [117–119]. The relationship between the

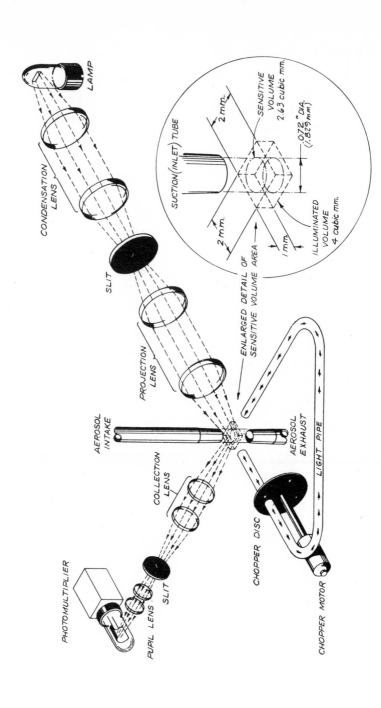

CONDENSATION LENS

LAMP

SLIT

PROJECTION LENS

AEROSOL INTAKE

COLLECTION LENS

SLIT

PUPIL LENS

PHOTOMULTIPLIER

AEROSOL EXHAUST

CHOPPER DISC

CHOPPER MOTOR

LIGHT PIPE

SUCTION (INLET) TUBE

2 mm.

SENSITIVE VOLUME 2.63 cubic mm.

.072" DIA. (1.829 mm.)

2 mm.

1 mm.

ILLUMINATED VOLUME 4 cubic mm.

ENLARGED DETAIL OF SENSITIVE VOLUME AREA

Fig. 3.7. Royco model 220 airborne particle monitor

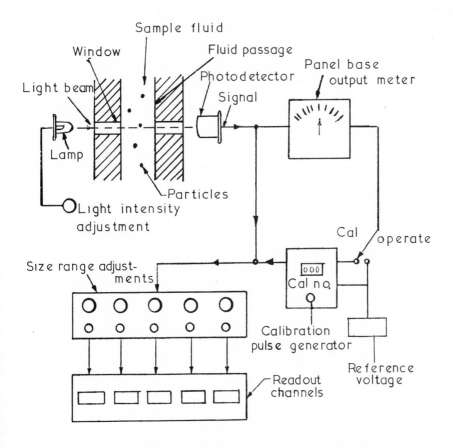

Fig. 3.8. HIAC automatic portable counter.

amplitude of particle vibration and particle size has been given by Heidemann [117] and suitable equipment has been designed by Schultz and Gucker [119].

A β-absorption impactor aerosol mass monitor has also been described [123]. New techniques include the use of ionization [125], gas chromatography [126] and a hot-wire anemometer [127] for aerosol droplets.

Olin [131, 132] describes a system in which aerosols are drawn into an electrostatic precipitator. A piezoelectric quartz oscillating crystal forms one electrode, the resonance frequency of which decreases linearly with the total mass of the particles thereby weighing them.

References

[1] Green, H.L., and Lane, W.R. (1957), *Particulate Clouds, Dusts, Smokes and Mists*, Spon.

[2] Drinker, P., and Hatch, T. (1954), *Industrial Dust*, McGraw-Hill, N.Y.

[3] Yaffe, C.D., Byers, D.H., and Hosey, A.S. (1956), *Encyclopedia of Instrumentation for Industrial Hygiene*, Univ. of Michigan.

[4] White, P.A.F., and Smith, S.E. (1964), *High Efficiency Air Filtration*, Butterworths.

[5] Clark, M.G., and Bradburn, J.A. (1970), 'Survey of Methods of Monitoring Particulate Contaminants', Inf. paper 122 and 122A. Welwyn Hall Research Establishments, Church Street, Welwyn, Herts.

[6] Schicketanz, W. (1969), *Staub*, **29**, 10, 417—20.

[7] Wright, B.M. (1960), British Patent 841, 698.

[8] Critchlow, A., and Proctor, T.D. (1965), Colliery Guard 211, 208—9.

[9] Dunmore, J.H., Hamilton, R.J., and Smith, D.S.L.E. (1964), *J. Sci. Instrum.*, **41**, 669.

[10] Harris, G.W., and Proctor, T.D. (1966), *Colliery Guard*, **213**, 690—1.

[11] Harris, G.W., and Maguire, B.A. (1968), *Ann. Occup. Hyg.*, **11**, 195—201.

[12] Maguire, B.A., and Barker, D. (1969), *Ann. Occup. Hyg.*, **12**, 197—201.

[13] Greenburg, L., and Smith, G.W. (1922), U.S. Bureau of Mines Report. Investigation 2392.

[14] Hatch, T., Warren, H., and Drinker, P. (1932), *J. Ind. Hyg. Taxicol*, **114**, 301.

[15] Katz, S.H., *et al.* (1925), *U.S. Public Health Bulletin*, **144**, 69.

[16] Owens, J.S. (1922), *Proc. R. Soc.*, **18**, A101.

[17] Ferry, R.M., Farr, L.E., and Hartmann, M.G. (1949), *Chem. Rev.*, **44**, 389.

[18] May, J.R. (1945), *J. Sci. Instrum.*, **22**, 187—95.

[19] Berner, A., and Preinig, O. (1964), *Staub*, **24**, 8, 295.

[20] Davies, C.N., and Aylward, M. (1951), *Proc. Phys. Soc.*, **B64**, 889.

[21] Ranz, W.E., and Wong, J.B. (1952), *A.M.A. Arch., Ind. Health*, **5**, 464—477; also Wong, J.B. (1952), *Ind. Chem.*, **44**, 1371.

[22] Laskin, S. (1949), *Pharmacology and Toxicology of Uranium Compounds*, (ed.) C. Voegtlin and H.G. Hodge, McGraw-Hill, N.Y.

[23] Gillespie, G.R. (1953), *Eng. Expt. Sta., University of Illinois Technical Report No. 9*, 50—1010.

[24] Gillespie, G.R., and Johnstone, H.F. (1955), *Chem. Eng. Progress*, **51**, 74F.

[25] Pilcher, J.M., Mitchell, R.L., and Thomas, R.E. (Dec. 1955), *Proc. Chem. Spec. Man. Assoc.*, N.Y., 1039—42.

[26] Wilcox, J.D. (1953), *A.M.A. Arch. Ind. Hyg. Occup. Med.,* **7**, 376—382.
[27] Wilcox, J.D., and Van Antwerp, W.R. (1955), *A.M.A. Arch. Ind. Health,* **11**, 422.
[28] Einbinder, H., *loc. cit.* [11].
[29] Sonkin, L.S. (1946), *J. Ing. Hyg. Toxicol,* **28**, 269.
[30] Brink, J.A. (1958), *Ind. Eng. Chem.,* **50**, 645—58.
[31] Anderson, A.A. (1958), *J. Bact.,* **76**, 471.
[32] Heneveld, W.H. (1959), Fifth Occupational Health Conference, University of Texas.
[33] Bucholz, H. (1970), *Staub Reinhalt Luft,* **30**, 4, 159—61.
[34] Bucholz, H. (1970), *Staub Reinhalt Luft,* **30**, 5.
[35] Bürkholz, A. (1970), *Chemic. Ing. Technik,* **42**, 5, 299—303.
[36] Jacobson, M., *et al.* (1970), *Am.Ind. Hyg. Assoc. J.,* **31**, 4, 442—5.
[37] Soole, B.W. (1971), *Aerosol Sci.,* **2**, 1, 1—14.
[38] Soloman, W.R. (1970), *J. Allergy,* **45**, 1.
[39] Littlefield, J.B., Schrenk, H.H., and Feicht, F.L. (1937), Bureau of Mines Impinger for Dust Sampling, Report Investigation 3360.
[40] Dubois, E., *et al.* (1967), Assessment Airborne Radioactivity Proc. Symp., Vienna 1967, 351—77.
[41] Glowiak, B., and Pilezynski, R. (1969), *Ochrona pivietrza 3,* **2**, 10, 12—15.
[42] Goetz, A. (1969), *Envir. Sci. Technol.,* **3**, 154—160.
[43] Hanel, G. (1969), *Atmos. Environ.,* **3**, 69—83.
[44] Noll, K.E. (1970), *Atmos. Environ.,* **4**, 1, 9—19.
[45] O'Donnell, H., Montgomery, T.L., and Corn, M. (1970), *Atmos. Environ.,* **4**, 1, 1—7.
[46] Renshaw, F.M., Bachman, J.M., and Pierce, J.O. (1969), *Am. Ind. Hyg. Assoc. J.,* **30**, 113—16.
[47] Green, H.L., and Watson, H.H. (1935), *Medical Res. Counc. Sp. Report Ser. No.199,* HMSO.
[48] Herdan, G. (1960), *Small Particle Statistics,* Butterworths.
[49] Gurney, S.W., Williams, S.R., and Meigs, R.R. (1938), *J. Ind. Hyg.,* **20**, 24.
[50] Cunning, P.T., Johnson, S.A., and Yang, R.T. (1973), 'Variations in the Chemistry of Airborne Particulate Material with Particle Size and Fine', Chem. Eng. Div. Argonne National Laboratories, Illinois.
[51] Hidy, G.M. (ed.)(1972), *Aerosols and Atmospheric Chemistry,* Academic Press, N.Y.
[52] Whitby, K.T., Liu, B.Y.H., Husar, R.B., and Barsic, N.J. (1972), *J. Colloid. Interface Sci.,* **39**, 1, 136—64.
[53] Whitby, K.T., Husar, R.B., and Liu, B.Y.H. (1972), *J. Colloid. Interface Sci.,* **39**, 1, 177—204.
[54] Husar, R.B., Whitby, K.T., and Liu, B.Y.H. (1972), *J. Colloid. Interface Sci.,* **39**, 1, 211—24.
[55] Lundgren, D.P. (1967), *J. Air Pollution Control Assoc.,* **17**, 225—28.
[56] Lundgren, D.A. (1971), *Atmos. Environ.,* **5**, 8, 645—651.
[57] Leary, J.A. (1951), *Indust. Eng. Chem. Anal.,* **23**, 853.
[58] Cowan, M., Sandia Corporation SCR — 296 (cit [4]).
[59] Sawyer, K.F., and Walton, W.H. (1950), *J. Sci. Instrum.,* **27**, 272—6.
[60] Keith, C.M., and Derrick, J.C. (1960), *J.Colloid Sci.,* **15**, 340.

[61] Goetz, A.H., and Kallai, T. (1962), *J. Air Polln. Control Assoc.,* **12**, 479.

[62] Ludwig, F.L., and Robinson, E. (1965), *J. Colloid Sci.,* **20**, 571−84.

[63] Stoeber, W., and Zenack, U. (1964), *Staub,* **24**, 8, 295.

[64] Tait, G.W.C. (1956), *Nucleonics,* **14**, 53.

[65] Kalmus, E.E. (1954), *J. Appl. Phys.,* **87**.

[66] Junge, C. (1951), 'Nuclei of atmospheric condensation', Compendium of Meteorology, A.M.S., Boston, Mass., U.S.A., 182−91 (loc. cit. [3]).

[67] Daniel, J., and Brackett, F. (1951), *J. Appl. Phys.,* **22**, 542−54.

[68] Orr, C., and Dallavalle, J.M. (1960), *Fine Particle Measurement,* Macmillan, N.Y., p.96.

[69] Yoshikawa, H.H., Swartz, G.A., MacWaters, J.T., and Fite, W.L. (1956), *Rev. Sci. Instrum.,* **359**.

[70] Howink, E.H., and Rolwink, W. (1957), *J. Hyg. Camb.,* **55**, 544.

[71] Agafonova, N.I., and Matalyavickus, V.P. (1968), *Hyg. Samit.,* **33**, 221−3.

[72] Morris, E.J., Darlow, H.N., Peel, J.S.H., and Wright, W.C. (1961), *J. Hyg. Camb.,* **59**, 487.

[73] Beadle, D.G., Kitto, P.H., and Blignaut, P.J. (1954), *A.M.A. Arch. Ind. Hyg. Occup. Med.,* **10**, 487.

[74] Lauterbach, K.E., Mercer, T.T., Hayes, A.D., and Morrow, P.E. (1954), *A.M.A. Arch. Ind. Hyg. Occup. Med.,* **9**, 69.

[75] Benarie, M., and Bodin, D. (1969), *Staub,* **29**, 3, 49.

[76] Hanson, D.N., and Wilkie, C.R. (1969), *Ind, Engng Chem.,* **8**, 3, 357−64.

[77] Gordon, M.T., and Orr, C. (1954), *J. Air. Polln. Control Assoc.,* **4**, 1.

[78] Cartwright, J. (1956), *B. J. Appl. Phys.,* **7**, 91.

[79] Epstein, P.S. (1929), *Z. Physik,* **54**, 537.

[80] Waldmann L. (1959), *Z. Naturforsch,* **14A**, 589.

[81] Strauss, W. (1966), *Industrial Gas Cleaning,* Pergamon.

[82] Watson, H.H. (1936), *Trans. Inst. Min. Metal.,* **46**, 176−87.

[83] Walton, W.H., and Harris, W.J. (1947), *Technical Paper 1.* Chemical Defence Res. Est., Porton, Hants., England.

[84] Prewett, W.G., and Walton, H.H. (1948), *Technical Paper 53.* Chemical Defence Res. Est., Porton, Hants., England.

[85] Schadt, C.F., and Cadle, R.D. (1957), *J. Colloid Sci.,* **12**, 356−62.

[86] Watson, H.H.,(1958), *B. J. Appl. Phys.,* **2**, 78−9.

[87] Hodkinson, J.R., Critchlow, A., and Stanley, N. (1960), *J. Sci. Instrum.,* **37**, 182−3.

[88] Hodkinson, J.R. (1962), Air Sampling Instruments, American Conf. Governmental Industrial Hygienists, 1014 Broadway, Cincinnati 2, Ohio, U.S.A.

[89] Donague, J.K. (1953), *J. Sci. Instrum.,* **30**, 59.

[90] Walkenhorst, W. (1952), *Beiträge zur Silikoseforschung,* **18**, 29−62.

[91] Burdenkin, J.T., and Davies, J.G. (1956), *B. J. Ind. Medicine,* **13**, 196−201.

[92] Gruszka, J. (1961), (*cit.* [88]).

[93] Beadle, D.G., and Kitto, P.M. (1952), *J. Chem. Met. and Min. Soc., S. Africa,* **52**, 284−311.

[94] Wright, B.M. (1954), *J. Sci. Instrum.,* **31**, 263−4.

[95] Cember, H., Hatch, T., and Watson, J.A. (1953), *Am. Ind. Hyg. Assoc. Quart.,* **14**, 191−4.

[96] Walton, W.H. (1950), *J. R. Micro. Soc.,* **70**, 51.

[97]   Orr, C., and Martin, R.A. (1958), *Rev. Sci. Instrum.*, **29**, 129–30.
[98]   Hamilton, R.J. (1956), *J. Sci. Instrum.*, **33**, 395–9.
[99]   Balashov, V., Bradwig, J.G., and Rendall, R.E.G. (1961), *J. Min. Vent. Soc., S. Africa*, **14**, 98–100.
[100] Wright, B.M. (1953), *Science*, **118**, 195.
[101] Gucker, F.T., O'Konski, C.T., Pickard, H.B., and Pitts, J.H. (1949), *J. Am. Chem. Soc.*, **69**, 2422.
[102] Gucker, F.T., and O'Konski, C.T. (1949), *J. Colloid,Sci.*, **4**, 541.
[103] O'Konski, C.T., and Doyle, G.J. (1955), *Analyt. Chem.*, **27**, 694.
[104] Fisher, M.A., Katz, S., and Lieberman, A. (1955), *Proc. Third Nat. Air Polln. Symp., Pasedena, California, U.S.A.*
[105] Martens, A.E., and Keller, J.D. (1968), *Am. Ind. Hyg. Assoc. J.*, **29**, 257–67.
[106] van de Hulst, H.C. (1957), *Light Scattering by Small Particles*, Wiley, N.Y.
[107] Moroz, W.J., Withstandley, V.D., and Anderson, G.W. (1970), *Rev. Sci. Instrum.*, **41**, 7, 978–83.
[108] Kratel, R. (1970), *Staub-Reinholt Luft.*, Engl. ed., **30**, 5, 40.
[109] Rimberg, D., and Keafer, D. (1970), *J. Colloid Interf. Sci.*, **33**, 4, 628.
[110] Langer, G. (1969), U.S. Patent 3, 434, 335.
[111] Langer, G. (1969), *Powder Technol.*, **2**, 307.
[112] Kennedy, D.A. (1970), Colorado University report.
[113] Langer, G. (1972), *Powder Technol.*, **6**, 5–8.
[114] Goldschmidt, V.W. (1965), *J. Colloid Sci.*, **20**, 617.
[115] Thomas, J.W. (1955), *J. Colloid Sci.*, **10**, 246.
[116] Thomas, J.W. (1956), *J. Colloid Sci.*, **11**, 107.
[117] Brandt, O., Freund, M., and Heidemann, E. (1937), *Z. Physik*, **104**, 511–33.
[118] Cassel, H.M., and Schultz, M. (1952), *Air Pollution*, (ed.) Lewis McCabe, McGraw-Hill.
[119] Gucker, F.T. (1949), *Proc. First National Air Polln. Symp. Sandford, California, U.S.A.*
[120] Hurd, F.K., and Mulling, J.C. (1962), *J. Colloid Sci.*, **17**, 2, 91–100.
[121] Lundgren, D.A., and McFarland, A.R. (1970), *Am. Ind. Hyg. Ass. J.*, **31**, 2, 36.
[122] Lundgren, D.A. (1971), *Atmos. Environ.*, **5**, 8, 645–51.
[123] Lilierfield, P. (1970), *Amer. Ind. Hyg. Assoc. J.*, **31**, 35.
[124] Chmara, P. (1969), *CIM Bull.*, 1171.
[125] Gourdine Systems Inc. (1969), Br. Pat. Spec. 1. 161. 190.
[126] Kovar, V. (1970), *Ochrana Ousdusi 7*, 104–11.
[127] Goldschmidt, V.W., and Householder, M.K. (1969), *Atmos. Environ.*, **3**, 643.
[128] Hounam, R.F. (1964), *Atomic Energy Research Est. Rep. M132*, 8.
[129] Hounam, R.F., and Sherwood, R.J. (1965), *Am. Ind. Hyg. Assoc. J.*, **26**, 122.
[130] O'Connor, D.T. (1971), U.K.A.E.A., AHSB-RP-R-108, HMSO.
[131] Olin, J.G., Trautner, R.P., and Gilmore, J. (1971), Sixty-fourth Ann. Meeting, Air Pollution Control Assoc.
[132] Olin, J.G., Sem. G.J., and Christenson, D.L. (1971), *Am. Ind. Hyg. Assoc. J.*, **32**, 209–20.

4 *Particle Size, Shape and Distribution*

4.1 Particle size

The size of a spherical homogeneous particle is uniquely defined by its diameter. For a cube the length along one edge is characteristic, and for other regular shapes there are equally appropriate dimensions. With some regular particles, it may be necessary to specify more than one dimension. For example: cone, diameter and height; cuboid, length, width and height.

Derived diameters are determined by measuring a size dependent property of the particle and relating it to a linear dimension. The most widely used of these are the equivalent spherical diameters. Thus, a unit cube has the same volume as a sphere of diameter 1·24 units, hence this is the derived volume diameter.

If an irregularly shaped particle is allowed to settle in a liquid, its terminal velocity may be compared with the terminal velocity of a sphere of the same density settling under similar conditions. The size of the particle is then equated to the diameter of the sphere. In the laminar flow region, the particle moves with random orientation, but outside this region it orientates itself to give maximum resistance to motion so that the free-falling diameter for an irregular particle is greater in the intermediate region than in the laminar flow region. The free-falling diameter, in the laminar flow region, becomes the Stokes' diameter. Stokes' equation, can be used for spherical particles, up to a Reynolds' number of 0·2, at which value it will give a diameter underestimation of about 2%. Above 0·2 corrections have to be applied. Corrections may also be applied for non-spherical particles, so that the derived diameter is independent of settling conditions becoming purely a function of particle size. These diameters are particularly useful for characterizing suspended particles in the atmosphere and other cases where the settling behaviour of suspended solids is being examined.

For irregular particles, the assigned size usually depends upon the method of measurement, hence the particle sizing technique should, wherever possible, duplicate the process one wishes to control. Thus, for paint pigments, the projected area is important, while for chemical reactants, the total surface area should be determined. The projected area diameter may be determined by microscopy for each individual particle, but surface area is usually determined for a known weight or volume of powder. The magnitude of this surface area will depend on the method of measurement; permeametry, for example, giving a much lower area than gas adsorption. The former gives the surface area accessible to the gas molecules and, therefore, depends

Table 4.1 Definitions of particle size

Symbol	Name	Definition	Formula
d_v	Volume diameter	Diameter of a sphere having the same volume as the particle	$V = \dfrac{\pi}{6}d_v{}^3$
d_s	Surface diameter	Diameter of a sphere having the same surface as the particle	$S = \pi d_s{}^2$
d_{sv}	Surface volume diameter	Diameter of a sphere having the same external surface to volume ratio as a sphere	$d_{sv} = \dfrac{d_v{}^3}{d_s{}^2}$
d_d	Drag diameter	Diameter of a sphere having the same resistance to motion as the particle in a fluid of the same viscosity and at the same velocity (d_d approximates to d_s when R_e is small)	$\begin{cases} F_D = C_D A \rho_f \dfrac{v^2}{2} \\ \text{where } C_D A = f(d_d) \end{cases}$ $\begin{cases} F_D = 3\pi d_d \eta v \\ R_e < 0 \cdot 2 \end{cases}$
d_f	Free-falling diameter	Diameter of a sphere having the same density and the same free-falling speed as the particle in a fluid of the same density and viscosity	
d_{st}	Stokes' diameter	The free-falling diameter of a particle in the laminar flow region ($R_e < 0 \cdot 2$)	$d_{st}{}^2 = \dfrac{(d_v{}^3)}{d_d}$
d_a	Projected area diameter	Diameter of a circle having the same area as the projected area of the particle resting in a stable position	$A = \dfrac{\pi}{4}d_a{}^2$
d_p	Projected area diameter	Diameter of a circle having the same area as the projected area of the particle in random orientation	Mean value for all possible orientations $d_p = d_s$ for convex particles
d_c	Perimeter diameter	Diameter of a circle having the same perimeter as the projected outline of the particle	$d_F = d_c$
d_A	Sieve diameter	The width of the minimum square aperture through which the particle will pass	
d_F	Feret's diameter	The mean value of the distance between pairs of parallel tangents to the projected outline of the particle	
d_M	Martin's diameter	The mean chord length of the projected outline of the particle	

on the size of the gas molecules if the solid contains very small pores.

The sieve diameter, for square-mesh sieves, is the length of the side of the minimum square aperture through which the particle will pass, though this definition needs modification for sieves which do not have square apertures. In a sieving operation, such a particle will not necessarily pass through the appropriate mesh, particularly if it will only pass through when presented in a particular orientation as with elongated particles. For all such particles to pass through, the sieving time would approach infinity. There is also a range of aperture sizes in any sieve mesh and certain particles may only pass through the largest apertures.

Microscopy is the only widely used particle-sizing technique in which individual particles are observed and measured. A single particle has an infinite number of linear dimensions, and it is only when they are averaged that a meaningful value results. Similarly, for a large number of particles. When a linear dimension is measured parallel to some fixed direction (Martin, Feret or Shear diameter), the size distribution of these measurements reflects the size distribution of the projected areas of the particles. These are called statistical diameters. Comparing the projected area of the particle with series of circles, gives a diameter which describes that particle for the orientation in which it is measured. In microscopy, this is usually the projected area diameter in stable orientation but, in certain cases, the particle may rest in an unstable position to give a lower value. Some definitions of particle size are given in table 4.1 (p. 75).

4.2 Particle shape
It is known that particle shape influences such properties as the flowability of powders, packing, interaction with fluids and the covering power of pigments, although little quantitative work has been carried out on these relationships. Qualitative terms may be used to give some indication of the nature of particle shape and some of these, extracted from the British Standard 2955: Glossary of Terms Relating to Powders, are given in table 4.2.

Table 4.2 Definitions of particle shape

Acicular	needle-shaped;
Angular	sharp-edged or having roughly polyhedral shape;
Crystalline	freely developed in a fluid medium of geometric shape;
Dentritic	having a branched crystalline shape;
Fibrous	regularly or irregularly thread-like;
Flaky	plate-like;
Granular	having approximately an equidimensional irregular shape;
Irregular	lacking any symmetry;
Modular	having rounded, irregular shape;
Spherical	global shape.

Such general terms are inadequate for the determination of shape factors that can be incorporated as parameters into equations concerning particle properties where shape is involved as a factor. In order to do this, it is necessary to be able to measure and define shape quantitatively.

Some work has been carried out on the measurement of individual particles. Church [15] uses the ratio of Feret's and Martin's diameter to represent monosize elliptical particles. Cole [20] uses the Quantimet 720 to compare longest chord, perimeter and area for large numbers of particles. Hausner [16] assesses particle shape with an enveloping rectangle of minimum area, and other methods have been proposed by Krumbein and Lees [17, 18].

Wadell [8] defines sphericity as:

$$\psi = \frac{\text{surface area of sphere having the same volume as particle}}{\text{surface area of particle}}$$

$$\psi = \left(\frac{d_v}{d_s}\right)^2$$

The most promising approach is the use of shape coefficients as defined by Heywood [1, 5], although as yet their use has not been widely exploited. Heywood's work is summarized in section 4.2.1.

4.2.1 Shape factors

If it is required to define the size of a particle by a single dimension, it is usual to do so by expressing the size in terms of one of the diameters defined in table 4.1. The variation between these diameters increases as the particles diverge more from the spherical shape, and hence shape is an important factor in the correlation of sizing analyses made by various procedures.

Heywood recognized that the word 'shape' in common usage refers to two distinct characteristics of a particle. These two characteristics should be defined separately, one by the degree to which the particle approaches a definite form such as cube, tetrahedron or sphere, and the second by the relative proportions of the particle which distinguishes one cuboid, tetrahedron or spheroid from another of the same class.

There are two especially important properties of the particle: the surface and the volume, and these are proportional to the square and cube respectively of some characteristic dimension. The constants of proportionality depend upon the dimension chosen to characterize the particle and the projected area diameter is used for the following discussion:

$$\text{surface of particle} \qquad S = \alpha_{s,a} da^2 = \pi d_s^2 \ (= x_s^2)$$

$$\text{volume of particle} \qquad V = \alpha_{v,a} da^3 = \frac{\pi}{6} d_v^3 \ (= x_v^3)$$

where α_s and α_v are the surface and volume shape coefficients, the additional suffix denoting that the measured diameter is the projected area diameter. The symbol x denotes size, as opposed to diameter, and includes the shape coefficient. This artifact is found to be very useful for general treatment of data.

When three mutually perpendicular dimensions of a particle may be determined, Heywood's ratios [5] may be used:

$$\text{elongation ratio} \qquad n = L/B \qquad\qquad (4.1)$$

$$\text{flakiness ratio} \qquad m = B/T \qquad\qquad (4.2)$$

where:

(i) the thickness T is the minimum distance between two parallel planes which are tangential to opposite surfaces of the particle, one plane being the plane of maximum stability;

(ii) the breadth B is the minimum distance between two parallel planes which are perpendicular to the planes defining the thickness and are tangential to opposite sides of the particle;

(iii) the length L is the distance between two parallel planes which are perpendicular to the planes defining thickness and breadth and are tangential to opposite sides of the particle.

Consider a particle circumscribed by a rectangular parallelepiped of dimensions L by B by T, then:

$$\text{projected area of the particle } A = \frac{\pi}{4} da^2 = \alpha_a BL \qquad (4.3)$$

where α_a is the area ratio.

Volume of particle equals projected area by mean thickness:

$$\alpha_{v,a} \, da^3 = \alpha_a BL \, p_r T \qquad\qquad (4.4)$$

where p_r is the prismoidal ratio (see figure 4.1).

Combining equations (4.3) and (4.4) gives:

$$\alpha_{v,a} = \frac{\pi\sqrt{\pi}}{8} \frac{p_r}{m\sqrt{\alpha_a}n} \qquad\qquad (4.5)$$

If the particle is equidimensional, i.e. $B = L = T$ and $n = m = 1$, then the volume coefficient takes on a special value α_e where:

$$\alpha_e = \frac{\pi\sqrt{\pi}}{8} \frac{p_r}{\sqrt{\alpha_a}} \qquad\qquad (4.6)$$

α_e may therefore be used to define particle form. When the particle is not equidimensional, the appropriate value of $\alpha_{v,a}$ is $\alpha_e/m\sqrt{n}$ which substantiates the reasoning given earlier that shape is a combination of the proportions and geometrical form.

Heywood classified particles into tetrahedral, prismoidal, sub-angular and rounded. Values of α and p_r for these classes are given in table 4.3 [22].

$\alpha_{v,a}$ can be calculated using equation (4.5) combined with direct observation to determine the shape group into which the particle fits and the values of m and n. This is practicable down to sizes as small as 5 μm by measurements on the number, mean size, weight and density of closely graded fractions. Indeed, $\alpha_{v,a}$ may be determined directly by weighing a known number of particles of known mean size.

Table 4.3 Values of α and p_r for particles of various shapes

Shape group		α_a	p_r
Angular	tetrahedral	0·5 −0·8	0·4 −0·53
	prismoidal	0·5 −0·9	0·53−0·9
Sub-angular		0·65−0·85	0·55−0·8
Rounded		0·72−0·82	0·62−0·75

$\alpha_{s,a}$ is more difficult to determine, but Heywood developed the following relationship on the basis of a large number of experimental measurements:

$$\alpha_{s,a} = 1\cdot57 + C\left(\frac{\alpha_{ea}}{m}\right)^{\frac{4}{3}} \frac{n+1}{n} \tag{4.7}$$

in which C is constant depending upon geometric form. Table 4.4 shows the values of α_{ea} and C for various geometrical forms and also for irregular particles.

Table 4.4 Values of α_{ea} and C for various geometrical forms and also for irregular particles.

Shape group		α_{ea}	C
Geometrical forms			
	tetrahedral	0·328	4·36
	cubical	0·696	2·55
	spherical	0·524	1·86
Approximate forms			
angular {	tetrahedral	0·38	3·3
	prismoidal	0·47	3·0
sub-angular		0·51	2·6
rounded		0·54	2·1

Table 4.5 gives some definitions of particle size and shape. These may be applied in the following manner to number and weight distributions respectively.

For spherical particles $\alpha_s = \pi$, $\alpha_v = \pi/6$ hence:

$$S = \pi d^2$$

$$V = \frac{\pi d^3}{6}$$

$$S_v = \frac{6}{d} \tag{4.8}$$

where d is the diameter of the sphere.

For non-spherical particles:

$$S = \pi d_s^{\,2}$$

Table 4.5 Table of shape factors and shape coefficients

Shape factors

Sphericity	The ratio of the surface area of a sphere having the same volume as the particle to its actual area; the reciprocal is known as the coefficient or rugosity or angularity	$\psi = \dfrac{d_v}{d_s}^2$ $\psi \leqslant 1$
Circularity	The ratio of the perimeter of a circle having the same area as the projected area of the particle to its actual perimeter	$\chi = \dfrac{d_a}{d_c}$ $\chi \leqslant 1$
Surface-shape coefficient	Coefficient of proportionality relating the surface area of the particle with the square of its measured diameter	$S = \alpha_{s,A} d_A^2$
Volume-shape coefficient	Coefficient of proportionality relating the volume of the particle with the cube of its measured diameter	$V = \alpha_{v,A} d_A^3$
Surface-volume shape coefficient	Ratio of surface to volume shape coefficient	$\alpha_{s,v,A} = \dfrac{\alpha_{s,A}}{\alpha_{v,A}}$

$$V = \frac{\pi}{6} d_v^3$$

$$S_v = \frac{6}{d_{sv}} \tag{4.9}$$

where

$$d_{sv} = \left(\frac{d_v^3}{d_s^2} \right)$$

d_s, d_v and d_{sv} are the surface, volume and surface-volume diameters.
For an assembly of particles:

(a)   based on microscopy, where there are n_r particles of projected area diameter d_a.

$$\Delta S = \alpha_{s,a} n_r d_a^2$$

$$\Delta V = \alpha_{v,a} n_r d_a^3$$

$$S_v = \frac{\Sigma \alpha_{s,a} n_r d_a^2}{\Sigma \alpha_{v,a} n_r d_a^3} \tag{4.10}$$

For most materials the shape coefficients are reasonably constant over a limited size range and may be taken outside the summation brackets to give:

$$S_v = \alpha_{sv,a} \frac{\Sigma n_r d_a^2}{\Sigma n_r d_a^3} \tag{4.11}$$

(b)   based on sieving, where the fractional weight residing between sieves of a mean between sieves aperture $d_{A,r}$ is X_r, ρ_s is the powder density and W is the total weight of powder.

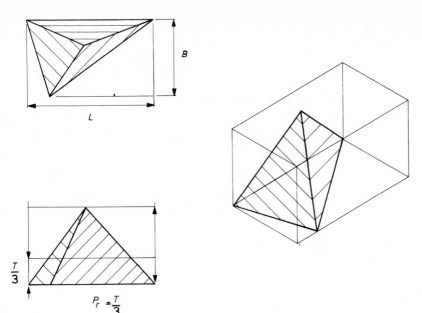

Fig. 4.1. Heywood's dimensions.

$$\Delta S = \alpha_{s,A} n_r d^2_{A\,r}$$

$$X_r W = \alpha_{v,A} n_r d^3_{A\,r}$$

$$\frac{\Delta S}{W} = \frac{\alpha_{sv,A}}{\rho_s} \frac{X_r}{d_{A,r}}$$

$$S_W = \frac{\alpha_{sv,A}}{\rho_s} \sum \frac{X_r}{d_{A,r}} \tag{4.12}$$

Equation (4.11) is used whenever a number count is taken and yields a specific surface if the shape coefficient is known and vice versa. If α_{sv} is assumed equal to 6 (this is to assume the particles are spherical), one obtains a specific surface. For microscope counting by projected area diameter, this gives $S_{v,a}$.

Equation (4.12) is used whenever a weight analysis is carried out. If $\alpha_{sv,A}$ is known S_v can be found and vice versa as before. If α_{sv} is assumed equal to 6, the specific surface obtained, for the quoted example, is the specific surface by sieve analysis $S_{v,A}$. $(S_v = \rho_s S_W)$.

The surface-volume shape coefficient has been determined for quartz and silica from surface area measurements using nitrogen adsorption giving $14 < \alpha_{sv} < 18$ with no significant variation with particle size [9]. Fair and Hatch [10] found that by measuring smoothed surfaces, values of $\alpha_{sv,a}$ as low as 7 were found ($\alpha_{sv,a} = 6$

for spheres). Crowl [11] found that with prussian blue, the specific surface by nitrogen adsorption applied to the primary particles of which each single particle is made up (figure 4.1). With red iron oxide, however, the specific surface applied to the single primary particle.

If the shape of the particles in an assembly of particles is known, by microscope examination, the average shape may be determined. Tables 4.6 and 4.7 give values of shape coefficients for regular and irregular shaped particles. If the particle shape is cylindrical, it can be seen that as the height–diameter ratio decreases, flaky particles, $\alpha_{sv,a}$ increases above 6 as the ratio increases, rod-shaped particles $\alpha_{sv,a}$ decreases below 6.

Example
Consider two cuboids of similar shape but different sizes; i.e. side lengths 1: 2: 3 and 2: 4: 6:

maximum projected areas $\qquad\qquad$ $6 + 24; A = 30$

total surface areas $\qquad\qquad$ $22 + 88; S = 110$

total volume $\qquad\qquad$ $6 + 48; V = 54$

projected area diameter $\qquad$ $A = \dfrac{\pi}{4} n\bar{d}_a{}^2$ $\qquad\qquad;\qquad \bar{d}_a = 4{\cdot}36$

mean surface diameter $\qquad$ $S = \pi n\bar{d}_s{}^2$ $\qquad\qquad;\qquad \bar{d}_s = 4{\cdot}18$

surface shape coefficient $\qquad$ $S = \alpha_{s,a} n\bar{d}_a{}^2$ $\qquad\qquad;\qquad \alpha_{s,a} = 2{\cdot}9$

mean volume diameter $\qquad$ $V = \dfrac{\pi}{6} n\bar{d}_v{}^3$ $\qquad\qquad;\qquad \bar{d} = 3{\cdot}72$

volume shape coefficient $\qquad$ $V = \alpha_{v,a} n\bar{d}_a{}^3$ $\qquad\qquad;\qquad \alpha_{v,a} = 0{\cdot}326$

surface-volume mean diameter $\qquad$ $d_{sv} = \dfrac{d_v{}^3}{d_s{}^2}$ $\qquad\qquad;\qquad \bar{d}_{sv} = 2{\cdot}94$

volume specific surface $\qquad$ $S_v = \dfrac{S}{V} = \dfrac{6}{d_{sv}}$ $\qquad\qquad;\qquad S_v = 2{\cdot}04$

volume specific surface by microscopy $\qquad$ $S_{v,a} = \dfrac{6}{\bar{d}_a}$ $\qquad\qquad;\qquad S_{v,a} = 1{\cdot}37$

(assuming $\alpha_{sv,a} = 6$). (See B.S. 4359:1970, Part 3, for further examples.)

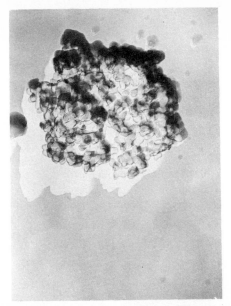

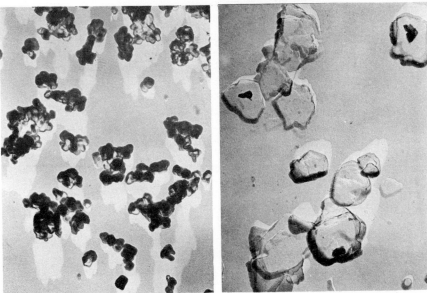

Fig. 4.2. Electron photomicrographs of two paint pigments, showing how particles can be aggregates of finer particles (Crowl [11]). (a) A single particle of Prussian blue about 1 μm in diameter. The nitrogen adsorption surface area is $61 \cdot 3 \text{m}^2 \text{g}^{-1}$ from which the surface volume mean diameter is $0 \cdot 051$ μm. This is seen to be the diameter of the individual primary particles of which the aggregate is made up. Similarly, the micronized Prussian blue (b) has approximately the same surface volume mean diameter. (c) With the red oxide the diameter is $0 \cdot 21$ μm which is approximately the same as the solid particle seen in the micrograph.

Table 4.6 Calculated values of shape coefficients

Form	Proportions	Linear dimensions used as d_r	α_s	α_v	α_{sv}
Sphere		diameter	3·14	0·52	6·00
Spheroid	1:1:2	minor axis	5·37	1·05	5·13
	1:2:2	minor axis	8·67	2·09	4·14
	1:1:4	minor axis	10·13	2·09	4·83
	1:4:4	minor axis	28·50	8·38	3·40
Ellipsoid	1:2:4	shortest axis	15·86	4·19	3·79
Cylinder	height = diameter	diameter	4·71	0·79	6·00
	height = 2 diameter	diameter	7·85	1·57	5·00
	height = 4 diameter	diameter	14·14	3·14	4·50
	height = $\frac{1}{2}$ diameter	diameter	3·14	0·39	8·00
	height = $\frac{1}{4}$ diameter	diameter	2·36	0·20	12·00

Table 4.7 Measured values of surface-volume shape coefficient

Material	Approximate sizes	α_{sv}	Specific surface method	Particle size method
Alumina	15−45	16		
Coal	15−90	12−17	permeametry	microscope
Dolomite	25−45	11		(d_a)
Silica	15−70	11		
Tungsten carbide	15−45	14		
Coal	15−90	10−12		Coulter
Silica	15−70	9	permeametry	counter (d_v)
Coal	0·5−10	9−11	light	weight
Diamond	0·5−12	8	extinction	count (d_v)
Quartz	0·5−10	9		

Tables from B.S. 4359: (1970), Part 3, reproduced by permission of the British Standards Institution, 2 Park Street, London W.1, from whom copies of the complete Standard may be obtained.

    These dimensions may be determined for a limited number of irregular small particles using microscopy, but the operation is too laborious as a method for the determination of the separate proportions of a particulate system unless an automatic microscope is available. Other ratios are, however, indicative of particle shape; for example, since particles fall with random orientation in the Stokes' region it is possible to obtain some indication of shape by comparing the mean Stokes' diameter with the mean projected area diameter by microscopy with the particles resting in stable orientation on the microscope slide.

Further, if an analysis has been carried out by two different techniques, the two results can usually be brought into coincidence by multiplying by a shape factor. For example, if the mean size by Coulter analysis is 32 μm and by gravitational sedimentation is 24 μm, the Coulter diameter divided by the Stokes' diameter is 4/3 (see section 4.5.6); i.e. $d_v/d_{st} = 4/3$.

This is in itself a shape factor, but it can be extended by writing the alternative form of the Stokes' diameter (table 4.1):

$$d_v^2 \frac{d_s}{d_v^3} = \frac{16}{9}$$

$$d_s = 1.78 d_v.$$

If the particles are cylindrical of length kD where D is the diameter, then k can be found since:

$$d_s^2 = (\tfrac{1}{2} + k)D^2 \; ; d_v^3 = \tfrac{3}{2} kD^3 \; .$$

The mean volume shape may be determined from a knowledge of the number, mean size, weight and density of the particles composing a fraction graded between close limits. Further, if the surface area is determined by permeametry, a surface shape may be evaluated though this will differ from that obtained from the gas adsorption surface area. Hence, when any shape is quoted, the method of obtaining it should also be given.

Ellison [6] obtained the value 0.9 for the ratio of the sizes of silica particles determined by settling experiments and mounted in agar in random orientation. Hodkinson [7] found, from measurements of quartz particles by light scattering, a diameter ratio of 0.8 between particles in a liquid suspension and settled particles. These factors for the mean ratio of projected diameter for random and stable orientation are indicative of the properties of the powder and are therefore of use to the analyst.

4.3 Average diameters

The purpose of an average is to represent a group of individual values in a simple and concise manner in order to obtain an understanding of the group. It is important, therefore, that the average should be representative of the group. All average diameters are a measure of central tendency which is unaffected by the relatively few extreme values in the tails of the distribution. Some of these are illustrated in table 4.8 (a) and (b) and figures 4.3 and 4.4.

The most commonly occurring value , the mode, passes through the peak of the relative frequency curve, i.e. it is the value at which the frequency density is a maximum. The median line divides the area under the curve into equal parts, i.e. it is the 50% size on the cumulative frequency curve. The vertical line at the mean

Table 4.8 (*a*) Cumulative percentage undersize distribution

Particle size (μm) x_2	Cumulative percentage undersize $\phi = \sum\limits_{0}^{x} d\phi$
5	1·4
9	9·4
11	18·0
14	32·0
17	49·5
20	64·0
23	76·0
28	88·0
33	94·0
41	98·0
50	99·4
60	99·9

ϕ, the frequency function $= \Sigma dN$ for a number distribution
$= \Sigma x dN$ for a size distribution
$= \Sigma x^2 dN$ for an area distribution
$= \Sigma x^3 dN$ for a volume or weight distribution where dN is the percentage of the total number of particles lying in the size range x_1 to x_2.

Table 4.8 (*b*) Relative percentage frequency distribution: tabular calculation of mean size

Particle size range x_1 to x_2	Interval dx	Average size x	Percentage in range dϕ	Percentage per micrometre dϕ/dx	xdϕ
0 to 5	5	2·5	1·4	0·3	4
5 to 9	4	7·0	8·0	2·0	56
9 to 11	2	10·0	8·6	4·3	86
11 to 14	3	12·5	14·0	4·7	175
14 to 17	3	15·5	17·5	5·8	271
17 to 20	3	18·5	14·5	4·8	268
20 to 23	3	21·5	12·0	4·0	258
23 to 28	5	25·5	12·0	2·4	306
28 to 33	5	30·5	6·0	1·2	183
33 to 41	8	37·0	4·0	0·5	148
41 to 50	9	45·5	1·4	0·2	64
50 to 60	10	55·0	0·5	0·1	28

$\Sigma x d\phi \quad 1847$

Mean size $= \dfrac{\Sigma x d\phi}{\Sigma d\phi} = 18\cdot47$

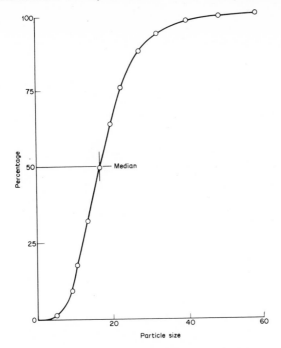

Fig. 4.3. The cumulative percentage frequency curve.

passes through the centre of gravity of a sheet of uniform thickness and density
cut to the shape of the distribution. Hence, for the mean, the moment of the sum
of all the elementary areas of thickness δx about the ordinate equals the sum of all
the moments:

$$\bar{x} \sum \frac{d\phi}{dx} \delta x = \sum x \frac{d\phi}{dx} \delta x$$

$$\bar{x} = \frac{\Sigma x d\phi}{\Sigma d\phi} . \qquad (4.13)$$

For a weight distribution $d\phi = x^3 dN$ giving:

$$\bar{x} = \frac{\Sigma x^4 dN}{\Sigma x^3 dN} . \qquad (4.14)$$

The mode and the median may be determined graphically but the above summation has to be carried out for the determination of the mean. However, for slightly
skewed distribution, the approximate relationship mean—mode = 3 (mean—median)
holds. For a symmetrical distribution, they all coincide. In the illustration, the
values are: mode = 15·0; median = 17·2; yielding mean = 18·2, as compared with
the summated value of 18·47 (table 4.8).

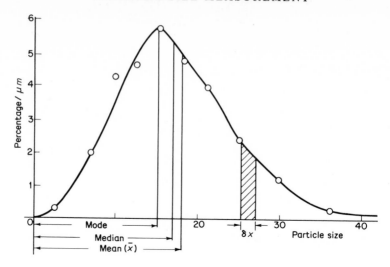

Fig. 4.4. The relative percentage frequency curve.

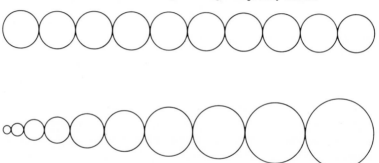

Fig. 4.5. The homogeneous distribution that represents in number and length a
       heterogeneous distribution of ten particles of size 1 to 10 with unit
       separation in size.

The characteristics of a particle distribution are its total number, length, area
and volume. A system of unequally-sized particles may be represented by a system
of uniformly-sized particles having two, and only two, characteristics of the original
distribution. The size of the particles in the uniform system is then the mean size
of the non-uniform system with respect to these two properties.

The sizes may be expressed mathematically by dividing the system of particles
into small intervals of size δx with assumed diameters of $x_1, x_2, ...$ The symbol x
is used because the method of measurement for individual particles is not specified,
and all particles are assumed to have the same shape. Let the number of particles in
these groupings be $\delta N_1, \delta N_2, ...$ respectively. Then the aggregate length, surface
and volume of the particles in each grouping are $x\delta N$, $x^2\delta N$ and $x^3\delta N$ and the

Table 4.9

Number, length mean diameter	x_{NL}	$= \dfrac{\Sigma dL}{\Sigma dN} = \dfrac{\Sigma x dN}{\Sigma dN}$
Number, surface mean diameter	x_{NS}	$= \sqrt{\left(\dfrac{\Sigma dS}{\Sigma dN}\right)} = \sqrt{\left(\dfrac{\Sigma x^2 dN}{\Sigma dN}\right)}$
Number, volume mean diameter	x_{NV}	$= \sqrt[3]{\left(\dfrac{\Sigma dV}{\Sigma dN}\right)} = \sqrt[3]{\left(\dfrac{\Sigma x^3 dN}{\Sigma dN}\right)}$
Length, surface mean diameter	x_{LS}	$= \dfrac{\Sigma dS}{\Sigma dL} = \dfrac{\Sigma x^2 dN}{\Sigma x dN}$
Length, volume mean diameter	x_{LV}	$= \sqrt{\left(\dfrac{\Sigma dV}{\Sigma dL}\right)} = \sqrt{\left(\dfrac{\Sigma x^3 dN}{\Sigma x dN}\right)}$
Surface, volume mean diameter	x_{SV}	$= \dfrac{\Sigma dV}{\Sigma dS} = \dfrac{\Sigma x^3 dN}{\Sigma x^2 dN}$
Volume, moment mean diameter	x_{VM}	$= \dfrac{\Sigma dM}{\Sigma dV} = \dfrac{\Sigma x^4 dN}{\Sigma x^3 dN}$
Weight, moment mean diameter	x_{WM}	$= \dfrac{\Sigma dM}{\Sigma dW} = \dfrac{\Sigma x dW}{\Sigma dW} = \dfrac{\Sigma x^4 dN}{\Sigma x^3 dN}$

total for the system by the summation of these expressions. Table 4.9 is a summary of the mathematical expressions for the various mean diameters [5].

The method of sizing may also be incorporated into the symbol. Hence, for particle sizing by microscopy, the arithmetic mean diameter becomes $d_{a,\,NL}$. The surface volume diameter calculated from the results of a sedimentation experiment is $d_{St,sv}$. The mean value of a cumulative weight percentage curve obtained by sieving would be $d_{A,vm}$ or $d_{A,wm}$.

Consider the system illustrated (figure 4.5) consisting of one particle of size 1, 2, 3, 4, 5, 6, 7, 8, 9, 10.

Hence ten particles, each of length 5·50, will have the same total length as the original distribution.

Similarly ten particles, each of length 6·21, will have the same total surface as the original distribution.

Each of these mean diameters characterizes the original distribution in two properties only. For example, the length-surface-mean diameter is 7·00. Therefore, the uniform system contains $N = (L/x) = (S/x^2)$, which is 7·87 in each case. Hence, the uniform system consists of 7·87 particles, each of length 7·00. Thus, the total length and the total surface of the particles are the same as in the original distribution, but the total number, volume and moment are all different, e.g. $V = x^3 N = 343 \times 7.87 = 2700$.

Table 4.10

$x_{NL} = 5 \cdot 50;$	$x_{LS} = 7 \cdot 00;$	$x_{VM} = 8 \cdot 37;$	$\Sigma dV = 3025$
$x_{NS} = 6 \cdot 21;$	$x_{LV} = 7 \cdot 43;$	$\Sigma dL = 55;$	$\Sigma dM = 25\,335$
$x_{NV} = 6 \cdot 71;$	$x_{SV} = 7 \cdot 87;$	$\Sigma dS = 385;$	

The arithmetic mean is the sum of the diameters of the separate particles divided by the number of particles; it is most significant when the distribution is normal:

$$x_A = x_{NL} = \frac{\Sigma x dN}{\Sigma dN} . \tag{4.15}$$

The geometric mean is the nth root of the product of the diameters of the n-particles examined; it is of particular value with log-normal distributions:

$$x_g = (\Pi x^{dN})^{\frac{1}{N}} . \tag{4.16}$$

$$N \log x_g = \Sigma dN \log x$$

$$\log x_g = \frac{\Sigma dN \log x}{N} . \tag{4.17}$$

The harmonic mean is the number of particles divided by the sum of the reciprocals of the diameters of the individual particles; this is related to specific surface and is of importance where surface area of the sample is concerned [12].

$$x_H = \frac{\Sigma dN}{\Sigma dN/x} . \tag{4.18}$$

4.4 Methods of presenting size analysis data

An example of the tabular method of presenting size distribution data is shown in table 4.11. The significance of the distribution is more easily grasped when the data is presented pictorially, the simplest form of which is the histogram. The data in table 4.11 give the size grading of 1000 particles in twelve class intervals which are in a geometric progression. The choice of class widths is of fundamental importance, the basic requirement being that the resolution defined as the class interval divided by the mean class size should be kept fairly constant. With narrowly classified powders, an arithmetic distribution is acceptable but it is more usual to use a geometric progression.

Consider an analysis of a sub-sieve powder. For an arithmetic progression of sizes, let the intervals be 2·5 to 7·5, 7·5 to 12·5, and so on, to 67·5 to 72·5 μm. The resolution will then vary from 1 to 0·071 as the particle size increases. A geometric progression with the same number of size intervals is 0·14 to 1·18, 1·18 to 1·68, 1·68 to 2·36, and so on, to 53·7 to 75·5 with geometric means of 1, $\sqrt{2}$, $2\sqrt{2}$, 4 to 64. The resolution for each size range is constant at 0·34. If there is a constant error in defining the class intervals, say, a 1 μm undersizing, the effect of this error will be dependent on the size with an arithmetic progression being greater for small

Table 4.11

Particle size range x_2 to x_1	Interval (dx)	Average size x	Number frequency in range dN	Percentage in range dφ	Percentage per micron $\dfrac{d\phi}{dx}$	$\dfrac{d\phi}{d \log x}$
1·4 to 2·0	0·6	1·7	1	0·1	0·2	1
2·0 to 2·8	0·8	2·4	4	0·4	0·5	3
2·8 to 4·0	1·2	3·4	22	2·2	1·8	15
4·0 to 5·6	1·6	4·8	69	6·9	4·3	46
5·6 to 8·0	2·4	6·8	134	13·4	5·6	89
8·0 to 11·2	3·2	9·6	249	24·9	7·8	167
11·2 to 16·0	4·8	13·6	259	25·9	5·4	173
16·0 to 22·4	6·4	19·2	160	16·0	2·5	107
22·4 to 32·0	9·6	27·2	73	7·3	0·8	49
32·0 to 44·8	12·8	38·4	21	2·1	0·2	14
44·8 to 64·0	19·2	54·4	6	0·6	0·0	4
64·0 to 89·6	25·6	76·8	2	0·2	—	1
			1000			

where $y = \dfrac{d\phi}{dx}$

particles, whereas with a geometric size interval, the effect is independent of particle size.

Three methods of presenting the histogram are available. In the first, a rectangle is constructed over each class interval, the height of which is proportional to the number of particles in that interval (figure 4.6).

A far more useful way is to construct rectangles whose areas are proportional to the number of particles in the intervals. The total area under the histogram is equal to the number of particles counted, and it is useful to reduce this number to 100 by making the areas under the rectangles equal to the percentage of particles in the intervals so that histograms may be compared irrespective of the number of particles counted (figure 4.7).

If a sufficient number of particles have been counted, a smooth curve may be drawn through the histogram to give a frequency distribution. It is usual to have more than twelve intervals for this reason, with an upper limit of about twenty in order that the number of particles in each interval remains high and the work involved does not become too great.

It is often more convenient to plot the information as a cumulative distribution, the abscissa is particle size and the ordinate, the percentage smaller than or larger than the size. This method has the advantage that the median size and the percentage between any two sizes may be read off directly. The cumulative curve does often conceal detail and for comparison of similar size gradings, the relative percentage frequency should be used. If the range of particle size is very great, particularly if the intervals are in a geometric progression, it is advisable to use a logarithmic scale. In order that the distribution be plotted according to an equidistant log scale

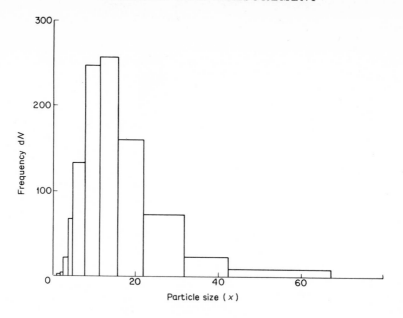

Fig. 4.6. Number frequency histogram.

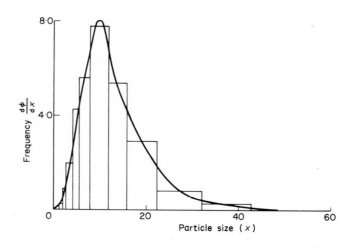

Fig. 4.7. The relative percentage frequency distribution by number.

$x\,(\mathrm{d}\phi/\mathrm{d}x)$ is plotted against $\ln x$ instead of $\mathrm{d}\phi/\mathrm{d}x$ against x as with the distribution curve using a linear abscissa [14, p. 90]. Alternatively, $\mathrm{d}\phi/\mathrm{d}(\log x)$ may be plotted against $\log x$ (figure 4.8).

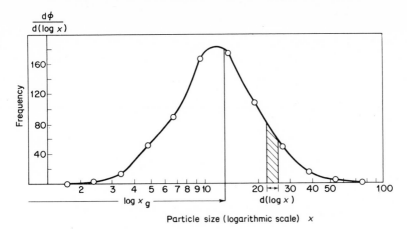

Fig. 4.8. A log-normal distribution plotted as a relative percentage frequency distribution using a logarithmic scale for particle size.

The mean size in this case is the geometric mean given by:

$$\log x_G \sum \frac{d\phi}{d(\log x)} \cdot d(\log x) = \sum \log x \frac{d\phi}{d(\log x)} \cdot d(\log x)$$

$$\log x_g = \frac{\sum \log x \, d\phi}{\sum d\phi} \tag{4.19}$$

(cf. equation (4.13)). ϕ is a general term for the variables W, S and N, i.e. weight, surface and number.

4.5 Devices for representing the cumulative distribution curve as a straight line

4.5.1 Arithmetic normal distributions
It is common practice to plot size distribution data in such a way that a straight line results, with all the advantages that follow from such a reduction. This can be done if the distribution fits a standard law, such as the normal law. This distribution occurs when the measured value of some property of a system is determined by a large number of small effects, each of which may or may not operate. If a large number of the measurements of the value are made, and the results plotted as a frequency distribution, the well-known, bell-shaped curve results.

Although it might be expected that this type of distribution would be common, it seems to occur only for narrow size ranges of classified material. Actual distributions are skewed, usually to the right.

The equation representing the normal distribution is:

$$y = \frac{1}{\sigma\sqrt{2\pi}} \exp\left[-\frac{(x-\bar{x})^2}{2\sigma^2}\right] \tag{4.20}$$

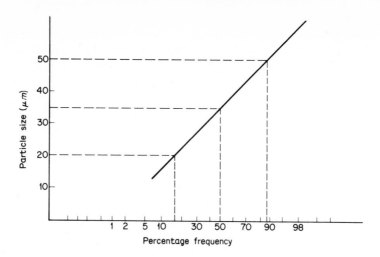

Fig. 4.9. A normal distribution plotted on normal probability paper.

$\bar{x}$ is the arithmetic mean value of x, the particle diameter, and σ, the standard deviation, is defined by:

$$\sigma^2 = \frac{\Sigma\,(x - \bar{x})^2}{N - 1} \tag{4.21}$$

where N is the number of measurements made.

A powder whose size distribution fits the normal equation can therefore be represented by two numbers, the mean value and the standard deviation. The fraction of particles lying between given sizes can then be found from the tables giving the areas under the graph between any two ordinates; such tables are published in Herdan's book [14, p. 77]. One advantage of this method of plotting is that experimental and operator errors may be smoothed out and the median and standard deviation can be read off the graph. In the illustrated example (figure 4.9), the median size, i.e. the 50% size, is 35 μm, and the standard deviation is half the difference between the 84% and the 16% sizes (15 μm).

It can be seen from the graph (figure 4.9) that a 1% unit around 95% probability is of about four times the size range as that round the 50% probability. This tends to aggravate the errors discussed under the theory of compensating errors, hence it is usual to draw a best straight line through the central points.

If all particles greater or smaller than a certain particle size have been removed, the curve becomes asymptotic towards these sizes. It is also possible to determine whether the distributions are homogeneous or heterogeneous since, in the latter case, points of inflection occur. These and other cases are discussed in detail by Irani and Callis [13, p. 47].

4.5.2 The log-normal distribution

According to the normal law, it is differences of equal amounts in excess or deficit from a mean value which are equally likely. With the log-normal law, it is ratios of equal amounts which are equally likely. In order to obtain a symmetrical curve of the same shape as the normal curve, it is therefore necessary to plot relative frequency against log size (figure 4.8).

The equation of the log-normal distribution is obtained by substituting $z = \ln x$. Then:

$$y = \frac{1}{\sigma_z \sqrt{2\pi}} \exp \left[-\frac{(z - \bar{z})^2}{2\sigma_z{}^2} \right] \qquad (4.22)$$

where $\qquad y = \dfrac{d\phi}{d(\ln x)}$, $\quad \sigma_z$ is the standard deviation of z

and $\qquad \bar{z} = \dfrac{\Sigma z d\phi}{\Sigma d\phi} \qquad (\phi = N, S \text{ or } W)$

$$\bar{z} = \frac{\Sigma z d\phi}{\phi}$$

or $\qquad \ln x_g = \dfrac{\Sigma \ln x \, d\phi}{\phi}$

therefore $\qquad \bar{x}_g = \phi\sqrt{\Pi x^{d\phi}}$. $\qquad (4.23)$

$\Pi x^{d\phi}$ is the product of the group data in which the frequency of particles of size x is $d\phi$, that is,,the mean of a log-normal distribution is the geometric mean, i.e. the arithmetic mean of the logarithms:

$$x_g{}^\phi = x_1{}^{d\phi_1} x_2{}^{d\phi_2} \ldots x_r{}^{d\phi_r} \ldots x_n{}^{d\phi_n}$$

Since the particle size is plotted on a logarithmic scale, the presentation of data on a log-probability graph is particularly useful when the range of sizes is large.

As before, the median particle size of the data presented on the graph (figure 4.10) is the 50% mediam size (20 μm) and this is equal to the geometric mean size x_g. The geometric standard deviation is:

$$\log \sigma_g = \log x_{84} - \log x_{50}$$

$$= \log x_{50} - \log x_{16}$$

or $\qquad 2 \log \sigma_g = \log x_{84} - \log_{50}$

$$= \log \frac{x_{84}}{x_{16}} . \qquad (4.24)$$

From figure 4.9:

$$\log \sigma_g = \tfrac{1}{2} \log \frac{40}{10} .$$

$$= \log 2$$

Therefore:

$$\sigma_g = 2 .$$

As a rule, if the number distribution of a given variable obeys a certain distribution law, the weight distribution does not and vice versa. This is not true for the log-normal distribution. If the number distribution is log-normal, the surface and weight distributions are also log-normal with the same standard deviation. Conversion from one distribution to another is easy using the following equations (see appendix):

(a) $$\ln x_{NL} = \ln x_{gN} + 0.5 \ln^2 \sigma_g$$

(b) $$\ln x_{NS} = \ln x_{gN} + 1.0 \ln^2 \sigma_g$$

(c) $$\ln x_{NV} = \ln x_{gN} + 1.5 \ln^2 \sigma_g$$

(d) $$\ln x_{NM} = \ln x_{gN} + 2.5 \ln^2 \sigma_g \qquad (4.25)$$

where x_{gN} is the geometric mean (median) of the number distribution and:

$$x_{NL} = \frac{\Sigma x dN}{\Sigma dN} ; \quad x_{NS}{}^2 = \frac{\Sigma x^2 dN}{\Sigma dN} ; \quad x_{NV}{}^3 = \frac{\Sigma x^3 dN}{\Sigma dN} ; \quad x_{NM}{}^4 = \frac{\Sigma x^4 dN}{\Sigma dN} .$$

Derived sizes are obtained in the following manner:

Example

Particle size range (μm)	Average size (x)	$\log x$	Cumulative % oversize ϕ	Percentage in range $d\phi$	$\dfrac{d\phi}{d(\log x)}$	$\log x \, d\phi$
$\sqrt{2}-2$	1·68	0·225	0·4	0·4	2·7	0·09
$2-2\sqrt{2}$	2·38	0·376	3·5	3·1	20·5	1·17
$2\sqrt{2}-4$	3·36	0·526	14·5	11·0	72·8	5·79
$4-4\sqrt{2}$	5·76	0·677	36·3	21·8	144·2	14·77
$4\sqrt{2}-8$	6·72	0·827	63·6	27·3	180·8	22·58
$8-8\sqrt{2}$	9·52	0·978	85·6	22·0	145·7	21·52
$8\sqrt{2}-16$	13·4	1·029	95·7	10·1	66·9	10·40
$16-16\sqrt{2}$	19·0	1·179	99·6	3·9	25·8	4·60
$16\sqrt{2}-32$	26·9	1·430	100·0	0·4	2·7	0·57
						81·49

Surface-volume

$$x_{sv} = \frac{\Sigma x^3 dN}{\Sigma x^2 dN}$$

$$= x^3{}_{NV}/x^2{}_{NS} .$$

Therefore:

$$\ln x_{sv} = 3\ln x_{NV} - 2\ln x_{NS}$$

$$= \ln x_{gN} - 2.5\ln^2 \sigma_g . \qquad (4.26)$$

If the initial analysis was a weight analysis, the above equations may be utilized using the conversions.

(a) $$\ln x_{gS} = \ln x_{gN} + 2\ln^2 \sigma_g \cdot$$

(b) $$\ln x_{gV} = \ln x_{gN} + 3\ln^2 \sigma_g \cdot \qquad (4.27)$$

where x_{gN}, x_{gS} and x_{gV} are the number, surface and volume geometric mean diameters.

Assuming a weight distribution ($d\phi = dW = x^3 dN$):

$$\log x_{gV} = \frac{\Sigma \log x d\phi}{d\phi}$$

$$= 0\cdot 815$$

$$x_{gV} = 6\cdot 53$$

σ_g may also be obtained from the table, but both these values may be obtained more readily from the graph giving:

$$x_{gV} = x_{median} = 6\cdot 6 \,\mu m$$

$$\sigma_g = 1\cdot 64 \,(\log \sigma_g = 0\cdot 215)\,.$$

The number distribution will have a median:

$$\log x_{gN} = \log x_{gV} - 6\cdot 9 \log^2 \sigma_g$$

$$= 0\cdot 815 - 6\cdot 9 \times 0\cdot 215^2$$

$$x_{gN} = 3\cdot 28\,.$$

Similarly:
$$\log x_{gS} = \log x_{gV} - 4\cdot 6 \log^2 \sigma_g$$

$$= 0\cdot 815 - 4\cdot 6 \times 0\cdot 215^2$$

$$x_{gS} = 4\cdot 00\,.$$

In each case the slope of the log-normal line, hence the standard deviation σ_g, will be the same; from equations (4.25):

$$X_{LS} = 3\cdot 67$$

$$X_{VS} = 4\cdot 10$$

$$X_{VM} = 4\cdot 55$$

$$X_{NL} = 3\cdot 30$$

$$X_{NS} = 3\cdot 48$$

$$X_{NM} = 3\cdot 87$$

4.5.3 The Rosin-Rammler distribution [21]

For broken coal, a distribution function has been developed which has since been found to apply to many other materials.

Let the size distribution of broken coal be obtained by sieving and let the weight percentage retained on the sieve of aperture x be denoted by R; a plot of R against x gives the cumulative percentage oversize curve.

From the probability considerations the authors obtain:

$$\frac{dF(x)}{dx} = 100n \, bx^{n-1} \exp(-bx^n) \qquad (4.28)$$

where n and b are constants, b being a measure of the range of particle size present and n being characteristic of the substance being analysed. Integrating gives:

$$R = 100 \exp(-bx^n) \qquad (4.29)$$

This reduces to:
$$\text{log-log} \frac{100}{R} = \text{const} + n \log x \; . \qquad (4.30)$$

If log log $100/R$ is plotted against $\log x$, a straight line results. The peak of the distribution curve for $n = 1$ is at $100/e = 36\cdot8\%$, and denoting the mode of the distribution curve by x_m equation (4.29) gives $b = 1/x_m$.

The sieve opening for $R = 36\cdot8\%$ is used to characterize the degree of comminution of the material, and since the slope of the line on the Rosin-Rammler graph depends on the particle size range, the ratio of $\tan^{-1}(n)$ and x_m is a form of variance

This treatment is useful for monitoring grinding operations for highly skewed distributions, but should be used with caution since the device of taking logs always reduces scatter, hence taking logs twice is not to be recommended.

4.5.4 Mean particle sizes and specific surface evaluation for Rosin-Rammler distributions

The moment-volume mean diameter is given by:

$$x_{vm} = \frac{\Sigma \, x\Delta W}{\Sigma \, \Delta W} \qquad (4.31)$$

since $\Delta W = \Delta F(x)$, defining $F(x)$ as 100 gives from equations (4.28) and (4.31):

$$x_{vm} = \frac{1}{100} \int_0^\infty 100n \, bx^n \exp(-bx^n) \, dx$$

$$= \frac{1}{n\sqrt{b}} \, \Gamma\left(\frac{1}{n} + 1\right) .$$

The surface-volume mean diameter may be similarly evaluated as:

$$x_{sv} = \frac{1}{n\sqrt{b} \, \Gamma\left(1 - \frac{1}{n}\right)} , \quad n > 1 .$$

These can be evaluated from tables of gamma functions for experimental values of n and the specific surface determined.

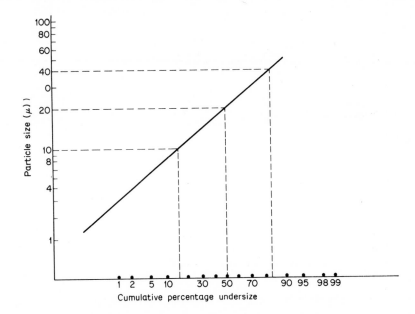

Fig. 4.10. A log normal distribution plotted on log probability paper.

4.5.5 Evaluation of non-linear distributions on log-normal paper

A bimodal distribution is detectable on log-probability paper by a change in slope of the line. It is also possible to deduce further features of the distribution. Figure 4.11 shows a bimodal distribution in which the parent distributions do not intersect on a log-probability plot. These distributions are asymptotic to the parent distributions. The geometric means of the parent distributions may be obtained by plotting relative percentage frequency against particle size on log-linear paper (figure 4.12). The area under the two quite distinct curves gives the proportions of the two constituents. From the modes to the 34% levels in areas gives the two standard deviations.

Figure 4.13 shows a bimodal distribution in which the parent distributions intersect on a log-probability plot. These distributions are asymptotic to the parent distribution having the widest size range (i.e. high standard deviation). The point of inflection passes through both distributions. If the separation of means is large, these may be obtained from a plot of relative percentage frequency against particle size on log-linear paper. If the separation of means is small, it is difficult to resolve these distributions (figure 4.14).

Figure 4.15 shows a trimodal distribution. This may also be easily resolved into its component parts if the parent distributions do not intersect on log-probability paper (figure 4.16).

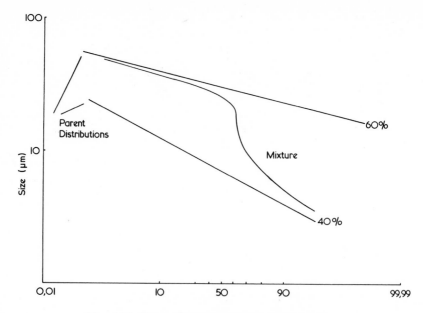

Fig. 4.11. Bimodal non-intersecting distributions.

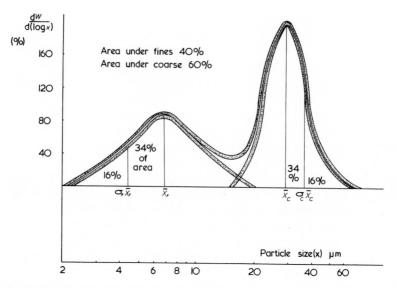

Fig. 4.12. Relative percentage per log-micrometre of a bimodal distribution with little overlap.

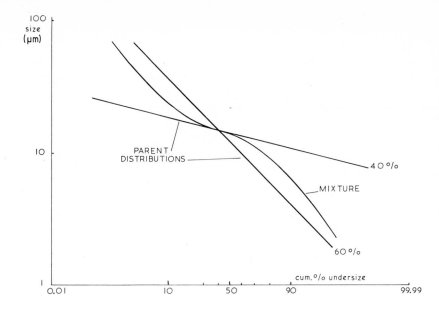

Fig. 4.13. Bimodal intersecting distributions

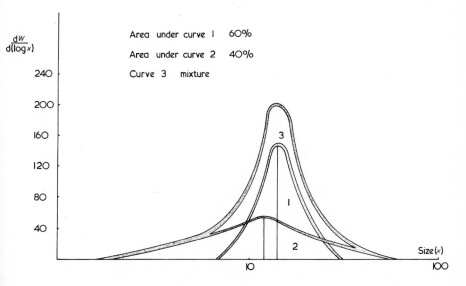

Fig. 4.14. Relative percentage per log-micrometre of a bimodal distribution with small separation of means.

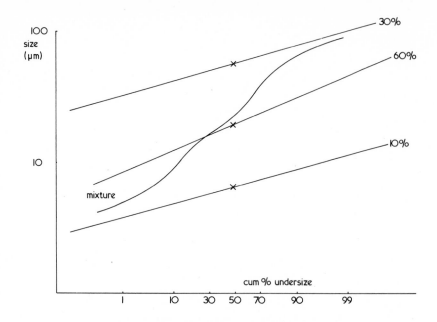

Fig. 4.15. Trimodal distribution with parent distributions.

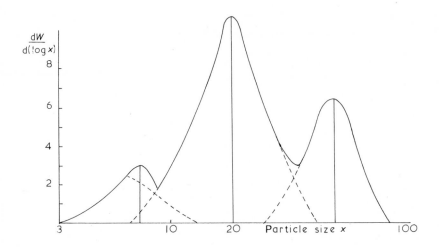

Fig. 4.16. Relative percentage per log-micrometre of a trimodal distribution with little overlap.

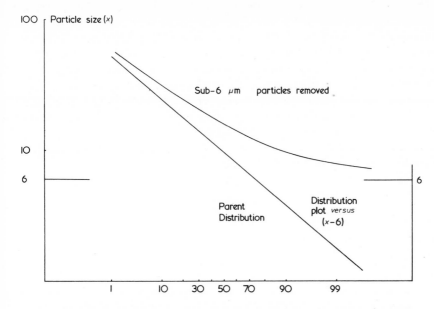

Fig. 4.17. Log-normal distribution with deficiency of sub-6 μm particles.

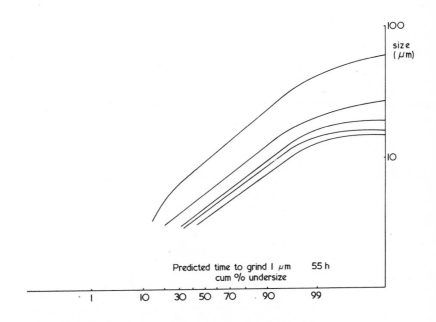

Fig. 4.18. Andreasen analysis monitoring a grinding operation (1).

Figure 4.17 shows a log-normal distribution of geometric mean size 10 μm and geometric standard deviation 2. This distribution is deficient in sub-6 μm particles and is asymptotic to this size. If $(x - 6)$ is taken as the particle size, a straight line results to give the original distribution. A similar sort of plot occurs when there is a deficiency of coarse particles and this may be similarly resolved.

Figure 4.18 shows Andreasen analyses monitoring a grinding operation. Since, in this case, the new surface created is proportional to grinding time, it is possible to predict future performance. Similarly, less accurately, maximum size is inversely proportional to grinding time, see table below.

Grinding time (hours) (t)	Mean particle size (μm)	Maximum particle size (x_g) (μm)	$x_g t$	$x_m t$
9	5·3	27·5	47·7	239
13	4·1	19	53·3	247
15	3·75	16	56·3	240
16	3·42	14	54·7	224

Hence, predicted time to grind to 1 μm mean size is 55 hours; predicted time to produce sub-10 μm particles in 24 hours.

Figure 4.19 gives six analyses from a grinding operation. For samples 4 and 5, the grinding variables have been altered.

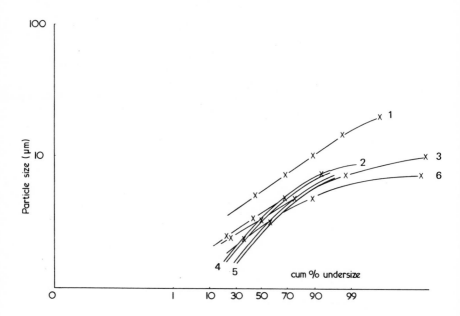

Fig. 4.19. Andreasen analysis monitoring a grinding operation (2).

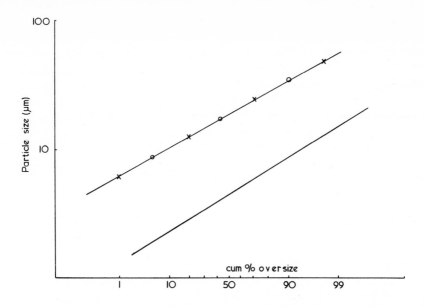

Fig. 4.20. Comparison between Coulter Counter analysis, X-ray and pipette methods.

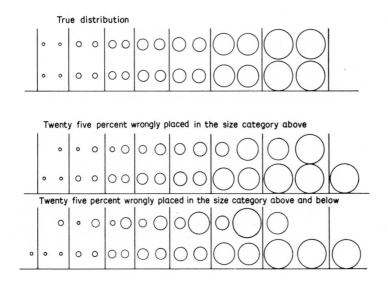

Fig. 4.21. Law of compensating variables.

4.5.6 Derivation of shape factors from parallel log-normal curves

The two curves on figure 4.20 are analyses of the same powder using gravimetric (X-ray and pipette sedimentation) and volumetric (Coulter) techniques.

Multiplying the diameter by the latter technique by a factor of 2·62, brings the two curves into coincidence, hence:

$$2·62 \, d_{st} = d_v$$

since: $\qquad\qquad d^2{}_{st} \doteqdot \dfrac{d_v{}^3}{d_s} \qquad$ this gives:

$$\frac{d_v}{d_{st}} = 2·62 ; \qquad \frac{d_s}{d_v} \doteqdot 2·62^2 .$$

For a spherical particle, these ratios are unity, increasing with increasing divergence from sphericity.

4.6 The law of compensating errors

In any method of size analysis, it is always possible to assign the wrong size to some of the particles. If this error is without bias, the possibility of assigning too great a size is equally as probable as assigning too small a size. This will modify the extremes of the distribution, but will have little effect on the central region. An illustration with particles of mean size $1, \sqrt{(2)}, 2, 2\sqrt{(2)}, 4, 4\sqrt{(2)}, 8$, in which, 25% in each size range are placed in the size category below and 25% in the size category above, is shown in figure 4.21. An illustration with bias is also shown with particles having the same size ranges as in the first example, but with 25% in each category being placed in the category above.

Table 4.12

Upper size limit (μm)	Mean size (μm)	Cumulative percentage undersize		Percentage in range	
		true	*error*	*true*	*error*
1	1·2	0	0·08	0·3	0·08
$\sqrt{2}$	1·7	0·3	0·50	1·1	0·42
2	2·4	1·4	2·15	4·1	1·65
$2\sqrt{2}$	3·4	5·5	6·85	9·5	4·70
4	4·8	15·0	17·38	19·0	10·53
$4\sqrt{2}$	6·8	34·0	35·25	24·0	17·87
8	9·6	58·0	57·00	20·0	21·75
$8\sqrt{2}$	13·4	78·0	76·28	13·0	19·25
16	19·0	91·0	89·385	6·4	13·10
$16\sqrt{2}$	28·9	97·4	96·30	2·0	6·95
32	38·0	99·4	99·03	0·5	2·73
$32\sqrt{2}$	53·8	99·9	99·80	0·1	0·77
64	76·0	100	99·98		0·18
			100		0·02

It can be seen that there is the same number of particles in each of the central-size categories, irrespective of whether bias is present or not. If the number distribution is converted into a weight distribution, this is still true, but by wrongly assigning a size of $8\sqrt{(2)}$ to 25% by number of the particles in the top-size category gives an apparently coarser distribution. For measurement sizes in arithmetic progression of sizes, the effect is small provided sizing is carried out at 10 or more size intervals and, for a log-normal distribution plotted as a relative frequency curve against the logarithm of particle size, the position of the mode is only slightly affected.

Table 4.12 is for a log-normal distribution having a mean size of 8·6 μm and a standard deviation of 0·320. Wrongly placing 25% of each category by weight in the size category above and 25% in the size category below, gives a mean size of 8·6 μm and a standard deviation of 0·284.

APPENDIX

4.7 Manipulation of log-probability equation
Consider the log-normal equation:

$$\frac{d\phi}{d(\ln x)} = \frac{1}{\sqrt{2\pi}\cdot\ln\sigma_g} \exp\left[-\left\{\frac{\ln\left(\frac{x}{x_g}\right)}{2\ln\sigma_g}\right\}^2\right] \qquad (4.32)$$

ϕ being a general term for the frequency, being number length, surface or volume (weight) (i.e. $\phi = N, L, S,$ or V).

Let:
$$X = \frac{\ln\left(\frac{x}{x_g}\right)}{\sqrt{2}\,\ln\sigma_g} \qquad (4.33)$$

then:
$$\sqrt{2}\,\ln\sigma_g\,dX = d(\ln x) \qquad (4.34)$$

$$\int d\phi = \frac{1}{\sqrt{\pi}} \int \exp(-X^2)\,dX \qquad (4.35)$$

The fraction undersize the geometric mean size x_g is obtained by inserting the limits $x = 0, x = x_g$ i.e. $x = -\infty, x = 0$.

$$\phi_{xg}\,\frac{1}{\sqrt{\pi}} \int_{-\infty}^{0} \exp(-X^2)\,dX$$

$$= \tfrac{1}{2}$$

Therefore, the geometric mean size is the median size.

The fraction lying within one standard deviation of the mean is obtained by inserting the limits $x = x_g, x = \sigma_g x_g$, i.e. $X_1 = 0, X_2 = 1/\sqrt{2}$.

$$\phi(\sigma_g x_g - x_g) = \frac{1}{\sqrt{\pi}} \int_{0}^{\frac{1}{\sqrt{2}}} \exp(-X^2)\,dX$$

$$= \frac{1}{\sqrt{\pi}}\left[X - \frac{X^3}{3} + \frac{X^2}{10} - \frac{X^7}{21} + \cdots\right]$$

$$= 0\cdot3413.$$

Hence, σ_g is the ratio of the 84·13% to the 50% size and the 50% to the 15·87% size.

Average sizes

Let:
$$d\phi = dn \; ; \; \sum_{r=0}^{r=0} n_r = \int_0^1 d\phi = 1.$$

n_r is the number of particles of size x_r ; x_0 ; x_x are the sizes of the smallest and largest particles present in the distribution. x_{gn} will, therefore, be the geometric mean of the number distribution:

$$x_{NL} = \frac{\sum x_r n_r}{\sum n_r} = \frac{1}{\sqrt{2\pi}\ln\sigma_g} \int_{-\infty}^{+\infty} \exp\left[-\left\{\frac{\ln\left(\frac{x}{x_g}\right)}{2\ln\sigma_g}\right\}^2\right] x \, d(\ln x). \qquad (4.36)$$

$$x^2_{NS} = \frac{\sum x^2_r n_r}{\sum n_r} = \frac{1}{\sqrt{2\pi}\ln\sigma_g} \int_{-\infty}^{+\infty} \exp\left[-\left\{\frac{\ln\left(\frac{x}{x_gN}\right)}{2\ln\sigma_g}\right\}^2\right] x^2 \, d(\ln x). \qquad (4.37)$$

$$x^3_{NV} = \frac{\sum x^3_r n_r}{\sum n_r} = \frac{1}{\sqrt{2\pi}\ln\sigma_g} \int_{-\infty}^{+\infty} \exp\left[-\left\{\frac{\ln\left(\frac{x}{x_gN}\right)}{2\ln\sigma_g}\right\}^2\right] x^3 \, d(\ln x). \qquad (4.38)$$

Substituting from equations (4.33) and (4.34) gives:

$$x_{NL} = \frac{x_{gn}}{\sqrt{\pi}} \quad \exp\left\{2\ln\sigma_g X - X^2\right\} dx. \qquad (4.39)$$

$$x^2_{NS} = \frac{x^2_{gN}}{\sqrt{\pi}} \quad \exp\left\{2\sqrt{2}\ln\sigma_g X - X^2\right\} dx. \qquad (4.40)$$

$$x^2_{NV} = \frac{x^3_{gN}}{\sqrt{\pi}} \quad \exp\left\{3\sqrt{2}\ln\sigma_g X - X^2\right\} dx. \qquad (4.41)$$

Making the transformations:

$$Y_1 = X - \frac{\sqrt{2}}{2}\ln\sigma_g \text{ in equation (4.39)}.$$

$$Y_2 = X - \sqrt{2}\ln\sigma_g \text{ in equation (4.40)}.$$

$$Y_3 = X - \tfrac{3}{2}\sqrt{2}\ln\sigma_g \text{ in equation (4.41)}.$$

$$x_{NL} = X_{gN} \, \underline{\exp^{\frac{1}{2}} (\ln^2 \sigma_g)} \int_{-\infty}^{+\infty} \exp\left(-Y_1^2\right) dY_1. \qquad (4.42)$$

$$x^2_{NS} = x^2_{gN} \, \underline{\exp 2 (\ln^2 \sigma_g)} \int_{-\infty}^{+\infty} \exp\left(-Y_2^2\right) dY_2. \qquad (4.43)$$

$$x^3{}_{NV} = x^3{}_{gN} \exp^{\frac{9}{2}} (\ln^2 \sigma_g) \int_{-\infty}^{+\infty} \exp(-Y_3^2) \, dY_3 . \tag{4.44}$$

The integration yields a value $I = \sqrt{\pi}$ giving:

$$\ln x_{NL} = \ln x_{gN} + \tfrac{1}{2} \ln^2 \sigma_g. \tag{4.45}$$

$$2 \ln x_{NS} = 2 \ln x_{gN} + 2 \ln^2 \sigma_g. \tag{4.46}$$

$$3 \ln x_{NV} = 3 \ln x_{gN} + 4\cdot5 \ln^2 \sigma_g. \tag{4.47}$$

Similarly:

$$4 \ln x_{NM} = 4 \ln x_{gN} + 8 \ln^2 \sigma_g. \tag{4.48}$$

Derived average sizes
If the number-size distribution of a particulate system has been determined and found to be log-normal, equations (4.44) to (4.48) may be used to determine other average sizes.

For example, the mean size of a weight distribution is given by:

$$x_{VM} = \frac{\Sigma x_r^4 n_r}{\Sigma x_r^3 n_r}$$

$$x_{VM} = \frac{\Sigma x_r^4 n_r}{\Sigma n_r} \frac{\Sigma x_r^3 n_r}{\Sigma n_r}$$

$$= (x^4{}_{NM}/x^3{}_{NV})$$

$$\therefore \ln x_{VM} = 4 \ln x_{NM} - 3 \ln x_{NV} .$$

Substituting from equations (4.47) and (4.48):

$$\ln x_{VM} = \ln x_{gN} + 3\cdot5 \ln^2 \sigma_g. \tag{4.49}$$

Similarly, the mean size of a surface distribution is given by:

$$\ln x_{SV} = \ln x_{gN} + 2\cdot5 \ln^2 \sigma_g. \tag{4.50}$$

Using this equation, the specific surface of the particulate system may be determined since:

$$S_V = 6/x_{SV} . \tag{4.51}$$

Transformation of the log-normal distribution by count into one by weight
If a number distribution is log-normal, the weight distribution is also log-normal with the same geometric standard deviation. Using the same treatment as was used to derive equation (4.45) gives, for a weight analysis:

$$\ln x_{VM} = \ln x_{gV} + \tfrac{1}{2} \ln^2 \sigma_g. \tag{4.52}$$

Comparing with equation (4.49) gives:

$$\ln x_{gV} = \ln x_{gN} + 3\cdot0 \ln^2 \sigma_g. \tag{4.53}$$

Since the relations between the number-average sizes and the number-geometric mean are known (equations (4.45) to (4.48)), these can now be expressed as relation tionships between number-average sizes and the weight (volume) geometric mean x_{gV}.

$$\ln x_{NL} = \ln x_{gV} - 2\!\cdot\!5 \ln^2 \sigma_g. \tag{4.54}$$

$$\ln x_{NS} = \ln x_{gV} - 2\!\cdot\!0 \ln^2 \sigma_g. \tag{4.55}$$

$$\ln x_{NV} = \ln x_{gV} - 1\!\cdot\!5 \ln^2 \sigma_g. \tag{4.56}$$

$$\ln x_{NM} = \ln x_{gV} - 1\!\cdot\!0 \ln^2 \sigma_g. \tag{4.57}$$

Other average sizes may be derived from the above, using a similar procedure to that used to derive equations (4.49) and (4.50) to give:

$$\ln x_{VM} = \ln x_{gV} + 0\!\cdot\!5 \ln^2 \sigma_g. \tag{4.58}$$

$$\ln x_{SV} = \ln x_{gV} + 0\!\cdot\!5 \ln^2 \sigma_g. \tag{4.59}$$

Similarly, for a surface distribution, the equivalent equation to equation (4.53) is:

$$\ln x_{gS} = \ln x_{gN} + 2\!\cdot\!0 \ln^2 \sigma_g. \tag{4.60}$$

Substituting this relationship into equations (4.45) to (4.48), yields the equivalent relationships relating surface-average sizes with the surface-geometric mean diameter.

4.8 Phi-notation

In geological literature dealing with particle size distribution, a very advantageous transformation of particle size is commonly used. Because it is a logarithmic transformation, it simplifies granulometric computations in the same way as logarithms in mathematical operations. This transformation replaces ratio scale numbers, based on millimetre values of particle size, by interval scale numbers, based on the logarithms of those values. Although several transformations based on decadic logarithms were also suggested (zeta-transformation [23] and gamma-transformation [24], more than thirty years ago, it has been broadly adopted, particularly in the U.S.A. After the redefinition by McManus [26] and the comments of Krumbein [27], the transformation is:

$$\phi = -\log_2 X_i \quad \text{or} \quad X_i = 2^{-\phi}$$

where X_i is a dimensionless ratio of a given particle size, in millimetres, to the standard particle size of 1 mm.

Phi-values can be found if the common particle size, in millimetres of X_i, are multiplied by $(\log 10^2)^{-1} = 3\!\cdot\!3219282$. Conversely, phi-values can be converted into their millimetre (or more precisely X_i) equivalents if their decadic antilogarithms are multiplied by $\log 10^2 = 0\!\cdot\!30103$. For easy manipulation, a conversion chart [28, p. 244] or a conversion table [29, 30] can be used.

By using the phi-notation, the statistical measurements acquire a great simplicity. The standard deviation, σ_ϕ, used in this notation refers to its quantile estimate:

$$\sigma_\phi = 0.5(\phi_{84} - \phi_{16}).$$

Similarly the ϕ skewness:

$$\phi = \frac{\phi_{16} + \phi_{84} - 2\phi_{50}}{\phi_{84} - \phi_{16}}.$$

Other statistical measurements used in geology for particle size distribution characterization (moment, quantile and others) have been reviewed [31, 32].

References

[1] Heywood, H. (1947), *Symposium on Particle Size Analysis*, Inst. Chem. Eng. Suppl., **25**, 14.

[2] Schweyer, H.E., and Work, L.T. (1941), A.S.T.M., *Symposium on New Methods for Particle Size Determination in the Sub-sieve Range*, (*loc. cit.* [1]).

[3] Report by B.C.O.R.A., and B.C.U.R.A. (1942), *Determination of Particle Size in the Sub-sieve Range*, (*loc. cit.* [1]).

[4] Rabson, S.R. (1944), *J. Chem. Met. Min. Soc., S. Africa*, **45**, 34; see (1945), 'Discussion', **46**, 160 (*loc. cit.* [1])..

[5] Heywood, H. (1963), *J. Pharm. Pharmacol. Suppl.*, **15**, 56T.

[6] Ellison, J. McK. (1954), *Nature*, **173**, 948.

[7] Hodkinson, J.R. (1962), Lond. Univ., PhD. thesis.

[8] Wadel, H. (1934), *Physics*, **5**, 281.

[9] Cartwright, J. (1962), *Ann. Occup. Hyg.*, **5**, 163.

[10] Fairs, G.L., and Hatch, L.P. (1933), *J. Am. Water Works Assoc.*, **25**, 1551.

[11] Crowl, V.T. (1963), *Paint Research Station Report No. 325*.

[12] Morony, M.J., *Facts from Figures*, Pelican.

[13] Irani, R.R., and Callis, C.F. (1963), *Particle Size: Measurement Interpretation and Application*, Wiley, N.Y.

[14] Herdan, G. (1960), *Small Particle Statistics*, Butterworths.

[15] Church, T. (1968–9), *Powder Tech.*, **2**, 27–31.

[16] Hausner, H.H. (1966), *Planseeber*, **14**, 2, 75–84.

[17] Lees, G. (1964), *Sedimentology*, **3**, 2–21.

[18] Lees, G. (1964), *J. B. Granite Whimstone Fed.*, **4**, 2.

[19] Wadel, H., *J. Geology*, (1932), **40**, 243–53; ibid, (1935), **43**, 250–80.

[20] Cole, M. (June, 1971), *American Laboratory*, 19–28.

[21] Rosin, P., and Rammler, E. (1933), *J. Inst. Fuel*, **7**, 29; (1927), *Zemast*, **16**, 820, 840, 871, 897; (1931), *Ibid.*, **20**, 210, 240, 311, 343.

[22] Heywood, H. (1973), *Harold Heywood Memorial Lectures*, Loughborough Univ., England.

[23] Krumbein, W.C. (1937), *Neues Jb. Miner.*, **73**, 137.

[24] Baturin, V.P. (1943), Reports Ac. Sci., USSR (Moscow), **38**, No. 7 (in Russian).

[25] Krumbein, W.C. (1934), *J. Sediment. Petrol.*, **4**, 65 (particularly p. 76).

[26] McManus, D.A.,(1963), *Ibid.*, **33**, 670.

[27] Krumbein, W.C. (1964), *Ibid.*, **34**, 195.

[28] Krumbein, W.C., and Pettijohn, F.J. (1938), 'Manual of Sedimentary Petrography', Appleton-Century-Crofts, New York.

[29] Page, H.G. (1955), *Ibid.*, **25**, 285.

[30] Griffiths, J.C. and McIntyre, D.D. (1958), 'A Table for the Conversion of

Millimetres to Phi units', Mineral Ind. Expt. Sta., Pennsylvania State University

[31] Folk, R.L. (1966), *Sedimentology,* **6**, 73.

[32] Griffiths, J.C. in Milner, H.B. (1962), *'Sedimentary Petrography',* Vol. 1, Ch. 16, MacMillan, New York.

5 Sieving

5.1 Introduction
Sieving is probably the easiest and certainly the most popular method of size analysis, but it is restricted to powders having the greater proportion coarser than 75 μm. For finer powders, the method is not generally used because of the high cost of producing sieves with uniform small apertures.

A sieve is an open container, usually cylindrical, having definitely spaced and uniform openings in the base. The openings are square when wire mesh is used and circular when the openings are formed by punching holes in a metal plate. By stacking the sieves in order of ascending aperture size and placing the powder on the top sieve and agitating, the powder is classified into fractions. A closed pan, a receiver, is placed at the bottom of the stack to collect the fines and a lid is placed on top to prevent loss of powder; agitation may be manual or mechanical. Results are usually expressed in the form of a cumulative undersize percentage distribution in terms of the nominal apertures of the sieves used in the analysis.

The sieve size d_A is the minimum square aperture through which the particles can pass. Fractionation by sieving is a function of two dimensions only, maximum breadth and maximum thickness for, unless the particles are excessively elongated, the length does not hinder the passage of particles through the sieve apertures (figure 5.1).

5.2 Types of sieves
A variety of sieve aperture ranges are currently used, the most popular being the German Standard, DIN 1171 (1934); A.S.T.M. standard E11−61; the American Tyler series; the French series A.F.N.O.R., the Institute of Mining and Metallurgy Standard and the British Standard, B.S.S. 410: (1962). The International Organisation for Standardisation is at present attempting to standardize these ranges [45] and some of their recommendations have been implemented in the British Standard.

5.3 British Standard specifications
The Standard is divided into three parts. Part 1 covers a range of woven wire fine mesh test sieves of aperture width in a fourth root of two progression from a maximum of 3·35 mm to a minimum of 0·045 mm. The series incorporates a root-two progression proposed as ISO sieves for international co-ordination. Two grades are

113

provided of equal nominal dimensions but different tolerances. Also included is a range of woven wire medium test sieves of aperture width from a maximum of $\frac{1}{2}$ in to a minimum of $\frac{1}{32}$ in. In addition, requirements are given for the manufacture of the sieves, including the frame mounting cover and finish and the wire cloth, together with requirements for marking, and the method of examination for acceptance

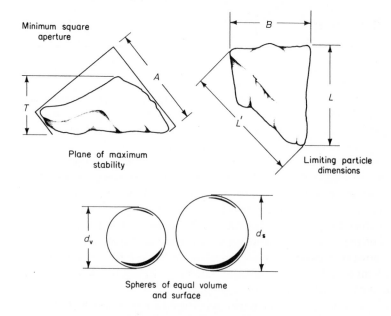

Fig. 5.1. Equivalent particle diameters (after Heywood).

Parts 2 and 3 of the Standard deal with coarse test sieves (perforated plates) having square apertures of width from 4 in to $\frac{3}{16}$ in for general purposes, and also a range of coarse heavy-duty test sieves for single-hole gauges specifically for use with blast-furnace coke, having square apertures of width from 8 in to $\frac{1}{8}$ in.

It is a matter of some interest that, of the 26 sizes in the B.S. fine mesh series, eleven are now identical with the corresponding values in the American series, and a further four are within one micrometre of the corresponding American values: The appendices include tabular summaries of the U.S.A. Standard series, the German Standard and the French.

The mesh for the sieves is woven wire of circular cross-section, the most commonly used materials being phosphor bronze for fine sieves (aperture < 250 μm), brass for coarser sieves and mild steel for apertures greater than 1 mm. The mesh number, a common method of designating sieves, is the number of wires per linear inch of sieve cloth.

From the table reprinted from B.S. 410: (1961) (table 5.1), it can be seen that the 200-mesh sieve has a nominal aperture of 75 μm and a nominal wire diameter

Table 5.1

Aperture width (μm)	Mesh number	Aperture tolerances		
		Average	Intermediate	Maximum
75	200	4·6	19	33
45	350	3·8	17	30

Tolerances

Average: The average aperture width must not deviate from the nominal aperture width by more than this amount.

Intermediate: Not more than 6% of the apertures may deviate from the nominal aperture width by more than this amount.

Maximum: No aperture may deviate from the average aperture width by more than this amount.

of 52 μm. The average aperture width must lie between 70·4 and 79·6 μm, with not more than 6% of the apertures outside the size range 56 to 94 μm and all the apertures in the size range 42 to 108 μm. For the 350-mesh sieve of nominal aperture 45 μm all apertures must be in the range 15 to 75 μm.

Since these requirements apply to the mesh and not to the sieve, individual sieves may have tolerances outside these limits. Examination of individual sieves, according to B.S. 410, suffices to show that in nearly every case the quality is far higher than required by the Standard.

5.4 Methods for the use of fine-mesh sieves [43, 44]

The British Standard applies to the sieving of material from 3350 to 53 μm in size (mesh nos. 5 to 300).

Modifications to the methods may be necessary for materials that are not free-flowing, are highly hygroscopic, very fragile, have abnormal particle shapes or possess other properties which cause difficulty in sieving. The recommended weight of powder varies from 25 to 100 g according to its density.

The sieving operation may be carried out wet or dry, by machine or by hand, for a fixed period of time or until less than 0·2% of the sample passes through the mesh in any 5-min sieving period (the rate test). Preliminary hand sieving on the finest sieve is recommended for the removal of dust.

If losses during sieving exceed 0·5% of the sample weight, the test should be discarded. The sieving operation is carried out in 5-min stages at the end of which the sieves should be emptied and brushed in order to reduce blocking of the apertures.

5.5 Sieving errors

The apertures of a sieve may be regarded as a series of gauges which reject or pass particles as they are presented at the aperture. The probability that a particle will present itself at an aperture depends on the following factors:

(1) The particle size distribution of the powder.

(2) The number of particles on the sieve (load).

(3) The physical properties of the particles (e.g. surface).

(4) The method of shaking the sieve.

(5) The dimension and shape of the particles.

(6) The geometry of the sieving surface (e.g. open area/total area).

Whether or not the particle will pass the sieve when it is presented at the sieving surface will then depend upon its dimension and the angle at which it is presented.

The size distribution given by a sieving operation depends also on the following variables:

(1) Duration of sieving.

(2) Variation of sieve aperture.

(3) Wear.

(4) Errors of observation and experiment.

(5) Errors of sampling.

(6) Effect of different equipment and operation.

It may be noted, therefore, that the rate method recommended in B.S. 1796 does not give the weight capable of passing a sieve but is an attempt to define an arbitrary reproducible end-point. Experimental investigation of these variables has been carried out by Fahrenwald and Stockdale [1].

The effect of sieving time and sieving load have been investigated by Shergold [5] The tests were carried out with 14- 52- and 200-mesh sieves using samples of sand specially prepared so that 50% by weight of each sample could pass through the appropriate sieve. Some of the results using the 200-mesh sieve are given in table 5.2 These results are of the form $P = k. \log_e t$. Shergold's results showed that the smaller the sieve aperture, the greater the effect of overloading .

Table 5.2

Sample weight (g)	Sieving time (min)			
	5	10	20	40
	Percentage retained on sieve (P)			
500	83·6	80·7	76·5	73·8
250	67·2	64·3	61·6	57·8
125	58·6	58·0	55·2	53·2
62·5	56·6	55·0	53·2	52·3

and the greater the discrepancies between the results for different loadings. He also showed that though, in general, there is no end-point for sieving, the approach to the true percentage is quicker for small sieve apertures. Since it is evident that a reduction in sample size is more effective than prolonging the sieving, he recommend that the sample should be as small as is compatible with convenient handling, 100–150 g for coarse sand and 40–60 g for fine sand with a sieving time of 9 min.

Fagerhalt [2], Whitby [3] and Kaye [4] have all attempted to predict sieving efficiency by mathematical treatment. Whitby found that the mechanism of sieving

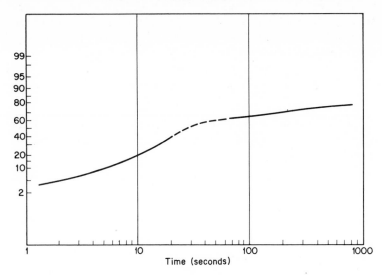

Fig. 5.2. The rate at which particles pass through a sieve plotted on
        log-probability paper (after Whitby [3]).

can be divided into different regions with a transition region in between, as illustrated
in figures 5.2 and 5.3. The first region relates to the passage of particles much finer
than the mesh openings and the law $P = at^b$ is obeyed where

a = fraction passing sieve per unit time or fraction per tap for hand sieving,
b = a constant very nearly equal to 1,
t = sieving time or number of taps for hand sieving,
P = cumulative weight fraction through the sieve.

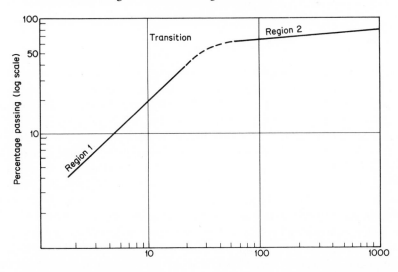

Fig. 5.3. The rate at which particles pass through a sieve plotted on log-log paper
        (after Whitby [3])

He assumed a to be a function of the variables, total load on sieve (W), particle density (ρ_s), mesh opening (S), sieve open area (A_o), sieve area (A), particle size (d), and bed depth on sieve (T).

This reduces to $a = f\left(\dfrac{W}{\rho_s SA_o}, \dfrac{S}{d}, \dfrac{A_o}{A}, \dfrac{T}{d}, \dfrac{A}{S^2}\right)$, an identity with seven variables and two dimensions; hence a is a function of five dimensionless groups.

Since A_o/A is constant for any sieve and A/S^2 is so large that it is unlikely to have any appreciable effect, and the effect of variation in T/d is negligible, the equation becomes:

$$a = f\left(\frac{W}{SA_o}, \frac{S}{d}\right).$$

Whitby found:

$$\frac{aW}{A_oS} = C_1\left(\frac{S}{k_s\bar{d}_m}\right) \frac{h}{\log\sigma}$$

where $k_s\bar{d}_m$ is a linear function of the geometric mass mean of the particle size distribution. C_1 and h are constants and σ is the geometric standard deviation at a particular size on the size distribution curve. This expression was found to hold for wheat products, crushed quartz, St Peter's sand, glass beads and other similar material

In the second region, all the particles capable of passing that remain on the sieve are near mesh-size and the rate of passing through decreases according to the log-normal law:

$$\frac{dW}{dt} = \frac{P}{t \log\sigma_g} \phi(Z)$$

where $\phi(Z)$ is the normal probability function

$$\text{and } P = \frac{dN}{Nd(\log t)} = \log\frac{\sigma_g}{\sigma_{gt}}.$$

P is a probability dependent on the material being sieved, the sieve motion and the type of sieve. N is the number of particles that can pass the sieve.

Whitby suggests that a good procedure would be to select as end-point a time at the beginning of region 2. This can be done by plotting the time–weight curve on log-probability paper (figure 5.2) and selecting as an end-point a time at the beginning of region 2. It is difficult to determine this point accurately in practice, and an alternative procedure used by the author is to transfer the straight line for region 2 on to a log-log scale (figure 5.3) and define as the end-point the intersection of the resulting curve with the straight line for region 1.

Using the rate test, the sieving operation is terminated some time during the second region. The true end-point, when every particle capable of passing through the sieve has done so, is not reached unless the sieving time is unduly protracted. However, Kaye [4] suggests that a plot of $\log(R_t - R_\infty)$ against time will yield this value where:

R_t is the weight retained on the sieve at time t, and

R_∞ is the estimated weight retained at infinite time.

The value of R_∞ which results in a straight line is accepted as the ultimate residue (figure 5.4). The above relationship is deduced from the equation:

$$\frac{dw}{dt} = k(W_t - W_r)$$

which Kaye derives from first principles.

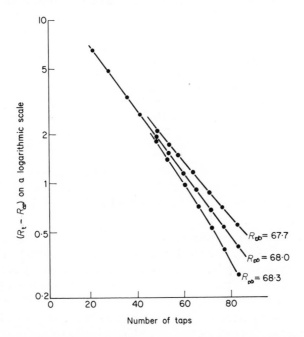

Fig. 5.4. Kaye's method of defining the end-point to a sieving operation [4].

Anderson [20] defines the particle size boundary from a rate test. When the rate passing is constant and fairly low the mean size of the particles that have passed during the last minute is determined by counting and weighing. This particle is the particle-size boundary under the applied sieving conditions. $C(k)$ is the fraction undersize k, k being defined as the edge of a cube of the same volume as the particle, the grains being counted in a weighed quantity of the fraction. Using this technique, good agreement is found between sieving and sedimentation.

Other variables investigated include sieve motion [1, 4], percentage open area [6], calibration [7, 8, 9], static [10], humidity [8] and accuracy for a particular application [11, 12, 13, 14].

Heywood [13], for example, describes experiments carried out at seven laboratories in which 50 g samples of coal dust were sieved on B.S. sieves of 72, 100, 150 and 200 mesh. The average percentage retained on a specified sieve in all the trials was taken to correspond to the quoted or nominal sieve aperture, and the percentage retained on that sieve in a single trial was taken to correspond to the effective sieve aperture. From a graph of the cumulative percentage passing through the sieve against the nominal sieve aperture, the effective sieve aperture may be read. For example, Heywood found that the average percentage passing through the 52-mesh (295 μm) sieve was 76·9%. In a particular analysis 74% passed through this sieve, the 76·9% on the graph being at an effective aperture of 280 μm, the aperture error being -15 μm. Heywood, by averaging over all the sieves, arrives at the following values for the standard deviations of aperture errors expressed as a percentage of the nominal aperture (table 5.3).

Table 5.3

Different sieves, different methods	8·30
Different sieves, same method	3·71
Same sieves, same method:	
machine sieving	0·61
hand sieving	0·80

Although differences between analyses are inevitable, standardization of procedure more than doubles the reproducibility of a sieving operation. A useful statistical analysis of Heywood's data is to be found in Herdan [15, p. 121].

5.6 Electroformed micromesh sieves

Micromesh sieves, first described by Daescher et al. [21] are made by electroforming nickel in square and circular mesh. These are available in aperture size from 5 to 150 μm in a fourth root of two progression openings 25 μm and larger (Buckbee Mears Ltd), although Zwicker reports using them down to 1 μm in size. Endecotts make electrodeposited sieves in the size range 5·5 to 31 μm in a root-two progression. These sieves have about twice the surface area as the Daescher sieves and are therefore more fragile. Burt [39] examined samples of British sieve cloth and found that the average width of metal between openings for each grade of cloth was one-third to one-half the minimum recommended for sieves of American manufacture [40]. Veco manufacture sieves with round apertures by a combination of etching and electrodeposition. The apertures are in the shape of truncated cones with the small circle uppermost [23]. This reduces blinding but also reduces the percentage open area and therefore prolongs the sieving time.

The tolerances with these sieves are much better than those for woven-wire sieves, the aperture being guaranteed to within 2 μm of nominal size. Each type of sieve has different advantages for specific problems [27]. When ultrasonics are not necessary and the sample retained in the apertures can be dissolved out, Endecotts are to be preferred because of their large percentage open area. For insoluble materials Buckbee Mears are recommended for sub-15 μm and Veco for plus-15 μm.

Dry sieving is often possible with the coarser mesh sieve, and this may be speeded up and the lower limit extended to about 15 μm with the air-jet technique. Aggregation of the particles may sometimes be reduced by drying or adding about 1% of a dispersant, stearic acid or fine silica being two possibilities. If this is unsuccessful, wet methods have to be used [27, 30]. Ultrasonic vibrations are often used as an aid to sieving or for cleaning blocked sieves; the danger of breakage of the delicate mesh becomes very likely under these conditions, readily occurring at frequencies of 50 Hz and sometimes at frequencies as high as 20 kHz. Endecotts sieves should never be subjected to ultrasonic [27], and a recommended safe frequency for other sieves, according to Colon [23], is 40 kHz for blockages which cannot be cleared by other means, though Crawley [28] recommends 800 kHz. Daescher [30] confirmed Rosenberg's [47] earlier findings that the rate of cavitation erosion is less in hydrocarbons than in alcohol and about six times greater in water than in alcohol. By saturating alcohols with carbon dioxide, the rate is less than in degassed alcohol. He tested three ultrasonic cleaners, 40 Hz, 60 W; 40 Hz, 100 W; 90 Hz, 40 W, and found that the high frequency cleaner produced the least amount of erosion. While very expensive, these sieves find a ready market in specialized fields [16].

5.7 Wet sieving

These techniques are useful for material originally suspended in a liquid and necessary for powders which form aggregates when dry-sieved. Woven-wire sieves are available down to 37 μm aperture size A.S.T.M. standard, (4 4 μm B.S.S.), and a full description of the techniques is given in B.S. 1796.

Automated wet sieving has been proposed by several authors [16]. In most of these methods a stack of sieves is filled with a liquid and the sample is fed into the top sieve. Sieving is accomplished by rinsing, vibration, reciprocating action, vacuum, ultrasonics or a combination [27]. A successful method is a combination of elutriation and sieving. Commercial equipment is available in which the sample is placed in the top sieve of a nest of sieves and sprayed with water while the nest is being vibrated.

Several methods of wet sieving with micromesh sieves have been described. Colon [27] rinses the fines through the sieve aperture with a suitable liquid after 0·5 to 1 g has been dispersed in a small volume of a suitable liquid. Sieving is then continued by moving the sieve up and down in a glass beaker filled with the sieving liquid, so that the direction of flow of the liquid through the sieve openings is continually reversed; this helps to clean blocked apertures and disperse agglomerates. Depending on the type of micromesh sieve and the resistance to breakage of the particles during sieving, ultrasonics may be used. After some time, which should preferably be standardized, the sieve is transferred to a glass beaker with fresh sieving liquid and sieving continued. Sieving is deemed complete when the number of particles passing through the sieve is negligible compared with the total number of particles.

If about 1 g of powder is dispersed in 1 l of liquid, this may be poured through a sieve supported in a retort stand. For woven-wire and coarse micromesh sieves, the sieves may be mechanically rapped to facilitate sieving. The powder is then rinsed off the sieve and weighed or the sieve is dried and weighed [48]. With fine sieves, an ultrasonic probe may be necessary and the sieving liquid must have a low surface tension, e.g. acetone, otherwise it will not flow through the sieve apertures. The liquid may be recovered by distillation.

Daescher [30] describes a method using a set of tared sieves mounted on a special funnel held in a filter flask. One to three grams of the powder is placed on the top sieve and washed through each sieve in turn with a suitable polar liquid or hydrocarbon containing a trace of dispersant. At the same time alternate pulses of pressure and suction are applied to the filter flask. This pulsating action orientates the particles in such a way as to speed up the sieving action. After the sample has been washed through each sieve they are dried and weighed. A full analysis can be completed in less than one hour.

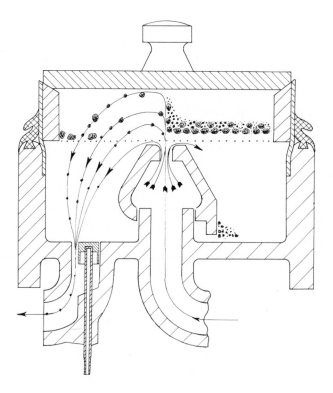

Fig. 5.5. Mode of action of the Alpine air-jet sieve.

5.8 Air-jet sieving
The principle of operation of this instrument (figure 5.5) is that air is drawn upwards, through a sieve, from a rotating slit so that material on the sieve is fluidised. At the

same time a negative pressure is applied to the bottom of the sieve which removes fine particles to a collecting device (a filter paper). With this technique, there is a reduced tendency to blind the apertures, and the action is very gentle, making it suitable for brittle and fragile powders. Sieving is possible with some powders down to 10 μm in size but with others balling occurs [34, 35]. The reproducibility is much better than by hand or machine sieving. Size analyses are performed by removal of particles from the fine end of the size distribution by using single sieves consecutively.

The end-point of sieving can be determined by microscopic examination of the cleanness of the sample [37], or by adopting the same criteria as are used in conventional dry sieving. Sieving is usually completed in 3 to 5 min using a 5 g to 10 g sample on 8-in diameter sub-75 μm sieves. Sieving time is more protracted with finer mesh sieves, and a sieving time of 20 min is usual with a 1 g load on a 3-in diameter 20 μm sieve.

A discussion of the techniques has been presented by Jones [33], and Lauer [38] has appraised it by microscopic examination of the powder fractions.

5.9 Felvation

The term *felvation* has been applied to a technique for grading powder using an elutriation process, with the sieves acting as stops for the coarse powder in suspension [25]. The apparatus used by Burt [39] is shown in figure 5.6.

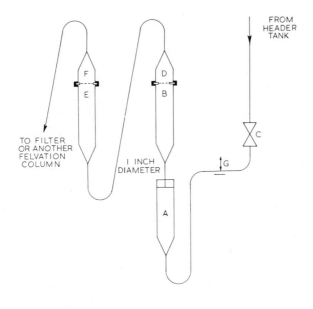

A = PREDISPERSION UNIT   D & F = SIEVING SURFACES
B & E = FELVATION COLUMNS   G = PULSATOR
C = NEEDLE VALVE

Fig. 5.6 Felvation apparatus.

The powder to be classified is dispersed in the predispersion unit A, which is connected to the bottom of the first felvation column B. The needle valve C is opened to allow liquid from the header tank to carry suspended particles into the conical base of the column, where they are fluidized. The flow rate is gradually increased until the finer particles are elutriated up the column to D, which consists of $\frac{1}{2}$-in square micromesh, or $\frac{3}{4}$-in diameter circular woven-wire, mesh cloth. The particles continue into the next felvation column E where they meet, and if fine enough pass through sieving surface F. The flow rate is increased in steps until larger and larger particles are elutriated and continues until the ascending particles are too large to pass through the sieves. The end-point is when the liquid above the sieves becomes clear. The powder passing the finest sieve is collected on a suction filter and the various fractions are contained in the bodies of the appropriate columns. Burt used 0·5 to 1·0 g for the micromesh sieves and found that the efficiency of separation increased with decreasing sample size and when only three felvation units were used. Separation efficiency increased if the fluid flow was pulsed 2 or 3 times per second, so a pulsator G was added to the equipment. British sieve cloth was used and found to be too fragile for this purpose. The technique was used more successfully with 2 g samples with woven-wire sieves.

The technique is not proposed as an alternative to standard sieving methods, but may well be useful if only small samples are available or, with hazardous materials, where small samples are desirable for safety reasons. The technique has also been used [39] to grade 5000 g samples in the size range 64 to 45 μm.

5.10 The sonic sifter [31]
The Allen-Bradley sonic sifter [41] is produced as a laboratory (LP3) and industrial (P60) model. It is claimed to be able to separate particles in the 2000 to 20 μm range for most materials and 5660 to 10 μm in some cases. It combines two motions to provide particle separation, a vertical oscillating column of air and a repetitive mechanical pulse. The sonic sifter moves the air in the sieve stack (figure 5.7). The oscillating air sets the sample in a periodic vertical motion which reduces sieve blinding and breaks down aggregates and yet produces very little abrasion, thus reducing sieve wear and particle breakage.

5.11 Calibration of sieves
The nominal aperture size of a sieve may differ from the true aperture size. Several methods of determining true aperture size are available [13, 19], the simplest being by microscope examination [46]. The easiest method for dealing with single sets of sieves is due to Stairmand [18]. It is known that the products of comminution are often log-normally distributed. Hence, if the sieve analysis is recorded on log probability paper, a best straight line can be drawn through the points, while a zig-zag is obtained by joining them. In this way the effective aperture of the sieves may be determined. If the same material is used for different sets of sieves, these can be corrected to a standard.

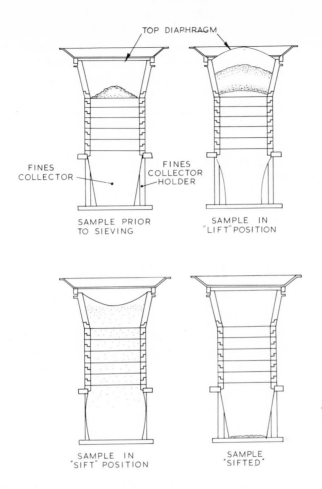

Fig. 5.7. Diagram of four conditions during sieving operation.

Kiff [26] states that commercial glass beads are also usually of a log-normal distribution and may be used similarly.

When spherical particles are sieved some are retained by the sieves in the sieve apertures. Removing these particles and determining their average size by microscopy will give a mean aperture size for the sieves.

5.12 Conclusion

There is always an element of chance as to whether a particle will or will not pass through a given sieve. The true end-point of a sieving operation is when every particle with a minimum square aperture smaller than the smallest sieve opening in the mesh has passed through. For the Kaye method of analysis, therefore, the cumulative percentage curve should be plotted against the smallest aperture in the mesh, not the nominal aperture. Other end-points are arbitrarily fixed and defined by a fixed time or a fixed rate of sieving. The first method is most popular for routine analysis because of its simplicity but yields the most unreliable data. The rate method is used for test analysis and the modifications of this method have been proposed in order to obtain more reproducible results.

References

[1] Fahrenwald, A.W. and Stockdale, S.W. (1929), U.S. Bur. Mines Rept., Investigation, 2933.
[2] Fagerhalt, G. (1945), G.E.C., Gads Forlag, Copenhagen.
[3] Whitby, K.T. (1958), *Symposium on Particle Size Measurement*, A.S.T.M. Sp. Publ. 234, 3.
[4] Kaye, B.H. (1962), Lond. Univ., Ph. D. thesis.
[5] Shergold, F.A. (1946), *Trans. Soc. Ch em. Ind.*, **65**, 245.
[6] Weber, M. and Moran, R.F. (1938), *Ind. Eng. Chem. Analyst. ed.*, **19**, 180.
[7] Carpenter, F.G., and Deitz, V.K. (1951), *J. Res. Nat. Bur. Std.*, **47**, 139.
[8] Moltini, E. (1956), *Ind. Mineraria (Rome)*, 7, 771; *Appl. Mech. Rev.*, **11**, 345.
[9] Carpenter, F.G., and Deitz, V.K. (1950), *J. Res. Nat. Bur. Std.*, **45**, 328.
[10] Allen, M. (1958), *Chem. Eng.*, **65**, 19, 176.
[11] Fritts, S.S. (1937), *Ind. Eng. Chem.*, **9**, 180.
[12] MacCalman, D. (1937), *Ind. Chem.*, **13**, 464; (1938), **14**, 64; (1939), **15**, 161.
[13] Heywood, H. (Mar., 1956), *Inst. Min. Met. Bull.*, **477**; also (1946), *Inst. Min. Met.*, **55**, 373.
[14] Ackerman, L. (1948), *Chem. Eng. Mining. Rev.*, **41**, 211.
[15] Herdan, G. (1960), *Small Particle Statistics*, Butterworths.
[16] Irani, R.R., and Callis, C.F. (1963), *Particle Size Measurement, Interpretation and Application*, Wiley, N.Y.
[17] Heywood, H. (1947), *Symposium of Particle Size Analysis*, Inst. Chem. Eng. Suppl. 25, 18.
[18] Stairmand, C.J., 'Some practical aspects of particle size analysis in industry', *op. cit.* [17, p. 77].
[19] Heywood, H. (1938), *Proc. Inst. Mech. Eng.*, **140**, 257.
[20] Andersen, J. (1931), *Zement*, **20**, 224, *cit.* Berg, S. (1954), *Atti del IV Congress Internationale della Ceramica Firenze* (French).
[21] Daescher, M.W., Seibert, E.E., and Peters, E.D. (1958), *Symposium on Particle Size Measurement*, A.S.T.M., 26—56 (ASTM Sp. Publ. 234).
[22] Lauer, O. (1960), *Staub*, **20**, 69.
[23] Colon, F.J. (Feb. 1965), *Chem. Ind.* 263.
[24] Mullin, J.W. (1966), *Chem. Ind.* (preprint).
[25] Kaye, B.H. (1966), Society for Analytical Chemistry Symposium on Particle Size Analysis, Loughborough, 1966.
[26] Kiff, P.R. (1973), *Proc. Soc. Analyst. Chem.*, **10**, 5, 114—15.
[27] Colon, F.J. (1970), *Proc. Soc. Analyst. Chem.*, 7, 9, 163—4.
[28] Crawley, D.F.C. (1968), *J. Sci. Instrum.*, series 2.
[29] Peterson, J.L. (1969), U.S. Patent 3, 438, 490; 1, 576.

[30] Daescher, M.W. (1969), *Powder Technol.*, **2**, 6, 349–55.

[31] Suhm, H.O., (1969), *Powder Technol.*, **2**, 6, 356–62.

[32] Burt, M.W. (1970), *Proc. Soc. Analyst. Chem.*, **7**, 9, 165–8.

[33] Jones, T.M. (1970), *Proc. Soc. Analyst. Chem.*, **7**, 9, 159–63.

[34] Brown, O.E., Bobrowski, G.S., and Kovall, G.E. (1970), A.S.T.M., Sp. Tech. Publ. No. 473, 82–97.

[35] Malhetra, V.M., and Zalderns, N.G. (1970), A.S.T.M. Sp. Tech. Publ. No. 473, 98–105.

[36] Mullin, J.W. (1971), *Chem. Ind.* no. 50, 1435–6.

[37] Lauer, O. (1958), *Staub*, **18**, 306.

[38] Lauer, O. (1966), *Grain size measurement on commercial powders,* Alpine A.G., Augsburg.

[39] Burt, M.W.G. (1970), *Proc. Soc. for Analyst. Chem.*, **7**, 9, 165–8.

[40] *A.S.T.M. Specification for Precision Micromesh sieves,* Designation E161–68.

[41] U.S. Patent 3 045 817.

[42] Peterson, J.L., *Method and Apparatus for Wet-sizing Finely-divided Solid Materials,* U.S. Patent 3 438 490.

[43] B.S. 1796 (1952), *Methods for the use of British Standard Fine Mesh Sieves.*

[44] I.S.O. 2591 (1973), *Test Sieving.*

[45] I.S.O. 565 (1972), *Test Sieves, Woven Metal Wire Cloth and Perforate plate. Nominal sizes of apertures.*

[46] A.S.T.M., D., 161–8.

[47] Rosenberg, L.D., (1960), *Ultrasonic News,* **4**, 16.

[48] Niedick, E.A. (1969), *Zeitschift für die Zuckesindustrie,* **19**, 9, 495–506, Berlin.

6 *Microscopy*

6.1 Introduction

Microscopy is often used as an absolute method of particle size analysis since it is the only method in which the individual particles are observed and measured. It also permits examination of the shape and composition of particles with a sensitivity far greater than for any other technique. The representativeness of the sample under analysis is critical since measurements are carried out on such minute quantities. Sampling techniques and sample preparation should, therefore, be carefully considered and the statistical factors governing accuracy should be well known.

The great advances in microscopy made during the past few years have led to a flood of papers and numerous new instruments, many of them having similarities. The difficulty of selecting the most suitable microscope technique has now reached similar proportions to the difficulty of selecting the most suitable size analysis technique from the many that are available. To aid in this choice there are certain guidelines, such as the range of sizes under consideration, cost, the number and frequency of analyses required, and so on. It is hoped that this chapter will help the reader make a wise decision and also to produce accurate and meaningful analyses.

6.2 Optical microscopy

The optical microscope is used for the examination of particles from about 150 to $0.8\ \mu m$ in size. Above $150\ \mu m$ a simple magnifying glass is suitable, while for smaller particles it is necessary to use electron microscopy.

Its most severe limitation is its small depth of focus, which is about $10\ \mu m$ at a magnification of $100 \times$ and about $0.5\ \mu m$ at $1000 \times$. The surface of particles larger than about $5\ \mu m$ can be studied by reflected light, but only transmission microscopy with which silhouettes are seen, can be used for sub $- 5\ \mu m$ particles. The edges of the images seen in a microscope are blurred due to diffraction effects. Charman [68], in an investigation into the accuracy of sizing by optical microscopy, showed that for particles greater than about $1\ \mu m$ in diameter the estimated size under ideal conditions was about $0.13\ \mu m$ too high; a $0.5\ \mu m$ particle gave a visual estimate of 0.68 μm and all particles smaller than about $0.2\ \mu m$ appeared to have a diameter of $0.5\ \mu m$. Rowe [72] showed that wide differences may occur between operators in particle sizing because of this effect. The limit of resolution of an optical microscope is about $0.25\ \mu m$ under ideal conditions. Two particles closer than this cannot be resolved separately due to diffraction effects. However, it is possible to detect particles as small as 0·3 μm and some operators routinely size down to these levels. The British Standard 3406 [31] is probably correct however, in stipulating a minimum size of 0·8 μm and limited accuracy from 0·8 up to 2·3 μm.

The images produced may be viewed directly or by projection. Binocular eye-pieces are preferable for particle examination but monoculars for carrying out a size analyses since, by using a single eyepiece, the tube length can be varied to give step-wise magnification. Most experienced operators prefer direct viewing, but projection viewing, less tiring to the eye, is often used for prolonged counting. Projection may be front or back. With the former, the operation is carried out in a darkened room due to the poor contrast attainable. Back projection gives better illumination, but image definition is poor; this can be rectified by using a system whereby two ground − glass screens are placed with their faces in contact and one is moved slowly relative to the other [73]. Some automatic and semi − automatic counting and sizing de-vices work from negatives or positives. The principal criticism that can be levelled against photographic methods, in conjunction with optical microscopy, is that only particles in good focus can be measured and this can lead to serious bias. Although photographic methods are often convenient and provide a permanent record, the processing time may well offset any advantage obtained by using a high − speed counting device. This is particularly true when a weight count is required since, on statistical considerations, a large number of fields of view are required for accurate results.

6.2.1 Preparation of slides

The most difficult problem facing the microscopist is the preparation of a slide con-taining a uniformly dispersed, representative sample of the powder. Many methods of carrying out this procedure have been suggested, but the final result often depends more on the skill of the operator than the procedure itself. Some acceptable pro-cedures for easily dispersed powders are described by Green [1] and Dunn [2]. The method of Orr and Dallevalle [3] for the production of permanent slides is to place a small representative sample of the powder to be analysed in a 10-ml beaker, add 2 or 3 ml of a solution containing about 2% colloidon in butyl acetate, stir vigorously and place a drop of suspension on the still surface of distilled water in a large beaker. The film produced as this drop spreads and evaporates may then be picked up on a clean microscope slide and completely dried. A dispersing agent may be added to prevent flocculation.

Alternative techniques are to produce a mounting medium of: colloidon in amyl acetate, Canada balsam in xylol, or polystyrene in xylene. With a 1% solution, this may be formed by dropping on to the surface of distilled water; with a ½% solution, it may be cast directly on to a microscope slide. The particle suspension may then be sprayed on, or a droplet can be allowed to evaporate, leaving the particles [4].

If a permanent slide is not required, an effective procedure is to place a small sample of the powder on a microscope slide and add a few drops of the dispersing fluid. Some operators work the powder into the fluid with a flexible spatula, others roll it in with a glass rod. Both these procedures may produce fracture of the particles and a preferable alternative is to use a small camel — hair brush. Further dispersing fluid is then added until the concentration is satisfactory. A drop of the suspension is then placed on another slide with the brush and a cover slip put carefully in place so as to exclude air bubbles. For a semi — permanent slide, the cover slip may be sealed with amyl acetate or glue. Cedar oil and glycerol are two satisfactory dispersing fluids; a dispersing agent may be added to eliminate flocculation.

Harwood [5] describes two methods for dispersing difficult powders. One involves the use of electrical charges to repel the particles and fixing the aqueous suspension with a gelatine — coated slide to overcome Brownian movement. The other, for magnetic materials, involves heating the sample to a temperature above the Curie point, dispersing and fixing them on a slide to cool. Rosinski *et al.* [6] have investigated several techniques in order to find which gave the best reproducibility. Allen [7] mounted the powder directly into clear cement, dispersing it by using sweeping strokes of a needle and spreading a film on a microscope slide to dry. Lenz [8] embedded particles on a solid medium and examined slices of the medium.

Variations in analyses may occur with operators and techniques due to orientation of particles on the slide. Ellison [9], for example, showed that if particles are allowed to fall out of suspension on to a microscope slide, they will do so with a preferred orientation. Also, if the dispersing is not complete, the presence of flocculates will give the appearance of coarseness (Green [10]).

Pidgeon and Dodd [91], who were interested in measuring particle surface area using a microscope, developed methods for preparing slides of particles in random orientation. For sieve — size particles, a thin film of Canada balsam was spread on the slide and heated until the material was sufficiently viscid, determined by scratching with a fine wire until there was no tendency for the troughs to fill in. Particles sprinkled on the slide at this stage were held in random orientation. After a suitable hardening time, cover glass coated with glycerol or warm glycerol jelly, was placed carefully on the slide.

Sub — sieve powders were dispersed in a small amount of melted glycerol jelly. When the mixture started to gel a small amount was spread on a dry slide. After the mount had set, it was protected with a cover slip coated with glycerol jelly. With this technique, it was necessary to refocus for each particle since they do not lie in a single plane.

The sizing of fibrous particles by microscopy presents serious problems including overlapping. Timbrell [74, 75] found that certain fibres show preferred orientation in a magnetic field, e.g. carbon and amphibole asbestos. He disperses the fibres in a 0·5% solution of colloidon in amyl acetate and applied a drop to a microsope slide, keeping the slide in a magnetic field until the film has dried. For SEM examination an aqueous film may be drained through a membrane filter held in a magnetic field.

Various means of particle identification are possible with optical microscopy. These include dispersion staining for identification of asbestos particles [92] and the use of various mounting media for particle identification [93].

6.3 Particle size

The image of a particle seen in a microscope is two dimensional. From this image an estimate of particle size has to be made. Accepted diameters are:

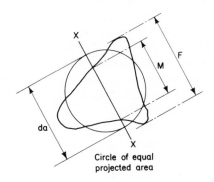

Fig. 6.1. Representative two − dimensional diameters.

(1) Martin's diameter (M) is the length of the line which bisects the image of particle. The lines may be drawn in any direction which must be maintained constant for all the image measurements (Martin [11], Heywood [12]).

(2) Feret's diameter (F) is the distance between two tangents on opposite sides of the particle, parallel to some fixed direction (Feret [13]).

(3) Longest dimension. A measured diameter equal to the maximum value of Feret's diameter.

(4) Maximum chord. A diameter equal to the maximum length of a line parallel to some fixed direction and limited by the contour of the particle.

(5) Perimeter diameter. The diameter of a circle having the same circumference as the perimeter of the particle.

(6) The projected area diameter (d_a) is the diameter of a circle having the same
(6 area as the particle viewed normally to a plane surface on which the particle is at rest in a stable position.

Mean diameters from these measurements are all independent of particle orientation since they are either taken in some preferred direction or, in the last two cases, are two dimensional measurements.

It has been shown [14, 15] that the relationship between specific surface, S_v, and Martin's diameter is:

$$M = \frac{4}{S_v} \ .$$

Herdan [16, p. 46] points out that the volume surface diameter

$$d_{vs} = \frac{6}{S_v}$$

the proportionality factor being a minimum of 6 for spherical particles. Thus the Martin's diameter is systematically different from the volume surface diameter. Experiments confirms that, on the whole, $M < d_a < F$. The ratios of these three diameters remain fairly constant for a given material and may be expressed as a shape function. For example, $F/M = 1 \cdot 2$ for Portland cement and $1 \cdot 3$ for ground glass [17].

Heywood [12] measured crushed sandstone which had passed a $1\frac{1}{8}$ in square sieve aperture and been retained on a 1 in square aperture. He determined the projected area of the particles using a planimeter and calculated the mean projected diameter; he next estimated the diameter using both the opaque and transparent circles on a globe and circle graticule and also determined Martin's and Feret's diameters. His conclusion, based on an examination of 142 particles, was that Feret's diameter was grossly in error for elongated particles, but that the Martin and projected area diameters are sufficiently in agreement for all practical purposes. Walton [20] disputed this and showed that Feret's diameter, averaged over all particle orientations is equal to particle perimeter$/\pi$. (See also [14]).

Herdan [16, p. 140] examined Heywood's data more rigorously. His results were:

(i) Feret's diameter was significantly different from the other four diameters;

(ii) Martin's diameter shows significant difference from that obtained using the globe and circle graticule, if the planimeter results are accepted as standard.

He concluded that there was no definite advantage to be gained by laboriously measuring profiles.

As one might expect, the projected area diameters gave the best estimate of the true cross – sectional areas of the particles. This does not rule out the use of the other diameters if they are conveniently measured, since the cross – sectional area diameter of a particle is not necessarily its optimum dimension.

6.4 Transmission electron microscopy [56]

The transmission electron microscope (TEM) is often used for the direct examination of particles in the size range 0·001 to 5 μm. The TEM produces an image on a fluorescent screen or a photographic plate by means of an electron beam. Although attempts have been made to perform analyses directly on the images visible on the fluorescent screen, this involves tying down the instrument for long periods of time hence it is more usual to carry out the analyses on the images recorded photographically.

Many particle size studies can be carried out at magnifications of less than 4000 and several relatively cheap instruments are now available giving magnifications up to 10 000.

Calibration is usually effected with narrowly classified polystyrene latices available from Dow Chemicals but for high accuracy work diffraction gratings are required.

6.4.1 Specimen preparation

Specimens for electron microscopy are usually deposited on or in a thin (100 to 200 Å) membrane which rests on a grid. These grids are usually made of copper and form a support for the film which is usually self — supporting only over a very small area (figure 6.2). Since most materials are opaque to the electron beam, even when only a few Angstroms thick, special problems exist in the production of suitable mounted specimens. Specimen support films are usually made of plastic or carbon, though other materials have also been used.

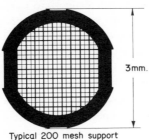

3mm.

Typical 200 mesh support

Fig. 6.2. Electron microscope grid.

Suitable film solutions may be made up of 2% W/V collodion in amyl acetate or 2% W/V formvar (polyvinyl formal) in ethylene dichloride or chloroform.

Films may be produced in the following manner [57]. A dish about 20 cm in diameter is filled with distilled water and a large circle of wire gauze (200-mesh) is placed at the bottom of the dish. A number of grids are placed on the wire gauze, then two drops of the film solution are dropped on to the surface of the water and the film that results after the solvent has evaporated is removed with a needle; this ensures that the water surface is clean. A second film, formed in the same way, is removed by raising the wire gauze containing the grids. The wire gauze and grids are then allowed to dry. A pre — examination of the film-covered grids in the electron microscope is desirable as this enables dirty films to be rejected and the film polymerizes in the electron beam, thus greatly increasing its strength.

An alternative procedure is to clean a microscope slide with a detergent solution and polish with a soft cloth without rinsing away the detergent, so as to form on the surface a hydrophilic layer to facilitate subsequent stripping of the membrane. The slide is dipped into a solution of formvar in ethylene dichloride (0·3 to 0·7% W/V depending on the thickness of film required) and allowed to drain dry. The film may then be floated on to a water surface and mounted on grids as before. If individual grids are required, the film may be cut into small squares with a needle or razor blade. The mounting operation is easier if a special jig is used [64]. The jig is a brass cylinder about 1 in long and ½ in diameter with a hole of the same diameter as the specimen grid drilled and tapped through its axis. A set screw in the threaded hole is adjusted so that its end is flush with the face of the plug and then withdrawn slightly to leave a shallow recess. The specimen grid is held in this recess and the membrane is lifted from the water surface with a wire loop of slightly larger diameter than the jig, surplus water being carefully removed with blotting paper. The wire loop is then lowered over the jig and when the membrane is dry the grid is raised by means of the screw, surplus membrane being removed by scoring round the grid with a needle. Special apparatus has also been described for producing plastic films of uniform thickness suitable for the preparation of replicas [58].

Carbon films are prepared under vacuum (10^{-3} mm Hg) by electrical discharge [59] from two pointed hard graphite rods. Films are best deposited on microscope slides cleaned with detergent and placed about 10 to 15 cm from the source. A thickness indicator, consisting of a drop of vacuum oil on a piece of white glazed porcelain, is placed beside the slide. During the discharge, the porcelain not covered with oil takes on a brownish colour changing to a light chocolate shade as the film thickness increases from 50 to 100 Å, the latter being a suitable thickness for general use. Evaporation is completed in about half a second with a current of about 50 Å. The film may then be floated on to the surface of distilled water and picked up as a whole or scored into small squares. A simple method of producing a suitable specimen is to place a few milligrams of the powder on a microscope slide, add a drop of 1 to 2% W/V suspension of formvar in a suitable solvent and rub out on the slide with a glass rod. Further solvent is added if required and the dispersion is spread out over the slide and allowed to dry. The film is removed from the slide and mounted on the grid as before.

Alternatively the sample may be dispersed in linseed oil which is then thinned with white spirit. The dispersion is next spread out on a microscope slide which is immersed in white spirits for a few minutes to remove the oil. After drying the slide a thin layer of carbon is deposited on the specimen to form a supporting film. Finally, this is floated off on water, as before, and picked up on a grid for examination [65].

A dispersed sample may also be obtained by means of one of the aerosol sampling devices described in chapter 3. A suitable technique is to form a sandwich of plastic film particles and 200 Å thick carbon. The underlying plastic may then be washed away with solvent and the specimen examined after shadowing [50, 57, 59].

A suspension of the powder may be made up and a drop placed on a grid by means of a pipette or hypodermic syringe. However, this often produces an uneven deposit. A more uniform deposit is often produced by spraying the suspension on to the grid; several suitable spray guns have been described [56, 60].

Timbrell [76] modifies the method of Hamilton and Phelps described in section 6.10, for the preparation of transparent profiles to facilitate electron microscopy. The metal film is floated on to a water surface and picked up on a grid. In cases of difficulty the slide is first dipped into 1% hydrofluoric acid to release the edge of the film and the process is completed in water. Although the metal film is strong enough to be floated off whole, it is usual to score it into small squares as described earlier and then remove the separate pieces.

In order to obtain reliable results for particle size analysis, as many separate grids as possible must be prepared and a large number of electron micrographs taken from each.

In an analysis of the errors involved in electron microscopy, Cartwright and Skidmore [64] examined the optical microscopy specimens produced by thermal precipitation. The specimens were then stripped from the microscope slides and the fines were counted, using an electron microscope. Good agreement was obtained by examining 1000 particles in the electron microscope using about sixty fields of view (60 micrographs) and almost 4000 particles in the optical microscope. To obtain accurate magnification calibration, four overlapping micrographs along the bar of a readily identifiable grid square were taken and the total length of the image of the grid bars was measured from the micrographs and directly, using an optical microscope. The surface areas of dust samples as determined by electron and optical microscopes have also been compared by Joffe [66].

6.4.2 Replica and shadowing techniques

Replicas are thin films of electron transparent material which are cast on opaque specimens in order that their surface structure may be studied. The basic procedure is to form a film on the substance to be examined, separate the two and examine the film. If a reverse of the original is unsatisfactory, a positive replica may be obtained by repeating the process. One method is to deposit the specimen on to a formvar-covered grid, vacuum deposit about 100 Å of carbon, remove the formvar by rinsing with chloroform and finally remove the specimen with a suitable solvent [61]. Instead of a backing film, it is sometimes possible to prepare a carbon replica of a dried sus-pension deposited on a microscope slide, the replica being washed off the slide in a water bath or a bath of hydrofluoric acid. The carbon film is then transferred to a bath containing a solvent for the specimen. The film may be strengthened immed-iately after being deposited by dipping the slide in a 2% W/V solution of Bedacryl 122X in benzene which is removed by a suitable solvent after the film has been deposited on a grid [56]. Numerous variations of these techniques have been used [3, 16, 50, 56, 62, 94, 95].

In order to determine surface characteristics and particle thickness, it is usual to deposit obliquely a film of heavy metal on to the specimen or its replica. The metal is applied by deposition in a hard vacuum by a small source in order that a nearly parallel beam may reach the specimen. The technique was originated by Williams and Wyckoff in 1946 [63] and has been used extensively since.

6.4.3 Chemical analysis

When particles are bombarded with electrons they emit radiation which depends upon their chemical composition. The Auger [69, 70] process can be studied by using monochromatic or polychromatic radiation or electron beams. It is a secondary elec-tron process which follows the ejection of an electron from an inner-shell level. The hole is filled by an electron falling to the vacant level which provides energy for another electron to be emitted. The energy of this Auger electron is characteristic of the molecule involved. There have been many studies on metal surfaces using vacuum ultra-violet techniques and the energy distribution curves (EDCs) obtained give in-formation on the band structure of the metals. The use of soft X-rays is known as electron spectroscopy for chemical analysis (ESCA). In addition to ejecting electrons from the valence shell orbits the X-rays have sufficient energy to eject electrons from some of the inner shells. These are essentially atomic in nature and the spectrums produced are characteristic of the atom concerned rather than the molecule of which it forms a part [71].

These, and other techniques, may be applied to electron microscopy to permit chemical assays and particle size analyses to be carried out concurrently.

6.5 Scanning electron microscopy

In the scanning electron microscope a fine beam of electrons of medium energy (5 − 50 keV) is caused to scan across the sample in a series of parallel tracks. These electrons interact with the sample, producing secondary electron emission (SEE), back scattered electrons (BSE) light or cathodoluminescence and X-rays. Each of these signals can be detected and displayed on the screen of a cathode ray tube like a television picture. Examinations are generally made on photographic records of the screen.

Samples as large as 25 mm × 25 mm can be accommodated and parts viewed at magnifications varying from 20 to 100 000 at resolutions of less than 200 Å in special cases. The depth of focus is nearly 300 times that of the optical microscope.

In both the SEE and BSE modes the particles appear as being viewed from above. In the SEE mode, where the particles appear to be diffusely illuminated, particle size can be measured and aggregation behaviour can be studied but there is little indication of height. The BEE mode in which the particles appear to be illuminated from a point source, gives a good impression of height due to the shadows. Several of the current methods of particle size analysis can be adapted for the measurement of images in SEM photographic records. There is also active interest in the development of analysis techniques that will make more use of the three-dimensional image presentation.

6.6 Manual methods of sizing particles

A frequently described method of measuring particle size is to use a microscope fitted with an optical micrometer, a moveable cross-hair being built into the ocular. The cross-hair is moved by a calibrated micrometer drum until it coincides with one edge of the particle. It is then moved to the other end of the particle, or some other conventionally adopted limit, precautions being taken to eliminate the effect of backlash. The difference in readings is a measure of the size of the particle. This technique is very time-consuming and has been largely superseded by the use of calibrated ocular scales.

The simplest form consists of a glass disc which is fitted on to the field stop of the ocular. Engraved upon the disc is a scale which is calibrated against a stage graticule. The stage graticule consists of a microscope slide on which is engraved a linear scale. The image of this scale is brought into coincidence with the ocular scale by focussing. With a single tube microscope the magnification may be varied somewhat by racking the tube in or out. The stage graticule is then replaced by a microscope slide containing the particles to be examined.

The slide is placed on a microscope stage which is capable of movement in perpendicular directions and is examined in strips (figure 6.3). As a particle image passes over the scale it is sized and recorded. For statistical accuracy, particles overlapping one end of the scale are neglected and particles overlapping the other end counted. Strips are selected so as to give complete coverage of the slide. The analyses are best carried out by two operators, one sizing and one recording, the operators alternating their duties at regular intervals to reduce eye strain. An alternative is to use a counting array with five or more size intervals and with a cumulative register so that the total count is also recorded [18].

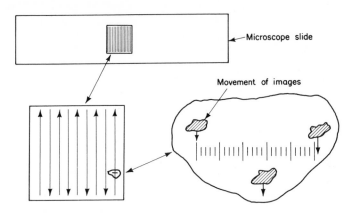

Fig. 6.3. Strip scanning using a calibrated scale.

6.6.1 Graticules

Ocular graticules having a linear scale are satisfactory for the measurement of linear dimensions of particles. Particle sizes obtained with a linear eyepiece are best classified arithmetically, hence it is most suited to particles having a narrow size range.

This type of eyepiece has been criticized on the grounds that the diameters so measured are greater than those derived by other methods. To overcome this objection, grids inscribed with opaque and transparent circles have been developed. These permit a direct comparison between the projected area of a particle and the area of the circles. According to Cauchy the projected area is a quarter of the surface area for a random dispersion of convex particles [24], hence this dimension may be related to other properties of the powder.

The first of this type, the globe and circle graticule, described by Patterson and Cawood (figure 6.4) [25], had 10 globes and circles ranging in diameter from 0·6 to 2·5 μm when used with a +2 mm × 100 objective eyepiece combination and was recommended by Watson [29] for thermal-precipitator work. Fairs [27] designed a graticule using reference circles with a $\sqrt{2}$ progression in diameter except at the smallest size. He considered this to be superior to the Patterson-Cawood where the series is much closer. May (figure 6.5) also describes a graticule with a $\sqrt{2}$ progression. Watson (figure 6.6) [29] has developed a graticule designed specifically to measure particles in the 0·5 to 5 μm range. This was compared with a line graticule and the

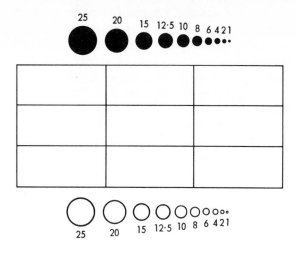

Fig. 6.4. Patterson-Cawood graticule.

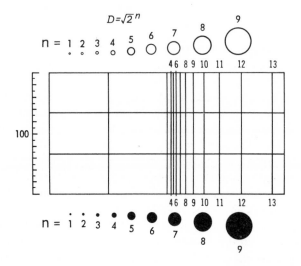

Fig. 6.5. May graticule.

Patterson-Cawood globe and circle graticule by Hamilton and Holdsworth [30]. As the sizing of particles by visual comparison with reference circles some distance from the particle may be subject to appreciable operator errors, the line graticule was included in order to determine whether more consistent results were obtained by this method. With this graticule, particles are sized as they cross the reference lines and the diameter so measured is Feret's diameter. Hamilton and Holdsworth found

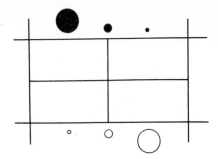

Fig. 6.6. Watson graticule

systematic differences in the mean counts or operators in the size range 1 to 5 μm, but no evidence that this was altered by the type of graticule used. It was also found that the Feret diameter overestimated the size of coal dust. Their conclusions were that all three graticules gave equally accurate and consistent results but the Watson and line graticules were preferred by the operators on the grounds that they were less trying to use.

Fairs [27] modified the Patterson-Cawood graticule to cover a wider size range (128 : 1) on three separate graticules, the diameters being in a constant $\sqrt{2}$ progression except for the smaller sizes. Fairs [77] also described a graticule for use with the projection microscope which was incorporated in the projection screen instead of being in the eyepiece; the nine circles were in a $\sqrt{2}$ progression. The method was adopted as the British Standard Graticule [31] (figure 6.7).

Guruswamy (78) has designed a graticule in which the diameters of eleven circles are arranged in a constant ratio of 1·2589 to use the fact that $\log_{10}$ 1·2589 = 1. This choice of the ratio and the novel system of marking the circles are claimed to facilitate the rapid calculation of size parameters from the data.

Particle thickness may be determined by a stereophotogrammetric procedure proposed by Aschenbrenner [19] (see also [3, p. 19]).

6.6.2 Training of operators

Although the use of linear diameters such as Martin's and Feret's give the most reproducible analyses, the projected area diameter is more representative of particle size; hence the globe and circle graticules are the most popular. When comparing an irregular profile with a circle, untrained operators have a tendency to oversize the profile. A method of correcting this is to compare the analysis of a trained operator with that of the trainee. When the trainee recognizes the bias, he readily corrects it. Heywood [33] produced a set of hand-held test cards. The trainee is required to compare each of the profiles with the reference circles and assign it to a size group. The area of each profile is previously determined by counting squares, hence the trainee can recognise and correct bias. Watson and Mulford [34] extended the technique by inscribing a number next to each profile and reducing them photographically

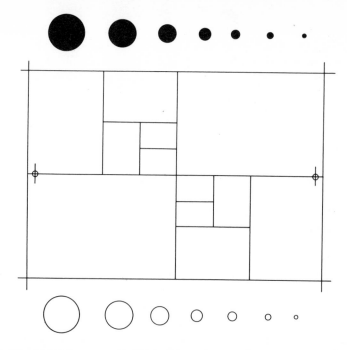

Fig. 6.7. The British Standard graticule (Graticules Ltd) Diagram from B.S. 3406: 1961, *Methods for the Determination of the Particle Size of Powders*, Part IV, *Optical Microscope Method*, reproduced by permission of the British Standards Institution, 2 Park Street, London W1, from whom copies of the complete standard may be obtained.

so that they could be examined under a reversed telescope, giving more realistic conditions. In a series of tests with nine operators, it was found that five were under-estimating and four overestimating, seven of the nine being badly biased. The nine operators were trained microscopists who were aware of the natural tendency to oversize and had overcorrected. It was also noticed that all nine observers were con-sistent in their bias but reduced it only slightly on a second reading.

Fairs [35] used a projection microscope for training purposes. A trained operator and a trainee can then examine given areas together and compare their results. This technique is also used for sizing (A.S.T.M., 1951, E20-SIT, 1539) but is not recom-mended for particle diameters less than 2 μm.

Holdsworth *et al.* (cit. [76]) demonstrated the necessity for training operators and showed that gross count differences on the same samples at different laboratories were much reduced after interlaboratory checks.

6.7 Semi-automatic aids to microscopy
Semi-automatic aids to counting and sizing have been developed to speed up analyses and reduce the tedium of wholly manual methods. The advantage of these aids over

automatic microscopy, apart from their relative cheapness, is that human judgment is retained. The operator can select or reject particles, separate out aggregates and discriminate over the choice of fields of view. Many such aids have been developed and these differ widely in degree of sophistication; price, ease, mode and speed of operation.

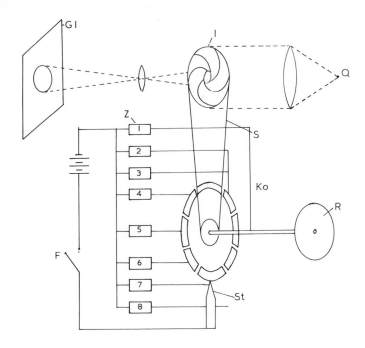

Fig. 6.8. Zeiss-Endter particle size analyser.

The Zeiss-Endter particle size analyser (figure 6.8)[32] has been developed so that a direct comparison may be made between the projected area of a particle and the area of a reference circle. The reference circle is a spot of light adjustable in size by an iris diaphragm and centred on a particle. After the spot of light has been made equal in area to the projected area of the particle, it is recorded in a preset size category by the depression of a foot-switch. The instrument has been designed to work with a photomicrograph which may be obtained from an electron microscope, thus its range of applicability is extended to around 0.01 μm. A modification of Endter's instrument which is rugged and simpler, but not as versatile, has been described by Becher [55].

Electron micrograph counts are greatly facilitated by the use of a projector, a transparent screen and a large transparent graticule connected to a counting device [65]. The micrograph is projected on to the screen and the area of each image compared directly with the areas of a series of circles, in a $\sqrt{2}$ progression, on the graticule. To record the size, an electrical contact by the appropriate circle is touched with a movable contact. This activates the appropriate counter as well as a counter to sum all the particles classified. A counting speed of over 1000 particles per hour is possible. The Spri particle analyser is a device on a similar principle to the above using a V-notch to give the size gradings. It may be interfaced with a computor or electronic counter unit. Particles may also be measured using specially constructed callipers [67].

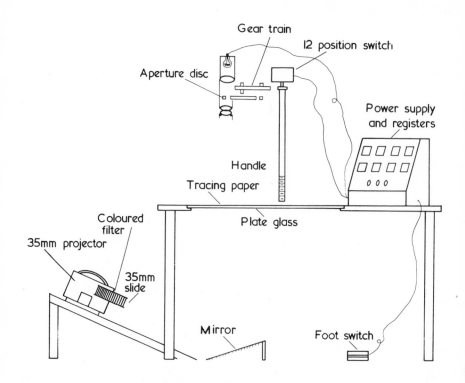

Fig. 6.9. Chatfield particle size analyser.

The Chatfield particle size comparator [79] (figure 6.9) was devised for the size classification of particles in the size range below 10 μm. The system operates on 35 mm film records and is based on the projection of a photograph on to a translucent screen and the comparison of the particle sizes with a superimposed spot of light projected from the other side. The photograph is projected by a standard projector via a surface-silvered mirror and the screen is a sheet of tracing paper put on a glass plate set into a bench top. The particle images can thus be seen from above by the operator seated at the bench. A second projector is used to project a spot of light downwards on to the sheet of paper. The diameter of this spot can be changed by rotation of a disc which has a number of apertures of different diameters. The aperture selected is illuminated by parallel light and its image is focussed on the tracing

paper at a magnification of about 4 when using a lens of 2 in focal length. Change
of aperture is controlled through a gear train by rotating a handle at bench level. The
whole spot projection system is supported at constant height above the bench by a
pantograph arrangement. This allows the projected spot to be moved over the screen
by moving the handle. Also coupled to the gear train is a 12-position rotary switch
connected to a series of electromagnetic counters. When an individual particle has
been sized by selecting the aperture with the area which best matches that of the
particle image, use of a foot switch causes the particle to be recorded on the appropriate counter. As each particle is counted it is marked on the tracing paper by a
pencil, thus eliminating the possibility of double counting. The spots are in $\sqrt{2}$ progression of diameter, starting with the smallest at 0·14 cm. With a total magnification
of 7000 the particle size range extends from 0·2 to 1·0 μm in eleven logarithmetically
equal steps. The smallest spot size complies with the requirement of B.S. 3406 that
the smallest size should be twenty times the limit of resolution of the unaided eye.
A performance trial showed that both experienced and untrained operators were able
to size particles at a speed in excess of 30 per minute.

In the Lark particle counter [80] designed for measuring particles in loose
powders the record of analysis consists of a series of pinholes in a chart 3½-in wide.
An electromechanical counter gives the total number of particles measured. The
system consists of an adjustable slotted eyepiece which is fitted to a microscope of
the stage focusing type. This eyepiece contains in its focal plane a fixed hairline and
a second moveable hairline. A particle to be measured is moved across the field of
view by a square mechanical stage until its image reaches the stationary hairline. The
second hairline is then brought up to the image by adjusting the free end of a lever
the other end of which is mechanically linked to this hairline. The free end of the
lever has a spring-loaded knob which can be depressed to make a pinpoint mark on
the chart. As this knob rises from the chart it activates a bar and ratchet which advances the chart by 1/16 in and also operates the counter. The chart is calibrated by
a stage micrometer. By ruling lines on the chart corresponding to a scale of sizes and
counting the pinholes between these lines, the size frequency distribution in terms
of Feret's diameter can be determined. About 1000 particles per hour can be counted.

In its original form the Humphries micrometer eyepiece (*cit.* [76]) made use of a
fixed and a moveable hairline. The modified form, developed in collaboration with
Malies Instruments Ltd can be attached to the microscope in which it replaces the
customary eyepiece, a × 10 ocular forming an integral part of the instrument. The
two vertical hairlines seen in the field of view are attached to frames and move towards or away from each other as a milled head to the side of the eyepiece is turned.
Grain-sizing is achieved by adjusting the position of the hairlines so that they bracket
the image symmetrically and then turning the milled head on the eyepiece so that
they touch the edges of the grain. When this has been effected a push-button at the
centre of the milled head is pressed. This closes a contact and operates one of a bank
of sixteen electromagnetic counters; a seventeenth records the total number of grains
examined. Classification and counting is carried out according to a scale of sizes with
a ratio of $4\sqrt{2}$:1 between classes. This scale is directly related to Krumbein's [81]

phi-scale and by adjustment of the overall tube length of the microscope the class limits can usually be made to fit these scales exactly. By the selection of suitable objectives, particles from 2 μm to 5 μm can be classified. The rate at which particles can be classified depends largely on the dimension chosen for the analysis. The measurement of the long axis involves rotation of the eyepiece in the body tube. It is claimed that the longest dimension and Feret's diameter can be measured at about 400 and 1000 grains per hour respectively. The counting can be made on slow-movin objects such as particles in liquid suspension without loss of accuracy.

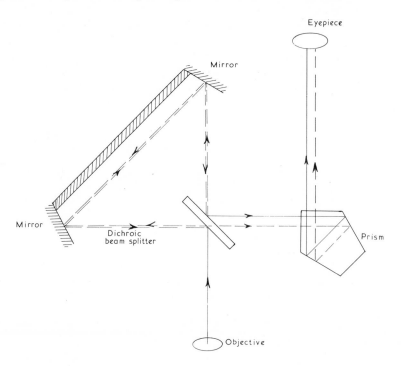

Fig. 6.10. The Watson image shearing eyepiece.

If the maximum width parallel to a fixed direction (shear size) is an acceptable measure of particle size, the use of a semi-automatic device is recommended. The Watson image shearing eyepiece (figure 6.10), developed by Dyson [52, 82], employs an image-shearing principle which is obtained by splitting the beam and separating the images by the rotation of two mirrors using a micrometer drum. The principle may be easily understood by referring to figure 6.11. With zero shear, the two images coincide; (a) with a small amount of shear the images overlap, (b) with greater shear a bright gap appear between the images. Since it is possible to change the direction of shear, selected diameters may be measured, a useful feature for particles with widely differing perpendicular diameters.

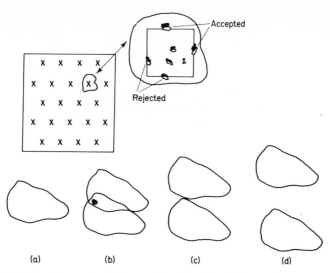

Fig. 6.11. Particle sizing using the image shearing principle.

The eyepiece is first calibrated and preset. It can be seen at a glance which particles are greater than the preset size. When a representative number of fields have been examined at this setting, a new setting is made and the particles oversize recorded. The number of fields examined at any size level may be chosen so as to give a statistically acceptable count. An improved optical and mechanical system is claimed for the Vickers-A.E.I. image-splitting eyepiece, in which two rotating prisms are used to produce shear (figure 6.12). Each prism consists of a rhomboidal and right-angled prism cemented together with a substantially neutral semi-reflecting interface. These are mounted so as to rotate about a vertical axis and are constrained by means of a simple linkage to rotate by equal amounts in opposite directions, the rotation being produced by using a micrometer head. Timbrell [22] modifies a normal microscope optical system by the introduction of a small mirror inclined at 45° to the vertical to reflect the light beam from the objective into a horizontal eyepiece. The mirror is mounted on to the diaphragm of a loudspeaker vibrating at about 50 Hz. The source of illumination is arranged to flash when the mirror is at the extremities of its vibration, the duration of the flash being short compared with the period of the vibration. Because of the persistence of vision, two images of each particle are seen. The amplitude of vibration of the mirror is controlled by varying the energizing current which is therefore proportional to the separation of the images.

Under ideal conditions, the accuracy of these instruments is 0·025 μm. The apparatus can be preset to chosen values of ten size limits. A manually operated switch enables the amount of shear to be increased in stepwise fashion to correspond to the preset limits in turn. Pressure on a foot-switch registers the particle on the appropriate one of ten electromagnetic counters which display the numbers together with the total. The apparatus can be connected to digital readout and printout on tape

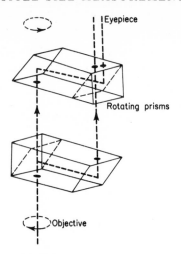

Fig. 6.12. The Vickers image-splitting eyepiece.

The operation of the eyepiece is based on the image-splitting principle. A single ray of light is split into two at the partially reflecting surface of the lower prism block. One ray is reflected along the prism block and then upwards into the eyepiece; the other ray is transmitted through the lower prism block and reflected along the upper prism where it is finally reflected upwards into the eyepiece.

facilities for processing the results by computer. Barnett and Timbrell [23] claim extremely high reproducibility for the instrument down to 2 μm.

This device was modified so that it could be inserted in an ordinary microscope tube and in this form is available from Microsizers. Fleming Instruments in collaboration with N.R.D.C. market a similar instrument. An Electrometer incorporating similar facilities but electronic rather than electrical, has been developed by Coulters, Hialeh, Florida. This instrument features a television display of the particles under examination. A particular feature of Timbrell's device is that particles can be made to vibrate in any direction and the two images from any one particle can be made to rotate about each other. This permits the measurement of maximum and minimum diameters as well as the Feret and shear size. The images can also be made to vibrate at two different amplitudes so that the overlap varies between, say, 10 μm and 12 μm hence particles can be classified into narrow size categories [76].

6.8 Automatic counting and sizing

The need to count and size large numbers of samples of airborne dust stimulated the development of automatic microscopes. In these instruments, the particles are passed through a light beam which then falls on a photocell. Changes in the intensity of the light beam due to the presence of particles are monitored and recorded. The instrument types may be categorized as spot scanners and slit scanners [36].

The spot scan methods [37, 38, 39] are based on the flying spot microscope of Roberts and Young [40]. In this, the scan is produced by a moving spot of light on a cathode-ray tube which is projected through a microscope on to the specimen. When a particle interrupts the light beam a photocell is activated and the particle is recorded. Special memory devices in the electronics prevent the same particle from being counted twice [41]. This technique forms the basis of the Rank Cintel instrument. Causley and Young [44], Furmidge [45] and Phillips [46], in discussing this technique, show that certain designs of apparatus are suspect and that there is always the probability that re-entrant particles will be counted twice.

The M.R. particle size distribution analyser utilizes the scanning spot of a television camera for determining particle size distribution. The instrument records the number of intercepts of the spot by particles and the size distribution may be derived by successive scans of the field at different discriminator levels. A conventional microscope is used with a beam splitter below the eyepiece, so that the image is passed both into the eyepiece and into a television camera. The output from the television camera is displayed on a screen, thus enabling the operator to select and focus on a field without the fatigue of peering through a microscope. The output is also fed to a selector unit which responds to the changes in intensity produced when the scanning spot passes over the particle. The selector unit output is displayed on a screen, so that the operator can check that the unit is operating at the correct level of discrimination and then passed to an indicating unit which displays on a meter the number of intercepts of the scanning spot with particles larger than the selected size.

In the Mullard film-scanning particle analyser [42], the principle of scanning a sample directly has been abandoned in favour of using an intermediate photographic image. This extends the range of the instrument, since electron micrographs may be used, and it also provides a permanent record. Against these advantages must be weighed the disadvantage of the extra operation of photographing and developing transparencies of the slide. Crowl [43] states that this innovation extends the lower range of the instrument to 0·08 μm and that improved performance is obtained by using negative images, i.e. white particles on black background. He concludes that the counting speed of 1000 particles in half an hour is little better than the counting speeds obtainable by a well-trained operator, and although its reproducibility is high, its inability to distinguish between single particles and aggregates produces errors. Crowl substantiates Phillips by stating that there is evidence that the instrument performs more satisfactorily with regularly-shaped particles.

The theory of slit scanning has been covered by Hawksley [47] and the technique is used in the Casella counter [48]. The method of operation is to project the image of a slide on to a slit using a conventional microscope. The slide is mechanically scanned and the signals produced as the particle images pass over the slip are electronically recorded. The effects of coincidence and overlap are eliminated by varying the width of the slit. The reproducibility are accuracy are found to be very good down to 2·0 μm using spherical opaque particles [49]. In recent years these instruments have been superseded by image analysers which have many advantages over the earlier systems.

6.9 Quantitative image analysers

Quantitative image analysers accept samples in a variety of forms; photographs, electron micrographs and direct viewing. The particles are scanned by a television camera and displayed on a console and electrical information describing the sample is passed to a detector. Parameters which can be measured include count, size distribution by area or some statistical diameter, projected length and intersect count and chord-size distribution; from these many secondary parameters may be evaluated. At the detector the features to be measured are selected and passed to an analog computer which counts the chosen data and stores it or presents it in one of a variety of ways.

A great number of basically similar instruments have been described and several of these are commercially available. These include the Ameda, Leitz Classimat, Millipore πMC, Bausch and Lomb quantitative metallurgical system and Quantimet image analysing computers. The latest version of the Quantimet, the 720 is not based on standard television scanning, but employs a digitally controlled scan which divides the field of view into 650 000 picture points and allows the use of more sophisticated logic.

Detailed descriptions of these instruments are given by Davies [83], Quantitative Image analysis is reviewed by Jesse [84] and discussed in several papers (in *Microscope* [85, 86]). The Quantimet has also been described by Williams [87] and the Classimat by Stutzer [88].

6.10 Specimen improvement techniques

Automatic and quantitative microscopes tend to give erroneous results for transparent particles. To overcome this problem, Amor and Block [89] have used the silver-staining technique to make the particles opaque. The particles are dry mounted onto a thin film of tacky colloidon on a microscope slide. Silver is then deposited from solution using the silver mirror reaction. Preliminary sensitizing of the crystalline surface ensures that much more silver is deposited on the particles than on the colloidon. They also give details for a method of staining particles in aqueous solution prior to deposition on a membrane filter for analysis.

Hamilton and Phelps [90] adapted the metal-shadowing technique for the preparation of transparent profiles of dust particles. The process consists of evaporating *in vacuo* a thin metal film in a direction normal to a slide containing particles. The particles are then removed by a jet of air or water, leaving sharp transparent profiles.

6.11 Statistical considerations governing the determination of size distributions by microscope count [51]

Since it is impracticable to size all the particles deposited on the microscope slide or electron microscope grid, a representative sample must be chosen. As with all sampling techniques, the measurement sample should be taken at random, or according to some predetermined pattern, from the analysis sample. The simplest procedure is to examine a number of fields spread uniformly over the slide or grid. Since it is necessary to size about 600 particles in order to obtain a statistically accurate count, and it is inadvisable to size more than six particles in any one field of view, it is necessary to examine at least 100 fields. The adopted procedure depends upon whether a number or a weight distribution is required, the former being the simpler of the two analyses.

(a) *Frequency distribution determination*. The percentage standard error of the mean size in a number distribution is $100/\sqrt{n}$, where n is the number of particles sized. Thus, if only a mean size is required, one may estimate the accuracy of the determination. For powders containing a narrow range of sizes, the necessary count may be substantially lower than that given by the above expression, and Irani and Callis [4] suggest that the mean size should be calculated as the count progresses. This will tend towards some fixed value and the count may be ended when this limit can be estimated.

For a full number distribution, the number to be counted in any size range to achieve a given accuracy is given by:

$$\sigma(F_1) = \left\{ \frac{F_1(100 - F_1)}{n_t} \right\}^{1/2}$$

where $\sigma(F_1)$ = standard deviation expressed as a percentage of the total by frequency,

$\quad F_1$ = frequency of particles in a given size range,

$\quad n_t$ = total number of particles of all size ranges counted.

The function $F_1(100 - F_1)$ has a maximum value for a size range containing 50% of the particles. Hence, if the required accuracy for $\sigma(F_1)$ is obtained in the size range containing most of the particles, it will hold for all other size ranges. In the case of a size analysis on a frequency basis, the same area should be examined for all classes.

(b) *Weight distribution determination*. The number of particles to be sized to achieve a given accuracy is given by:

$$\sigma(M_q) = M_q/\sqrt{n_d}$$

where $\sigma(M_q)$ = standard distribution expressed as a percentage of the total by weight,

$\quad M_q$ = percentage by weight in the given size range,

$\quad n_d$ = number of particles counted in the size range.

If, in a particular case, 10% by weight of the particles lie in the top range and an accuracy $\sigma(M_q) = 2\%$ is required, the number of particles (n_d) to be counted in that size range, is equal to twenty-five.

In order to maintain this accuracy for all other size ranges, the control factor

$$\Omega = \left\{ \frac{nd^6}{(ka)^2} \right\}^{1/2}$$

calculated for the top range exceeds that counted for all other ranges.

d = volume mean diameter of the size range,

a = area of one field,

k = number of areas examined.

In optical microscopy it is often necessary to examine the whole of the slide in strips in order to find 25 particles in the top size range and sometimes necessary to examine more than one slide. It is advisable to make a preliminary scan at the lowest magnification in order that an estimate of Ω may be made and the areas to be scanned for the next two size ranges estimated. Derivations of the above formulae and full operating instructions are given in B.S. 3406 [31].

6.12 Conclusion

The microscope is an invaluable tool to the particle size analyst. If there are relatively few particles present that are smaller than 1 μm in size, the optical microscope should be used. This should also be used to examine every sub-sieve (greater than 1 μm) powder awaiting analysis in order to reduce the possibilities or errors. For example, the Coulter counter will give a size analysis for a sub-micrometre powder although the size of the individual pulses generated by the particles is below the discriminator range of the instruments, since the counting system for this instrument will count doublets and triplets as single particles if the concentration is high enough.

Number counts can be carried out quickly and accurately, but it is not widely understood that weight counts can also be accurately carried out on as few as 600 particles. The method to be adopted however, is entirely different; hence B.S. 3406 should be carefully followed.

Image-shearing eyepieces are very useful for size-grading narrowly classified powders and are relatively inexpensive. The Timbrell system is more expensive, more rapid and easier to use. It is, therefore, useful if many analyses are required on a routine basis. The image analysing computers are even more sophisticated and expensive but provide for more information.

For sub-micrometre particles it is necessary to use a TEM or SEM, the latter being extremely useful for studies of surface topography.

References

[1] Green, M. (1921), *J. Franklin Inst.*, **192**, 657.
[2] Dunn, E.J. (1930), *Ind. Eng. Chem. Analyt. ed.*, **2**, 59.
[3] Orr, C. and Dallevalle, J.M. (1959), *Fine Particle Measurement*, Macmillan, N.Y
[4] Irani, R.R., and Callis, C.F. (1963), *Particle Size*, Wiley, N.Y.
[5] Harwood, M.G. (1954), *B. J. Appl. Phys.*, suppl. 3, S193.
[6] Rosinski, J., Glaess, H.E., and McCulley, C.R. (1956), *Anal. Chem.*, **28**, 486.
[7] Allen, R.P. (1942), *Ind. Eng. Chem., Analyt. ed.*, **14**, 92.
[8] Lenz, F. (1954), *Optik*, **11**, 524.
[9] Ellison, J. McK. (1954), *Nature*, **179**, 948.
[10] Green, M. (1946), *Ind. Eng. Chem.*, **38**, 679.
[11] Martin G., *et al.* (1923), *Trans. Ceram. Soc.*, **23**, 61; (1926), **25**, 51; (1928), **27**, 285.
[12] Heywood, H. (1946), *Trans. Inst. Min. Met.*, **4**, 391.
[13] Feret, R.L. (1931), *Assoc. Int. pour l'essai des Mnt.* 2, Group D, Zurich.
[14] Tomkieff, S.L. (1945), *Nature*, **155**, 24.
[15] Moran, P.A.P. (1944), *Nature*, **154**, 490.
[16] Herdan, G. (1960), *Small Particle Statistics*, Butterworths.

[17] Steinheitz, A.R. (1946), *Trans. Soc. Chem. Ind.*, **65**, 314.

[18] Crowl, V.T. (1961), *Paint Res. Station, Teddington, Memorandum No.* 291, **12**, 24.

[19] Aschenbrenner, B.C. (1955), *Photogrammetric Engng*, **21**, 376.

[20] Walton, W.H. (1948), *Nature*, **162**, 329.

[21] Watson image shearing eyepiece. See Appendix.

[22] Timbrell, V. (1952), *Nature*, **170**, 318–9.

[23] Barnet and Timbrell, V. (Oct., 1962), *Pharm. J.*, 379.

[24] Cauchy, A. (1940), *Compte Rendu*, **13**, 1060.

[25] Patterson, H.S., and Cawood, W. (1936), *Trans. Faraday Soc.*, **32**, 1084.

[26] Watson, H.H. (1936), *Trans. Inst. Min. Metall.*, **46**, 176.

[27] Fairs, G.L. (1943), *Chem. Ind.*, **62**, 374.

[28] May, K.R. (1965), *J. Sci. Instrum.*, **22**, 187.

[29] Watson, H.H. (1952), *B. J. Ind. Med.*, 19, 80.

[30] Hamilton, R.J., and Holdsworth, J.F. (1954), *B. J. Appl. Phys.*, suppl. 3, S101.

[31] B.S. 3406: 1963, Part. 4.

[32] Endter, F., and Gebauer, H. (1956), *Optik*, **13**, 87.

[33] Heywood, H. (1946), *Bull. Inst. Min. Met.*, nos. 477, 478.

[34] Watson, H.H. and Mulford, D.F. (1954), 'A particle profile test strip for assessing the accuracy of sizing irregularly shaped particles with a microscope', *B. J. Appl. Phys.*, suppl. 3, S105.

[35] Fairs, G.L., 'Discussion', *ibid.*, S108.

[36] Walton, W.H., 'Survey of the automatic counting and sizing of particles', *ibid.*, S121.

[37] Vick, F.A. (1956), *Sci. Prog.*, **94**, 176, 655.

[38] Morgan, B.B. (1957), 'Automatic particle counting and sizing', *Research (Lond.)*, **10**, 271.

[39] Taylor, W.K. (1954), 'An automatic system for obtaining particle size distributions with the aid of the flying spot microscope', *B. J. Appl. Phys.*, suppl. 3, S173.

[40] Roberts, F., and Young, J.Z. (1952), *Nature*, **169**, 962.

[41] Bell, H.A. (1954), 'Stages in the development of an arrested scan type microscope particle counter', *B. J. Appl. Phys.*, suppl. 3, S156.

[42] *Mullard Film Scanning Particle Analyser*, L. 188, Mullards Ltd, Technical leaflet.

[43] Crowl, V.T. (1960), 'The use of the mullard film scanning particle size distribution counting from electron micrographs', *Res. Memorandum No.* 284, Research Association of British Paint, Colour and Varnish Manufacturers.

[44] Causley, D., and Young, J. (1955), *Z. Research*, **8**, 430.

[45] Furmidge, C.G.L. (1961), *B. J. Appl. Phys.*, **12**, 268.

[46] Phillips, J.W. (1954), 'Some fundamental aspects of particle counting and sizing by linear scans', *B. J. Appl. Phys.*, suppl. 3, S133–7.

[47] Hawksley, P.G.W., 'Theory of particle sizing and counting by track scanning', *ibid.*, S125–132.

[48] *Casella Automatic Particle Counter and Sizer* (Booklet 906A), Cooke, Troughton & Simms Ltd.

[49] Allen, T., and Kaye, B.H. (1965), *Analyst*, **90**, 1068, 147.

[50] Walton, W.M. (1947), 'The application of the electron microscope to particle

size measurement', Symposium on Particle Size Analysis, *Inst. Chem. Eng.*, **25**, 64–76.

[51] Fairs, G.L. (1951), *J.R. Microsc. Soc.*, **71**, 209.

[52] Dyson, J. (1960), *J. Opt. Soc. Am.*, **50**, 754–7.

[53] Payne, B.O. (1964), *Microscope*, **14**, 6, 217.

[54] Dyson, J. (1961), *A.E.I. Engng*, **1**, 13.

[55] Becher, P. (1964), *J. Colloid Sci.*, **19**, 468.

[56] Kay, D.H. (1965), *Techniques for Electron Microscopy*, 2nd ed., Blackwell Scientific Publications, Oxford.

[57] Drummond, D.G. (ed) (1950), *The Practice of Electron Microscopy*, Royal Microscopical Society, London.

[58] Revell, R.S.M., and Agar, A.W. (1955), *B. J. Appl. Phys.*, **6**, 23.

[59] Bradley, D.E. (1954), *B. J. Appl. Physics.*, **5**, 65.

[60] Backus, R.C., and Williams, R.C. (1950), *J. Appl. Phys.*, **21**, 11.

[61] Bradley, D.E., and Williams, D.J. (1957), *J. Jen. Microbiol.*, **17**, 75.

[62] Bailey, G.W., and Ellis, J.R. (1954), *Microscope*, **14**, 6, 217.

[63] Williams, R.C., and Wyckoff, R.W.G. (1946), *J. Appl. Phys.*, **17**, 23.

[64] Cartwright, J., and Skidmore, J.W. (1953), S.M.R.E., Sheffield, Report No. 79.

[65] Crowl, V.T. (1961), Paint Research Station, Teddington, Report No. 291.

[66] Joffe, A.D. (1963), *B. J. Appl. Phys.*, **14**, 7, 429.

[67] Maclay, W.N., and Grindter, E.M. (1963), *J. Colloid. Sci.*, **18**, 343.

[68] Charman, W.N. (1961), Lond. Univ., Ph.D. thesis.

[69] Taylor, N.J. (1969), *Vacuum*, **19**, 575; *J. Vacuum Sci. Tech.*, (1969), **6**, 241.

[70] Chang, C.C. (1971), *Surface Sci.*, **25**, 23.

[71] Brundle, C.R. (1972), *Surface and Defect Properties of Solids*, vol. 6, chapter 6, Chemical Society, London.

[72] Rowe, S.H. (1966), *Microscope*, **15**, 216.

[73] Welford, G.A. (1960), *Optics in Metrology*, **85**.

[74] Timbrell, V. (1972), *J. Appl. Phys.*, **43**, 11, 4839.

[75] Timbrell, V. (1972), *Microscope*, **20**, 365.

[76] Timbrell, V. (1973), *Harold Heywood Memorial Symposium*, Loughborough Univ., England.

[77] Fairs, G.L. (1951), *J.R. Microsc. Soc.*, **71**, 209.

[78] Guruswamy, S. (1967), *Particle Size Analysis*, Society for Analytical Chemistry, 29–31.

[79] Chatfield, E.J, (1967), *J. Sci. Instrum.* **44**, 615.

[80] Lark, P.D. (1965), *Microscope,* **15**, 1–6.

[81] Krumbein, W.C. (1934), *J. Sedim. Petrol*, **4**, 65–7.

[82] Dyson, J. (1959), *Nature*, **184**, 1561.

[83] Davies, R. (1970), Illinois State Microscopical Society Seminar.

[84] Jesse, A. (1971), *Microscope*, **19**, 1, 21–30.

[85] Cole, M. (1971), *Microscope*, **19**, 1, 87–103.

[86] Huna, W. (1971), *Microscope*, **19**, 2, 205–18.

[87] Williams, G. (1971), *Bull. Soc. Fr. Ceram.* **90**, 59, 59–63.

[88] Stutzer, M. (1971), *Bull. Soc. Fr. Ceram.* **90**, 65, 65–8.

[89] Amor, A.F., and Block, M. (1968), *J.R. Microsc. Soc.*, **88**, 4, 601–5.

[90] Hamilton, R.J., and Phelps, B.A. (1956), *B. J. Appl. Phys.* **7**, 186.

[91] Pidgeon, F.D., and Dodd, C.G. (1954), *Analyt. Chem.*, **26**, 1823–8.

[92]   McCrone, W.C. (1970), *Microscope*, **18**, 1, 1.
[93]   Delly, J.G. (1969), *Microscope*, **17**, 205–11.
[94]   Corcoran, J.F. (1970), *Fuel*, **49**, 3, 331–4.
[95]   Eckert, J.J.D., and Caveney, R.J. (1970), *J. Phys. E.*, **3**, 413–4.

7 *Interaction between Particles and Fluids in a Gravitational Field*

7.1 Introduction

The settling behaviour of particles in a fluid is widely used for particle size determination. The simplest case to consider is the settling velocity, under gravity, of a single sphere in a fluid of infinite extent. Many experiments have been carried out to determine the relationship between settling velocity and particle size. A unique relationship between drag factor and Reynolds' number has been found, and this relationship reduces to a simple equation, the Stokes' equation, which applies at low Reynolds' number, relating settling velocity and particle size. In this chapter this equation is developed and its limits explored. It is shown, that for the purpose of particle size measurement, the time for a particle to reach a steady velocity (the acceleration time) is negligible.

If the concentration is monitored at a fixed depth below the surface for an initially homogeneous suspension of spheres, this will remain constant until the largest particle present in the suspension has fallen from the surface to the measurement zone. The concentration will then fall, being at all times proportional to the concentration of particles smaller than the diameter given by the Stokes' equation for that particular time and depth of fall.

Any sample removed from this depth should not contain particles with diameters larger than the Stokes' diameter. In practice this is not true, due to particle–particle interaction, and this is investigated here in some detail. In general, pairs of equally-sized spheres in close proximity will fall with a greater terminal velocity than for a single sphere. For unequally sized particles the situation is more complex, the larger particle may actually pick up the smaller one so that it revolves round the large one as a satellite. Assemblies of spheres tend to diverge due to the rotation effect caused by the greater velocity of the streamlines on the envelope of the assembly. A cluster of particles acts as a single large particle of appropriate density and reduced rigidity and has a much greater velocity than the settling velocities of the particles of which it is composed.

At volume concentrations as low as 1%, the suspension settles *en masse* and the rate of fall of the interface gives an average size for the particles with a modified Stokes' equation. This equation is very similar to the permeametry equation for a fluid passing through a fixed bed of powder. The settling velocities of particles are also reduced in the proximity of container walls through this effect is usually quite small.

As the Reynolds' number increases, so does the divergence between Stokes' equation and experimental results. Corrections should, therefore, be applied otherwise the experimentally determined diameters will be too low. At higher Reynolds numbers the streamlines around the particles break up and the particles carry fluid down with them thus reducing their velocity. Corrections may be applied using the tables in section 7.10.

For irregularly shaped particles, the Stokes' diameters are the diameters of spheres of the same material having the same settling velocities as the particles under the same conditions. Again it is necessary to apply corrections at higher Reynolds' number, otherwise the determined diameter will vary with varying fluid density or viscosity. At low Reynolds' number particles settle in random orientation, but as the number increases there is an increasing tendency for the particles to orientate themselves to give maximum resistance to motion.

As particle size decreases the particles are acted upon by the fluid molecules to give a variable settling rate to particles of the same size. Indeed, a proportion of the particles will actually rise during a time interval, although the concentration at a fixed depth, on the average, will fall. Impressed upon this effect there are convection currents which may be set up by surface evaporation or temperature differences. All settling suspensions appear to be basically unstable due to preferred paths up the sedimentation tank for the fluid displaced by the settling particles. The fluid tends to rise up the walls of the containing vessel and to dissipate itself as convection currents at the top of the sedimentation column and carry with it some of the finer particles. This leads to an excess of fines at the top of the container and an overestimation of the fines percentage in an analysis. For these reasons, for accurate results below about $2\,\mu\text{m}$, centrifugal techniques should be used.

7.2 Relationship between drag coefficient and Reynolds' number for a sphere settling in a liquid

When a particle falls under gravity in a viscous fluid, it is acted upon by three forces: a gravitational force W acting downwards; a buoyant force U acting upwards and a drag force F_D acting upwards. The resulting equation of motion is:

$$mg - m^1 g - F_D = m\frac{du}{dt} \tag{7.1}$$

where m is the mass of the particle, m^1 is the mass of the same volume of fluid, u is the particle velocity and g is the acceleration due to gravity.

When the terminal velocity is reached, the drag force is equal to the motive force on the particle, that is, the difference between the gravitational attraction and the Archimedes' upthrust.

For a sphere of diameter D and density ρ_s falling in a fluid of density ρ_f, the equation of motion becomes:

$$F_D = (m - m^1)g$$

$$F_D = \frac{\pi}{6}(\rho_s - \rho_f)g D^3. \tag{7.2}$$

Dimensional analysis of the general problem of particle motion under conditions of equilibrium [34] shows that there is a unique relationship between two dimension groups, the Reynolds' number, R_e, and the drag coefficient C_D where:

$$R_e = \frac{\rho_f u D}{\eta} \tag{7.3}$$

where η is the viscosity of the fluid:

$$C_D = \frac{\text{drag force}}{\text{cross-sectional area of particle} \times \text{dynamic pressure on particle}}$$

$$C_D = \frac{F_D}{\dfrac{D^2}{4} \times \rho_f \dfrac{u^2}{2}} \tag{7.4}$$

The experimental relationship between the Reynolds' number and the drag coefficient is shown graphically in figure 7.1. This graph is divided into three regions, a laminar flow or Stokes' region, an intermediate region and a turbulent flow or Newton region.

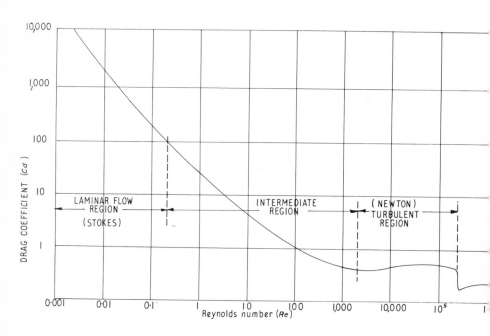

Fig. 7.1. Experimental relationship between drag coefficient and Reynolds' number for a sphere settling in a liquid.

7.3 The laminar flow region

Stokes [35] assumed that when the terminal velocity is reached, the drag on a spherical particle falling in a viscous fluid of infinite extent is due entirely to viscous forces within the fluid and deduced the expression:

$$F_D = 3\pi D \eta u_{st} \qquad (7.5)$$

where u_{st} is the terminal velocity in the Stokes' region. Alternatively u_{st} is the terminal velocity as given by Stokes' equation, the difference between this and the free-falling velocity increasing with increasing Reynolds' number.

Substituting in equation (7.2) gives, for a sphere:

$$u_{st} = \frac{(\rho_s - \rho_f)g D^2}{18\eta} . \qquad (7.6)$$

The assumption made in the derivation of Stokes' law of settling velocities are:
(1) The particle must be spherical, smooth and rigid and there must be no slip between it and the fluid.
(2) The particle must move as it would in a fluid of infinite extent.
(3) The terminal velocity must have been reached.
(4) The settling velocity must be low so that all inertia effects are negligible.
(5) The fluid must be homogeneous compared with the size of the particle.

The relationship between C_D and R_e in the laminar flow region is, from equations (7.4) and (7.5):

$$C_D = \frac{24}{R_e} . \qquad (7.7)$$

C_D tends to this value at low Reynolds' numbers (see figure 7.1). Equation (7.6), the Stokes' equation, may therefore be used for low Reynolds' numbers; the terminal velocities calculated thereby will be about 5% too great at $R_e = 0.2$.

7.4 Critical diameter for laminar flow settling

Writing the diameter as given by the Stokes' equation as D_{st}, the critical diameter above which Stokes' equation should not be used is given by making $R_e = 0.2$ and eliminating u from equations (7.3) and (7.6) giving:

$$\text{critical value of } D_{st}^3 = \frac{3.6\eta^2}{(\rho_s - \rho_f)\rho_f g} \qquad (7.8)$$

For quartz particles settling in water:

$$\rho_s = 2650 \text{ kg m}^{-3}$$
$$\rho_f = 1000 \text{ kg m}^{-3}$$
$$g = 9.81 \text{ m s}^{-2}$$
$$\eta = 0.001 \text{ Ns m}^{-2}$$

$$\underline{D_{st} = 60.6 \ \mu m}$$

The critical value for quartz particles settling in air, $\eta = 18 \times 10^{-6}$ Ns m^{-2}, $\rho_f =$ 1.39×10^{-4} kg m^{-3}, is 30 μm. Very many problems concerned with particle motion are beyond the validity of Stokes' equation and a rapid method of calculating the terminal velocity in such cases is required.

7.5 Particle acceleration

In sedimentation analyses it is assumed that the terminal velocity is reached instantaneously. The usual procedure is to agitate the suspension and assume that when this ceases the particles are all falling with their terminal velocities. In actual fact, the particles are in random motion, though a visual examination suffices to show that all the particles are falling within a few seconds. If it is assumed that the particles are initially at rest in a still fluid, the equation of motion, in the laminar flow region, becomes:

$$\frac{\pi}{6}(\rho_s - \rho_f)gD^3 - 3\pi D\eta u = \frac{\pi}{6}\rho_s D^3 \frac{du}{dt} \qquad (7.9)$$

Simplifying by putting $\rho = \dfrac{\rho_s - \rho_f}{\rho_s}$ and $X = \dfrac{18\eta}{\rho_s D^2}$

$$\frac{du}{dt} = \rho g - Xu \qquad (7.10)$$

$$\int_0^u \frac{du}{\rho g - Xu} = \int_0^t dt$$

$$u = \frac{\rho g}{X}[1 - \exp(-Xt)] \qquad (7.11)$$

As t approaches infinity, u approaches the Stokes' velocity u_{st} as given in equation (7.6).

Theoretically a particle never reaches its terminal velocity but, for practical purposes, it can be assumed that the velocity is sufficiently near the terminal velocity for the error to be neglected.

From equation (7.11), the velocity is 0.99 times the terminal velocity when:

$$u = 0.99\, u_{st}$$

$$1 - \exp(-Xt) = 0.99$$

$$Xt = \log_e 100$$

$$t = \frac{4.6\, D^2 \rho_s}{18\eta}.$$

For spheres of density 2650 kg m^{-3} in water, $\eta = 0.001$ Ns m^{-2} and in air, $\eta = 18 \times 10^{-6}$ Ns m^{-2}, the times taken to reach 99% of the terminal velocity for particles of different diameters are as follows:

Diameter (μm)	Times (ms)	
	Water	air
5	0·017	0·95
10	0·068	3·70
50	1·70	0·95

From this table it can be seen that the assumption that a particle falling from rest reaches its terminal velocity instantaneously does not introduce any appreciable errors in the Stokes' region.

The distance covered h during the acceleration time is given by integrating equation (7.11):

$$\int_0^h \mathrm{d}h = u_{st} \int_0^t [1 - \exp(-Xt)] \, \mathrm{d}t$$

$$h = u_{st}\, t \left\{ 1 - \frac{1}{Xt} [1 - \exp(-Xt)] \right\}. \qquad (7.12)$$

At 99% of the terminal velocity $1 - \exp(-Xt) = 0.99$, as before, and $Xt = 4.6$

$$h = 0.785\, u_{st}\, t.$$

Since t is very small, the distance fallen in achieving a velocity equal to 0·99 times the settling velocity is also very small at low Reynolds' number.

7.6 Errors due to the finite extent of the fluid

When the fluid is of finite extent, there are two effects, the fluid streamlines about the particle impinge on the walls of the containing vessel and are reflected back on the particle causing increased drag; also, since the fluid is stationary at a finite distance from the particle there is distortion of the flow pattern which reacts back on the particle.

Both effects increase the drag on the particle leading to too low an estimate of particle size in sedimentation. Thus the drag on a sphere is given by:

$$F = 3\pi D\eta u \left(1 + k\frac{D}{L} \right) \qquad (7.13)$$

where L is the distance from the centre of the particle to the walls of the containing vessel. The numerical constant k has been obtained theoretically for a sphere [1]. For a single wall $k = 0.563$, for two walls $k = 1.004$ and for a circular cylinder $k = 2.104$. Each extra wall increases the drag by an approximately equal amount, thus the settling velocity of a sphere in a cylinder is much the same over a large part of the central area, the increase in drag due to displacement towards one side being offset by the decrease due to displacement from the other. As long as the inertial terms are negligible, there is no force tending to move the sphere towards or away from the wall.

A sphere moving near a single plane wall will, however, rotate, as if it were rolling on the wall, at an angular velocity given by [2, p. 327]:

$$= \frac{3u}{2D} \left(\frac{D}{L}\right)^4 \left\{1 - \frac{3}{4}\frac{D}{L}\right\}.$$

Between two parallel walls with $D \ll L$, where the sphere is located such that its distance from one wall is three times its distance from the other, rotation is in the opposite direction to rolling on the near wall with angular velocity:

$$= \frac{1}{80}\frac{D}{L^2} \bigg/ \left(1 - 0.326\frac{D}{L}\right)$$

where L is the distance to the nearer wall.

Inserting equation (7.13) in Stokes' equation gives:

$$D = D_{st}\left(1 + \frac{1}{2}k\frac{D}{L}\right) \tag{7.14}$$

neglecting second and higher order terms, where D is the true diameter and D_{st} the diameter obtained using the unmodified Stokes' equation.

For a 100 μm sphere settling in a 0.5 cm diameter cylinder, $L = 0.25$ cm, the error in particle size is given by:

$$D = D_{st}\left(1 + \frac{1}{2}\frac{2.104}{0.25}\frac{10^{-4}}{10^{-2}}\right)$$

$$= 1.042\,D_{st}, \text{ an error of about 4\%.}$$

The effect of the bottom of the container has been evaluated by Lorentz [1] who modified equation (7.5) in the following manner:

$$F_D = 3\pi D\eta u\left(1 + \frac{9}{16}\frac{D}{L}\right). \tag{7.15}$$

The correction term is negligible if the sampling is carried out at a distance greater than 1000 diameters from the ends of the suspension and is very small for distance as small as 50 diameters.

7.7 Errors due to discontinuity of fluid

The Stokes' drag needs modification for the molecular nature of real fluids. At one extreme, when the pressure is very low and the mean free path length of the gas molecular (λ) is much larger than the particle size, the resitance to particle motion is due to bombardment by individual molecules acting independently and is very much less than the Stokes' drag, leading to an increased settling velocity:

$$u = u_{st} \frac{4 \cdot 49 \, \lambda}{BD} \qquad (7.16)$$

where B depends on the nature of the molecular reflections and lies between 1 and 1·4 [3].

At the other extreme, when the pressure is higher and the particles are much larger than the mean free path length, the discontinuity effect gives rise to 'slip' between the particle and the medium, leading to the following modification to Stokes' equation:

$$u = u_{st} \left[1 + \frac{2\lambda}{D} \left(\frac{2-f}{f} \right) \right] \qquad (7.17)$$

where f is the fraction of molecules undergoing diffuse reflection at the particle surface and is experimentally found to be of the order of 0·90. In the intermediate region, when the mean free path length and particle size are of the same order, neither treatment is applicable.

Cunningham [4] introduced a correction term to Stokes' law of the form:

$$u = u_{st} \left(1 + \frac{2A\lambda}{D} \right) \qquad (7.18)$$

where A is a constant approximately equal to unity. Experimental data, analysed by Davies [5], gave the more accurate empirical equations:

$$u = u_{st} \left\{ 1 + \frac{\lambda}{D} \left[2 \cdot 514 + 0 \cdot 800 \exp \left(-0 \cdot 55 \frac{D}{\lambda} \right) \right] \right\} \qquad (7.19)$$

For air at pressure p cm Hg and $20° $C, λ may be replaced by $(5 \cdot 0 \times 10^{-4}/p)$. For air at 76 cm Hg and $20° $C and D in micrometres, the equation becomes:

$$u = u_{st} \left\{ 1 + \frac{1}{D} \left[0 \cdot 1663 + 0 \cdot 0529 \exp \left(-8 \cdot 32D \right) \right] \right\}.$$

The mean free path is here defined as:

$$\lambda = \frac{2\eta}{P} \sqrt{\pi \frac{RT}{8M}}$$

where R is the molar gas constant, T the absolute temperature and M the molecular weight of the gas.

Lapple [6] gives the following typical values for spherical particles in air at $70° $F:

$D (\mu m)$	0·1	0·25	0·50	1·0	10·0
$\dfrac{2A\lambda}{D}$	1·88	0·68	0·33	0·16	0·016 .

The correction may be important for aerosols but not for particles in liquids.

7.8 Brownian motion

When a particle is sufficiently small, collisions with individual fluid molecules may displace the particle by a measurable amount. This results in a random motion of the particles in addition to any net motion in a given direction due to the action of external forces such as gravity [7, 8]. Quantitively, this random motion may be expressed as follows [2, p. 412]:

$$\bar{X}^2 = \frac{4RTK_m t}{3\pi^2 \eta N D} \qquad (7.20)$$

where $\bar{X}$ is the statistical average linear displacement in a given direction in time t, R is the gas constant, T the absolute temperature, N is Avogadro's number and K_m the correction for discontinuity of the fluid discussed above.

A comparison of Brownian movement displacement and gravitational settling displacement is given in table 7.1 [9].

Table 7.1 Comparison of Brownian movement displacement and gravitational settling displacement.

Particle diameter μm	Displacement in 1·0 second (μm)			
	in air at 70° F (1 atm)		in water at 70° F	
	due to Brownian movement*	due to gravitational settling†	due to Brownian movement*	due to gravitational settling†
0·10	29·4	1·73	2·36	0·005
0·25	14·2	6·3	1·49	0·0346
0·50	8·92	19·9	1·052	0·1384
1·0	5·91	69·6	0·745	0·554
2·5	3·58	400	0·334	13·84
10·0	1·75	1550	0·236	55·4

*Mean displacement given by equation (7.20).

† Distance settled by a sphere of density 2000 kg m^{-2}, including Cunningham's correction.

This effect limits the use of gravitational sedimentation in water for particle size analysis to particles greater than about 1 μm where, for a specific gravity of 2, the Brownian motion exceeds the gravitational motion. Even for specific gravities of 5, the magnitudes of the two motions are similar, i.e. 0·528 m s^{-1} and 2·22 m s^{-1} respectively.

Brownian motion is normally negligible [8, p. 16] when compared with even the most feeble convection currents and this further limits the smallest size at which gravitational sedimentation gives meaningful results.

7.9 Viscosity of a suspension

When discrete solid particles are present in a fluid, they themselves cannot take part in any deformation the fluid may undergo, and the result is an increased resistance to shear. Thus a suspension exhibits a greater resistance to shear than a pure fluid. This effect is expressed as an equivalent viscosity of the suspension. As the proportion of solids increases, so the viscosity increases. Einstein [10] deduced the equations:

$$\eta_T = \eta_0 (1 + kc) \tag{7.21}$$

where η_0 is the viscosity of the fluid, η_T the viscosity of the suspension, c the volume concentration of solids and k a constant which equals 2·5 for rigid, inertialess spherical particles.

The formula is found to hold for very dilute suspension, but requires some modification for c greater than 1% [1]. However, in the dilute suspensions used in sedimentation analysis, the effect is usually smaller than errors inherent in the determination of η by conventional methods.

7.10 Calculation of terminal velocities in the transition region

The general equation relating the size of a sphere with its settling velocity may be written:

$$C_D \frac{D^2}{4} \rho_f \frac{u^2}{2} = \frac{\pi}{6} (\rho_s - \rho_f) g D^3$$

(equations 7.2 and 7.4).

For Reynolds' number $R_e < 0\cdot2$, equation (7.7) may be inserted in the above to yield Stokes' equation. At higher Reynolds' numbers the equation is only soluble using experimental values of C_D (figure 7.1).

Attempts at theoretical solutions of the relationship between C_D and R_e have been made. Oseen [12] partially allowed for inertial effects and obtained:

$$C_D = \frac{24}{R_e} \left(1 + \frac{3}{16} R_e\right). \tag{7.22}$$

This equation is more complicated than Stokes, and in practice is found to be equally inaccurate, since the second term overcorrects Stokes' equation and gives a value of C_D as much in excess as Stokes is too low.

Proudman and Pearson [13] pointed out that Oseen's solution could only be used to justify Stokes' law and not as a first-order correction. They obtain as a first-order correction:

$$C_D = \frac{24}{R_e} \left(1 + \frac{3}{16} R_e + \frac{9}{20} R_e^2 \ln R_e\right) \tag{7.23}$$

Goldstein [14] solved the equation without approximation and obtained:

$$C_D = \frac{24}{R_e} (1 + 1\cdot88 \times 10^{-1} R_e - 1\cdot48 \times 10^{-2} R_e^2 +$$

$$3\cdot46 \times 10^{-3} R_e^3 - 8\cdot75 \times 10^{-4} R_e^4). \tag{7.24}$$

Schillar and Nauman [15] fitted an empirical equation to the experimental values and obtained for $R_e < 700$:

$$C_D = \frac{24}{R_e} (1 + 0\cdot15 R_e^{0\cdot687}). \tag{7.25}$$

The data, as expressed above, is most inconvenient for computation since C_D and R_e contain both the velocity and diameter. Davies [16] has given a statistical analysis of the published data and expressed the result in the form R_e as a function of $C_D R_e^2$, which is suitable for calculating the velocity when the diameter is known:

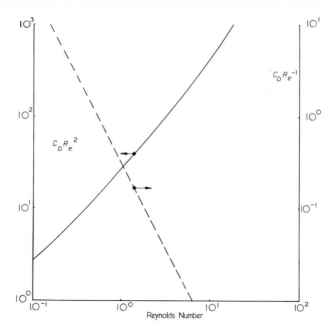

Fig. 7.2. Graphs of $C_D R_e^2$ against R_e (full line) and $C_D R_e^{-1}$ against R_e (broken line).

For $R_e < 0\cdot4$ or $C_D R_e^2 < 130$

$$R_e = \frac{C_D R_e^2}{24} - 2\cdot34 \times 10^{-4} (C_D R_e^2)^2 + 2\cdot02 \times 10^{-6} (C_D R_e^2)^3 -$$

$$- 6\cdot91 \times 10^{-9} (C_D R_e^2)^4. \tag{7.26}$$

For $3 < R_e < 10^4$, $100 < C_D R_e^2 < 4\cdot5 \times 10^7$

Table 7.2. Table of drag coefficients

1	2	3	4	5	6	7	8	9	10	11	12	13	14	15	16	17	18	19
R_e	C_D	$C_D R_e^2$	$C_D R_e^{-1}$	C_D for various $\alpha_{v,a}$ values				$\log R_e$	$\log C_D R_e^2$ for various $\alpha_{v,a}$ values					$\log C_D R_e^{-1}$ for various $\alpha_{v,a}$ values				
				0·4	0·3	0·2	0·1		$\alpha/6$	0·4	0·3	0·2	0·1	$\pi/6$	0·4	0·3	0·2	0·1
10^{-2}	2400	2.4×10^{-1}	2.4×10^{5}	3400	4400	6060	9300	$\bar{2}$·0000	$\bar{1}$·3802	$\bar{1}$·5315	$\bar{1}$·6435	$\bar{1}$·7825	$\bar{1}$·9685	5·3802	5·5315	5·6435	5·7825	5·9685
	1200	4.8×10^{-1}	6.0×10^{4}	1700	2200	3030	4650	$\bar{2}$·3010	$\bar{1}$·6812	$\bar{1}$·8325	$\bar{1}$·9445	0·0830	0·2695	4·7782	4·9294	5·0414	5·0414	5·3665
	484	1.21×10^{0}	9.78×10^{3}	680	880	1212	1860	$\bar{2}$·699	$\bar{2}$·0828	0·2304	0·3424	0·4814	0·6675	3·9903	4·1271	4·2455	4·3845	4·5705
10^{-1}	244	2.44×10^{0}	2.44×10^{3}	340	440	606	930	$\bar{1}$·000	0·3874	0·5315	0·6435	0·7825	0·9685	3·3874	3·5315	3·6435	3·7825	3·9685
	123	4.92×10^{0}	6.15×10^{2}	175	218	300	460	$\bar{1}$·301	0·6920	0·8325	0·9405	1·0792	1·2672	2·7889	2·9420	3·0374	3·1761	3·3617
	51·4	1.29×10^{1}	1.03×10^{2}	70	90	127	176	$\bar{1}$·699	1·1106	1·2430	1·3522	1·5017	1·6435	2·0128	2·1461	2·2553	2·4048	2·9445
10^{0}	27·2	2.72×10^{1}	2.72×10^{1}	36·3	50	69	93	0·000	1·4346	1·5599	1·6990	1·8388	1·9685	1·4346	1·5599	1·6990	1·8388	1·9685
	15·0	6.0×10^{1}	7.5×10^{0}	20·3	27·5	39	55	0·301	1·7782	1·9096	2·0414	2·1931	2·3424	0·8751	1·0065	1·1383	1·2900	1·4393
	7·12	1.78×10^{2}	1.424×10^{0}	10·4	13	18	28	0·699	2·2504	2·4150	2·5119	2·6532	2·8241	0·1535	0·3181	0·4150	0·5563	0·7482
10^{1}	4·35	4.35×10^{2}	4.35×10^{-1}	6·3	8·0	10·8	17·4	1·000	2·6385	2·7993	2·9031	3·0334	3·2405	$\bar{1}$·6385	$\bar{1}$·7993	$\bar{1}$·9031	0·0334	$\bar{1}$·2405
	2·74	1.10×10^{3}	1.37×10^{-1}	3·97	5·12	7·3	12·0	1·301	3·0414	3·2009	3·3114	3·4654	3·6812	$\bar{1}$·1367	$\bar{1}$·2978	$\bar{1}$·4082	$\bar{1}$·5623	$\bar{1}$·7782
	1·56	3.9×10^{3}	3.12×10^{-2}	2·40	3·2	4·45	8·6	1·699	3·5911	3·7782	3·9031	4·0882	4·3324	$\bar{2}$·4942	$\bar{2}$·6812	$\bar{2}$·8062	$\bar{2}$·9494	$\bar{1}$·2355
10^{2}	1·10	1.1×10^{4}	1.1×10^{-2}	1·70	2·35	3·7	7·7	2·000	4·0414	4·2304	4·3711	4·5682	4·8803	$\bar{2}$·0414	$\bar{2}$·2304	$\bar{2}$·3711	$\bar{2}$·5682	$\bar{2}$·8865
	0·808	3.23×10^{4}	4.04×10^{-3}	1·37	1·9	3·17	7·2	2·301	4·5092	4·1388	4·8573	5·1031	5·4594	$\bar{3}$·6064	$\bar{3}$·8357	$\bar{3}$·9777	$\bar{2}$·0354	$\bar{2}$·5563
	0·568	1.42×10^{5}	1.14×10^{-3}	1·12	1·48	2·68	7·1	2·699	5·1523	5·4472	5·5682	5·8261	5·2492	$\bar{3}$·0569	$\bar{3}$·3502	$\bar{3}$·4713	$\bar{3}$·7292	$\bar{2}$·1523
10^{3}	0·460	4.6×10^{5}	4.6×10^{-4}	1·00	1·42	2·40	7·0	3·000	5·6628	6·0000	6·1523	6·3802	6·8451	$\bar{4}$·6629	$\bar{4}$·0000	$\bar{4}$·1523	$\bar{3}$·3802	$\bar{3}$·8451
	0·420	1.68×10^{6}	2.1×10^{-4}															
	0·410	1.03×10^{7}	8.2×10^{-5}															
10^{4}	0·42	1.8×10^{8}	4.2×10^{-5}															
	0·45	1.2×10^{8}	2.25×10^{-5}															
	0·48	4.8×10^{9}	9.6×10^{-6}															
10^{5}	0·48	1.76×10^{9}	4.8×10^{-6}															
	0·44	5×10^{10}	4.0×10^{-7}															
	0·20		2.2×10^{-7}															
10^{6}	0·22	2.2×10^{11}	2.2×10^{-7}															

$$C_D R_e^2 = \frac{4(\rho_s - \rho_f)\rho_f g}{3\eta^2} D^3; \quad C_D R_e^{-1} = \frac{4(\rho_s - \rho_f)g}{3\rho_f \mu^3}; \quad V = \alpha_{v,a} d_a^3$$

$$\log R_e = -1\cdot29536 + 0\cdot986 \log (C_D R_e^2) - 4\cdot6677 \times 10^{-2} \log$$

$$(C_D R_e^2)^2 + 1\cdot1235 \times 10^{-3} \log (C_D R_e^2)^3. \tag{7.27}$$

A method for simplifying the calculation was proposed by Heywood [17], who presented the experimental data in tabular form. These data were embodied in tables presenting $C_D R_e^2$ in terms of $R_e C_D^{-1}$ and vice versa. Since the former expression is independent of velocity and the latter is independent of particle diameter, the velocity may be determined for a particle of known diameter and the diameter determined for a known settling velocity.

Heywood also presented data for non-spherical particles in the form of correction tables for four values of the volume-shape coefficient ($\alpha_{v, a}$) from microscopic measurement of particle projected areas.

The particle volume V is related to the projected area diameter d_a by the equation

$$V = \alpha_{v, a} d_a^3 \tag{7.28}$$

$$\left(\alpha_{v, a} = \frac{\pi}{6} \text{ for spherical particles}\right).$$

It is more convenient to present Heywood's data in the form shown in table 7.2. If settling velocities are required for spheres of known diameter, $C_D R_e^2$ is plotted against R_e on logarithmic paper and the velocities are derived from the graph (figure 7.2). If the converse is required, a graph of $C_D R_e^{-1}$ against R_e is plotted on logarithmic paper.

Example

Calculate the terminal velocity of a spherical particle of diameter 300 μm, density 2650 Kg m^{-3} falling in water at 150°C, from equations (7.2, 7.3 and 7.4)

$$C_D R_e^2 = \frac{4}{3} \frac{\rho_f (\rho_s - \rho_f)}{\eta^2} g D^3:$$

$$C_D R_e^2 = 448.$$

From figure 7.2, $R_e = 10\cdot2$.   *Data*

Hence: $D = 3 \times 10^{-4}$

$$u = \frac{\eta}{\rho_f D} \times 10\cdot2 \qquad\qquad \rho_s = 2650 \text{ g m}^{-3}$$

$$u = 3\cdot88 \text{ cm s}^{-1} \qquad\qquad \rho_f = 1000 \text{ g m}^{-3}$$

$$\eta = 0\cdot00114 \text{ Ns m}^{-2}$$

$$g = 9\cdot81 \text{ m s}^{-1}$$

An alternative to plotting the data is to use the tabulated values of $\log C_D R_e^2$ and $\log R_e$ (table 7.2, columns 10 and 9):

when $C_D R_e^2 = 448 \log C_D R_e^2 = 2\cdot651.$

From table 7.3:

Table 7.3

$\log R_e$	$\log C_D R_e^2$
1·301	3·0414
1·000	2·6385

Interpolating, when $\log C_D R_e^2 = 2\cdot651$, $\log R_e - 1\cdot0093$.

Hence $R_e = 10\cdot22$, giving $u = 3\cdot89$ cm s^{-1}.

7.11 The turbulent flow region

For $R_e > 500$, $C_D = 0\cdot44$ and is roughly constant. For low Reynolds' number, the drag is due mainly to viscous forces and the streamlines about a settling particle are all smooth curves. With increasing Reynolds' number, the boundary layer begins to detach itself from the rear of the particle and form vortices, figure 7.3(a). Further increase in R_e causes the vortices to increase in size and move further downstream, figure 7.3(b); at very high Reynolds' numbers, the wake becomes fully turbulent and the vortices break up and new vortices are formed, figure 7.3(c).

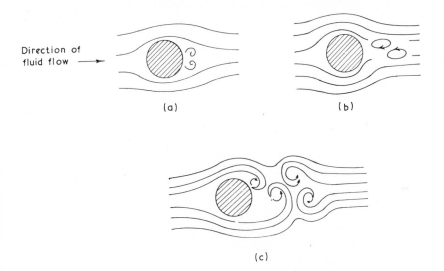

Fig. 7.3. Formation of vortices behind a spherical particle as the relative velocity between the fluid and the particle increases.

This effect may be demonstrated as follows:
A table-tennis ball held just under the surface of a container of water will, on release, rise to a much greater height than a ball initially held several inches below the surface.

Since the momentum carried by the balls on breaking the surface is much greater in the latter case, one would expect this ball to rise highest.

The explanation is that the mass of the ball is much greater in the latter case since it includes its associated vortices. Due to the low velocity the vortices have not formed in the first case.

7.12 Non-rigid spheres

Non-rigid particles, e.g. liquid droplets, will deform in such a way that the drag is reduced [2, p. 129]. The diameter calculated from the terminal velocity D_{st} will, therefore, be less than the true diameter D. It has been shown that the drag:

$$F_D = 3\pi D\eta_2 \, u \left\{ \frac{3\eta_1 + 2\eta_2}{3\eta_1 + 3\eta_2} \right\} \tag{7.29}$$

where η_1 and η_2 are the viscosities of the drop and fluid respectively.

For the case of a gaseous bubble rising slowly through a liquid, at a Reynolds' number in the Stokes' region, $\eta_1 \ll \eta_2$, and thus:

$$F_D = 2\pi D\eta u.$$

This result is, in fact, identical to that for a solid sphere at whose surface perfect slip occurs.

Comparing with Stokes' equation gives, for a sphere of diameter D,

$$D_{st}^2 = D^2 \left\{ \frac{3\eta_1 + 3\eta_2}{3\eta_1 + 2\eta_2} \right\} \tag{7.30}$$

For a raindrop falling in air; $\eta_1 = 1000 \times 10^{-6} \text{ Ns m}^{-2}$

$$\eta_2 = 180 \times 10^{-6} \text{ Ns m}^{-2}$$

$$D_{st} = 1 \cdot 04 \, D.$$

Experimentally, small bubbles behave like solid spheres having terminal velocities closely approaching Stokes' which, according to Levich [18] may be attributed to impurities at the interface.

7.13 Non-spherical particles

7.13.1 Stokes' region

Homogeneous symmetrical particles can take up any orientation as they settle slowly in a fluid of infinite extent.

Spin-free terminal states in all orientations is attainable for ellipsoids of uniform density and bodies of revolution with fore- and aft-symmetry, but the terminal velocities of such particles will depend on their orientation. A set of identical particles can, therefore, have a range of terminal velocities. This range is, however, fairly limited. Heiss and Coull [19], for example, found that the ratio of maximum to minimum velocities for discs and cylinders was less than 2:1, even with a length diameter ratio of 10:1.

Particles which are symmetrical in the sense that the form of the body is similarly related to each of three mutually perpendicular coordinate planes, as for example, a sphere or cube, not only fall stably in any orientation, but fall vertically with the same velocity in any orientation.

Asymmetric particles, such as ellipsoids and discs, do not generally fall vertically, unless they are dropped with a principle axis of symmetry parallel to a gravity field, but tend to drift to the side.

Not all bodies are capable of attaining steady motion, with unsymmetrical bodies spiralling and wobbling may occur.

For an oblate spheroid [8, p. 144] of eccentricity ϵ and equatorial diameter a, the maximum drag force is:

$$F_D = 3\pi a\eta \left(1 - \tfrac{1}{5}\epsilon\right) u \text{ for } \epsilon \longrightarrow 0. \tag{7.31}$$

For a sphere of equal volume as the above oblate spheroid:

$$F_D = 3\pi a\eta \left(1 - \tfrac{1}{3}\epsilon\right) u.$$

Hence a sphere of equal volume has a smaller resistance than the spheroid and the same can be shown to hold for a sphere of equal surface.

Happel and Brenner [2, p. 156] also determine the correction to Stokes' law for a prolate spheroid settling with its axis of revolution parallel to the direction of motion, and show that when the major diameter a greatly exceeds the equatorial diameter b, the spheroid behaves as a long thin rod.

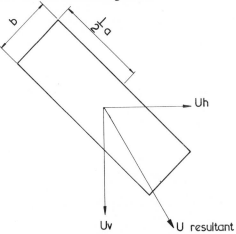

Fig. 7.4. Direction of motion of a disc settling in a fluid.

For this limiting case:

$$F_D = \frac{2\pi a\eta u}{(\ln a/b + 0.1935)}. \tag{7.32}$$

Because of the logarithmic term the resistance changes but slowly with the ratio (a/b).

A thin circular disc of diameter a, thickness b [2, p. 204], will have components of velocity, horizontally $u_h = \dfrac{\pi a b g}{128} \Delta\rho \sin 2\phi$

$$\text{vertically } u_v = \frac{\pi a b g}{128} \Delta\rho \, (5 - \cos 2\phi) \tag{7.33}$$

where ϕ is the angle between the normal to the plane of the disc and the vertical (figure 7.2).

If β is the angle between the downward vertical and the direction or motion of the disc, then:

$$\tan \beta = \frac{\sin 2\phi}{5 - \cos 2\phi}$$

The angle is a maximum when the disc orientation is:

$$\phi = 39 \cdot 2°$$

$$\beta = 11 \cdot 5°$$

corresponding to a maximum ratio of horizontal to vertical velocities of 0·204.

When $\phi = 0$, the disc will fall with its face horizontal.

$$F_D = 8\eta a u . \tag{7.34}$$

When $\phi = 90°$ the disc will fall edge on and

$$F_D = \tfrac{16}{3} \eta a u \tag{7.35}$$

averaging over all orientations:

$$F_D = 6\eta a u \tag{7.36}$$

with $b = 0 \cdot 1 a$, the value of the constants changes only slightly (e.g. the constant in equation (7.34) increases by about 0·4%).

These equations are similar to the Stokes' equation ($F_D = 3\pi d_a \eta u$) with the drag diameter, d_a, of the same order as the disc diameter.

Pettyjohn and Christiansen [20] made an extensive experimental study of isometric particles and proposed the following relationship:

$$d_{st} = d_v^2 \times 0 \cdot 843 \log \frac{\psi}{0 \cdot 065} \tag{7.37}$$

where ψ, the sphericity, is the ratio of the surface area of a sphere of the same volume as the particle to the surface area of the particle.

$$= d_v^2 / d_s^2 \tag{7.38}$$

Hawksley [3] showed that this was equivalent to stating that the drag diameter closely approximates to the surface diameter.

For the Stokes' region, the modified form of equation (7.6) is :

$$3\pi d_d \eta u_{st} = \frac{\pi}{6}(\rho_s - \rho_f)g d_v^3$$

giving

$$d_{st} = \sqrt{\frac{18\eta u_{st}}{(\rho_s - \rho_f)g}} \qquad (7.39)$$

where

$$d_{st}^2 = \frac{d_v^3}{d_d} \qquad (7.40)$$

d_f, the free falling diameter, is defined as the diameter of a sphere having the same free falling speed as the particle in a fluid of the same density and viscosity.

d_{st}, the Stokes' diameter, is defined as the free falling diameter in the laminar flow region ($R_e < 0.2$).

d_v, the volume diameter, is defined as the diameter of the sphere having the same volume as the particle.

Since the drag diameter is otherwise indeterminable, it is usual in practice to assume that in the Stokes' region $d_d = d_s$. This is found to hold at very low Reynolds number but as the Reynolds' number increases $d_d > d_s$.

7.13.2 *The Transition Region*

In the transition region particles fall with their largest cross-sectional area horizontal according to a report by Davies [5].

Hawksley (3) proposed that the C_D v R_e relation can be used provided the following definitions are employed.

$$C_D = \frac{4}{3}\left(\frac{\rho_s - \rho_f}{\rho_f}\right)\frac{d_v g}{u_m^2} \qquad (7.41)$$

$$R_e = \frac{1}{\sqrt{\psi}}\frac{u d_v \rho_f}{\eta} \qquad (7.42)$$

In figure 7.5 the friction factor C_D is plotted against Reynolds' number for different sphericities.

It is more convenient to extend Heywood's technique to non-spherical particles. Using data from figure 7.4, $C_D R_e^2$ may be evaluated in terms of the volume diameter d_v, and if this is known the free-falling velocity, u_f may be determined. Heywood determined u for particles of different projected area diameters d_a, as seen with a microscope.

The volume of such a particle is given by equation (7.28) as:

$$V = \alpha_{v, a} d_a^3.$$

Hence, modified values of Pd_a and u/Q were determined for $\alpha_{v, a} = 0.1, 0.2, 0.3, 0.4$. These data are plotted in table 7.2 in the form of $\log C_D R_e^2$ and $\log C_D R_e^{-1}$

which are applied as in the following worked example.

Worked example

In the earlier example the terminal velocity was found for a sphere of diameter 300 μm. Consider now a particle of projected area diameter 300 μm and volume-shape coefficient $\alpha_{v,\,a} = 0.25$.

As before, $\log C_D R_e^2 = 2.651$.

A section of table 7.2 is reproduced below (table 7.4).

Table 7.4

Column	9	11	12	Interpolating $\alpha_{v,\,a}$
	$\log R_e$	$\log C_D R_e^2$ $\alpha_{v,\,a}$		
Line		0·3	0·2	
9	0·699	2·5119	2·6532	2·5826
10	1·000	2·9031	2·0334	2·9683
Interpolating	0·706 ←			→ 2·651

Hence $R_e = 5.082$, giving

$u = 1.94$ cm s^{-1}, about half the velocity of a sphere with the same projected area diameter.

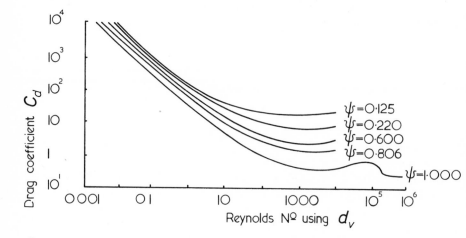

Fig. 7.5. Drag coefficient, *versus* Reynolds' number for particles of different sphericities.

7.14 Concentration effects

Most of the theoretical work on particle–particle interaction has been limited to the study of pairs of spheres. If the particles are close together, they may be considered as a single particle and a correction factor applied, provided their centre-to-centre distances are small compared to the distance from the container walls. As they move farther apart, their separate effects must be considered, and this must include the field reflections from the container walls. The net effect in the first case is a reduction of the drag on the individual particles so that they fall with a greater terminal velocity than for a single sphere. Happel [2, p. 27] plots the ratio of the drag force exerted on either sphere to that exerted on a single sphere, against L/D, the ratio of interparticle separation, (spheres touching when $L = D$), and against particle diameter for the cases of spheres falling (a) parallel, and (b) perpendicular to their line of centres. The results are shown in table 7.5:

Table 7.5. Ratios of drag force for pairs of spheres and single spheres for spheres falling (a) parallel, and (b) perpendicular to their line of centres, where L is the centre-to-centre separation of spheres of diameter D.

L/D	1	2	3	4	5	6	7
a	0·65	0·73	0·80	0·83	0·86	0·80	0·91
b	0·70	0·83	0·87	0·91	0·93	0·94	0·95

The particles will also rotate as shown in figure 7.6.

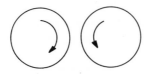

Fig. 7.6. Direction of rotation of two spheres falling close together.

For all practical purposes, this interaction becomes negligible for separations greater than about 10 diameters. For more than two spheres, interaction is more complex; assemblies of spheres will tend to diverge slowly, that is repel each other, due to the rotation effect. For three spheres in a vertical line, with the top two closer together so they fall more rapidly, the centre sphere will join forces with the lower sphere and, leaving its original companion behind, fall as a doublet (Kynch [21]). A large sphere falling in a vertical line close to a small sphere can pick it up so that it revolves as a satellite. Oseen [12] shows that, for two identical spheres falling in the same vertical line, the retardation on the trailing sphere is smaller than on the leading sphere so that they will move towards each other.

It is important to distinguish between two cases: an assembly of particles which completely fills the fluid, and a cluster of particles. The descent of a given particle creates a velocity field which tends to increase the velocity of nearby particles.

In opposition to this the downward motion of each particle must be compensated for by an equal volume upflow. If the particles are not uniformly distributed, the overall effect is a net increase in settling velocity, since the return flow will predominate in particle sparse regions. On the other hand, a system of uniformly distributed particles will be retarded to much the same extent.

A cluster of particles in an infinite fluid can be treated as a single large particle of appropriate density and reduced rigidity, that is as a liquid drop [3. p. 131]. A very large increase in settling rate could arise which is of importance at low concentrations.

For a dilute uniform assembly of uniform spheres of diameter D, the settling velocity is reduced by the factor:

$$\frac{u_h}{u} = \frac{1}{1 + 1 \cdot 3 \left(\dfrac{D}{L} \right)} \tag{7.43}$$

where u_h is the settling velocity of a particle in the presence of other particles, u is the free-falling velocity and L is the interparticle separation.

In a cubic assembly the concentration of particles by volume is

$$c = \frac{\pi}{6} \frac{D^3}{L}, \text{ hence:}$$

$$\frac{u_h}{u} = \frac{1}{1 + 1 \cdot 61 c^{\frac{1}{3}}} . \tag{7.44}$$

Famularo [22] investigated the problem further using a digital computer and found values of the constant for different assemblies as follows : cubic, $1 \cdot 91$; rhombohedral, $1 \cdot 79$; random, $1 \cdot 30$.

Burgers [23] considered a random assembly of particles and arrived at the expression:

$$\frac{u_h}{u} = \frac{1}{1 + 6 \cdot 88c} . \tag{7.45}$$

The numerical constant has been questioned by Hawksley [3, p.131], who suggests that in practice the particles will accelerate to an equilibrium arrangement with a reduced constant of $4 \cdot 5$. The form of the expression has also been criticized by Happel and Brenner [2, p. 376].

Maude and Whitmore [24] suggest that:

$$\frac{u_h}{u} = (1 - c)^\beta \tag{7.46}$$

where $4 \cdot 67 > \beta > 4 \cdot 2$ for $R_e < 1$ and β is a function of particle shape and size distribution. Richardson and Zaki [25] also propose a relationship similar to equation (7.46) with $\beta = 4 \cdot 65$.

Brinkman [26] proposes:

$$\frac{u_h}{u} = 1 + \frac{3}{4}(1-\epsilon)\left\{1 - \frac{8}{(1-\epsilon)} - 3\right\} \tag{7.47}$$

for $0.6 < \epsilon < 0.95$, where the porosity $\epsilon = 1 - c$.

Steinour [27] derived the following expression to fit his experimental data:

$$\frac{u_h}{u} = \epsilon^2 \, 10^{-2.82} \, (1-\epsilon). \tag{7.48}$$

If $0.3 < \epsilon < 0.7$:

$$\frac{u_h}{u} = 0.123 \frac{\epsilon^3}{(1-\epsilon)} \tag{7.49}$$

Powers [28] found that, in order to represent his experimental data, he had to modify the above equation by introducing a factor w_i, where w_i was included to compensate for the liquid dragged down by the settling particles.

Powers final equation was:

$$u_h = \frac{(\rho_s - \rho_f)g}{5\eta S_v^2} \frac{(\epsilon - w_i)^3}{(1-\epsilon)}.$$

For spherical particles $S_v = \frac{6}{D}$, hence:

$$\frac{u_h}{u} = 0.10 \frac{(\epsilon - w_i)^3}{(1-\epsilon)}. \tag{7.50}$$

Steinour defined the immobile liquid per unit of total volume as $a(1-\epsilon)$, where $a = \frac{w_i}{(1+w_i)}$. To correct equation (7.49), $a(1-\epsilon)$ must be subtracted from each value of ϵ giving:

$$\frac{u_h}{u} = 0.123 \frac{[\epsilon - d(1-\epsilon)]}{(1+a)(1-\epsilon)} \tag{7.51}$$

$$= 0.123 \frac{(1+a)^2}{(1-\epsilon)}\left(\epsilon - \frac{a}{1+a}\right)^3.$$

In terms of w_i, this becomes:

$$\frac{u_h}{u} = \frac{0.123 \, (\epsilon - w_i)^3}{(1-\epsilon)(1-w_i)^2}. \tag{7.52}$$

Similarly substitution into equation (7.53) gives:

$$\frac{u_h}{u} = \frac{(\epsilon - w_i)^2}{1 - w_i} 10^{-1.82} \frac{1-\epsilon}{1-w_i}. \tag{7.53}$$

7.15 Hindered settling

Several investigations have been carried out on the settling behaviour of spherical particles in a concentrated suspension [2, p.413] with best agreement with equations of the form (7.46). Equations of the form (7.47) indicate too high a concentration dependence of the rate of settling.

The highest settling rates observed were reported by Kaye and Boardman [29], and independently, using the same technique, by Johne [30]. Their results may be attributed to cluster formation which has been shown earlier to result in enhanced settling. For suspensions of spherical particles at volume concentrations less than about 1%, agreement between sedimentation analysis and other methods, e.g. microscopy, indicates that interaction between particles is relatively unimportant.

With polysized dispersions of irregularly-shaped particles, mutual interference can have a noticeable retarding effect, and it is usual to carry out analysis at as low a concentration as possible. A duplicate analysis at a higher concentration should not give a significantly coarser analysis. The highest concentration to be used is usually less than 1% *v/v*.

At higher concentrations particles tend to settle *en masse*, and the rate of fall of the interface (u_h) is given by equations of the form (7.43) to (7.53). With closely graded powder the interface is sharp becoming more diffuse for powders with a wide size range and in some cases forming more than one interface. The formation of more than one interface is due to fines being swept out as the bulk of the solids settle, forming a suspension of fines over the suspension of coarse and being, in its turn, subject to hindered settling.

If equation (7.46) holds, a plot of $\log u_h$ *versus* $\log \epsilon$ should yield a straight line of slope β with $u = u_h$, when $\epsilon = 1$ and u will give an average particle size when inserted into Stokes' equation ($\epsilon = 1 - c$).

If equation (7.48) holds, it is necessary to plot $\log u_h/\epsilon^2$ against $(1 - \epsilon)$ to determine u. Steinour found that equation (7.49) held for tapioca in oil and spherical glass beads in a 0·1% sodium hexametaphosphate solution. If a graph of $u_h (1 - \epsilon)^{\frac{1}{3}}$ against ϵ, equation (7.49), does not yield a straight line, it is necessary to apply equation (7.50) so that a graph of $u_h (1 - \epsilon)^{\frac{1}{3}}$ against ϵ will intercept the ϵ axis at w_i.

Both Steinour and Powers found that the more complex equation had to be used for non-spherical particles. This equation has also been used successfully by others [31, 32].

The general conclusions that can be made are that settling is extremely complex in the high concentration regions and several equations may apply according to the range of porosity considered and the presence or absence of flocculation. The determined particle size decreases with the addition of dispersing agents and it is suggested that the size so determined is floc-size [33]. The technique is a useful and simple one for determining average particle size, the equations being very similar to the permeametry equations.

References
[1] Lorentz, H. (1906), *Abh. u. Th. Phys.* **82**, 541.
[2] Happel, J., and Brenner, M. (1965), *Low Reynolds Number, Hydrodynamics,* Prentic Hall, (1951).
[3] Hawksley, P.G.W. (1951), *British Coal Utilization Research Association Bulletin,* **15**, 4.
[4] Cunningham, E. (1910), *Proc. R. Soc.,* **A83**, 357.
[5] Davies, C.N. (1954), *Proc. Phys. Soc.,* **57**, 259.
[6] Lapple, C.E. (1950), *Chemical Engineering Handbook,* (ed). J.M. Perry, McGraw-Hill, N.Y.
[7] Green, M.L., and Lane, W.R. (1957), *Particulate Clouds: Dusts, Smokes and Mists,* Spon, p. 58.
[8] Boothroyd, R.G. (1971), *Flowing Gas Solids Suspensions,* Chapman & Hall.
[9] Fuchs, N.A. (1964), *Mechanics of Aerosols, Trans.,* (ed.) C.N. Davies, Pergamon.
[10] Einstein, A. (1906), *Ann. Phys. Leipzig,* **19**, 289; (1911), **34**, 591.
[11] Kynch, C.J. (1954). *B. J. Appl. Phys.,* suppl. 3.
[12] Oseen, C.W. (1927), 'Neuere Methoden und Ergebrisse in der Hydrodynamik', *Leipzig Akademische Verlag.* 4, 166, 181, 182.
[13] Proudman, I., and Pearson, J. R. A. (1957), *J. Fluid. Mech.,* **2**, 237.
[14] Goldstein, S. (1938), *Modern Developments in Fluid Dynamics,* Clarendon Press.
[15] Schillar, L., and Nauman, A.Z. (1933), *Ver. Dtsch. Ing.,* **77**, 318.
[16] Davies, C.N. (1947), *Suppl. Trans. Instn. Chem. Engrs,* **25**, 39.
[17] Heywood, H. (1962), *Proc. Symp. on the Interaction between fluids and particles,* Inst. Chem. Engrs (London).
[18] Levich, V.G. (1962), *Physiochemical Hydrodynamics,* Prentice Hall, Englewood Cliffs, N.J.
[19] Heiss, F., and Coull, J., *Chem. Eng. Progress,* **48**, 3; (1952), 133–140.
[20] Pettyjohn, E.A., and Christiansen, E.B. (1968), *Chem. Eng. Prog.,* **44**, 157.
[21] Kynch, G.J. (1959), *J. Fluid. Mech.,* **5**, 193.
[22] Famularo, J. (1962), New York Univ. Engng. Sci. D. thesis,
[23] Burgers, J.M. (1941), *Proc. K. Ned. Aka. Wet.,* **44**, 1045; (1942), **45**, 9.
[24] Maude, A.D., and Whitemore, R.L. (1958), *Brit. J. Appl. Phys.,* **4**, 477.
[25] Richardson, J.F., and Zaki, W.N. (1954), *Chem. Eng. Sci.,* **3**, 65.
[26] Brinkman, H.C. (1947), *Appl. Sci. Res.,* **A1**, 27; (1948), **A1**, 81; (1949), **A2**, 190.
[27] Steinour, H.H. (1944), *Ind. Eng. Chem.,* **36**, 618, 840, 901.
[28] Powers, T.C. (1939), *Proc. Am. Concrete Inst.,* **35**, 465.
[29] Kaye, B.H., and Boardman, R.P. (1962), Proc. Symposium Interaction between Fluids and Particles, London, Bulletins *Inst. Chem. Engrs,*
[30] Johne, R. (1966), *Dissertation Karlsruhe 1965;* also *Zeitschr.* **38**, 428–30.
[31] Dollimore, D., and Real, G.R. (1962), *J. Appl. Chem.,* **12**, 445.
[32] Ramakrishna, V., and Rao, S.R. (1965), *J. Appl. Chem.,* **15**, 473.
[33] Dollimore, D. (1972), *J. Powder Technol.,*
[34] Rayleigh, Lord, (1892), *Phil. Mag.,* **5**, B4. 59.
[35] Stokes, Sir, G.G. (1891), *Mathematical and Physical Paper III,* Cambridge University Press.

8 *Dispersion of Powders*

8.1 Discussion

In many size analyses methods it is necessary to incorporate a powder into a liquid medium such that the particles are evenly dispersed. If the powder surface is lyophobic the powder is difficult to disperse, if it is lyophilic the powder disperses easily (for water dispersions the terms are hydrophobic and hydrophilic respectively. Dispersing agents are, therefore, added to wet the surface of lyophobic materials to make them lyophilic [16].

Starting with a dry solid and a liquid medium, several separate stages in the dispersion process may be distinguished. Firstly, there is the process of wetting which is defined as the replacement of the solid – air interface by a solid – liquid interface Secondly, there is the process of disaggregation of clusters of particles, and thirdly the process of dispersion stabilization.

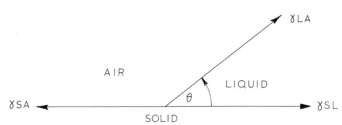

Fig. 8.1. The spreading of a liquid on the surface of a solid.

If a liquid is placed on a solid, it will spread if (see figure 8.1):

$$\gamma_{SA} \geqslant \gamma_{SL} + \gamma_{LA} \cos \theta \qquad (8.1)$$

where γ_{SL}, γ_{SA}, γ_{LA} are the interfacial tensions between the solid and the liquid, solid and air and liquid and air and θ is the angle of contact between the solid and the liquid. (γ_{SA} and γ_{LA} will rapidly fall to γ_{SV} and γ_{LV} as the solid surface becomes saturated with vapour, but for simplicity the former suffixes will be retained.)

The spreading coefficient is defined as:

$$S_{LS} = \gamma_{SA} - \gamma_{SL} - \gamma_{LA}. \qquad (8.2)$$

The liquid will spread on the solid if the spreading coefficient is positive:

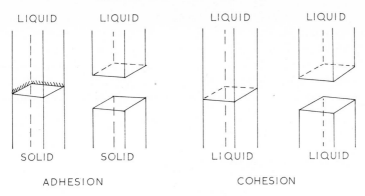

LIQUID   LIQUID   LIQUID   LIQUID

SOLID   SOLID   LIQUID   LIQUID

ADHESION   COHESION

Fig. 8.2. Work of adhesion and work of cohesion.

The work of adhesion is defined as the work necessary to separate one square centimetre of interface between two phases:

$$W_{SL} = \gamma_{SA} + \gamma_{LA} - \gamma_{SL}. \qquad (8.3)$$

The work of cohesion is defined as the work necessary to separate one square centimetre of one phase;

$$W_{LA} = 2\gamma_{LA}. \qquad (8.4)$$

Hence, the spreading coefficient may be defined as:

$$S_{LS} = W_{SL} - W_{LA} \qquad (8.5)$$

and, if positive, infers a greater affinity between the liquid and the solid than between the liquid's own molecules.

The energy of immersion is defined as the surface energy loss per unit area of surface on immersion:

$$W_i = \gamma_{SA} - \gamma_{SL}. \qquad (8.6)$$

Equations (8.1) and (8.3) may be combined to give:

$$W_A \geqslant \gamma_{LA} (1 + \cos \theta). \qquad (8.7)$$

The ease of displacement of air from the surface of a powder is thus enhanced if W_A is increased. This is frequently accomplished in aqueous systems by the use of surface-active agents to reduce the contact angle θ to zero if possible. Since, at equilibrium, from equation (8.1):

$$\cos \theta = \frac{\gamma_{SA} - \gamma_{SL}}{\gamma_{LA}}. \qquad (8.8)$$

The addition of a surface-active agent usually causes a reduction in γ_{LA}, and if absorbed a reduction in γ_{SL}. Both effects lead to better wetting. The change in γ_{SA}

is probably negligible in most cases so the dominating factor is γ_{LA}, the surface tension of the liquid phase.

The difficulty in the use of these equations in practice is the experimental one of determining θ for fine powders. Bartell and co-workers [5] developed a method in which a pressure was applied to prevent liquid from penetrating a plug of powder. The required pressure to prevent penetration is given by the Laplace equation:

$$\Delta P = \frac{2\gamma_{LA}\cos\theta}{r}.$$ (8.9)

For a liquid which wets the solid, one has:

$$\Delta P_0 = \frac{2\gamma_{LA}{}^0}{r}$$

so that:

$$\cos\theta = \frac{\Delta P}{\Delta P_0}\left(\frac{\gamma_{LA}{}^0}{\gamma_{LA}}\right).$$ (8.10)

The principle of the method is to obtain the effective capillary radius r using a non-wetting liquid and repeat the measurement with a wetting liquid.

This method is difficult to use and the following simpler method has been described [3]. The distance of penetration L in time t into a horizontal capillary, or in general when gravity may be neglected, is given by the Washburn equation [2]:

$$\frac{L^2}{t} = r\frac{\gamma_{LA}\cos\theta}{2\eta}$$ (8.11)

where η is the viscosity of the liquid.

For a packed bed of powder this equation becomes:

$$\frac{L^2}{t} = \frac{r}{(K^2)}\frac{\gamma_{LA}\cos\theta}{2\eta}$$ (8.12)

where the bracketed term is an unknown factor dependent on the packing. If several liquid are used with the same powder, uniform high values of $(r/K^2)\cos\theta$ are found and it is assumed that these correspond to $\cos\theta = 1$. This factor is then used to obtain values of θ with other liquids.

The next stage in the dispersion process is the breakdown of aggregates and agglomerates after wetting. For easily wetted material penetration of liquid into the voids between particles may provide sufficient force to bring about disintegration. Often, however, mechanical energy is required and this is usually introduced by spatulation or stirring, though the use of ultrasonics is now quite widely practised.

The stability of a wetted, dispersed system depends upon the forces between particles. The random motion of the particles brings them into close contact and under certain circumstances causes them to flocculate. The frequency of collision depends upon the concentration, viscosity and temperature. Whether two approaching particles will combine or not depends on the potential barrier between them.

The potential energy can be considered to consist of two terms, the attractive, due to London-van der Waal's force and the repulsive, due to the electrical double layers which exist around particles; this double layer consists of an inner layer of ions at the surface of the particle and a cloud of counter-ions surrounding it. The interaction curve (figure 8.3) follows an exponential decay pattern; the sum for the attraction A and repulsion R is the total energy curve B and if the maximum has an energy of more than $15\,KT$ the system is stable [4]. With large particles, the net potential energy curve may show a minimum at appreciable distances of separation. This concept cannot account for the action shown by many non-ionic, surface-active agents, and in these cases it has been suggested that the size of the agent could lead to a repulsion due to the steric nature of the absorbed layer; i.e. the molecules extend so far out into the media that two approaching particles do not get close enough to flocculate.

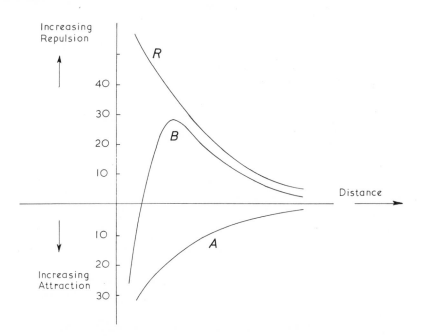

Fig. 8.3. Potential energy (net) curve against distance from particle: A, force of attraction, R, force of repulsion, B, resultant force.

In non-aqueous media of low dielectric constant ionic charge stabilization is unlikely to be very important. In such cases stabilization depends on steric or entropic repulsion and polymeric agents are preferred against the long-chain paraffinic types which are so successful in aqueous media.

In practice it is necessary to decide whether an agent is required to wet out the solid so that it will disperse in the liquid concerned or whether the problem is one of stabilization. The minimum of wetting agent to ensure adequate dispersion is added. Any combination which causes foaming should be rejected since this may cause separation of the finer particles. If this is not feasible, an anti-foaming agent may be used. The present state of the art is such that dispersing agents are chosen almost at random, but with some knowledge of the surface chemistry involved [14].

A simple test for wetting efficiency is to make up suspensions using the same concentration of powder but different agents and allow the suspension to settle out. About a gram of powder is mixed with the dispersing liquid in a 10 ml container. Slow settling, a clear interface between the clear liquid and turbid lower layers and small depth of sediment indicate the best agent or, if several concentrations of the same agent are being tested, the best concentration [6, 7]. It is important that no vibration be imparted to the containers during settlement which may take several hours. Another test for the degree of flocculation of a paste is to measure the difference between the smear and flow points. The test is made by adding known quantities of dispersing medium to a known weight of the powder and working it in with a spatula. The difference is noted between the amount required for the powder to smear and to flow, the more dispersed the sample the smaller the difference [9].

It has been found that for pigments in solvents a high dielectric constant leads to a more dispersed system. In general, polar liquids disperse polar solids and non-polar liquid disperse non-polar solids. For polar solids dispersed in non-polar liquids, it is possible to use the polarity of the surface as a means of anchoring a stabilizing molecule to the surface. The effectiveness is characterized by the heat of wetting which may be determined by calorimetry.

A guide to the choice of dispersing medium and dispersing agents is given in tables 8.1 and 8.2. It is also necessary to adjust the density and viscosity of the medium to suit the density and particle size of the powder so that settling is within the Stokes' region. These values are best taken from a comprehensive standard book such as Perry [18].

Effectiveness of deflocculants in dilute suspensions may be studied by light absorption using the photosedimentometer [10]. If the optical density of an agitated suspension falls with time this is an indication of either flocculation or dissolution, whereas an increasing optical density indicates breakdown of flocs. Neither of these situations is tolerable.

Dilute suspensions in electrolytes may be studied with a Coulter counter. It is frequently found using the instrument that the count level at the lower sizes decreases with time, and this may usually be attributed to flocculation or dissolution (this loss is usually not marked enough to significantly effect the resulting particle size analysis). A problem that arises with this technique is that the dispersing liquid is an electrolyte and one would expect that this would reduce the energy barriers and decrease the stability of the system [15].

The final criterion is the practical test; if size analyses are carried out with two systems, the one showing the finest distribution will be more accurate than the other. This, however, is not conclusive since both systems may have some flocculation.

One test which is often suggested is to examine, by transmission microscopy, a drop of suspension placed on a microscope slide. Although a visual examination of particles in order to determine their approximate size is always recommended, a false impression may be obtained as to their state of dispersion due to the wide difference in environment between this testing situation and the actual analysis.

Many wetting agents are hygroscopic, hence the dried residue should be cooled in a desiccator and contact with the atmosphere during weighing reduced to a minimum. It is suggested, though there is very little evidence in support, that some wetting agents are preferentially absorbed onto finer powders leading to errors in powder concentration derived from the weight of dried residue.

8.2 Density determination

One of the parameters that is often required for particle size analysis is particle density. The usual method for determining this physical constant has been by liquid pyknometer or specific gravity bottle and full details of the relevant techniques may be found in B.S.733: 1952. This method has, to a large extent, been supplanted by the use of gas pyknometers [11-13] with these instruments the gas displaced by a known weight of solids is determined, yielding results which are accurate and rapid.

The values obtained by this method are in agreement with values obtained by liquid pyknometer methods, provided the solids are non-porous. Liquid will not normally enter the pores of porous solids unless they have been degassed immediately prior to immersion in the liquid, since the air trapped in the pores will resist liquid penetration [1, p.359]. Hence, porous particles have two densities, the envelope density and true density, and in a sedimentation analysis the determined size will be dependent on which density is used.

A pyknometric method [17] has been described which is particularly suitable for fine powders and utilizes a centrifugal force to effect rapid sedimentation of the fines and to provide a realistic degree of de-aeration.

8.3 Viscosity

The viscosity of the suspending media should have a value that will fulfil the following conditions:

    (1) The largest particle in the suspension should settle under laminar flow conditions, i.e. the Reynolds' number should be less than 0·2.

    (2) The free-falling velocity of the largest particle should be restricted so that it takes at least one minute for it to reach the measurement zone.

For the first condition, the relationship between Stokes' diameter and viscosity is given by inserting a value of 0·2 for the Reynolds' number,

$$R_e = \frac{\rho_f v d}{\eta} \quad \text{in Stokes' equation:}$$

$$d^3{}_{st} = \frac{3\cdot6\,\eta^2}{(\rho_s - \rho_f)\rho_f g}. \tag{8.13}$$

For a particle of density $\rho_s = 2\cdot7$ g ml^{-1} in a suspending media of density $\rho_f = 1\cdot0$ g ml^{-1}, the required viscosity for a particle of size 75 μm is therefore 0·014 poise.

Stokes' law does not apply when the Reynolds' number exceeds 0·2, and the diameters calculated using Stokes' equation are smaller than the correct values. This is due to flow being no longer laminar, eddies are set up behind the particle which retard its motion. Further, it is generally accepted that under streamline conditions particles fall in random orientation, whereas particles orientate themselves for maximum drag under turbulent motion conditions. Corrections may be applied using Heywood's table. Alternatively, for comparison purposes, a frequency may be plotted or tabulated against free-falling velocity.

8.4 Sedimentation systems

The usual concentration of wetting agent used is 0·1% weight by volume.

Table 8.1. List of wetting and dispersing agents

A,	sodium linoleate
B,	potassium silicate
C,	sodium hexametaphosphate (calgon)
D,	dispersal T
E,	potassium citrate
F,	calcium chloride (0·05 M/L)
G,	trisodium phosphate
H,	aerosol OT 1%
I,	gallotannic acid
J,	sodium tartrate
L,	sodium silicate
M,	trinatrium phosphate
N,	perminal BX
O,	sodium oxolate
P,	sodium pyrophosphate
R,	oleic acid
S,	sodium citrate
T,	tannic acid
U,	sodium carbonate
V,	potassium chloride 0·001M
W,	sodium hydroxide
X,	xylene
Y,	Daxad 23 0·02%
	Cetrimide B.P. (cetyl − trimethyl − ammonium − bromide) cationic [17]
β,	Dispersal T (sodium − methylene − dimaphthalene − sulphonate) anionic
θ,	Lissapol N.X. (alkylphenol/ethylene oxide condensate) non-ionic
	Nonidet P40 (alkylphenol/ethylene oxide condensate) non-ionic

Table 8.2. Dispersing solutions for powders

Material	Liquid	Wetting agent
Alkali salts	cyclohexanol	—
Alumina	n-butanal, n-butylamine,	
	linseed oil	xylene
Aluminium	cyclohexanol	—
	carbon tetrachloride	—
	water	C, J or O
	dilute hydrochloric acid	
	(pH adjusted to 3)	
Aluminium oxide	water	P
Anthracite	water	M or N
Antimony trioxide	water	P or C
Arsenates	water	P
Arsenious oxide	octyl alcohol	—
	cyclohexanol	—
	liquid paraffin	2% fatty acid
Ash	water	P
Barium carbonate	methyl alcohol	—
	methanol	—
Barium strontium		
carbonate	water — ethyl alcohol mixture	—
Barium sulphate	water	C or θ
	water — methanol mixture	—
Barytes	water	C or P
Beryl	water	L or C
Blast-furnace slag	water	C
Bronze powder	cyclohexanol	—
Brown coal	cyclohexanol + 10% methanol	—
	phthalsaurediatheylester	
Cadmium sulphide	water	P
	ethylene glycol	—
Calcium arsenate	1:1, ethyl alcohol: water	—
Calcium carbonate	water	P, D or X
	xylene	—
Calcium compounds	water	C
Calcium oxide	ethylene glycol	—
Calcium phosphate	water	P
Calomel	cyclohexanol	
Carbon black	water	H, I or T
Carborundum	water	C
Cellulose powder	benzene	M
Cement	methyl alcohol saturated	
	with glycerol	—
	ethylene glycol	F
	ethyl alcohol	F
	kerosene	R

Table 8.2. (Cont.)

Material	Liquid	Wetting agent
	benzene	—
	isopropanol	—
	absolute alcohol	F (anhydrous)
	methyl alcohol	P
	butyl alcohol	—
Ceramic grog	water	C
Cerussite	water	C
Chalk	water	L
	water	E
	acetone	—
	petroleum	—
Chalk (precipitated)	isopropanol	—
Charcoal	water	O, A or P
	aqueous ammonia ($\rho = 0.91$, $5.8^v/_v\%$)	
Chromium oxide	water	P
Chromium pigment	water	P
Chromium powder	isobutyl alcohol	—
Clay china	water	G
Coal	water	F
	ethyl alcohol	—
	cyclohexanol	—
	1·1, cyclohexanol: methyl alcohol	—
Cobalt	95% ethyl alcohol in water	—
	isobutyl alcohol	—
	diethylester of phthalic acid	—
Coke	water	N or A
	isobutyl alcohol	—
	alcohol	F
	1:1, ethylene glycol: ethyl alcohol	F
Haematite	water	—
Hydrated lime	ethyl alcohol	—
	isopropanol	—
Ilmenite	water	—
Iron and iron alloys	rape oil and acetone	—
	1:1, soya bean oil + acetone	—
Kaolin	water	L or P
	water + few drops of ammonia	
Kieselguhr	water	—
Lead	acetone	—
	water	—
	cyclohexanol	—
	isoamylalcohol	—
Lead cyanamide	water	P
Lead monoxide	xylene	—

Table 8.2. (Cont.)

Material	Liquid	Wetting agent
Lead oxide	water	P
Lead pigments	water	P
Lignite	cyclohexanol + 10% methanol	—
	isobutyl alcohol	
	diethyl ester or phthalic acid	
Limestone	water	(L+ P) or (P+ S)
	25% aqueous glycerol	—
Lithopone	water	D
	33% aqueous glycerol	—
Magnesite	ethyleneglycol	
Magnetite	water/ethyl alcohol/methyl alcohol/	
	nitrobenzene	
Manganese	isobutyl alcohol	—
Manganese dioxide	water	P
Methyl methacrylate	water	—
Molybdenum	ethyl alcohol	—
	acetone	—
	glycerol	—
	aqueous glycerol	—
Moulding sand	water	W
Nickel	rape oil + acetone	—
	aqueous glycerol	—
	cyclohexanol + 10% acetone	—
Organic powders	isobutyl alcohol and diethyl	
	phthalate mixtures	—
	octyl alcohol	—
	isoamyl alcohol	—
Phosphate ores	water	C
Phosphorus	water	B or B + Y
Pigments	water	P
	isopropanol	—
Plaster	water	E
	alcohol − glycol	E
Polyvinyl acetate	water	C
Polyvinyl chloride	water	T
Pulp	water	L
Pumicite	water	
Quartz	water	—
Red lead	paint prepared in linseed oil	
	and dispersed in white spirit	
	(aluminium stearate)	
Red phosphor	4% conc. in methylated spirits	
Sand	water	L
	butyl phthalate + alcohol	—
Shales	alcohol	F

Table 8.2. (Cont.)

Material	Liquid	Wetting agent
Silica	water	C, O or P
	1:1, water and xylene	—
	water + alcohol	—
Silicates	water	P
Sillimanite	1:1, water + ethyl alcohol	—
	1:1, water + ethyl alcohol	—
	water	P
Slag (cement)	isopropanol	—
	water	—
Soils and clays	water	O
	butyl phethalate + alcohol	—
Starch	isobutyl alcohol	—
	diethyl ester of phthalie acid	—
	isobutyl alcohol + diethyl phthalate	—
Steel powder	water	θ
Sugar	isobutyl alcohol	—
	diethyl ester of phthalic acid	—
	isoamyl alcohol	—
Sulphides	ethyline glycol	—
Talcum	water	C
Thorium	33% aqueous glycerol	—
Tin	butyl alcohol	or C
Titanium dioxide	water	C
	xylene, linseed oil	
Tricalcium phosphate	water	—
Tungsten	glycerol	—
	acetone + rape oil	—
	ethyl alcohol	—
Tungsten ores	water	P
Tungsten carbide	ethylene glycol	—
	oil	—
Uranium oxides	aqueous glycerol	—
	isobutyl alcohol	—
	water	C
Zinc	ethyl alcohol	
	butyl alcohol	
	acetone	
Zinc oxide	water	C or P
Zirconium	0·0001N hydrochloric acid in methyl alcohol	—
	isobutyl alcohol	—
Zirconium oxide	water	C or R

8.5 Densities and viscosities of some aqueous solutions

Aqueous glycerol solutions

Some relationships between temperature T (°C), density (ρ) g ml^{-1}, viscosity η centipoise and fractional volume concentration of glycerol C are given below:

$$T = 20°C \qquad \rho = 1 + 0.26C; \text{ for all } C. \tag{8.14}$$
$$\eta = 1.0 + 4.4C; 0 < C < 0.25. \tag{8.15}$$
$$\eta = 24.0 - 139.4C + 207.2C^2; 0.25 < C < 0.75. \tag{8.16}$$
$$C = 0.50 \qquad \eta = 29.1 - 1.86T + 0.036T^2$$
$$20 < T < 25. \tag{8.17}$$
$$C = 0.75 \qquad \eta = 99.5 - 5T + 0.08T^2; 15 < T < 25. \tag{8.18}$$

Change in density with temperature may be neglected over limited temperature ranges. For example, $\rho = 1.195 \pm \hat{0}.002$ for T = 20 ± 5,

$$C = 0.75. \tag{8.19}$$

From equation (8.16) it can be seen that

$$\frac{\Delta\eta}{\eta} = \frac{(414C - 139)\,\Delta C}{24 - 139.4C + 207.2C^2}.$$

For $C = 0.75$

$$\frac{\Delta\eta}{\eta} = \frac{0.171\,\Delta C}{36} = \frac{4.7\,\Delta C\%}{}.$$

Therefore, at $C = 0.75$ an error of $\Delta C = 1\%$ leads to a 4.7% error in viscosity, hence a 2.2% error in Stokes' diameter.

Alcohol – Water
$$0.30 < C < 0.80 \qquad 30\rho = 31.2 - 8.3C + C^2$$
$$\eta = 1.2 + 7.4C - 8C^2.$$

Ethylene glycol – water
$$0.25 < C < 0.75 \qquad \rho = 1 + 0.12C$$
$$\eta = 2 - 4.2C + 13.6C^2.$$

References

[1] Adamson, A.W. (1963), *Physical Chemistry of Surfaces*, Wiley, N.Y.
[2] Washburn, E.D. (1921), *Phys. Rev.* **17**, 374.
[3] Crowl, V.T., and Wooldridge, W.D.S. (1967), *Wetting*, SCI Monograph No. 25, 200.
[4] Crowl, V.T. (1967), *Agriments*, (ed.) D. Patterson, Elsevier, p.192.
[5] Bartell, F.E., and Walton, C.W. (1934), *J. Phys. Chem.*, **38**, 503.
[6] Rossi, C., and Baldocci, R. (1951), *J. Appl. Chem.*, **1**, 446,
[7] Buzagh, A. von (1937), *Colloid Systems*.
[8] Herdan, G. (1960), *Small Particle Statistics*, Butterworths, p.347.
[9] B.S. 3406: (1963), Part 2, p.39.

[10] Koglin, B. (1969), Turbidimetric investigation of the activity of surface active agents in dispersing suspension. private communication: Lerstuhl für Mechanische Verfahrenstechnik, Universität Karlsruhe (TH), W. Germany.

[11] Galatchi, G.L. (1969), *Stud. Cercet. Fiz.*, **21**, 7.

[12] Dollimore, D., *et al.* (1970), *J. Phys. E.*, **3**, 465 − 6.

[13] Keng, E.Y.H. (1970), *Powder Technol.*, **3**, 3, 179 − 80.

[14] Bryant, D.P. (1968), *Proc. Soc. Analyt. Chem.*, **5**, 8, 165 − 6.

[15] Groves, M.J., *ibid.*, 166 − 8.

[16] Parfitt, G. (1973), *Dispersion of Powders in Liquids*, Applied Science Publishers.

[17] Burt, M.W.G., Fewtrell, C.A., and Wharton, R.A. (1973), *Powder Technol.*, **8**, 223 − 30.

[18] Perry, J.H. (1963), *Chemical Engineers' Handbook*, McGraw-Hill.

9 Incremental Methods of Sedimentation Size Analysis

9.1 Basic theory

The particle size distribution of a fine powder may be determined by examining a sedimenting suspension of the powder. The powder may be introduced as a thin layer on top of a column of clear liquid, the two layer technique; or it may be uniformly dispersed in the liquid, the homogeneous suspension technique. In the incremental method of size analysis by sedimentation, changes with time in the concentration or density of the suspension at known depths are determined and from these the size distribution may be found. In the cumulative method, the rate at which the powder is settling out of suspension is determined and, from a knowledge of this, the size distribution may be found. Incremental methods may be divided into fixed time and fixed depth methods, the latter being more popular, although a combination is sometimes used.

9.1.1 Variation in concentration within a settling suspension

Let a mass $m_s = \rho_s v_s$ of a solid be dispersed in a mass $m_f = \rho_f v_f$ of fluid, ρ and v being density and volume respectively.

Initially, the concentration throughout the suspension will be uniform and equal to:

$$C(h, 0) = \frac{\text{mass of solids}}{\text{volume of solids} + \text{volume of fluid}}$$

$$C(h, 0) = \frac{m_s}{v_s + v_f} \tag{9.1}$$

where $C(h, 0)$ is the concentration at depth h, time $t > 0$.

Consider a small horizontal element in the suspension at a depth h. At the commencement of sedimentation the particles leaving the element are exactly balanced by the particles entering it from above. When the largest particles, initially present at the surface of the suspension leave the element, there are no similar particles entering to replace them. Hence the concentration within the element falls and becomes equal to the concentration of particles smaller than D in the suspended phase, where D is the size of the particle which falls with a velocity h/t. The concentration of the suspension at depth h at time t may be written:

191

$$C(h, t) = \frac{m'_s}{v'_s + v_f} = \int_{D_{min}}^{D} F(D) \mathrm{d}D \qquad (9.2)$$

where m'_s is the mass and v'_s the volume of solids in a volume v_s of fluid at time t from commencement of sedimentation and at a depth h from the surface of the suspension. Hence:

$$C(h, 0) = \frac{m_s}{v_s + v_s} = \int_{D_{min}}^{D_{max}} F(D) \mathrm{d}D . \qquad (9.3)$$

From these three equations:

$$\frac{C(h, t)}{C(h, 0)} = \frac{m'_s}{m_s} = \frac{\int_{D_{min}}^{D} F(D) \mathrm{d}D}{\int_{D_{min}}^{D_{max}} F(D) \mathrm{d}D} . \qquad (9.4)$$

It has been assumed that the difference between v'_s and v_s is negligible compared with v_s.

Thus, if a graph of $100 \, C(h, t)/C(h, 0)$ is plotted against D, the resulting curve shows the cumulative percentage undersize by weight.

9.1.2 Relationship between density gradient and concentration

Let $\phi(h, t)$ be the density of the suspension at a depth h and at time t. Then:

$$\phi(h, t) = \frac{m'_s + m_f}{v'_s + v_s}$$

$$= \frac{\rho_s v'_s + \rho_f v_f}{v'_s + v_s}$$

$$= \frac{\rho_s(v'_s + v_s) + (\rho_s - \rho_f)v'_s}{v'_s + v_s}$$

$$= \rho_s + \frac{\rho_s - \rho_f}{\rho_s} \cdot \frac{m'_s}{v'_s + v_f}$$

$$= \rho_s + \frac{\rho_s - \rho_f}{\rho_s} \cdot C(h, t) .$$

Also

$$\phi(h, 0) = \rho_s + \frac{\rho_s - \rho_f}{\rho_s} C(h, 0) .$$

Therefore

$$\frac{C(h, t)}{C(h, 0)} = \phi = \frac{\phi(h, t) - \rho_f}{\phi(h, 0) - \rho_f} \qquad (9.5)$$

where ϕ is the fraction undersize D.

Thus a plot of $100 \times \dfrac{\phi(h, t) - \rho_f}{\phi(h, 0) - \rho_f}$ against D gives a cumulative percentage curve.

9.2 Resolution for incremental methods

Assuming Stokes' law to apply:

$$D^2 = k(h/t)$$

differentiating with respect to h:

$$2D(dD/dh) = k/t$$
$$= D^2/h$$
$$dD/dh = D/2h$$

or
$$dD/D = dh/2h . \tag{9.6}$$

The variation in size within an element of thickness dh, from the calculated Stokes' diameter is therefore $\pm \frac{1}{2}dD$ which equals $\pm \frac{1}{4}(D \cdot d/h)$.

States [1] defines the resolution for incremental techniques as the reciprocal of the variation in particle size in the sampling zone, i.e.

Resolution $1/dD = 2h/aD$ where $a = dh$ is the width of the sampling zone.

Heywood [2] points out that this is misleading since the relative size variation is the important factor. This is greatest for the hydrometer method, although the effect depends on the type of size distribution concerned.

Consider the following cases.

Table 9.1

h (cm)	dh (cm)	$\dfrac{dD}{D} = \dfrac{dh}{2h}$
10	10	0·5
20	2	0·05
5	0·2	0·02

The first case applies to the hydrometer method of analysis and, at a nominal Stokes' diameter of 50 μm, the size variation within the sampling zone is 25 μm. If the weight frequency of particles in the 50 to 62·5 μm range is equal to that in the 37·5 μm range, the effect is balanced out, otherwise a bias results. The general effect of such a bias is to mask peaks in a multimodal distribution.

Heywood carried out experimental work on the relationship between width of sampling zone and resolution and concludes that if the sampling zone is less than one-sixth of the mean depth, the practical error introduced is negligible. The hydrometer, in spite of the low resolution, gives reasonably accurate results for clay particles, but is not, in general, recommended for other types of powdered materials.

9.3 The pipette method

In the pipette method of particle size analysis, the concentration changes occurring within a settling suspension are followed by drawing off definite volumes by means of a pipette.

The method was described first in 1922 by Robinson [3], who used a normal laboratory pipette, and Jennings *et al.* [50], who used a pipette taken out downwards from the sedimentation vessel with a suction system consisting of nine tubes of which eight were bent outwards, four on each of two different radii. In 1923 Krauss [51] suggested a variable height system of three suction tubes closed at the bottom, each having six to eight horizontal bores. Koettgen [52] used a normal pipette with a bent top and recommended that the pipette should be rotated during the withdrawal of the sample. Köhn [53] used a pipette closed at the tip and with several horizontal holes. Lehmann [54] and Lorenz [55] in 1932 reported a pipette closed at the tip with four or six horizontal apertures.

Andreasen [4] in 1928 was the first to leave the pipette in the sedimentation vessel for the duration of the analysis. The apparatus described in 1930 by Andreasen and Lundberg [7] is the one in general use today [5, 6].

The question that arises is whether some of these complicated constructions are really necessary. By making certain assumptions, an estimate may be made of the magnitude of the various errors and the modifications required to reduce them to acceptable limits [53, 9]. Before discussing these a description of the basic equipment is given. The Andreasen equipment (figure 9.1) consists of a graduated sedimentation vessel (0 to 20cm) which holds between 500 and 600 ml when filled to the 20-cm mark. The stem of the pipette is fused to a ground glass socket which fits the neck of the sedimentation vessel, so that the stem is centrally positioned in the sedimentation vessel and its tip is level with the zero fiduciary mark. Above the socket is a two-way tap so that suspension may be drawn into a 10 ml container, which may then be emptied into a 25 ml beaker or centrifuge tube.

The recommended procedure is to take representative sample of powder to make up a volume concentration of between 0·5 and 1·0% by volume. The powder is made into a paste and then a slurry by the slow addition of dispersing liquid while the powder is being mixed with a spatula. At this stage, dispersing agent may be added, e.g. two or three drops of Nonidet P42. Other systems may be made up in bulk beforehand, e.g. 0·1% sodium hexametaphosphate in distilled water, and the mixing is done with this liquid. Further dispersing may be carried out in an ultrasonic bath. The suspension is washed into the sedimentation vessel and the level made up to the top fiduciary mark. The analysis is preceded by violent agitation, preferably not with a stirrer, since this imparts a centrifugal motion to the suspension A recommended method is continually to invert the container by hand for about a minute. Zero time is the time at which agitation ceases. Since the particles are not at rest when $t = 0$, an error is introduced. Because of this, it is not advisable to withdraw samples for times shorter than 1 min. Acceptable time scales are 2 : 1 progression of t-values to give a $\sqrt{2}$ progression in particle size D as calculated from Stokes' equation.

Ten seconds before withdrawal time, suction is applied to the withdrawal pipette, either orally or with a suction bulb. Rate of withdrawal should be such that the

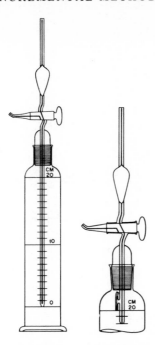

Fig. 9.1. Andreasen's fixed-position apparatus (Gallenkamp).

10 ml sample is withdrawn in 20 s. The two-way tap is turned and excess pressure applied to empty the pipette into a tared container (a 25-ml capacity beaker). About 5 ml of fill liquid, without dispersing agent, is then drawn into the pipette from a beaker and the beaker is then removed, so that air is drawn into the 10 ml container. This is also blown into the sample container, leaving the pipette clean in preparation for the next sample.

The concentration of solids in the samples may be determined by centrifuging, drying and weighing or simply drying and weighing. The drying temperature should not be too high or 'spitting' and subsequent loss of powder may occur. With hygroscopic dispersing agents, special care must be taken to eliminate uptake of moisture from the atmosphere as the containers cool. They are, therefore, cooled in a desiccator and some desiccant is placed in the balance so that the air near the pan is dry. The containers are removed from the desiccator singly and weighed as quickly as possible. Alternatively, the dispersing agent may be removed by filtering off the liquid instead of evaporating it [9, 61].

The equation yielding the percentage undersize D_{st} is:

$$P = 100 \frac{m_t}{v_t} \cdot \frac{v_t}{m_s}$$

$$= Km_t \qquad (9.7)$$

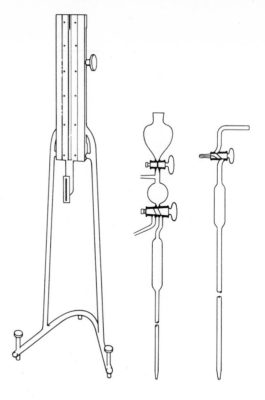

Fig. 9.2. The fixed-depth pipette.

where m_t is the weight of powder in the aliquot sample of volume v, and m_s/v_s is the solid concentration in the initial homogeneous suspension. The largest size present in each sample d_{st} is calculated from Stokes' equation, due allowance being made for the fall in height of the suspension due to withdrawing samples.

If $C(h, 0)$ is too large, i.e. greater than 1·0% by volume, hindered settling may occur, leading to erroneous results, whereas low values of $C(h,0)$ lead to inaccuracies in weighing the small samples withdrawn. It is therefore advisable to carry out duplicate analyses, one at about 1% by volume and one at about 0·5% by volume. If the former gives a significantly coarser distribution than the latter, further analyses are required to determine the optimum concentration, which is usually between these two limits. Fixed-position pipettes of varying stem length are available and the final sample may be taken with one of these in order to complete the analyses in a shorter time.

A modification to this technique is to use a fixed-depth pipette [6] (figure 9.2). This pipette is inserted immediately before the sample is required. After the sampling procedure has been carried out, the pipette is withdrawn so that the collected sample may be emptied into a container. If several suspensions have been prepared,

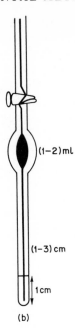

(1–2) mL

(1–3) cm

1 cm

(b)

Fig. 9.3. (*a*) The side-arm pipette (Berg [20]). (*b*) Berg's pipette for fine material
[15]. The pipette is immersed in the suspension immediately prior to
sampling with the bottom of the pipette resting on the bottom of a container holding the suspension.

each sample may be taken from a different suspension which has previously been
undisturbed. This makes the analysis more complex, but gives a marginal increase in
accuracy.

An alternative apparatus [7] consists of a sedimentation vessel (figure 9.3) with
a horizontal sampling tube and a loose pipette. When the pipette is connected to the
sampling tube, the pressure inside the vessel will make the suspension rise into the
pipette beyond the two-way stopcock which is then closed and the pipette removed,
the sampling tube being closed with a glass rod. The suspension above the stopcock
is then blown out through the side tube of the stopcock and the pipette is emptied
into a weighed vessel, which is evaporated and weighed.

If a dispersing agent is used, the weight in the aliquot sample withdrawn is deduced from the weight added to the whole sample and a correction applied. Errors
can arise with hygroscopic dispersing agents or if the dispersing agent is adsorbed by
the solid. These errors may be eliminated by washing out the dispersing agent [9].

9.3.1 Experimental errors
Since the sample is not withdrawn instantaneously, the size of the largest particle

present in the sampling zone will vary throughout the sampling time. The error due to this will be greater at the commencement of the analysis but soon becomes negligible. Rapid withdrawal of the sample is not recommended since preferential sampling always occurs when sampling is not isokinetic. Small particles beyond the sampling zone are drawn into it due to their low inertia, thus suggesting a finer distribution. This has been confirmed experimentally by Johnson [8], who varied the sampling time between 12 and 140 seconds. In B.S. 3406 a compromise time of 20 seconds is recommended. For reproducible results, this time should be strictly adhered to.

In the theory it is assumed that the sample is withdrawn from a narrow cylindrical element, whereas with the Andreasen pipette the sampling zone is, to a first approximation, a sphere. Leschonski [9] showed that the error introduced is less than 1%, provided the ratio of sphere radius to sedimentation height remains below 0·1.

With a vertically downward positioned pipette, such as the Andreasen, there is a liquid volume below the tip of the pipette into which no solid particles can sediment from the layers lying above. This situation creates an instability which results in the setting up of density difference convection currents around the lower end of the pipette. Johnson [8] found that a horizontally directed pipette gave a coarser analysis than one directed downwards and attributed it to thi· effect. Similar experiments conducted by Allen [25] showed no significalnt difference between these two types. Kast [56] used pipettes with open tips and different external diameters of the capillary and found that with large external diameters there was a displacement of the percentage undersize curves towards smaller values.

Leschonski [9] designed a pipette to conform with theory (figure 9.4). The pipette is extended to the bottom of the vessel and the sample withdrawn through a series of holes around its circumference at a fixed depth. Leschonski pointed out that this idea was not new since Andreasen [4] employed a pipette extending to the bottom of the vessel for the sake of sturdiness and for accurate height adjustment. Lorenz [55] also reported on a similar system which was not incorporated in the resulting commercial apparatus, and Berg's pipette for fine material [15] also rests on the bottom of the container holding the suspension.

With the Andreasen pipette, a small amount of liquid is retained in the capillary tube after each withdrawal and gives rise to a systematic positive error, i.e. an overestimation of the percentage undersize. Leschonski [9] showed theoretically that this error could be substantial for narrow distributions. This error can be reduced by shortening the capillary volume. In the MSO-Maschinen und Schleifmittelwerke [57]- the capillary runs out of the side of an 80-cm-long sedimentation column. Kuncweicz and Krzyzewski [58] prefer the pipette by Esenwein on account of its shorter capillary which, again, projects laterally from the sedimentation cylinder.

If the error is to be completely avoided, the sample residue must be removed from the capillary shortly before taking the next sample. This measure was recommended by Andreasen in 1928 [4], but in the apparatus described in 1930 [7] this instruction is missing.

The pipette described by Leschonski [9] incorporates a subsidiary bulb with a

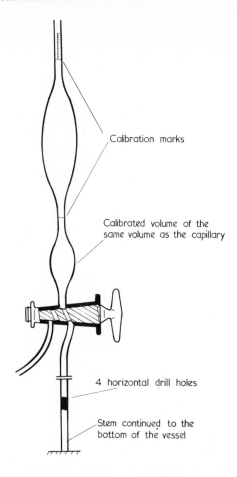

Calibration marks

Calibrated volume of the
same volume as the capillary

4 horizontal drill holes

Stem continued to the
bottom of the vessel

Fig. 9.4. Improved pipette design (Leschonski [9]).

volume matched to that of the capillary (figure 9.4). The capillary extends to the
bottom of the vessel and has four withdrawal apertures staggered by 90°, located
about 30 mm above the bottom of the vessel. The shape of the bulb is also uncon-
ventional with a gradual transition from the bulb to the stem. This design reduces
the possibility of overrunning the upper fiduciary mark. As a further precaution an
additional volume scale is provided in the vicinity of this mark to eliminate the
practice of allowing excess suspension to run back into the sedimentation cylinder,
one which is to be deprecated since more solids are flushed back than were originally
present in the excess volume.

Agitation prior to analysis causes convection currents which may introduce considerable errors in the early readings [59]. With apparatus which on account of its
size could not be shaken by hand, Andreasen [4] used a long hollow tube through

which air was blown, a method also used in [57] but rejected by Leschonski due to the possibility of flotation occurring. His preferred method is with a perforated plate plunger-type stirrer.

Convection currents may also be set up due to temperature variations and it is advisable to keep the temperature constant to $\pm 0.01°C$ min^{-1}. Oden [60] states that for colloidal gold suspensions the upper limit is 0.2°C per day. For extended analyses it is usual to immerse the container in a thermostated bath taking care that no vibrations are imparted to the system. An acceptable alternative method of lagging the sedimentation bottle has been suggested by Heywood [10].

If the sedimentation vessel is not set up absolutely vertically, convection currents are detectable, whereas these are not seen when the vessel is set up correctly. Further errors are caused by disturbance to the suspension when samples are withdrawn, and, with the variable-depth pipette, when the pipette is inserted and withdrawn. These errors could be reduced by using several sedimentation vessels and taking each sample from a different vessel, but this more elaborate procedure is not recommended for tourine work.

This technique was recently reviewed by Alex [21] and compared with other methods by Grandillo [23]. It has also been the subject for an American Standard for cement [22] and used for pharmaceutical powders [24]. It is a highly reproducible method, the cost of the equipment is low and several analyses may be carried out by semi-skilled labour per day.

9.4 The photosedimentation technique

9.4.1 Introduction

The photosedimentometer combines gravitational settling with photoelectric measurement. The principle of the technique is that a narrow horizontal beam of parallel light is projected through a suspension at a known depth h on to a photo-cell. Assuming an initially homogeneous suspension, the concentration of particles in the light beam will be the same as the concentration in the suspension. If the particles are allowed to settle, the number of particles leaving the light beam will be balanced by the number entering it from above. However, after the largest particle present in the suspension, d_m, has fallen from the surface to the measurement zone, the emergent light flux will begin to increase since there will be no more particles of this size entering the measurement zone from above. Hence, the concentration of particles in the light beam at any time, t, will be the concentration of particles smaller than d_{st}, where d_{st} is given by Stokes' equation (equation (7.39)):

$$d_{st} = \sqrt{\frac{18\eta h}{(\rho_s - \rho_f) g t}} \tag{9.8}$$

the symbols having their usual meaning.

It can be shown that the attenuation of the beam of light is related to the projected surface area of the particles in the light beam and from this relationship the particle-size distribution may be determined.

9.4.2 Theory

Consider a sedimentation tank of length L cm, measured in the direction of the light beam, containing the suspension of powder under analysis; the concentration of the powder being $C g\,cm^{-3}$ of suspension.

Let the incident light intensity on an element of thickness δL be I and the emergent light intensity be $I - \delta I$. If the area of the light beam is A, the reduction in flux due to the presence of particles may be attributed to a fall in the overall intensity of the light beam or a reduction in the area of the light beam.

The emergent flux may be written:

$$(I - \delta I)A = (A - \delta A)I$$

$$\frac{\delta I}{I} = \frac{\delta A}{A} \qquad (9.9)$$

where δA is the effective cross-sectional area of particles in the beam perpendicular to the direction of propagation. This equation holds, provided the beam of light becomes homogeneous again between adjacent particles.

If there are n_r particles of size d_r in 1 g of powder.

$$\delta A = -AC\delta L \sum_{r=0}^{r=St} K_r k_r n_r d_r^2 \qquad (9.10)$$

where k is a constant depending on the shape of the particles ($k = \pi/4$ for spheres) d_0 and d_{St} are the smallest and largest particles present in the light beam.

The extinction coefficient K_r is defined as:

$$K_r = \frac{\text{light obscured by particles of size } d_r}{\text{light which would be obscured by this particle}}$$
$$\text{if the laws of geometric optics held.}$$

From equations (9.9) and (9.10):

$$\int_{I_0}^{I_t} \frac{dI}{L} = -\int_0^L CdL \sum_{r=0}^{r=St} K_r k_r n_r d_r^2 \ .$$

Integrating gives:

$$\ln \frac{I}{I_0} = -CL \sum_{r=0}^{r=St} K_r k_r n_r d_r^2 \ .$$

Taking logarithms to base 10 and defining the optical density as:

$$D = \log_{10} I/I_0$$

gives:

$$D = -CL (\log_{10} e) \sum_{r=0}^{r=St} K_r k_r n_r d_r^2 \ . \qquad (9.11)$$

Consider a small change in optical density; ΔD_x, as the maximum size of particle in the beam changes from d_x' to d_x'' where $d_x = \frac{1}{2}(d_x' + d_x'')$.

$$\frac{\Delta D_x}{K_x} = - k_x \, CL \, (\log_{10} e) \, n_x \, d_x^2 \; .$$

The cumulative projected surface area distribution undersize of the particles is given by:

$$\frac{\sum\limits_{x=0}^{x=St} n_x d_x^2}{\sum\limits_{x=0}^{x=max\,m} n_x d_x^2} = \frac{\sum\limits_{x=0}^{x=St} \dfrac{\Delta D_x}{K_x}}{\sum\limits_{x=0}^{x=max\,m} \dfrac{\Delta D_x}{K_x}} \; . \tag{9.12}$$

The cumulative weight distribution undersize is given by:

$$\frac{\sum\limits_{x=0}^{x=St} n_x d_x^3}{\sum\limits_{x=0}^{x=max\,m} n_x d_x^3} = \frac{\sum\limits_{x=0}^{x=St} \dfrac{\Delta D_x}{K_x}}{\sum\limits_{x=0}^{x=max\,m} \dfrac{\Delta D_x dx}{K_x}} \; . \tag{9.13}$$

Further, the weight specific surface of the powder in suspension is derivable from the initial concentration of the suspension and the maximum optical density:

$$S_w = \alpha_s \sum\limits_{r=0}^{r=max\,m} n_r d_r^2$$

$$S_w = \frac{\alpha_s}{kL} \left(\frac{D}{C} \right) \frac{1}{K_m (\log_{10} e)} \; . \tag{9.14}$$

It is generally assumed that k is constant for the restricted size range of any powder under analysis. Further, for non-re-entrant particles the ratio of the surface and projected area shape coefficient (α_s/k) is equal to 4. For re-entrant particles, the surface area obtained by making these assumptions is the envelope surface area. Equation (9.14) simplifies to:

$$S_w = \frac{9 \cdot 2}{K_m L} \left(\frac{D}{C} \right) . \tag{9.15}$$

9.4.3 The extinction coefficient

The photosedimentation technique has many advantages over most other particle size-analysis methods. The attenuation of a beam of light can be measured accurately; the suspension is not disturbed by the insertion of a probe of other measuring device; the sample of powder required is small; a test can be carried out rapidly; the required concentration is low which reduces the possibility of particle–particle inter-action and experimental results are obtained in a form which lends itself to auto-matic recording and remote-control techniques. The method has not yet become popular due to the breakdown in the laws of geometric optics which occurs as the particle size approaches the wavelength of the incident radiation.

For small particles (around $80 \, \mu m$ with light of wavelength $0 \cdot 60 \, \mu m$), an amount of light flux, equal in magnitude to that incident upon the particle, is bent away from the forward direction. As the particle size decreases the scattered light is contained in an increasing solid angle; however, no matter how small the receiver, some of the light is accepted until the particle size is similar to the wavelength of light when the light is predominantly back-scattered. Thus large opaque particles will obstruct an amount of light proportional to their cross-sectional area. With a narrow-angle receiver, this amount will double as the particle size decreases from about 80 to $6\,\mu m$.

With a partially transparent particle, interference due to the light transmitted by the particle will also occur. If a $6\,\mu m$ particle attenuates a fraction F of the light incident upon it , a fraction $1 + F$ will not be collected by a small-angle receiver, hence the extinction coefficient will more than double. It cannot, therefore, be assumed that each particle obstructs the beam with its own geometric cross section, and complex diffraction, scattering, interference and absorption effects have to be considered. These effects are compensated for in the equations by the insertion of an extinction coefficient K.

Early experimenters were either unaware of , or neglected, the parameter K, and this attitude has persisted because of the difficulty in determining it [30, 31]. Some research workers have used monochromatic light and determined K theoretically [32, 33]. Rose and Lloyd [34-36] attempted to derive a universal calibration curve for K against d for white light. This curve has been challenged by Allen [37], who shows that an alternative interpretation may be placed on Rose's experimental data. In later papers [26, 27] Allen showed that a correction curve for diffraction effects could be derived from Fraunhoffer diffraction theory. This correction curve depends upon the receiving angle of the detector; at a particle size of about $6\,\mu m$ an amount of light flux equal to that incident on the particle is diffracted away from the forward forward direction and not picked up by the receiver. For particles smaller than $6\,\mu m$, the shape of the extinction curve becomes more heavily dependent on the optical properties of the particulate fluid system under investigation. Allen's theoretical approach results in an extinction curve for opaque particles which is applicable to the EEL photosedimentometer (a narrow-angle instrument). On the basis of this work, a wide-angle scanning photosedimentometer (WASP) was developed.

9.4.4 Photosedimentometers

The Wagner photosedimentometer, a single standard turbidimeter for use in the determination of the fineness of cement, has a variable height platform for the sedimentation tank and a galvanometer with whcih to record the output of a barrier layer photocell.

The EEL (figure 9.5) uses a white light beam of circular cross section collimated by a lens and a series of stops. The beam passes through the sedimentation cell and, after another series of stops, to a selenium barrier layer photocell which feeds a galvanometer. Six sedimentation cells are housed in a moveable carriage so that the beam may traverse them in turn. Hence, in theory, five samples may be analysed simultaneously, the sixth cell being filled with clear liquid and used as a reference cell. In practice a more realistic number is three.

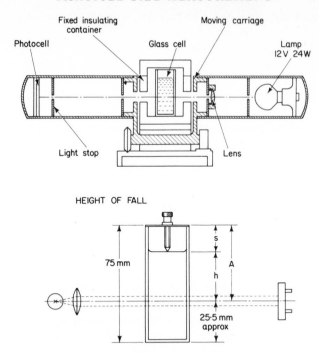

Fig. 9.5. The EEL photosedimentometer, optical system.

The small size of the sedimentation cells limits the height of fall to 2 cm, so that only a limited size range may be analysed in one cell. Further, continuous operator attention is needed. Since this is a narrow-angle instrument, correction has to be applied for the breakdown in the laws of geometric optics. The correction curve supplied with the instrument is based on wrong premises and, although it partially corrects for the error it was intended for, the accuracy of the final analysis is very doubtful. Similarly, as a surface-area measurer the validity of the correction equations is very doubtful.

The Bound Brooke photosedimentometer is a more complex instrument, comprising a sophisticated optical system and a pen-recorder for automatic and continuous recording of variations in optical density (figure 9.6). Since a beam of

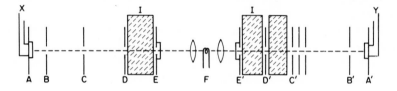

Fig. 9.6. Prototype of the Bound Brooke photosedimentometer as used by Morgan [31].

rectangular cross section is used, the instrument has a narrow angle in the vertical plane and a wide angle in the horizontal plane. No correction for changes in extinction coefficient is provided.

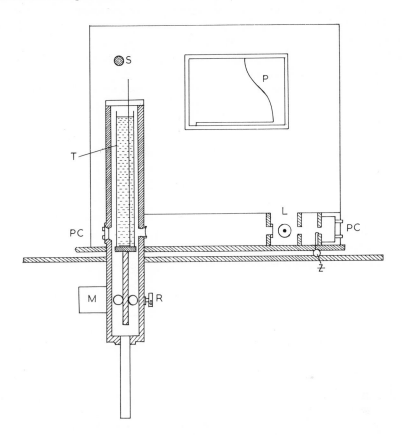

Fig. 9.7. The wide-angle scanning photosedimentometer (WASP): T, sedimentation tank; L, light cell; PC, photocell; S, sensitivity control; Z, zero setting; M, scanning motor; R, manual return; P, pen-recorder.

In the wide-angle scanning photosedimentometer (WASP), the beam of light is split into two components which are passed to separate photocells. One of the beams, after being made parallel, passes through the sedimentation cell and is attenuated by the suspension, the other is a reference beam (figure 9.7).

The two photocells are connected in opposition and thence to a potentiometric recorder. The light flux falling on the reference photocell may be varied (zero set) to balance the electrical output of the two photocells; this zeros the **pen** recorder. Since the two beams of light originate from the same source, any variation in light intensity affects both photocells equally giving a stable zero. A sensitivity control is then adjusted so that the pen-recorder registers full-scale deflection when no light falls on the measurement photocell. The pen-recorder chart has an optical density scale to facilitate subsequent evaluation of the size distribution.

The sedimentation cell has a capacity of 600 ml, allowing a height of fall of up to 20 cm. With the scanning version, the suspension is scanned at a rate of 1 cm min^{-1} after a variable preset time in a static position. This enables accurate determination of the top size to be made together with a rapid complete analysis (usually between 15 and 60 min). Operator time is limited to setting up the instrument and evaluating the results, the time for each of these being of the order of 5 min, although evaluation takes longer if a weight distribution rather than a surface distribution is required.

9.4.5 Discussion

The particle-size limits for photosedimentation techniques are those common to all sedimentation methods. A suitable upper limit for the EEL is a particle that will fall 2 cm in thirty seconds, whereas for the WASP a settling speed of 40 cm min^{-1} is possible. This is because the extinction readings at times less than thirty seconds are unreliable due to the effects of stirring. (For particles of density 2·65 in water, these top sizes are 27·3 and 86 μm respectively, and may be increased four to five-fold by using a more viscous liquid such as ethylene glycol.) The lower size limit is governed by the onset of convection currents at a falling speed of about 14 μm min^{-1}.

Limitation on top size also occurs due to deviations from streamline flow, the breakdown in Stokes' law leading to 5% errors in terminal velocity for particles of 61 μm in size for the example above (450 μm in ethylene glycol). Corrections may be applied using Heywood's tables, but these may only partially correct since it is an inherent assumption that the particles fall in random orientation. If flow is not streamlined, the particles may orientate themselves to give maximum drag, thus reducing the cross-sectional area obstructing the light beam. It is, therefore, strongly recommended that this technique should not be used outside the lamina-flow range.

It is often suggested that independent settling only occurs for the very low volume concentrations possible with this technique (less than 0·05 %). Although not always true, repeat analyses using other sedimentation techniques at volume concentrations of 0·5 and 1·0 % give reproducible results with easily dispersed solids. However, it is often necessary and always preferable to use as low a concentration as possible.

9.5 X-ray sedimentation

A natural extension to the use of white light is to use X-rays. In this case the X-ray density is proportional to the weight of powder in the beam

$$I = I_0 \exp(-BC) \tag{9.16}$$

and D, the X-ray density is defined as:

$$D = \log_{10}(I/I_0) \tag{9.17}$$

where B is a constant, D the X-ray density and C the concentration of powder in the beam.

Brown and Skrebowski [28] in 1954 first suggested the use of X-rays for use in an incremental sedimentation technique. This instrument was built by I.C.I. and described by Nonhebel [38] and others [29]. In this I.C.I. instrument a system is used in which the difference between the intensity of an X-ray beam which has passed through the suspension in one half of a twin sedimentation tank, and the intensity of a reference beam which has passed through an equal thickness of clear liquid in the other half, produces an imbalance in the current produced in a differential ionization chamber. This eleminates errors due to the instability of the total output of the source, but assumes a good stability in the beam direction. Since this is not the case the instrument suffers from a zero drift, which affects the results. A water-cooled X-ray tube is used for generation of 18 keV radiation, which, after traversing the tank, is detected in an ionization chamber. The chamber measures the difference in X-ray intensity in the form of an electric current which is amplified and displayed in a pen-recorder. The intensity difference is taken as directly proportional to the powder concentration in the beam. The sedimentation curve is manually converted to a cumulative percentage frequency using this proportionality and Stokes' law.

Kalshoven in 1966 described an instrument [41], employing the X-ray absorption technique with a special programme for scanning the sedimentation tank. As the concentration measurement by means of X-rays is very rapid, it is possible to change the height of measurement during the analysis. In this instrument it is done in such a way that the concentration is not recorded as a function of time, but as a function of the Stokes' diameter and the cumulative percentage frequency is directly obtained. The analysis is speeded up by scanning and can be as short as a few minutes. An X-ray tube is used as the X-ray source and a scintillation counter as the detector. The difference in intensity between the reference and measuring beams, in which the emitted beam is alternately split, is measured by a rotating wedge that automatically sets the difference to zero. Sub-micrometre particles can be measured if the sedimentation tank is spun in a centrifuge for some time, the time integral of the centrifugal force is measured and the tank is scanned after the centrifugation. The author claims that initial concentrations in the range 0·01 to 1 % by volume can be used, depending on the atomic number of the analysed material. The experiments proved that the concentrations can be measured at short distances below the surface of the suspension without seriously affecting the results. When the centrifuge was used the results were independent of the time of centrifugation. No comparison analyses were presented. The principle was patented [42] in 1965.

Oliver, Hickin and Orr [40] in 1969 patented a gravitational X-ray particle size analyser that incorporated the absorption technique and improves the systems used by Kalshoven [41]. The same instrument was also reported by Hendrix and Orr in 1970 [47] and is now available commercially [48]. This instrument automatically presents results as a cumulative percentage frequency, and the sedimentation tank is driven in such a way that the concentration is recorded directly as a function of the Stokes' diameter. An air-cooled, low-power X-ray tube is used for generation of

X-rays, these are collimated into a narrow beam and pass through 0·14 in (approx. 3·6 mm) thickness of suspension. The sedimentation tank, only 1·375 in (35 mm) high, is closed at the top, and, in use, completely filled with suspension. Filling and emptying of the tank is accomplished with a built-in circulating pump. The transmitted radiation is detected as pulses by a scintillation detector and these are fed into a counting electronics, which in conjuction with an operational amplifier with a diode feedback, gives a voltage proportional to the logarithm of the X-ray intensity and therefore proportional to the powder concentration. The instrument can analyse powders containing an element with atomic number higher than 13, but rather high initial volume concentrations of powder have to be used (0·5–3·0 %). This is due to the need for the initial decrease in X-ray intensity, due to the powder in the suspension, to be greater than 20 % of the intensity, with clean liquid. An absolute system is used here in which the initial intensity with clean liquid is first measured and the zero set, and the suspension is then introduced. This system assumes an excellent stability of the source, which is, in the case of X-ray tubes, a rather unreliable assumption. The authors [47] claim a good reproducibility and present several comparison analyses with microscopy, etc. The range of use is said to be 50 to 0·2 μm for most powders. The lower limit is unreal since it is generally accepted that gravitational sedimentation is limited to particle sizes in excess of 1 or 2 μm. The instrument is a good piece of instrumentation engineering, but the results are affected by the necessary damping and the doubtfulness of its lower size limit. The acceptance by the manufacturers of this lower size has affected the design in that only a 35 mm fall-height is possible and this restricts the upper size limit.

A review of these and other methods is contained in a thesis by Svarovsky [45] and a paper by Svarovsky and Allen [46].

Allen and Svarovsky developed two versions of the LADAL [43] X-ray sedimento meter, a gravitational [44] and a centrifugal [49] instrument.

In both versions, gravitational and centrifugal, the X-ray beam is generated from a Promethium 147/aluminium isotope source with a half-life of 2·6 years, an energy level of 22·6 keV and activity of 3 Curies. A xenon-filled proportional counter at 1300 V is used to detect the beam. The gravitational version uses the X-ray absorption technique in the gravity field. The powder is dispersed in a liquid at a volume concentration of less than 1·0%, a necessary condition for free settling. An X-ray beam passes through the suspension at a known depth below the surface and the changing intensity of the transmitted beam is measured as a function of time. To speed up the analysis, after a preset time, the beam is made to scan up to the surface of the suspension. Typically, the analysis will begin with the beam 18 cm below the surface; it then scans to within 1 cm of the surface in 11 minutes. It is usual to maintain a fixed depth until the largest particles present in the suspension pass through the beam in order to define the top size accurately. For particles of density 3·0 g ml^{-1} in water, using a preset time of 3 min, a full analysis from 30 to 3·3 μm would take 14 min.

Results are presented by a pen-recorder as X-ray intensity against time. A typical curve is shown in figure 9.13. Conversion to cumulative percentage undersize by

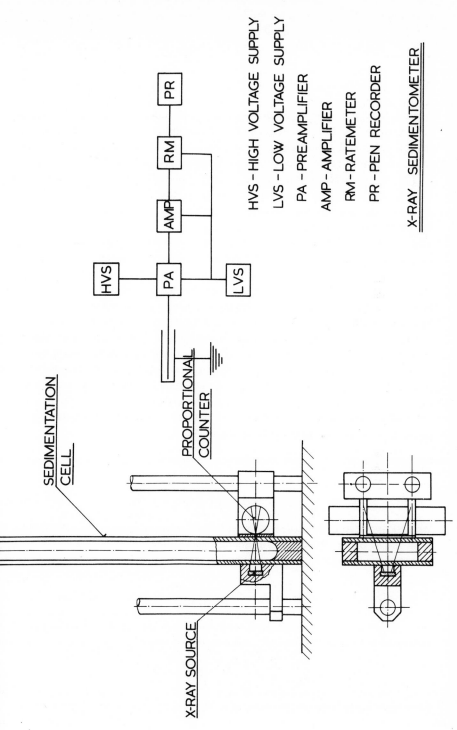

SEDIMENTATION CELL

PROPORTIONAL COUNTER

X-RAY SOURCE

PR

RM

AMP

HVS

PA

LVS

HVS – HIGH VOLTAGE SUPPLY
LVS – LOW VOLTAGE SUPPLY
PA – PREAMPLIFIER
AMP – AMPLIFIER
RM – RATEMETER
PR – PEN RECORDER

X-RAY SEDIMENTOMETER

Fig. 9.8. Schematic diagram of the sedimentometer and block diagram of the electrical circuit.

weight against Stokes' diameter can be carried out manually in about ten minutes or, more conveniently, by digital computer.

The following form of equation (9.16) is used:

$$BC = D = -\log \left(1 - \frac{I_c - I}{I_c}\right) \tag{9.18}$$

where I_c is proportional to the pen-recorder deflection with clear liquid in the sedimentation tank and I is the deflection with suspension in the tank. Adequate sensitivity is obtained by suppressing the zero and expanding the scale by $\times 1$, $\times 3$ or $\times 10$ so that I_c may be made proportional to 20, 60 or 200 cm.

The recorder trace suffers a small amount of instability due to statistical variation of the count level. This can be reduced by integrating the count over 3·3 or 10 s.

9.6 Hydrometers [11, 12]

The variations in density of a settling suspension may be followed with a hydrometer, a method widely used in the ceramic industry. The suspension is made up with a known amount of powder and thoroughly agitated, usually be shaking. The container is then placed in a thermostat and the change in density of the suspension at known depths recorded as the solid phase settles out. Some workers remove the hydrometer after each reading and replace it slowly immediately before the next, others object to the resulting disturbance and reshake the container after each reading. From the series of readings, the size distributions may be determined.

With the hydrometer immersed, its weight W, which is constant, equals the weight of suspension displaced. Let the length of stem immersed in the clear suspending liquid be L, i.e. the same as would be immersed in the suspension at infinite time, the length immersed in the suspension at the commencement of the determination L_0, and the length immersed at time t be L_t; then:

$$W = V\phi(h_0, 0) + L_0 \alpha \rho_1 \tag{9.19}$$

$$W = V\rho_f + L\alpha\rho_f \tag{9.20}$$

$$W = V(h_t, t) + L_t \alpha \rho_2 \tag{9.21}$$

where V is the volume of the hydrometer bulb, α the cross-sectional area of the stem and h_t the depth of the hydrometer bulb at time t.

From equation (9.5):

$$\phi = \frac{(h, t) - \rho_f}{(h, 0) - \rho_f} \, .$$

Since the density of the suspension around the stem (ρ_1, ρ_f, ρ_2) varies negligibly compared with the variation in L, this may be written:

$$\phi = \frac{L_t - L}{L_0 - L} = \frac{w_t - w}{w_0 - w} \tag{9.22}$$

where w is the specific gravity marked on the hydrometer.

If the suspension is made up of W g of powder made up to 1 litre of suspension, equation (9.16) may be written:

$$\phi = \frac{1000}{W} \frac{\rho_s(\rho_t - \rho_f)}{\rho_s - \rho_f} \tag{9.23}$$

where ρ_t is the density of the suspension at the given time t.

An equivalent formula for powders which are present as a slurry in water removes the necessity for drying out the slurry. A specific gravity bottle is filled with water and weighed and the water is then replaced by the sample under test and reweighed, the difference in weights being ΔW. The sample is then taken out of the bottle and used for the analysis. The equivalent formula is:

$$= \frac{1000(\rho_t - \rho_f)}{\Delta W}. \tag{9.24}$$

With the hydrometer technique, both density and depth of immersion vary with each reading. If the temperature is maintained constant at the calibration temperature for the hydrometer, the determination of the former presents no problems since it may be read directly from the hydrometer stem. If the temperature varies, corrections have to be applied for thermal expansion and misreading of the meniscus [13].

The chief difficulty lies in determining the point of reference below the surface to which this density refers, for when the hydrometer is put into the suspension the level rises in the container, thus giving a false reference point (figure 9.9). If the cross-sectional area of the container is A, the depth to be used in Stokes' equation, from geometrical consideration is [14] :

$$L = L_1 + \frac{1}{2}L_2 - \frac{1}{2}\frac{V}{A}.$$

This simple formula has been challenged by several workers who claim that corrections have to be applied for the density gradient about the bulb and the displacement of suspension by the stem. Johnson [8], for example, gives:

$$L = L_1 + \frac{1}{2}L_2 - \frac{1}{2}\frac{V}{A} - 0.5 \text{ cm}.$$

In order to achieve sufficient accuracy in the specific gravity readings, it is necessary to use a concentration of at least 40 g l^{-1}, which is well into the hindered settling region. The only justification for this that has been advanced is that the method gives reproducible results.

Most hydrometers are calibrated to be read at the bottom of the meniscus and this is usually not possible in a suspension. The readings are therefore taken at the top of the meniscus, and an experimentally determined correction, which is usually of the order 0.003 g ml^{-1}, applied.

It is usual to disregard calibration errors, although these may be substantial.

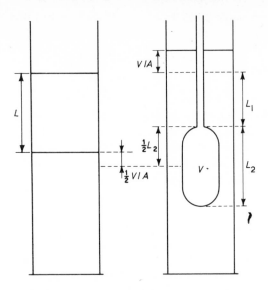

Fig. 9.9. Depth of immersion using a hydrometer.

Good-quality hydrometers are usually guaranteed to ± 0·0005 g ml^{-1}, which corresponds to a percentage error of around ± 1·5 % under normal operating conditions. Johnson [8] recognized this error and suggested that the error should be determined at several points by calibration in a series of dilute suspension of common salt.

A correction to meniscus reading error and density should also be applied if a wetting agent is used.

Although the hydrometer cannot be recommended as an absolute instrument, it is useful for control work. It is of little use with discontinuous size distributions, since these give sharp boundaries in the settling suspension, which lead to peculiar results.

9.7 Divers

An extension of the hydrometer technique which overcomes many of the objections to it is to use miniature hydrometers, which are completely immersed in the suspension. The method was developed by Berg [15] who called the miniature hydrometers 'divers' [figures 9.10(a) and (b)]. The first type was designed for gravitational and the second for centrifugal sedimentation. Onee the diver had been constructed, its density was brought as close as possible to the required density by adding mercury. The bulb was then sealed and its density adjusted to the required density by etching with hydrofluoric acid. During the analysis, the diver was inserted into the suspension and sank to the level at which the density of the suspension was equal to its own. A number of divers are required since each one gives only one point on the size distribution curve. Since the divers were not visible in the suspension, Berg located them by drawing them to the side of the sedimentation tube with

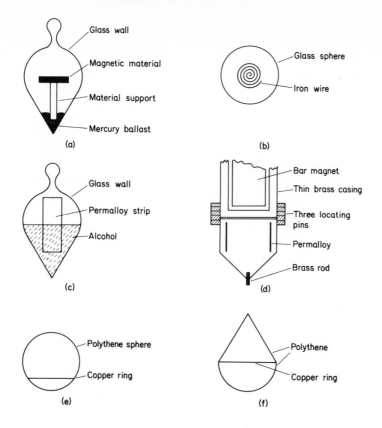

Fig. 9.10. (a)–(f) Divers.

a magnet. This method of location has the disadvantage that the magnet may displace the diver in a vertical as well as a horizontal direction.

Jarrett and Heywood [16] located their divers (figures 9.10 (c) and (d)) with an alternating-current inductance resistance bridge; the balance was destroyed when a thin search coil surrounding the sedimentation tube was moved past the diver. In the roof diver technique which they developed (figure 9.10 (d)), the diver is placed at the foot of a vertical column, the locating device being placed just below it. The diver is held on to the column with a magnetic rod which is afterwards withdrawn. Due to the excess pressure, it remains in position until the density of the surrounding suspension equals its own and it then falls. Jarrett and Heywood found it necessary to vibrate the vertical column to prevent sticking and this is obviously a disadvantage.

Johnson [17] used six divers, consisting of small sealed bulbs containing iron powder, and located them using a magnet. He found a density range 1·0242 to 1·004 g ml^{-1} satisfactory for ceramic materials.

The problem with all the above divers is that they are difficult to construct and calibrate. These difficulties were overcome by Kaye and James [18], who used polythene spheres, 0·6 cm diameter, containing copper rings (figure 9.10 (e) and (f). There were located with a thin search coil fed with high-frequency alternating current. When the plane of the search coil coincided with that of the copper ring, there was an increase in the power consumption which was recorded by pen-recorder.

Kaye and James showed that the diver fell to a greater depth than its density level because of its kinetic energy. It should then have oscillated about its density level with damped simple harmonic motion but did not, due to the picking up and shedding of powder. This fault is confined to divers that are asymmetrical about their centres of gravity, which are therefore unsuitable for density determination. Polythene spheres coated with copper on graphite are symmetrical and develop a continuous spin giving reproducible satisfactory results.

9.8 The specific gravity balance

The changes in density within a settling suspension may be followed by using a specific gravity balance [19]. This instrument comprises a bob on each arm of a beam balance, one bob being immersed in clear suspension fluid and the other in the suspension. The depth of immersion of the bobs may be varied, the change in buoyancy being counterbalanced by means of solenoids which are connected to a pen-recorder. From the trace on the pen-recorder, the particle size distribution may be determined.

9.9 Appendix: Worked Examples

9.9.1 Wide-angle scanning photosedimentometer: Analysis of silica

Horizontal scales
    Time: recorder chart travels at 1 cm min^{-1}.
    Depth: initially 18 cm. After 16 min, delay scanning commences at a rate of
        1 cm min^{-1}.
    Diameter: Stokes' diameter evaluated by:

$$d_{st} = 175 \sqrt{\frac{0 \cdot 01 \times 18h}{(2 \cdot 60 - 1 \cdot 10)\, T\, 18}}$$

$$= 58 \cdot 7 \left(\frac{h}{18\,T}\right)^{\frac{1}{2}}.$$

Vertical scales
D is optical density, pen-recorder scale, cumulative
S is D converted to a percentage, the surface undersize by weight.

Evaluation

Time (min)	1	2	4	8	16	20	24	28	32
Height of fall (cm)	18	18	18	18	18	14	10	6	2
Stokes' diameter (μm)	58·7	41·5	29·4	20·8	14·7	11·6	8·9	6·4	3·45
Optical density D	0·495	0·475	0·407	0·321	0·240	0·194	0·152	0·172	0·060
Cumulative % undersize by surface D (%)	100	96	82·2	64·8	48·5	39·2	30·8	22·6	12·1
Average diameters d		45·7	35·5	25.1	17·7	13:2	10·2	7·65	4·9	1·7
ΔD		0·20	0·68	0·86	0·81	0·46	0·42	0·40	0·52	0·60
ΔDd		9·1	24·2	21·6	14·3	6·1	4·3	3·1	2·5	1·0
Cumulative % undersize by weight ΔDd (%)	100	89·6	61·5	36·4	19·7	12·7	7·7	4·1	1·1

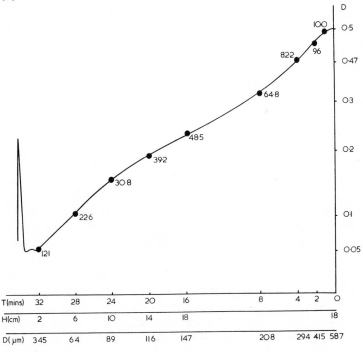

Fig. 9.11. Pen-recorder trace of a photosedimentation analysis (optical density D against time T).

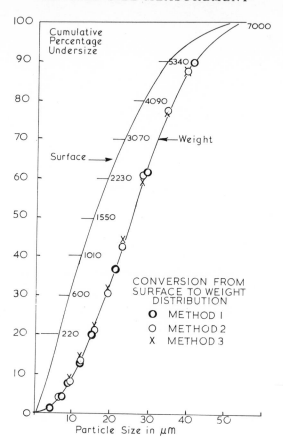

Fig. 9.12. Size distribution using the wide-angle scanning photosedimentometer (WASP).

9.9.2 Conversion from surface distribution to weight distribution

Conversion may be carried out by a tabular method as illustrated above (method 1). An improvement on this is to tabulate with data from the surface distribution curve, this permits smoothing out of experimental variations and extrapolation (method 2). For reliable cumulative undersize weight results, the top size needs to be accurately known since small errors in top size can lead to gross errors when the integration is performed (i.e. when the area ΔDd is evaluated). Such accuracy is not generally required at the lower end of the size spectrum and the analysis may often be terminated when 20 % or so by surface remains unmeasured. The most rapid and accurate method is to perform the integration graphically, by counting squares say, (method 3). The results from all three methods are illustrated graphically (figure 9.12).

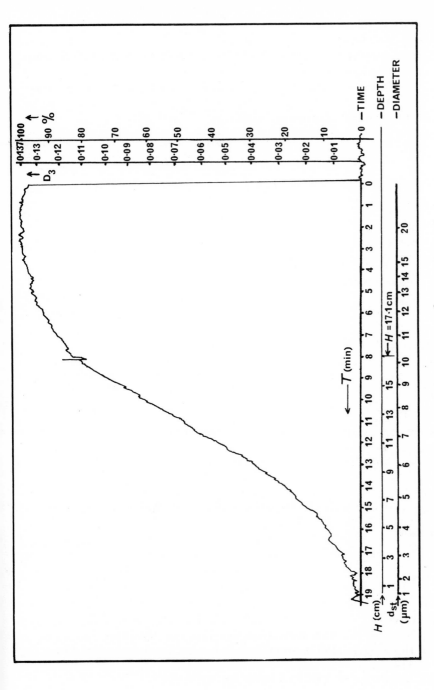

Fig. 9.13. Pen-recorder trace of an X-ray analysis (X-ray density D^3 against time T).

9.9.3 The LADAL X-ray sedimentometer: Analysis of tungstic oxide

Horizontal scales

Time: recorder chart travels at 1 cm min^{-1}.

Depth: initially 17·1 cm. After 8 min delay, scanning commences which causes a kick on the chart.

With a scanning rate of 1·515 cm min^{-1}, the decrease in depth is evaluated.

Diameter: Stokes' diameter evaluated by

$$d_{st} = 175 \sqrt{\frac{0 \cdot 01 \times 17 \cdot 1 h}{(7 \cdot 16 - 1 \cdot 00) T \, 17 \cdot 1}}$$

$$= 27 \cdot 8 \sqrt{\frac{h}{17 \cdot 1 T}}.$$

Vertical scales

D_3 is the X-ray density which may be converted to cumulative percentage undersize by weight using equations 9.18: e.g.

Maximum deflection $L_{max} = 18 \cdot 6$ cm   F.S.D. = 60 cm

$$D_{max} = BC(h, 0) = -\log\left(1 - \frac{18 \cdot 6}{60}\right) = 0 \cdot 137$$

Evaluation

Time (min)	2	2·8	4	5·6	8	10	12	14	16	18
Height of fall (cm)	17·1	17·1	17·1	17·1	17·1	14·0	11·0	8·1	5·1	2·0
Stokes' diameter (μm)	2·0	17·5	14·6	12·3	10·0	8·4	6·8	5·3	3·9	2·3
X-ray density D	0·137	0·137	0·135	0·128	0·109	0·084	0·0555	0·0274	0·0092	0·006
Cumulative % under-size D% by weight	100	100	98·5	93·5	79·5	61·5	40·5	20·0	8·7	4·8

References

[1] States, M.N. (1939), *Proc. Amer. Soc. Test. Mat.*, **39**, 795.

[2] Heywood, H. (1947), Symposium on Particle Size Analysis, *Inst. Chem. Engrs.*, 114.

[3] Robinson, G.W. (1922), *J. Agric. Sci.*, **12**, 3, 306−21.

[4] Andreasen, A.H.M. (1938), *Kolloid Beith.*, **27**, 405.

[5] Andreasen, A.H.M. (1939), *Ingen. Vidensk. Skr.*, **3**.

[6] B.S. 3406, Part 2.

[7] Andreasen, A.H.M., and Lundberg, J.J.V. (1930), *Ber. Deut. Keram. Ges.*, **11**, 5, 312–23.

[8] Johnson, R. (1956), *Trans. B. Ceram. Soc.*, **55**, 237.

[9] Leschonski, K. (1962), 'Vergleichende Undersuchungen der Sedimentation Analyse', *Staub*, **22**, 11, 475–86.

[10] Heywood, H. (1938), *Proc. Inst. Mech. Engrs.*, **140**, 27.

[11] B.S. 1377: (1961).

[12] A.S.T.M. (1961), 1272, Part 4.

[13] Orr, C., and Dallavalle, J.M., *Fine Particle Measurement*, Macmillan, N.Y., p.64

[14] Bauer, E.E. (1937), *Engng. News-Record*, No. 118, McGraw-Hill, 662.

[15] Berg, S. (1940), Ingeniorvidenskab, Skrifter, 2, Danish Acad. Tech. Sci., Copenhagen.

[16] Jarrett, B.A., and Heywood, H. (1954), *B. J. Appl. Phys.*, suppl. No. 3, S21.

[17] Johnson, R. (1955), *Trans. B. Ceram. Soc.*, **55**, 237.

[18] Kaye, B.H., and James, G.W. (1962), *B.J. Appl. Phys.*, **13**, 415.

[19] Suito, E., Arakawa, M., Mishima, H., Yano, S., and Okamoto, N. (1964), *J. Soc. Matl. Sci. Japan*, **13**, 133, 825.

[20] Berg, S. (1958), *Symposium on Particle Size Measurement*, Sp. Publ. No. 234, A.S.T.M., p.143.

[21] Alex, W. (1970), *G.I.T.*, **11**, 5, 637–40, 643–6.

[22] Grinrod, P.S. (1970), A.S.T.M. Sp. Tech. Publ. No. 473, 45–70.

[23] Grandillo, A.D. (1970), *J. Powder Metall.*, **6**, 1, 3–16.

[24] Joos, P., Rvyssen, R., and Haners, Y. (1970), *J. Pharm. Belg.*, **25**, 2, 133–51.

[25] Allen, T. (1967), Univ. of Bradford, Ph. D. thesis.

[26] Allen, T. (1968), *J. Powder Technol.*, 132–40.

[27] Allen, T. (1968), *ibid.*, 141–53.

[28] Brown, J.F., and Skrebowski, J.N. (1954), *B.J. Appl. Phys.*, suppl. No. S27.

[29] Conlin, S.G., *et al.* (1967), *J. Sci. Instrum.* **44**, 606–10.

[30] Jarrett, B.A., and Heywood, H. (1954), *B. J. Appl. Phys.*, suppl. No. 3, 21.

[31] Morgan, V.T. (1954), Symposium on Powder Metallurgy.

[32] Vouk, V. (1948), London Univ., Ph. D. thesis.

[33] Lewis, P.C., and Lothian, G.F. (1954), *B. J. Appl. Phys.* suppl. 3, S571.

[34] Rose, H.E., and Lloyd, H.B. (1946), *J. Soc. Chem. Ind.*, **65**, 52.

[35] Rose, H.E. (1946), *ibid.*, **65**, 65.

[36] Rose, H.E. (1952), *J. Appl. Chem.*, **2**, 80.

[37] Allen, T. (1962), Lond. Univ., MSc. thesis.

[38] Nonhebel, G. (ed.)(1964), *Gas Purification Processes*, Newnes.

[39] Kratohvil, J.P. (1964), *Ann. Chem.*, **36**,5, 485R.

[40] Oliver, J.P., Hickin, G.K., and Orr, C. (1969), *US Patent 3*, 449, 567.

[41] Kalshoven, J. (1967), '*Particle Size Analysis' Conference Proceedings*, publ. Society for Analytical Chemistry, London.

[42] Kalshoven, J. (1965), *Br. Pat. Spec.* 1, 158, 338.

[43] Allen, T. (1970), *Br. Pat. Appl.*, 1764/70. (1971), U.S. Patent Application 106, 013.

[44] Allen, T., and Svarovsky, L. (1970), *J. of Phys. E.*, **3**, 458–60.

[45] Svarovsky, L. (1972), University of Bradford, Ph. D. thesis.

[46] Svarovsky, L. and Allen, T. (1973), paper presented at Heywood Memorial Symposium, Univ. of Loughborough.

[47] Hendrix, W.P., and Orr, C. (1970), *'Particle size analysis' Conference Proceedings,* publ. Society for Analytical Chemistry, London.

[48] Sedigraph. See list of Manufacturers and Suppliers.

[49] Allen, T., and Svarovsky, L. (1974), *J. Powder Technol.,* accepted for publication.

[50] Jennings, D.S., Thomas, M.D., and Gardner, W. (1922), *Soil Sci.,* **14**, 485–99.

[51] Krauss, G. (1923), *Int. Mitt. Bodenkunde,* **13**, 1, 2, 147–60.

[52] Koettgen, P. (1927), *Z. Pflanzenernähr Düng Bodenkunde,* **9**, 35–46.

[53] Köhn, M. (1928), *Landwirtsh. Jahrb.,* **67**, 1, 485–546.

[54] Lehman, H. (1932), *Sprechsaal Keram. Glas. Email.,* **65**, 36.

[55] Lorenz, R. (1932), *Ber. Deutsch. Keram. Ges.,* **13**, 3, 124–39.

[56] Kast, W. (1960), *Staub,* **20**, 8, 253–66.

[57] Report from the abrasives laboratory of the MSO-Maschinen und Schleifmittelwerke AG, (1954), *Sprechsaal Keram. Glas. Email,* **87**, 19.

[58] Kuncewicz, L., and Krzyzewski, Z. (1960), *Staub,* **20**, 2, 47–8.

[59] Joos, E. (1954), *Staub,* **35**, 18–34.

[60] Oden, S. (1920), *Kolloid Z.,* **26**, 1, 100–121.

[61] Gille, F. (1952), *Zement-Kalk-Gips,* **5**, 10, 309–314.

10 *Cumulative Methods of Sedimentation Size Analysis*

10.1 Introduction

There are two approaches to the determination of the size distribution of a sedimenting suspension. The incremental method involves the determination of the rate of change of density or concentration with time or height or both. In the cumulative method the rate at which the powder is settling out of suspension is measured. In either of these techniques, two-layer or homogeneous suspensions may be used. Usually it is preferable to use incremental methods since analyses can be carried out more rapidly by these methods. The big advantage of cumulative techniques is that the amount of powder required is small (about 0·5 g), which reduces interaction between particles to a minimum. This is particularly useful when only a small quantity of powder is available or when one is dealing with toxic materials.

10.2 Two-layer methods

If the powder is initially concentrated in a thin layer floating on the top of the suspending fluid, the size distribution may be directly determined by plotting the fractional weight settled against the free-falling diameter of the particles. Marshall [1] was the first to use this principle. Eadie and Payne [2] developed the micromerograph, the only method in which the suspending fluid is air.

The Werner [3] and Travis [4] methods also operate on the layer principle but utilize a liquid suspension on top of clear liquid. These methods have found little favour since the basic instability of the system, a dense fluid on a less dense fluid, is responsible for what is commonly known as 'streaming'; some of the suspension settles *en masse* in the form of pockets of particles which fall rapidly through the clear liquid leaving a 'tail' of particles behind (see [5, p.78]).

Whitby eliminated this fault by using a clear liquid with a density greater than that of the suspension. He also extended the range of the technique by using centrifugal settling for the finer fraction. A description of the apparatus and method is given by Whitby [6, Pt. 1] and procedures [6, Pt. 1] and applications in [6, Pt. 2]; Whitby *et al.* [7] describe the equipment in use. The apparatus has been commercialized under the name M.S.A. particle size analyser.

An objection that can be levelled at all these methods, apart from the micromerograph, is that the amount settled is determined by the height of the sediment. As the settled volume is not independent of particle size this introduces errors unless a correction is applied.

The two-layer technique has also been used to size and fractionate UO_3 particles [8]. The weight that had sedimented out was determined by a device to measure the radio-activity at the bottom of the tube and the settled powder was washed out at fixed time intervals without disturbing the settling suspension.

10.3 Homogeneous suspensions

The principle of this method is the determination of the rate at which particles settle out of a homogeneous suspension. This may be determined by extracting the sediment and weighing it, allowing the sediment to fall on to a balance pan or determining the weight of powder still in suspension by using a manometer.

The theory outlined below was developed by Oden [9] and later modified by Coutts and Crowthers [10] and Bostock [11].

If one considers a distribution of the form $W = F(D)$ where W is the percentage having a diameter greater than D, the weight per cent P which has settled out at time t is made up of two parts; one consists of all the particles with a free-falling speed greater than D_t as given by Stokes or some related law, where D_t is the size of particle which has a velocity of fall h/t and h is the height of suspension; the other consists of particles smaller than D_t which have settled because they started off at some intermediate position in the fluid column. If the free-falling velocity of one of these smaller particles is v, the fraction of particles of this size that have fallen out at time t is vt/h giving:

$$P = \int_{D_t}^{D_{max}} F(D)dD + \int_{D_{min}}^{D_t} \frac{vt}{h} F(D)dD.$$

By differentiating with respect to time and multiplying by t:

$$t\frac{dP}{dt} = \int_{D_{min}}^{D_t} \frac{vt}{h} F(D)dD$$

i.e.

$$P = W + t\frac{dP}{dt}. \tag{10.1}$$

where W is the percentage oversize D_t.

Since P and t are known, it is possible to determine W using this equation. It is preferable, however, to use the form of equation (10.1) suggested by Gaudin, Schumann and Schlechter [12]:

$$W = P - \frac{dP}{d \ln t}. \tag{10.2}$$

Several methods have been suggested for the determination of W using these equations. The most obvious is to tabulate t and P, hence derive dP, dt and finally W.

Alternatively, P may be plotted against t and tangents drawn. A tangent drawn at point $(P_1 t)$ will intercept the abscissa at W_1, the weight oversize t_1. This method is particularly useful when pen-recorders are used in association with a cumulative method and the data presented as graphs of P against t.

Another tabulation method suggested by Stairmand [13] (see appendix) is dependent on tabulating P against t at times such that the ratio of (t/dt) remains constant, i.e. a time interval in a geometric progression. In order to smooth out experimental and operator errors it is probably better to plot P against t, determining the values of P from the smoothed curve. Stairmand's method is illustrated in table 10.2.

Many powders have a wide size distribution and, in such cases, the time axis on a linear plot tends to become cramped at the lower end or unduly extended; the use of equation (10.2) is then recommended. Evaluation proceeds from a plot of P against $\ln t$; one can then plot $dW/\ln t$ on the same scale, measuring the difference between the abscissae at specific times [6]. The determination is simplified by using a special protractor devised by Edwald [14].

A far less cumbersome technique is to draw tangents. This has been further simplified by Bostock [11] who differentiates graphically every half-unit of $\ln t$; the point where the tangent cuts the ordinate line one $\ln t$ unit less than the value at which it was drawn gives the weight per cent oversize W at that value. These methods are illustrated in table 10.1 and figure 10.1.

The cumulative method of size analysis has been criticized by Nissan [15] and Jarrett and Heywood [16] because of the need for differentiation. Donoghue [17], however, states that these criticisms are baseless, particularly if the weight of sediment is determined at times increasing by a factor of not more than 2.

10.4 Sedimentation balances

By far the most popular method of carrying out a cumulative sedimentation size analysis is the balance method, in which the weight of powder settling out on to a balance pan is recorded against time. The use of an analytical beam balance with counterbalancing as sedimentation proceeded was first described by Oden [9, 18], and the first automatic recording sedimentation beam balance was described by Svedberg and Rinde [20]. As sediment collected on the pan, electrical points made contact and current was fed to a motor which acted on the other arm to restor equilibrium. The time — current plot was automatically recorded to be later converted into a time — weight plot. Other instruments have also been described [21 — 24]. In an ideal system all the powder intially in suspension will eventually settle on to the pan. If the pan is situated in the suspension, allowance has to be made for the particles settling between the rim of the pan and the sides of the sedimentation column, also the particles originally below the pan at the start of the run. The density unbalance as particles settle out from under the pan results in particles streaming over it [10]; a size-selective phenomenon, since fine particles are more likely to be lost than coarse ones, hence difficult to correct for. With balance systems using counterpoising, such as the Shimadzu and Sartorious, this effect is aggravated by the pumping action resulting from the periodic movement of the pan.

It is necessary to know the final weight to be expected after complete sedimentation since it is rarely possible to prolong   a run until all the suspension has settled

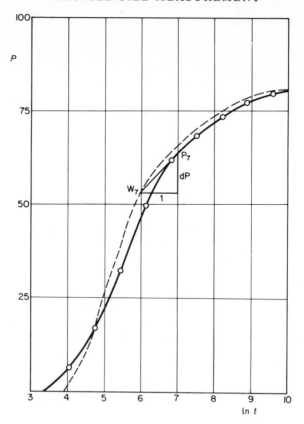

Fig. 10.1 a. Determination of weight percentage oversize (W) from the graph of weight of powder sedimented (P) against ln t by Bostock's method of drawing tangents.

out. The manufacturers of the Sartorious balance suggest that 8% is deducted to compensate for weight losses due to the effects mentioned above, hardly a satisfactory correction since it has been shown that weight losses vary with the mean size of the powder in suspension from 93% at 32 μm to 28·80% at 4·5 μm [59].

The Recording Sedibal or Sartorious balance was developed by Bachman and Gerstenberg [28]. In this instrument, when 2 mg of sediment has deposited, electron circuitry activates a step by step motor which twists a torsion wire to bring the beam back to its original position. A pen records each step on chart paper.

This instrument was modified by Leschonski [56] (figure 10.2), so that the balance pan was situated at the bottom of the sedimentation column but was otherwise surrounded by clear liquid. This eliminated powder losses and resulted in much more accurate analyses [57, 60]. This improvement results in a considerable loss in

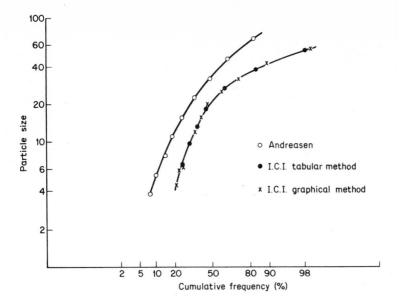

Fig. 10.1 b. Frequency distribution using I.C.I. apparatus using Stairmand's method
and also using the theoretical equation. A comparison is made with an
Andreasen analysis.

ease and simplicity of operation and makes it impossible to carry out repeat runs on
the same sample. Furthermore, the actual loss for coarse powders is close to 8% and the
the standard method give results of sufficient accuracy, making it unnecessarily inconvenient to use the Leschonski modification for every sample [59].

Scott and Mumford [59] suggest the following correction procedure, first proposed by Harris and Jowett [61], for the unmodified balance which they show gives
reasonable agreement with results using the modified balance.

Assume that the final approach to the unknown asymptote represented by complete sedimentation is a simple first-order exponential function:

$$W_t = W_\infty [1 - \exp(-\alpha t)] \qquad (10.3)$$

where W_t is the weight collected at time t, and W_∞ is the weight expected at infinite
time, then, as shown by Mengelsdorf [62], a plot of $W_{(t + \Delta t)}$ against W_t with constant Δt should give a straight line which intersects the 45° line at the point
(W_∞, W_∞), the value of the correct end-weight.

This technique should not be regarded as a panacea for all the ills of current balance techniques since it is necessary that the losses be representative for the correction to apply. It is, therefore, recommended that whenever possible accurate experimental results should be sought.

Improvements to the electronics of the Sartorious balance have also been suggested
[63, 64]. The instrument is described in detail by Friedrich [29], a critical comparison

Table 10.2. Illustration of various methods of determining the cumulative percentage undersize by weight from cumulative weight deposited data

Experimental data			Stairmand's method (see table 10.1) (a)			Experimental data		From the graph of P v, ln t (equation 10.2) (b)			Andreasen analysis (c)	
(1) Extraction time (s)	(2) Stokes' diameter (μm)	(3) Incremental weight of sediment (g × 10⁻⁵)	(4) Weight in grade	(5) Percentage in grade	(6) Percentage undersize	(7) ln t	(8) P (%)	(9) ln t	(10) W	(11) Particle size μm	(12) Particle size (μm)	(13) Cumulative percentage oversize
57	75	4333			100	4·043	6·5	5·0	1·7	53·7	65·3	15·9
114	53	7064	1243	1·9	98·1	4·736	17·1	5·5	10·0	41·7	45·7	34·9
228	37·5	10 154	8754	13·1	85·0	5·429	32·2	6·0	26·0	32·7	31·9	41·1
456	26·5	11 554	15 107	22·8	62·2	6·123	49·8	6·5	39·5	25·1	22·3	65·6
912	18·8	8001	11 528	17·4	44·8	6·816	61·8	7·0	53·2	19·9	15·7	74·8
1824	13·3	4473	5566	8·3	36·5	7·509	68·1	7·5	59·7	15·8	10·9	81·7
3648	9·4	3382	4402	6·6	29·9	8·202	73·7	8·0	65·4	12·1	7·7	85·8
7296	6·6	1625	3097	4·7	25·2	8·895	77·2	8·5	69·4	9·5	5·4	89·6
14 592	0	13 523*	16 773	25·2		9·588	79·6	9·0	73·8	7·4	3·8	91·7
								9·5	76·8	5·8		
								10·0	78·7	4·5		
TOTAL		66 470	66 470									

*Extrapolated value.

Columns 6 and 2, 11 and 10 and 13 and 12 are presented graphically in figure 10.1 (b)
Theoretically the first value in col.3 cannot be greater than half the second. However, in the theory a cylindrical tube is assumed and the reduction in cross-sectional area due to the conical portion reduces the weight sedimented at the commencement of the analysis.
The tabular solution (col. 6) agrees well with the graphical solution (col. 10), but these disagree with the Andreasen analysis (col. 13). This is due to the shape of the container which results in an underweighting of the coarse fraction and to loss of powder (ca. 12% in this instance). This loss is added to the fines and biases the analysis in favour of the fines.

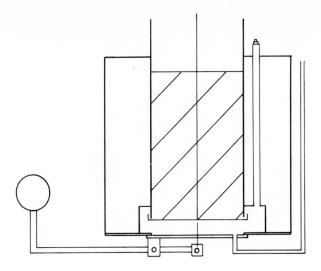

Fig. 10.2. Schematic representation of the Leschonski modification of the Sartorious balance.

with the Andreasen technique has been carried out by Loos [30] and a comparison with the Coulter and Fisher subsieve sizer has been carried out by Grandillo [65].

One automatic recording beam balance is sold under the name Shimadzu [25] (figure 10.3). In this balance, as sediment falls on to one pan, electrical points make contact and operate a solenoid which in turn operates a ratchet. As the ratchet turns, ball-bearings fall into the other pan, thus causing the electrical circuit to be broken. A subsidiary feed from the ratchet leads to a pen on a recording drum which yields a plot of sediment against time (P versus t).

The Shimadzu suffers from an inertia in reading due to the excess pressure required to activate the electrical contact which energizes the ball-bearing release and pen-recorder setup; this has the effect of moving the resulting distribution curve towards the fines. Other sources of error are due to the pan being in the suspension and the pumping action due to rebalancing; the former leads to streaming and powder loss errors as discussed earlier and the latter to a general instability in the system. Although reproducible results may be obtained with the Shimadzu instrument, the size distribution is finer than that obtained by other methods due to the reasons mentioned earlier. The high concentration required (1 to 5% by weight) with the apparatus may cause hindered settling which will also act in such a way as to give a finer distribution than actually exists.

In 1954, Kiffer [26] described a continuous weighing chain-link balance. Rabatin and Gale [27] developed a simple spring balance operated in conjunction with photocells and shutter mechanism to intercept a beam of parallel light. Additional damping circuits were incorporated to prevent excessive oscillations of the system. This instrument needs frequent recalibration to compensate for ageing of the spring.

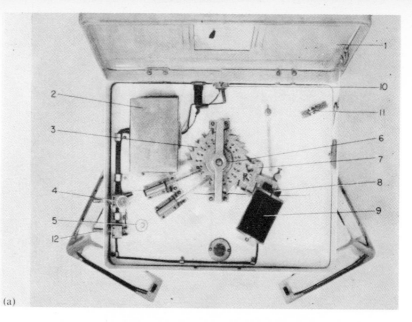

(a)

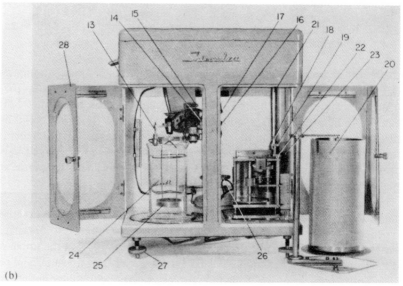

(b)

Fig. 10.3. (*a*), (*b*) The Shimadzu sedimentation balance.
(1) Case top. (2) Transformer. (3) Rotary disc. (4) Steel ball reservoir (L). (5) Steel ball reservoir (S). (6) Pulley wheel. (7) Ratchet (8) Iron piece for magnet. (9) Electromagnet. (10) Receptacle for source. (11) Intermediate pulley wheel. (12) Switch. (13) Contact point. (14) Contact point. (15) Stopper. (16) Right pan. (17) Ball receptacle. (18) Balancing weight. (19) Knob for changeover to clockwork. (20) Clockwork drum. (21) Slide pole. (22) Pen-holder. (23) Pen. (24) Sedimentation bottle. (25) Sedimentation pan. (26) Balancing weight. (27) Levelling screw. (28) Door.

Palik [31] designed a torsion-type balance, in which alteration in pan height due to particles settling on it is recorded by light and photocell systems. Special precautions are proposed to minimize the error due to flow of liquid of lower density below the pan to its upper region which interferes with the free vertical fall of the particles.

In 1942 Gaudin *et al.* [70] proposed placing the balance pan below a sedimentation cylinder with an open bottom. The internal diameter of this pan is larger than the external diameter of the cylinder. The whole arrangement is placed in a second vessel filled with sedimentation liquid. During a run the suspension is located only above the balance pan in the sedimentation cylinder. This arrangement was adopted by Bostock [11, 32] in a balance manufactured by Gallenkamp.

In Bostock's torsion balance [11, 32] (figure 10.4), the weight settled is read at chosen intervals of time directly from the deflection of the torsion wire. The instrument has been automated by the makers by the incorporation of a camera which photographs a scale reading of deflection at fixed intervals of time. A more elegant way of automating this balance was suggested by Ames *et al.* [33], who fastened the core of a linear variable differential transformer to the balance beam. The output of the transformer was amplified and recorded and the weight − sedimented − time curve derived from the data.

Bostock eliminated most of the faults associated with balances by situating the balance pen immediately below the sedimenting column and surrounding it with clear suspension fluid.

Faults are found, however, in the commercial version of this instrument. The balance system tends to stick, tapping with a pencil prior to taking a reading can cause the pointer to move one or two divisions. Loss of powder can be quite high The mode of operation is to premix about half a gram of powder and pour the suspension into the upper container. With the pan clamped the two clips are released to all the suspension to enter the column, displaced air passing to the top container. The balance pan is then released. This filling operation is such that some suspension tends to leak round the pan into the clear water reservoir. Powder is also lost on the walls of the upper container. These losses can be reduced if the glass surfaces are treated with a silicone antistatic agent. Some balances are found to have non-linear scales, this may be checked by placing ball-bearings on the pan under operating conditions with water replacing the normal suspension [66]. Although this system incorporates most of the requirements for a good sedimentation balance, its design could be greatly improved.

The granulometer (figure 10.5) is a two-layer balance intended for the particle size range 60 to 1000 μm [67, 68]. Two settling tubes are used for continuous operation. While one run is being made in one tube, a second sample is prepared for the other.

The sample release gate consists of a Venetian blind, that is a system of parallel, horizontal overlapping, metal shutters. A sample is introduced by 90° rotation of the shutters which are opened electrically and closed manually. The particle-size distribution is recorded directly as phi-grain size.

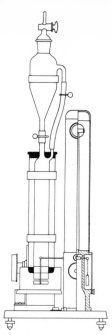

Fig. 10.4. Bostock's torsion balance (Gallenkamp).

10.4.1 The Micromerograph

The micromerograph is a two-layer sedimentation balance which uses a gas as the sedimentation fluid [2]. The sample is placed in a chamber at the top of the sedimentation column. A blast of nitrogen at high pressure forces the sample through the annulus between two cones to break up the aggregates. The particles then settle down the sedimentation tube on to the pan of a servo-electric balance. The accumulating weight is recorded on a strip chart giving a graph of weight against time. By use of a template incorporating Stokes' law a continuous particle-size distribution curve is obtained. The makers recommend the instrument for the size range 1 to 250 μm, but the best operating range is 2 to 70 μm. Reproducible results are obtained easily and rapidly without the need for highly trained operators and the instrument is largely automatic. Difficulties arise if a substantial fraction of the powder is smaller than 1 μm since it is not possible to correct for the weight of sample below the lowest measured size. The major difficulty with this instrument is that not all the sample is recorded [5] and losses may be as high as 80%. The assumption that has to be made is that this loss, which is due to powder adhering to the walls of the settling column, is representative. It is more probably, however, that the loss is selective, the fines being more readily attracted to the walls. In such cases the results from this instrument should be accepted with caution. The instrument, is therefore, only suitable for a limited range of material. The micromerograph is the only instrument in which terminal velocities can be measured in a gas, so that it is useful when no dispersing liquids can be found.

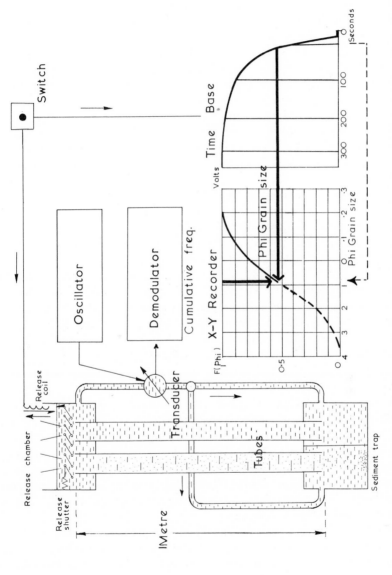

Fig. 10.5. Granulometer, pressure version. Micropressure difference is sensed electrically by a transducer and recorded as cumulative weight frequency (ordinate). Time base controls every y-plot to be recorded in phi-grain-size scale.

A recent study [58] of the micromerograph confirms its reproducibility but demonstrates the preferential loss of the finer fractions by recovering the material collected on the balance pan and passing it through the instrument again.

10.5 Sedimentation columns

The I.C.I. equipment (figure 10.6) was described in 1947 by Stairmand [13] in its original and in a modified form. The sedimentation tube is connected near its base to a reservoir of clear liquid. The sedimentation tube is one-third filled with clear liquid through which air is gently bubbled. Stopcock B is kept closed and stopcock A is replaced with the stirring funnel. About 0·1 ml of powder is dispersed in about 10 ml of clear liquid with a suitable agent and transferred to the sedimentation tube. The sedimentation tube is filled by opening stopcock B to allow liquid to enter from the reservoir. The stopcock is then closed, and, after 5 min the sampling cock is closed, thus isolating the system from the air supply, and the funnel is replaced by stopcock A. Stopcock A is then closed and cock B opened. The stopclock is started when the air agitation ceases, this being considered to be the commencement of sedimentation. At recorded times the sedimented powder is flushed out into a centrifuge tube, dried and weighed. If 10 ml of clear fluid is insufficient to remove all the powder, it is recommended that a 25 ml beaker be used instead of a centrifuge tube. If a 2:1 time progression is used the size distribution may be calculated (section 10.11), otherwise the size distribution may be derived in the usual way by plotting P against t and differentiating.

The B.C.U.R.A. equipment [34,35] (figure 10.7) is similar to the I.C.I. sedimentation column, except that a reservoir of clear liquid is not used. Instead the lower end of the tube is constructed of 1·0 mm bore glass tubing. When the tube is isolated from the air supply, surface tension prevents the suspension leaving the tube. A small sampling tube filled with clear liquid is then fitted over the outlet; this breaks the meniscus and allows the sediment to fall into the tube. At convenient time intervals the sampling tubes are replaced. The tubes are then dried and weighed as before. Recommended volume concentration is again 0·1%.

The two types of equipment described above are cheap and may be operated by semi-skilled assistants and, although continous attention is required, several analyses may be carried out concurrently. The concentration required is far lower than for incremental sedimentation, hence the possibility of hindered settling is greatly reduced. The surrounding water jacket maintains the temperature within the suspension tolerably constant and reduces thermal convection within the suspension. Disturbance of the suspension due to sampling is reduced with the I.C.I. and eliminated with the B.C.U.R.A. equipment.

Since the tubes are not cylindrical, the early samples are deficient in solids and the analysis is finer than the actual distribution. If the analysis is carried out in the tabular way described in section 10.11, an error of opposite sense but similar magnitude is introduced. For this reason the tabular method is recommended but it is suggested that the experimental points should be plotted and a smooth curve drawn through them to reduce operator curve. A common way of interpreting the results

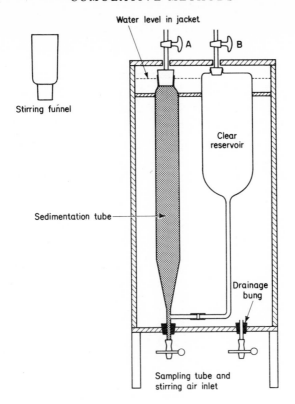

Fig. 10.6. I.C.I. sedimentation column

is to assume that at infinite time all the powder would be collected. This assumption may lead to large errors if much powder is lost in handling or if any powder sticks to the side of the tube. The latter can be considerable if the conical portion of the tube is rippled and any such tube should be rejected. Treatment with an antistatic agent (silicone M.441 as a 10% solution in carbon tetrachloride), can reduce this loss and with a Perspex tube and many powders the loss is negligible. A more accurate way of determining the weight of powder still in suspension is to carry out a sub-sidiary experiment, decanting at an appropriate time and height and drying and weighing the sediment or the suspension to determine the fractional weight of powder still in suspension at the Stokes' diameter for which the final sample was withdrawn in the experiment. This procedure is applicable to all cumulative sedi-mentation techniques when the loss of powder is small. One problem experienced with the B.C.U.R.A. equipment is some loss of liquid at the beginning of the experi-ment. The surface-tension force is unable to support the column unless aided by a partial vacuum above the column. The error introduced by this loss is slight and can be easily corrected. Alternatively, agitation may be carried out by using a vacuum pump connected to the top of the column instead of an air supply at the bottom

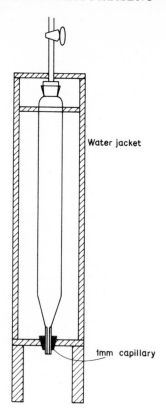

Fig. 10.7. B.C.U.R.A. sedimentation column.

and the residual vacuum when the pump is disconnected helps to support the column of liquid. These methods have some value for comparison work, but no advantage can be gained by using them for routine analyses since the analyses they give, though reproducible, are inaccurate.

10.6 Manometric methods

The manometric method was first described by Wiegner [36] and later by Kramer and Stamm [37] who used it with emulsion. In it a vertical capillary side tube filled with pure dispersion medium is joined to the lower end of a sedimenting column. The pure liquid has a greater height than that of the suspension due to is lower density. Measurement of this excess height at various times gives the variation of mean density of the suspension between the surface of the suspension and the sampling level. From these data the size distribution curve may be determined. This technique was later improved by Dotts [19] by use of a more consistent technique, simplified calculations and simpler apparatus. Dotts claimed an accuracy of 1%. The apparatus is commercially available as the Fisher − Dotts apparatus.

In 1942, Kelly [38] produced a modification of an earlier apparatus by Ostwald and Hahn by constructing the side tube at a small angle to the horizontal instead of the vertical in order to increase the sensitivity. He claimed an accuracy of 0·5%. A variation was proposed by Goodhue and Smith [39] who increased the sensitivity of a Kelly-type instrument by using two immiscible liquids to magnify the reading zone. Duncombe and Withrow [40] made an extensive study of the above instrument, improved the apparatus further and applied corrections for leakage of clear fluid into the suspension as the manometer level fell. The instrument was automated by Knapp [41] who magnified the pressure change by an optical lever system and recorded it photographically. More recent work has been carried out by Soper [42] who added clear immiscible fluid to the manometer to maintain a constant level. This remedied the fault of the earlier instruments in that manometer fluid entered the sedimentation tube and disturbed the settling powder (Gessner [43]). Other faults of the method are that the change in excess height is small so that accurate measurement is difficult, the manometer tends to be sluggish in action and the fluid in the manometer can be contaminated with powder that has migrated from the sedimentation vessel. The last fault can be minimized by making a constriction in the manometer tube [37]. A review of manometric methods was made by Hawksley in 1951 [44]. The method was not recommended by Jarret and Heywood who, in 1954, compared various types of size analysis equipment [16].

10.7 Pressure on the walls of the sedimentation tube
This is a method used by Edwald [45], who recorded the change in pressure on the wall of the sedimentation vessel as sedimentation proceeded, and assumed it to be proportional to the amount of sediment.

10.8 Decanting
In this method a homogeneous suspension is allowed to settle for a predetermined time. The supernatant liquid is then decanted off and replaced by fresh dispersing liquid. This process is repeated several times for the same sedimentation time until the supernatant liquid is clear. The decanted liquid will only contain particles finer than size $D = k \sqrt{(h_2/t)}$, where h_2 is the depth at which the liquid is siphoned off at time t and k is a constant. The process is repeated for shorter times so that the particles removed become progressively coarser. Herdan [46] suggests that six repeats are sufficient to remove substantially all the particles under the selected size and Allen [47] found that fifteen repeats are necessary to produce a clear supernatant liquid.

A theoretical approach is to consider a cylindrical vessel containing a depth h_1 of homogeneous suspension, the siphoning being carried out at a depth h_2. No particles coarser than $D = k \sqrt{(h_2/t)}$ will be removed. Particles of size $xD, x < 1·0$ will have fallen a distance h in the same time, where:

$$xD = k \sqrt{(h/t)}.$$

Hence, from these two equations:

$$x^2 = h/h_2.$$

The fraction F_1 of particles of size xD removed

$$= (h_2 - h)h_1$$

$$= (h_2/h_1)(1 - x^2).$$

The fraction of particles of this size still in suspension

$$= \left[1 - \frac{h_2}{h_1}(1 - x^2) \right]$$

If the suspension is made up to its original volume, redispersed and a second fraction removed after a further time t, the fraction of particles of size xD removed will be:

$$F_2 = \frac{h_2}{h_1}(1 - x^2) \left[1 - \frac{h_2}{h_1}(1 - x^2) \right]$$

The fraction of particles of this size still in suspension will be:

$$\left[1 - \frac{h_2}{h_1}(1 - x^2) \right]^2.$$

After n decantings the fraction still in suspension

$$= \left[1 - \frac{h_2}{h_1}(1 - x^2) \right]^n. \tag{10.4}$$

Therefore, the fraction removed

$$= 1 - \left[1 - \frac{h_2}{h_1}(1 - x^2) \right]^n. \tag{10.5}$$

The effect of h_2/h_1 is negligible over quite a wide range compared with x, hence there is little to be gained from making $h_2 - h_1$ very small with subsequent risk of disturbing the solids that have settled out. For example, if h_2/h_1 is reduced from 1 to 0·9, the number of decantings to achieve the same separation will be increased from n to m, where:

$$\frac{m}{n} = \frac{\log [1 - (1 - x^2)]}{\log [1 - 0\cdot9(1 - x^2)]} = \frac{\log x^2}{\log (0\cdot1 + 0\cdot9x^2)}$$

for $x = 0\cdot5$, $m/n = 1\cdot23$.

Some values of separation are given in table 10.2 for $h_2/h_1 = 0\cdot9$.

Table 10.3. Percentage of particles removed after
a known number of decantings

Relative particle size (x)	Number of decantings (n)					
	1	2	4	8	16	32
0·9	17·1	31·3	52·7	77·6	95·3	97·7
0·8	32·4	54·4	79·3	95·7	98·2	99·7
0·7	45·9	70·6	91·4	99·3	–	–
0·6	57·6	82·0	96·8	99·8	–	–
0·5	68·5	90·1	99·0	–	–	–

A large number of decantings are required to remove particles whose size is close to the cut size. Hence the wider the size range of the original suspension, the fewer the decantings required.

Although the method would not normally be used for size analysis, it is a useful means of obtaining closely graded samples. Several descriptions of apparatus are available [46, 48 – 51]. Apparatus has also been devised so that the whole operation may be carried out automatically [52].

10.9 The β – back-scattering method

In this technique the thickness of the deposited solid is determined by recording the intensity of β-radiation scattered from the base of a sedimentation column [53 – 55]. The apparatus (figure 10.8) consists of a 100 cm^3 Perspex centrifuge tube with a thin flat base (0·015 in), situated above a 3 mC^{90}Sr – ^{90}Y source, which rests in the wall of a thick lead ring placed on tope of a β-scintillation counter, the output of which is fed to a rate meter and recorder.

The intensity of the radiation scattered back from the base of the tube is proportional to both the atomic number and the thickness of the scattered material. The graph of scattered radiation against concentration of deposit exhibits an initial linear portion before saturation is reached. If this portion only is used, the increase in count rate is proportional to the increase in weight of deposit. The maximum thickness of deposit for this condition is of the order of 0·07 g cm^{-2}. The technique is applicable to materials having an effective atomic number $\bar{z}$ greater than 12·5, where:

$$\bar{z} = \frac{n(A_b Z_b) + m(A_c Z_c)}{\text{mol. wt of } B_n C_m}$$

where A_b and A_c are the atomic weights of B and C, and Z_b and Z_c their atomic numbers in a compound $B_n C_m$.

Settling under gravity allows size distributions from approximately 80 to 1 μm and this may be extended to 0·1 μm by centrifuging the tube.

An alternative method is described in [69]. The apparatus consists of a Pyrex glass tube about 120 cm in length and 2·5 cm internal diameter. One end is tapered

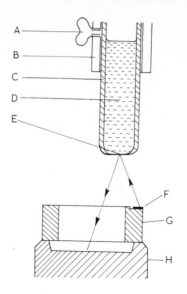

A = Perspex locating screw
B = Perspex tube holder
C = Perspex sedimentation tube
D = Sedimentation liquid

E = Sedimented material
F = 3mC⁹⁰Sr ⁹⁰Y source
G = Lead ring
H = β-Scintillation counter
    or ionisation chamber

Fig. 10.8. Arrangement of source, sedimentation tube and counter for
β-back-scattering method

to an 8 mm internal diameter outlet tube, as shown in figure 10.9. A piece of soft
rubber tubing is attached to the outlet tube and this is closed with a spring clip.
The tube is calibrated along its length in centimetres, the zero position at the outlet
end of the tube being determined as follows. A quantity of water is placed in the
tube with the outlet clip closed, sufficient being added to bring the level above the
tapered portion of the tube. The level of the water is then marked. A further volume
of water is added to the tube and the level again marked. From this difference in
volumes and levels, the volume of water per unit length of tube is established. The
tube is then emptied by opening the clip and the quantity of water corresponding to
a 5 cm length of tube again added. The water level is permanently marked with the
figure 5 and subsequently a linear centimetre scale is marked on the tube from 5 to
100 cm.

For an analysis, a sample of powder weighing about 4 g is dispersed in 100 ml of
distilled water and added to the tube which is then inverted repeatedly for about a
minute to give a uniform dispersion. After some 20 − 30 inversions a stopwatch is
started on the last inversion immediately the air bubble has left the lower end of the
tube. The tube is immediately placed in a rack and held in a vertical position. After

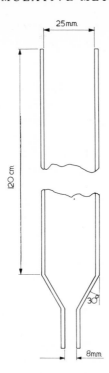

Fig. 10.9. Sedimentation tube.

about 90 s, the spring clip is opened carefully and sufficient of the suspension is allowed to run out under gravity into a 100 ml centrifuge tube (pre-weighed), so that the suspension surface falls from the 100–cm mark to the 86-cm mark. Timing should be such that exactly 100 s should have elapsed when the clip is closed and the suspension level reach 86 cm. The temperature of this sample is taken and recorded. The process is repeated after 3, 6, 12, 30 and 90 min at levels of 72, 58, 44, 30 and 15 cm. After 180 min, the remaining suspension is withdrawn, down to 5 cm in one centrifuge tube and the remainder in the last tube. The suspension is now distributed among the eight centrifuge tubes used. The amount of sediment is found by centrifuging and removing the supernatant, or filtering and drying. For quantities less than 1 g, the suspended material can be filtered off on a glass fibre or membrane filter, dried, and the weight again found.

The calculation of results is shown in example 1. Columns 4, 5 and 6 are self-evident. Column 7 is the summation of col. 6, starting at the bottom (i.e. col. 7, line 7, is col. 6, line 8; col. 7, line 6, is col. 6, line 7 and 8; col. 7, line 5, is col. 6, line 6 + 7 + 8, etc.).

Column 8, the depth factor, is applied to restore the cumulative weight and time to that required for a full 100-cm depth of fall. Column 8 is 100/col. 2. Column 9 is the corrected weight − col. 7 × col. 8. Column 10 is the corrected time − col. 3 × col. 8. The percentage in col. 11 is expressed as a percentage of the total weight.

Graphical interpretation of results
The results calculated in columns 10 and 11 of example 1 (p. 242) are plotted on 5-cycle semi-logarithmic graph papers. The points are uniformly spaced, thus allowing the curve to be drawn with maximum accuracy.

A piece of tracing paper, or thin Perspex sheet, is then taken and horizontal lines are drawn to correspond with the upper and lower limits of the graph (0 and 100% cumulative weight). Vertical lines are drawn, their distance apart being equal to the distance between log 1·0 and log e on the graph (i.e. 1·72). If now the tracing paper is placed on the curve and moved horizontally, the lower horizontal line following the axis through 0%, until the line log e is at the time corresponding to the settling time for a selected grain diameter, a tangent to the curve at this point will intersect the line log 1 at a point whose ordinate is the cumulative percentage finer than the chosen size. This process is continued for as many points as desired. The grain-size distribution curve is then obtained by plotting these points against particle diameter on another semi-logarithmic sheet.

Particle size is given using Stokes' equation, allowance being made for the fall in height after multiplied by $(100/h)$, where h is the height immediately prior to withdrawal. This factor is necessary in order to restore the cumulative weight deposited to that required for a full 100 cm depth of fall. A plot of corrected weight deposited against corrected time ($100/h$ × true time) is essentially P versus t from which the weight undersize may be determined.

10.10 Discussion
The main advantage that most cumulative methods have over incremental methods of sedimentation analysis is that the concentration required is much lower, thus reducing the risk of hindered settling. The technique is most useful for normal distributions, but the need to differentiate leads to errors when the size distribution is irregular in any way (e.g. bimodal).

The B.C.U.R.A. and I.C.I. equipment give similar and reproducible analyses but the latter is simpler in use. This apparatus is of most use when nearly all the powder is finer than about 50 μm since, if there is a substantial weight of powder above this size, repeat analyses produce wide variations in the weight of the initial aliquot sample. The shape of the sedimentation tube limits the method to comparison work and justifies the use of the approximate theory derived in section 10.6. Loss of powder on the conical portion of the tube also leads to errors which are usually negligible but may be significant with some powders.

The cumulative effect of the many disadvantages of the manometric method make it highly unlikely that it will ever be widely used for routine analysis. Repeated decanting will continue to prove attractive to many industries because of the low cos of equipment and the by-product of closely graded fractions. Manual decanting is too time-consuming to merit general approval but machine decanting is a more attractive proposition.

Balance methods continue to be most attractive, the best of these is probably the Cahn. The Bostock is the cheapest of these systems and a modified version to eliminate its faults could be most useful. It could also be improved by being made a continuous recording balance. The Sartorious has this advantage, combined with the disadvantage that the pan is immersed in the suspension, which leads to errors in the record. The Shimadzu is completely unsuitable due to its sluggish response.

10.11 Appendix: An approximate method of calculating size distribution from cumulative sedimentation results

All particles larger than 75 μm are removed by sieving. The top sedimentation size of the remainder is taken as 106 μm, due to the overlapping of sieve size and Stokes' diameter. The sieve range is then extended to the following sizes:

Grade size (μ)   106 – 75 – 53 – 37·5 – 26·5 – 18·8 – 13·3 – 9·4 – 6·6 – 4·7 – 3·3

Mean size (μ)   89 63 44·5 31·5 22·3 15·8 11·2 7·9 5·6 4·0

It is assumed that the mean size may be attributed to the whole range, e.g. in the 75 to 106 μm range all particles are assumed to have the size 89 μm.

Since the sizes diminish in a $\sqrt{(2)}$:1 ratio, the free-falling speed will decrease in a 2:1 ratio. Thus when the 89 μm particles have fallen the full length of the sedimentation tube, the 63 μm particles will have fallen half the length, hence half of them will have fallen out of suspension.

The first sample is withdrawn when all the 89 μm particles have fallen out of suspension at time t; the second sample when all the 63 μm particles have fallen out of suspension at t and so on.

Let:

W_{89} be the weight of solids in the size range 75 to 105 μm,

X_{89} be the total weight of sediment at time t_{89},

Y_{63} be the weight of the increment at time t_{63}.

Figure 10.10 shows the upper levels for the various sizes at the times given below the figures.

The first sample, withdrawn at t_{89}, will be:

$$X_{89} = W_{89} + \tfrac{1}{2}W_{63} + \tfrac{1}{4}W_{44\cdot5} + \tfrac{1}{8}W_{31\cdot5} + \tfrac{1}{16}W_{22\cdot3} + ... + \tfrac{1}{512}W_4. \qquad (10.6)$$

The first increment will be:

$$Y_{63} = \tfrac{1}{2}W_{63} + \tfrac{1}{4}W_{44\cdot5} + \tfrac{1}{8}W_{31\cdot5} + \tfrac{1}{16}W_{22\cdot4} + ... + \tfrac{1}{512}W_4 \qquad (10.7)$$

therefore:

$$W_{89} = X_{89} - Y_{63}.$$

The second increment will be:

$$Y_{44\cdot5} = \tfrac{1}{2}W_{44\cdot5} + \tfrac{1}{4}W_{31\cdot5} + \tfrac{1}{8}W_{22\cdot5} + ... + \tfrac{1}{256}W_4. \qquad (10.8)$$

From equations (10.5) and (10.6):

$$W_{63} = 2Y_{63} - Y_{44\cdot5}$$

Example I — SEDIMENTATION TUBE RESULT SHEET

1	2	3	4	5	6	7	8	9	10	11
Tube No.	Height (cm)	Time	Weight of tube + sample (g)	Weight of tube (g)	Weight of sample (g)	Cumulative weight $(g)(P)$	Depth factor $\left(\frac{h_0}{h}\right) = \left(\frac{100}{h}\right)$	Weight in 100 cm suspension (g)	Corrected time (mins) $\left(\frac{100}{h}\right)T$	%
	$\frac{h_0}{100}$									
1	86	100 secs	66·6800	66·5175	0·1625	0·9640	1·000	0·9640	1·94	100
2	72	3 min	66·5791	66·4241	0·1550	0·8015	1·163	0·9322	4·17	96·7
3	58	6 min	67·6784	67·5212	0·1572	0·6465	1·389	0·8980	10·30	93·2
4	44	12 min	67·1532	66·9886	0·1646	0·4893	1·724	0·8436	27·3	87·5
5	30	30 min	73·8796	73·7008	0·1788	0·3247	2·273	0·7380	100	76·6
6	15	90 min	73·1364	73·0001	0·1363	0·1459	3·333	0·4863	600	50·5
7	5	180 min	65·2502	65·2414	0·0088	0·0096	6·667	0·0640	3600	6·6
8		180⁺ min	73·3064	73·3056	0·0008	0·0008	20	0·0160		1·7

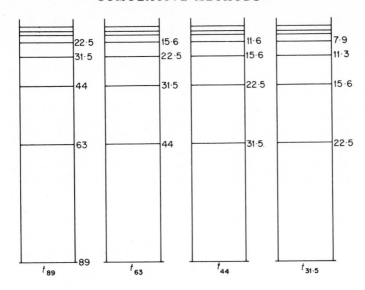

Fig. 10.10. Theory for the I.C.I. technique.

The third increment will be:

$$\gamma_{31\cdot5} = \tfrac{1}{2}W_{31\cdot5} + \tfrac{1}{4}W_{22\cdot5} + \tfrac{1}{8}W_{15\cdot6} + \dots + \tfrac{1}{256}W_4 \qquad (10.9)$$

From equations (10.8) and (10.9):

$$W_{44\cdot5} = 2\gamma_{44\cdot5} - \gamma_{31\cdot5}.$$

This form of solution continues until the final withdrawal, which we shall assume is at t_4. The solids still remaining in suspension after t_4 we shall call γ_0.

Total weight of solids = total weight of increments

$$W_{89} + W_{63} + W_{44\cdot5} + W_{31\cdot5} + \dots + W_4 + W_{3\cdot3}$$

$$= X_{89} + \gamma_{63} + \gamma_{31\cdot5} + \dots + \gamma_4 + \gamma_0.$$

Substituting in the solutions for W:

$$(X_{89} - \gamma_{63}) + (2\gamma_{63} - \gamma_{44\cdot5}) + (2\gamma_{63} + \gamma_{31\cdot5}) + (2\gamma_{5\cdot6} - \gamma_4) + W_{<3\cdot3}$$

$$= X_{89} + \gamma_{63} + \gamma_{44\cdot5} + \gamma_{31\cdot5} + \dots + \gamma_4 + \gamma_0 - \gamma_4 + W_{<3\cdot3} = \gamma_4 + \gamma_0$$

$$W_{<3\cdot3} = 2\gamma_4 + \gamma_0$$

These results may be summarized: (see table 10.1)

Table 10.1

Size of grade	Mean size	Time of sampling	Weight of increment	Weight in grading
106−75	89	t_{89}	x_{89}	$x_{89} - \gamma_{63}$
75−53·3	63	t_{63}	γ_{63}	$2\gamma_{63} - \gamma_{44}$
53·5−37·5	44·5	$t_{44·5}$	$\gamma_{44·5}$	$2\gamma_{44·5} - \gamma_{31·5}$
31·5−26·5	31·5	$t_{31·5}$	$\gamma_{31·5}$	$2\gamma_{31·5} - \gamma_{22·4}$
26·5−18·8	22·3	$t_{22·4}$	$\gamma_{22·5}$	$2\gamma_{22·4} - \gamma_{15·6}$
18·8−13·3	15·6	$t_{15·6}$	$\gamma_{15·6}$	$2\gamma_{15·6} - \gamma_{11·2}$
13·3− 9·4	11·2	$t_{11·2}$	$\gamma_{11·2}$	$2\gamma_{11·2} - \gamma_{8}$
9·4− 6·6	7·9	t_{8}	γ_{8}	$2\gamma_{8} - \gamma_{5·6}$
6·6− 4·7	5·6	$t_{5·6}$	$\gamma_{5·6}$	$2\gamma_{5·6} - \gamma_{4·0}$
4·7− 3·3	4·0	$t_{4·0}$	$\gamma_{4·0}$	
		t_{0}	γ_{0}	$2\gamma_{4·0} - \gamma_{0}$
			W TOTAL	W TOTAL

γ is obtained by difference. γ_0 = initial wt of sample − sum of increments up to and including γ_4

t_{89} is determined using Stokes' equation:

$$t_{89} = \frac{18\eta h}{(\rho_s - \rho_f) g(89)^2} \times 10^8$$

and $t_{63} = 2t_{89}$; $t_{44·5} = 2t_{63}$ and so on.

References

[1] Marshall, C.E. (1930), *Proc. R. Soc.* **A126**, 427.
[2] Eadie, F.A., and Payne, R.E. (1954), (*a*) (1954) *Iron Age*, **174**, 99; (*b*) (1956) *Brit. Chem. Eng.*, **1**, 306.
[3] Werner, D. (1925), *Trans. Faraday Soc.*, **21**, 381.
[4] Travis, P.M. (1940), *A.S.T.M. Bull.*, **29**, 102.
[5] Irani, R.R., and Callis, C.F. (1963), *Particle Size: Measurement, Interpretation and Application,* Wiley, N.Y.
[6] Whitby, K.T. (Jan., 1955), *Heating, Piping and Air Conditioning,* (Jan. 1955) Part 1, 231; (June 1955) Part 2, 139.
[7] Whitby, K.T., Algren, A.B., and Annis, J.C. (1958), A.S.T.M. Sp. Publ. No. 234, 117.
[8] Imris, P., and Landspersky, H. (1956), *Silikaty,* **9**, 4, 327.
[9] Oden, S. (1916), *Kolloid Z.,* **18**, 33 − 47.
[10] Coutts, J., and Crowthers, E.M. (1925), *Trans. Faraday Soc.,* **21**, 374.
[11] Bostock, W. (1952), *J. Sci. Instrum.,* **29**, 209.
[12] Gaudin, A.M., Schumann, R., and Schlechter, A.W. (1942), *J. Phys. Chem.,* **46**, 903.
[13] Stairmand, C.J. (1947), Symposium on Particle Size Analysis, *Inst. Chem. Eng.,* **25**, 110.
[14] Edwald, P. (1942), *Ind. Eng. Chem., analyt. ed.,* **14**, 66.
[15] Nissan, A.H. (1951), *Faraday Soc. (Discussion),* **11**, 15.
[16] Jarrett, B.A., and Heywood, H. (1954), *B. J. Appl. Phys.,* suppl. 3, 21s.

[17] Donoghue, J.K. (1956), *Brit. J. Appl. Phys.*, suppl. 5, 7, 333.
[18] Oden, S. (1925), *Soil Science,* 19, 1.
[19] Dotts, W.M. (1946), *Ind. Eng. Chem. analyt. ed.,* 19, 326.
[20] Svedberg, T., and Rinde, H. (1934), *J. Am. Chem. Soc.,* 45, 173.
[21] Bishop, D.L. (1934), *Bur. Stand. J. Res.,* 12, 173.
[22] Knapp, R.T. (1934), *Ind. Eng. Chem., analyt. ed.,* 6, 66.
[23] Muller, R.H., and Garman, R.L. (1936), *Analyt. Chem.,* 10, 436.
[24] Jacobsen, A.E., and Sullivan, W.G. (1947), *Analyt. Chem.,* 19, 855.
[25] Suito, E., and Arakawa, M. (1950), *Bull. J. Chem. Res., Kyota University,* 23, 7.
[26] Kiffer, C. (1954), (*a*) *Bull. Soc. Franc. Ceram.,* 17, 22; (*b*) (1954) *Abs. Trans. Ceram. Cos.,* 53, 392A.
[27] Rabatin, G.J., and Gale, R.H. (1956), *Analyt. Chem.,* 28, 1314.
[28] Bachmann, D., and Gerstenberg, H., (1957), *Chem. Eng. Tech.,* 8, 589.
[29] Friedrich, W. (1959), *Staub,* 19, 281.
[30] Loos, E. (1959), *Staub,* 19, 392.
[31] Palik, E.S. (1962), *Ceramic Age,* 78, 8, 49.
[32] Cohen, L. (1959), *Instrum. Practice,* 13, 1036.
[33] Ames, D.P., Irani, R.R., and Callis, C.F. (1959), *J. Phys. Chem.,* 63, 531.
[34] Kabak, J., and Loveridge, D.J. (1960), *J. Sci. Instrum.,* 37, 266.
[35] Kabak, J. (1955), *J. Sci. Instrum.,* 32, 153.
[36] Weigner, G. (1918), *Landwirtsh. vers. Sta.,* 91, 41.
[37] Kramer, E.O., and Stamm, A.J. (1924), *J. Am. Chem. Soc.,* 46, 2709.
[38] Kelly, W.S. (1924), *Ind. Eng. Chem.,* 16, 928.
[39] Goodhue, L.D., and Smith, C.M. (1936), *Ind. Eng. Chem., analyt. ed.,* 8, 469.
[40] Duncombe, C.G., and Withrow, J.R. (1932), *J. Phys. Chem.,* 36, 31.
[41] Knapp, R.T. (1934), *Ind. Eng. Chem., analyt. ed.,* 6, 66.
[42] Soper, A.K. (1947), Symposium on Particle Size Analysis, *Inst. Chem. Eng.* 110.
[43] Gessner, H. (1928), Akademische Verlagsgesellschaft, Leipzig.
[44] Hawksley, P.G.W. (1951), *British Coal Utilisation Research Assoc. Bull.,* 15, 4, 129.
[45] Edwald, P. (1942), *Ind. Eng. Chem., analyt. ed.,* 14, 66.
[46] Herdan, G. (1960), *Small Particle Statistics,* Butterworths.
[47] Allen, T. (1962), London Univ., M.Sc. thesis.
[48] Truog, E., *et al.* (1936), *Proc. Soil Sci. Soc. Am.,* 1, 10.
[49] Davies, R.J., Green, R.A., and Donnelly, H.F.E. (1937), *Trans. Ceram. Soc.,* 36, 181.
[50] Birchfield, H.P., Gullaston, D.K., and McNew, G.L. (1948), *Anal. Chem.,* 20, 1168.
[51] Johnson, E.I., and King, J. (1951), *Analyst,* 76, 661.
[52] Horsfall, F., and Jowett, A. (1960), *J. Sci. Instrum.,* 37, 4, 120.
[53] Connor, P., Hardwick, W.H., and Laundy, B.J. (1958), *J. ApplyChem.,* 8, 716.
[54] *ibid.,* (1959), 9, 525.
[55] Hardwick, W.H., and Laundy, B.J. (1966), International Symposium on Particle Size Measurement, Loughborough, 1966, *Soc. for Analyt. Chem.*
[56] Leschonski, K. (1962), *Staub.,* 22, 475.
[57] Pretorius, S.T., and Mandersloot, W.G.B., *Powder Technol.* (in the press).
[58] Bryant, A.C., Freeman, D.S., and Tye, F.L., Particle Size Analysis Conference, 1966, *Soc. Analyt. Chem.*

[59] Scott, K.J., and Mumford, D. (1970), *C.S.I.R. Special Report Chem.*, 156; and Scott, K.J. (1972), *Addendum,* Pretoria, South Africa.

[60] Van Tonder, J.C., Viljoen, N.J.S., Birkhill, R.S., and Geertsma, J.C. (1969), *R.A.K. Verslag No. 10.*

[61] Harris, C.C., and Jowett, A. (1963), *Nature,* **197**, 4873, 1192.

[62] Mengelsdorf, P.C. (1959), *J. Appl. Phys.,* **30**, 442.

[63] Alex, W., and Putz, R. (1971), *Messtechnik,* **78**, 3, 69 − 73.

[64] Leschonski, K., and Alex, W. (1972), *Proc. International Symposium on Particle Size Analysis, Bradford 1971,* Soc. Analyt. Chem.

[65] Grandillo, A.D. (1970), *J. Powder Metall.,* **6**, 1, 3 − 16.

[66] Allen, T. (1967), Univ. of Bradford, Ph.D. thesis.

[67] Brezina, J. (1969), *J. Sedimentary Petrology,* (1627 − 1631).

[68] Brezina, J. (1972), *Particle Size Analysis 1970,* Soc. Analytical Chem., 225 − 6

[69] *Report No. 7* (1943), 'A study of methods used in measurement and analysis of sediment loads in streams', St. Paul, U.S. Engineer District Sub-office Hydraulic Laboratory, University of Iowa, Iowa City, U.S.A.

[70] Gaudin, A.M., Schumann, R., and Schlechten, A.W. (1942), *J. Phys. Chem.,* **46**, 902 − 4.

11 Fluid Classification

11.1 Introduction

Fluid classification is a process for separating dispersed materials, based on the movement of suspended particles to different points under the effect of different forces. The fluid is usually water or air and the field force either gravity, as with elutriators, or centrifugal and Coriolis, in rotary classifiers. The other forces of importance are the drag forces due to relative flow between the particles and flow medium, and the inertia forces, due to accelerated particle movement. A wide variety of equipment is available, ranging in capacity from many tons per hour with the larger units to a few grams per hour with laboratory machines.

The results of classification processes may be presented as size distributions, the accuracies of which depend on the sharpness of cut. The ideal is when the cut size is well defined and there are no coarse particles in the fine fraction and vice versa. In practice, however, there is always overlapping of sizes. The cut size may sometimes be predicted from theory, but this usually differs from the actual cut size due to difficulties in accurately predicting the flow patterns in the system. It is, therefore, necessary to be able to predict the performance of classifiers based on their actual performance.

11.2 Assessment of classifier efficiency [18, 20]

Consider a single stage of a classifier, where: W, W_c, W_f are the weight of feed, coarse produce and fine product respectively; $F(x)$, $F_c(x)$, $F_f(x)$ are the cumulative fraction oversize of feed, coarse product and fine product; x is particle size.
Then:

$$W = W_c + W_f \qquad (11.1)$$

and

$$W. \frac{dF(x)}{dx} = W_c \frac{dF_c(x)}{dx} + W_f \frac{dF_f(x)}{dx}. \qquad (11.2)$$

The total coarse efficiency may be defined as:

$$E_c = \frac{W_c}{W} \qquad (11.3)$$

and the total fine efficiency as:

$$E_f = \frac{W_f}{W} \qquad (11.4)$$

$$= 1 - E_c . \tag{11.5}$$

The value of E_c is meaningless for a general characterization of the classifier since it depends upon the quality of the feed.

The grade efficiency, which is independent of the feed, is defined by:

$$\text{coarse grade efficiency} = \frac{\text{amount of coarse product of size } x}{\text{amount of feed of size } x}$$

$$G_c(x) = W_c \frac{dF_c(x)}{dx} \div W \frac{dF(x)}{dx}$$

$$= \frac{W_c}{W} \frac{dF_c(x)}{dF(x)}$$

$$= E_c \frac{dF_c(x)}{dF(x)} \tag{11.6}$$

Similarly, the fine grade efficiency is defined by:

$$G_f(x) = E_f \frac{dF_f(x)}{dF(x)} \tag{11.7}$$

which, from equation (11.2) and (11.4) may be written:

$$G_f(x) = 1 - G_c(x) . \tag{11.8}$$

These equations enable one to determine the grade efficiency of a classification process from the total efficiency and the size distributions of any two streams. Results are usually plotted as *grade efficiency curves* of $G_c(x)$ or $G_f(x)$ against x.

Table 11.1. Example of grade efficiency calculation

Particle size (x)	F(x)	$\dfrac{dF(x)}{dx}$	$F_c(x)$	$\dfrac{dF_c(x)}{dx}$	$G_c(x)$	$\bar{x}$
2	0	1		0		2·8
4	2	2·25	0	1	0·13	5·6
8	11	2·75	2	2·25	0·25	11
16	33	2·00	12	4·00	0·60	22
32	65	0·73	44	1·94	0·80	44
64	88·5	0·15	81	0·50	1·00	90
128	98	0·02	97	0·05	1·00	180
256	100		100			

Total weight of feed = 100 g; total weight of coarse product = 60 g.

These data are plotted in figure 11.1. The 50% size on the grade efficiency curve is called the *equiprobable* size (e), since particles of this size have an equal chance

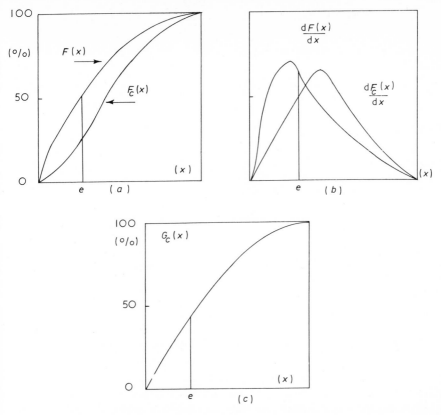

Fig. 11.1. (a) Cumulative percentage undersize by weight curves for feed and coarse product. (b) Relative percentage per micrometre for feed and (c) Grade efficiency curves.

of being found in the coarse or fine produce and are usually taken as the cut size.

The grade efficiency is often expressed as a single number. This number is the sharpness index, ϕ, and is related to the slope of the grade efficiency curve at the equiprobable size:

$$75\phi25 = \frac{x_{75}}{x_{25}} \tag{11.9}$$

where x_{75} and x_{25} are the particle sizes at which the grade efficiency is 75% and 25% respectively. For perfect classification $\phi = 1$, while values above 3 are considered poor. Alternatively, $90\phi10$ has been used.

Leschonski [1] is of the opinion that these ratios are not always adequate to define the sharpness of cut. In many cases it is important to keep the proportions finer or coarser than the cut size as small as possible in both, or at least one of both, fractions. For these cases a measure of the effectiveness of the separation process is given by [19]:

$$\psi_c = \frac{\text{weight of coarse particles larger than } e \text{ in the coarse fraction}}{\text{weight of coarse particles larger than } e \text{ in the feed}}$$

$$\psi_c = E_c \frac{\sum\limits_{e}^{x_{max}} F_c(x)}{\sum\limits_{e}^{x_{max}} F(x)}. \tag{11.10}$$

Similarly:

$$\psi_f = E_f \frac{\sum\limits_{x_{min}}^{e} F_f(x)}{\sum\limits_{x_{min}}^{e} F(x)}. \tag{11.11}$$

11.3 Systems

All classifiers can be divided into two systems, the counterflow equilibrium and the transverse flow separation.

Counter flow can occur either in a gravitational or centrifugal field. The field force and the drag force act in opposite directions and particles leave the separation zone in one of two directions according to their size. Particles of a certain size are acted upon by two equal and opposite forces, hence stay in equilibrium in the separation zone. In gravitational systems these particles remain in a state of suspension, while in a centrifugal field the equilibrium particles rotate at a fixed radius which is governed by the rate at which material is withdrawn from the system. They would, therefore, accumulate to very high concentrations in a continually operated classifier if they were not distributed to the fine or coarse fraction by a stochastic mixing process.

In a transverse-flow classifier, the feed material enters the flow medium at one point of the classification chamber at a certain angle with a component of velocity transverse to the flow and is fanned out under the action of field, inertia and resistance forces. Particles of the same size describe identical trajectories which differ from the trajectories of particles of a different size, and it is possible to separate them according to size.

11.4 Counterflow equilibrium classifiers in the gravitational field-elutriators

Elutriation is a process of grading particles by means of an upward current of fluid, usually water or air. The process is therefore the reverse of gravity sedimentation and Stokes' law applies. The grading is carried out in a series of vessels, usually of cylindro-conical form and of successively increasing diameter. Hence the fluid velocity decreases in each stage, the coarsest particles being retained in the smallest vessel and relatively finer particles in the following vessels. The operation is considered completed when, for air elutriation, the rate of change in the weight of the residue is deemed negligible, say 0·2% of the initial weight in half an hour. For water elutriation, the end-point is reached when there are no visible signs of further classification taking place.

In most elutriators Stokes' law does not apply, since the ratio of tube length to tube diameter is too small for laminar flow conditions, i.e. the fluid disturbances at inlet and outlet overlap. Combined with this, the tube shape is not always conductive to laminar flow.

Due to the viscosity of the fluid, a parabolic velocity front exists which is flattened only in the case of large-diameter tubes. The cut is not sharp, therefore, since the upward force on a particle depends on its axial position in the tube. In spite of these defects, elutriation methods are still useful for design or control work. Roller [2] showed that the effect of the uneven cut is the removal of some coarse above the theoretical cut-point, while leaving behind some of the fines. Thus, while the separate fractions are not accurately sized, the final mass fraction is often reasonably close to the correct value. This has been confirmed by Stairmand [3], who points out that the method is not applicable to bimodal distributions.

The parameter by which particles are classified is their falling speed, which is not uniquely related to size, but which is of greater significance than size in many applications, e.g. in determining the respirability of dust or the point of deposition of particulate matter emitted from a chimney stack.

A particular advantage of elutriation is the production of closely graded fractions which are often useful for further investigations.

Theory

If it is assumed that the fluid flow is streamline, the velocity profile is parabolic, the velocity at a point at a distance r from the axis of the tube, being given by Poiseuille's equation:

$$v = \frac{p}{4\eta L}(a^2 - r^2) \qquad (11.12)$$

where p is the pressure drop across the elutriator tube,
  η is the fluid viscosity,
  L is the tube length,
  a is the tube radius.

The flow rate through the tube is:

$$Q = \frac{pa^4}{8\eta L} \qquad (11.13)$$

giving an average velocity:

$$v_m = \frac{Q}{\pi a^2} = \frac{pa^2}{8\eta L} \qquad (11.14)$$

By putting $r = 0$ in equation (11.12), the maximum velocity may be found:

$$v_{max} = \frac{p}{4\eta L}a^2 = 2v_m. \qquad (11.15)$$

From equations (11.12) and (11.13):

$$v = v_{max} \left(1 - \frac{r^2}{a^2}\right) = 2v_m \left(1 - \frac{r^2}{a^2}\right).$$

(11.16)

If it is assumed that there is no radial flow of particles, the possibility of a particle being elutriated depends on its position in the tube. Since v_m is the velocity usually taken as the elutriation velocity, from equation (11.16):

$$\frac{r^2}{a^2} = 1 - \frac{v}{2v_m}.$$

(11.17)

Thus a particle of terminal velocity v can ascend if it is in a coaxial circle of radius r. Assuming a homogeneous distribution of particles, the fraction of this size ascending is the fraction contained in a cylinder of radius r:

$$F = \pi r^2 / \pi a^2$$

$$= 1 - v/2v_m.$$

(11.18)

Since, from Stokes' equation, v is proportional to particle size squared:

$$F = 1 - \frac{1}{2}\left(\frac{D}{D_m}\right)^2.$$

(11.19)

The collection efficiency may be calculated using equation (11.19).

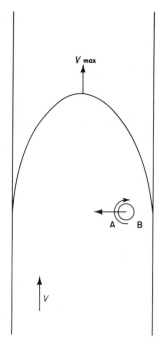

Fig. 11.2. The pressure gradient across a particle.

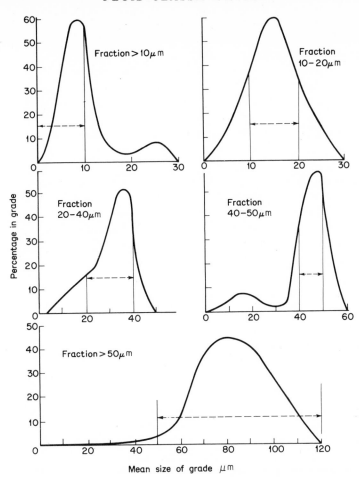

Fig. 11.3. Efficiency curves for the Gonell elutriator (Stairmand [3]). The fractions were analysed using Stairmand's photographic method.

Table 11.2. Theoretical efficiency of elutriators

D/D_m	0·1	0·2	0·3	0·4	0·5	0·6	0·7	0·8	0·9	1·0	1·1	1·2	1·3	1·4	$\sqrt{2}$
Percentage elutriated $(100F)$	99·5	98	99·5	92	87·7	82	75·5	68	59·5	50	39·5	28	15·5	02	0

The cut, however, is better than one would expect from the theoretical grade efficiency curve due to a radial flow of particles from the outer to the inner areas. This is due to the pressure difference across the particle in a radial direction.

At A (figure 11.2), the particle rotates in the same direction as the gas flow, this increases the gas velocity at A and at B the reverse occurs. The energy to accelerate is drawn from the pressure energy of the gas, hence the pressure is lower at A than B, therefore the particles move from the regions of low velocity to the regions of high velocity.

The cut velocity is therefore v_{max} since, if elutriation is carried out to completion all particles smaller than $\sqrt{(2)}\,D_m$ will be removed.

Experimental results [3] are in general agreement with the above, some typical curves being given in figure 11.3. It can be seen that the top size elutriated is approximately $\sqrt{(2)}\,D_m$ and the fraction of cut size retained is of the order of 0·5.

11.4.1 Water elutriators

Water elutriators are recommended for the size range 10 to 200 μm for powders with densities greater than 2·0 g ml^{-1}. With the Andrews elutriator [4] (figure 11.4), the sample of known weight is placed in the feed tube in the form of a dispersion. With wet samples, such as pottery slip, the weight of solids is determined by weighing the feed tube full of water W_w, then weighing it full of mixture W_m. The weight of solid is then:

$$W = \frac{W_m - W_w}{\rho_s - 1}$$

where ρ_s is the specific gravity of the solids.

A screw pinchcock at the inlet is first adjusted to give the required water velocity, which is evaluated by determining the volume rate of flow. The stopcock N is then closed to stop the upward flow of water; the bung at the top of the instrument is then removed and the feed tube inserted.

The stopcock N is then reopened. Next the air vent D is opened, thus releasing the air lock between the surface of the water and the bottom of the feed tube, thereby starting the feed. As the particles fall out of the feed tube B, they are replaced by water rising through the inner tube E. The density gradient produces a circulatory motion from the outer vessel H into the central fitting. Aggregates are caused to impinge on the stationary cone F where they are broken up; fines are carried out through the overflow. After the solid material has all passed into H, the tap P is closed and the vent A opened. Closing P allows the feed to fall into L, while opening A allows the water to drain out of B, thus washing out any solid residue.

When the solid material has all fallen into L, P is reopened, thus restarting the water flow. When the upper portions of L and H are clear, the clamp at J and the stopcock at N are shut. The coarse fraction then gravitates into M from where it can be removed and weighed. M may then be replaced and the clamp at J opened so that the intermediate fraction may fall into M and its weight determined. The weight of fines is determined by difference.

Other water elutriators have been described by Schöne [5], Werner [3], Andreasen [6] and Blythe [7]. The Blythe elutriator (figure 11.5) consists of six beakers almost filled with water and connected in series by siphons; the

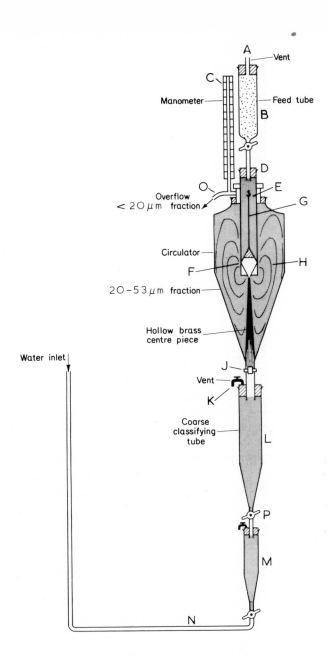

Fig. 11.4. The Andrews kinetic elutriator.

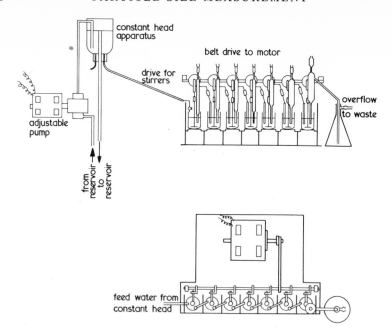

Fig 11.5. The Blythe elutriator.

diameter of the up-going tube of each siphon is $\sqrt{2}$ times that of the preceding one. Each of the beakers is mechanically stirred and water from a constant head tank flows at a controlled rate through the system.

A dispersed powder is washed into the first beaker, where the coarsest particles are retained. All particles below a specific size, determined by the water velocity up the first siphon, are carried over to the second beaker. The entraining velocity in the second siphon is only half that of the first, so that again, the coarsest particles remain in the second beaker and the finer ones are carried along. It is thus possible to separate into seven grades. Though the process is lengthy, no attention is needed.

11.4.2 Air elutriators
Air flow is especially useful for powders which are, in practice, subject to grading by air flow, e.g. fine dust, which contains particles of different density with settling velocities which are not uniquely related to particle size. The major difficulties involved in air elutriation are to ensure the breaking up of aggregates of particles and to prevent fine particles from adhering to the sides of the elutriator tube.

The three main types of air elutriator are the up-blast, the down-blast and the circulating type. The disadvantage of the up-blast type is that at low rates of air flow, the powder tends to choke the air inlet, causing a fluctuation of the velocity

The Gonell elutriator (figure 11.6) has three cylindrical brass tubes of decreasin

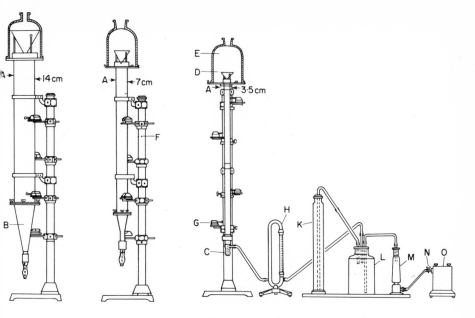

Fig. 11.6. Air operated elutriator (Gonell [8]). A, air sifter tube (large, diameter 140 mm); B, conical tube, attached to A by a flange; C, glass projection, connected to B by a rubber sleeve; D, top attachment, for discharging the air stream; E, glass bell-jar on top place; F, stand with contact-holders for G; G, rappers; H, rotameter; K, pressure governor with height-adjustable supply tube; L, buffer volume (4–5 l flask); M, air cleaner and oil separator; N, regulating valve; and O, blower.

diameter. Ancillary equipment consists of a blower, pressure-stabilizing and air-cleaning equipment and a rotameter for measuring volume rate of flow. The sample tube has a down-blast arrangement to prevent choking. The effect of electrostatic charges, which causes particles to adhere to the walls of the tube, is reduced by continual mechanical rapping of the tube. This effect may be further reduced by the use of an antistatic agent. Fines are collected in glass containers at the top of the tubes, collection being aided by the use of deflector cones, though these also create some turbulence in the column. The analysis times may be greatly reduced if a modification suggested by Hughes [9] is employed. This consists of altering the shape of the dust reservoir and commencing the analysis with a high velocity blast to carry all the dust into the tube, but of such duration that the particles do not have time to reach the top of the tube.

The circulating type of elutriator as developed by Roller [10], (figure 11.7), is a modification of the up-blast, but the sample of powder is caused to circulate in a U-tube at the base of the elutriator tube. The elutriator has four chambers, to each of which is attached a paper extraction thimble collector for the fines. Ancillary

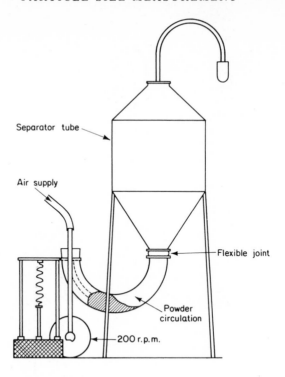

Separator tube

Air supply

Flexible joint

Powder
circulation

200 r.p.m.

Fig. 11.7. The Roller particle size analyser.

equipment, including mechanical rappers, is included and the instrument is enclosed
in a sound-insulated cabinet. In the miniature elutriator [11] a high-velocity air jet
blows downward into a thimble at the base of the elutriating tube containing 0·1 to
0·5 g of the powder under test. The tube is much smaller than that of other elutriator
being 14 in long and 1 in diameter. The infrasizer described by Haultain [12]
consists of six elutriating tubes in series, air-flow entry being to the smallest. Air
enters through a conical seating supporting a golf ball, which, by rotation and impact
breaks down agglomerations of particles.

The velocity distribution in a model Gonell elutriator was investigated by
Weilbacher [14]. He found that the flow at the lower end of the tube was characteri
by strong turbulence and instability and that separation was governed by this region.
Because of this and other disadvantages, he developed a new classifier [1, 13, 14],
shown in figure 11.8. The elutriation zone consists of a 1-cm-high vertical tube with
a height-to-diameter ratio of one-tenth. The material to be classified is dispersed on
to an air-permeable medium, for instance, a membrane filter or fine mesh sieve. The
emergent air flow is uniform and accelerates immediately after the short separation
zone by a conical tube to eliminate redispersion of eluted material. With this
classifier, an exact predetermination of cut size is possible. Leschonski [1] showed

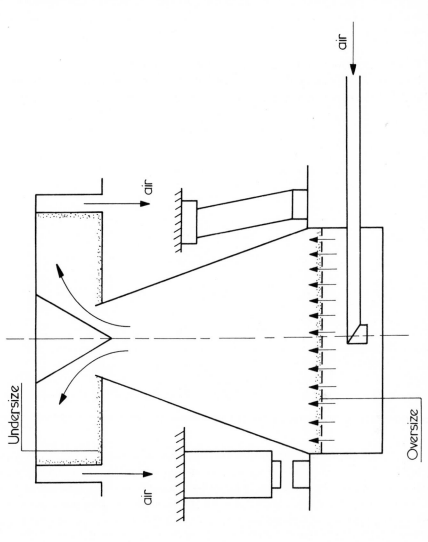

Fig. 11.8. Schematic design of the Fritsch Analysette 8 with a short cylindrical separation zone and accelerated removal of fines.

that to achieve a residue of about 60% for a cut size of 10 μm about 1000 minutes of separation was required with the Gonell elutriator, and 200 minutes with the Analysette. This is reduced to 80 min with the addition of a dispersing agent (Aerosil). Because of the long classification times, the method is not recommended below 10 μm.

11.5 Counterflow equilibrium classifiers in the centrifugal field
This system is used preferably in spiral classifiers, investigated for the first time by Rumpf [15] in 1939 and subsequently improved by Rumpf *et al.* [16, 17, 22].

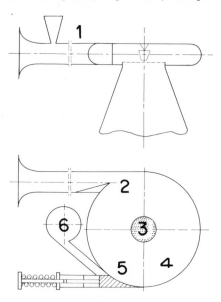

Fig. 11.9. Schematic design of the Analysette 9 centrifugal transverse-flow classifier.

As a result the Analysette 9 centrifugal transverse-flow classifier was developed (figure 11.9). The feed material is dispersed and accelerated in tube 1 and enters the flat classification chamber almost tangentially at a point on the circumference 2. The air leaves the chamber together with the fine fraction on spiral paths through the orifice 3 at the centre while the coarse fraction gathers at the circumference 4, constituting a ring of coarse material that spins along the peripheral wall of the classification chamber. The rotating ring of material enters the constant velocity jet of air at 2 transversely at a very acute angle with a definite velocity and is distributed fanwise under the influence of drag and inertia forces.

The procedure repeats itself very frequently, i.e. of the order of 2000 times per minute. This high number of classifications coupled by the dispersion of agglomerate by friction forces in the rotating ring are claimed to lead to a sharpness of cut at very low sizes not previously obtainable in a spiral classifier. The coarse material is

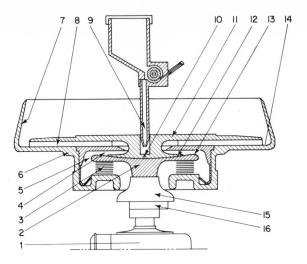

Fig. 11.10. Simplified schematic diagram of a Bahco-type microparticle classifier showing its major components: 1, electric motor; 2, threaded spingle; 3, symmetrical disc; 4, sifting chamber; 5, container; 6, housing; 7, top edge; 8, radial vanes; 9, feed point; 10, feed hole; 11, rotor; 12, rotary duct; 13, feed slot; 14, fan-wheel outlet; 15, grading member; 16, throttle.

removed intermittently through a special outlet 5 and is collected on a small filter 6. The Analysette 9 provides a good sharpness of cut in the size range 2 to 12 μm. In this range it is claimed to be superior to the Bahco [1], described next, but the Bahco permits separation at coarser cut sizes with equally good sharpness. The cut size may be varied by altering the amount of coarse material in the classifier and this can be estimated theoretically [22].

The Bahco microparticle classifier (figure 11.10) is a combination air centrifuge-elutriator. The sample is introduced into a spiral-shaped air current created by a hollow disc rotating at 3500 rev min^{-1}. Air and dust are drawn through the cavity in a radially inward direction against centrifugal forces. Separation into different size fractions is made by altering the air velocity. Since no two instruments perform identically, instrument calibration is necessary [23, 24]. About 20 g of dust are required for the sample, which can be graded in the size range 5 to 100 μm.

The B.C.U.R.A. centrifugal elutriator [25] consists of two parallel concentric discs of equal radius mounted on a motor driven spindle in a short cylindrical coaxial chamber. The discs are spun at a controlled rate and dusty air is drawn through the system entering the chamber axially and flowing outward over the surface of the first disc, then between the two from the periphery to the centre and leaving axially. Centrifugal forces act outwards and drag forces inwards, hence coarse particles are deposited on the circumference of the chamber and fine particles pass through the exit. There is considerable turbulence in the grading zone so that an empirical calibration has to be made. The range of the instrument is from 5 to 40 μm.

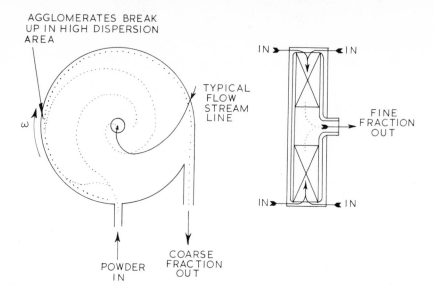

Fig. 11.11. Schematic diagram of Donaldson classifier.

The Donaldson classifier [21] is shown schematically in figure 11.11. Feed particles are subjected to a high degree of dispersion prior to being classified so that reagglomeration is minimized. Eluting air enters the rotor radially around its outer edge, carrying with it dispersed fine particles as it spirals inward to a central fine-fraction outlet. Coarse particles and any remaining agglomerates of fine particles are continuously dispersed as they move around the rotor periphery to the coarse-fraction outlet. The desired cut size is selected by adjustment of air-flow rate and rotor speed. Quantities of 1 to 100 lb can be classified at cut sizes ranging from 0·5 to 20 μm.

The Micromeritics model 1001 [26] works on the following principle. A de-agglomerated stream of particles is sucked from a dispersion device into the centre of a rotor where it divides into two streams. Air of either stream flows radially outward to the rotor wall, while the particles follow curvilinear paths depending on their size and density. At the wall they contact either of two paper or plastic films which can be removed once a sufficient deposit is collected. The film can then be cut into segments, each containing discrete sizes, or the particles can be scraped off into a series of separate containers.

Some other commercial classifiers, which are intended mainly for separating rather than size analysis, are listed in table 11.3.

Table 11.3. Commercially available classifiers

Type	Cut size	Capacity
Walther air vortex classifier	$2 - 20 \ \mu m$	$3 - 4$ tph and $1 - 60 \ \text{lb h}^{-1}$
Multiplex laboratory zig-zag classifier	$+ 1 \ \mu m$	$< 5 \ \text{kg h}^{-1}$ to tn h^{-1}
Double-cone air separator	< 30 mesh	tn h^{-1}
Head Wrightson air classifier	$75 \ \mu m$	$-$
Alpine Microplex spiral-air classifier	$3 - 90 \ \mu m$	$-$
Hosokawa micron separator	$10 - 140 \ \mu m$	$50 - 1500 \ \text{kg h}^{-1}$
Self-contained mechanical air separators		up to 100 tph
Revolving-blade air classifier	$325 - 10$ mesh	
British Rema microsplit	$3 - 60 \ \mu m$	circ. 1000 16 h^{-1}

References

[1] Leschonski, K., and Rumpf, H. (1968−9), *Powder Technol.*, **2**, 175−85.

[2] Roller, P.S. (April, 1931), *Ind. Eng. Chem.*,

[3] Stairmand, C.J. (1947), Symposium on Particle Size Analysis, *Inst. Chem. Engrs.*, **25**, 77.

[4] Andrews, L. (1927−8), *Proc. Inst. Engng, Inspection*, **25**; also (May, 1929), *Min. Mag.*, 301.

[5] Schöne, E. (1867), *Über Schlammanalyse und einen neuen Schlammapparat*, Berlin (*loc. cit.* [2]).

[6] Andreasen, A.H.M. (1930), *Ber. deut. Keram. Ges.*, **11**, 675.

[7] Blythe, H.N., Pryor, E.J., and Eldridge, A. (1953), *Recent Development in Mineral Dressing*, Inst. Min. Metal. Lond., Symposium, 23−5 Sept., 1952, p. 11.

[8] Gonell, H.W. (1928), *Z. Ver dt. Ing.*, **72**, 945.

[9] Hughes, T.H. (1957), Paper 9, Inst. Fuel 2nd Conference on Pulverized Fuel, London, November 1957.

[10] Roller, P.S. (1932), *A.S.T.M. Proc*, **32**, Part 11, 607; also (1937), *J. Am. Ceram. Soc.*, **20**, 167.

[11] Stairmand, C.J. (May, 1951), *Engineering*, **171**, 585−7.

[12] Haultain, H.E.T. (1937), *Trans. Canad. Min. Met.*, **40**, 229.

[13] Berns, E.G. (1954), *Br. J. Appl. Phys.*, supplement No. 3, S208.

[14] Weilbacher, M., and Rumpf. H. (1968), *Aufbereitungstechnik*, **9**, 7, 323−30.

[15] Rumpf, H. (1939), Univ. of Karlsuhe, thesis, *cit.* [1].

[16] Rumpf, H., and Kaiser, F. (1952), *Chem. Ing. Tech.* **24**, 129–135.

[17] Rumpf, H., and Leschonski, H. (1967), *Chem. Ing. Tech.* **39**, 1231.

[18] Richards, J.C. (1966), 'The efficiency of classifiers', *BCURA Monthly Bulletin,* **30**, 4, 113.

[19] Newton, H.W., and Newton, W.H. (1932), *Rock Products,* V35.

[20] Wessel, J. (1967), *Aufbereitungs Technik,* No. 2, p. 53.

[21] Schaller, R.E., and Lapple, C.E. (1971), 'Particle size separation of plastic powders, paper presented at 162nd National Meeting of the Am. Chem. Soc., Washington D.C., U.S.A.

[22] Rumpf, H., and Leschonski, K. (1967), *Chem. Ing. Tech.,* **39**, 21, 1231–41.

[23] Weilbacher, M. (1968), Univ. of Karlruhe, thesis, *cit* [1].

[24] Crandall, W.A. (1964), *Am. Soc. Mech. Engrs,* Winter Annual Meeting, Publ. 64–WA/PTC–3.

[25] Godridge, A., Badzioch, S., and Hawksley, P. (1962), *J. Sci. Instrum.,* **13**, 611.

[26] Burson, J.H., Keng, E.Y.H., and Orr, C. (1967–8), *Powder Technol.,* 305–15.

12 Centrifugal Methods

12.1 Introduction

Gravitational sedimentation techniques have limited worth for particles below about 5 μm in size due to the long settling times involved. In addition, most sedimenation devices suffer from the effects of convection, diffusion and Brownian motion. These difficulties may be reduced by speeding up the settling process by centrifuging the suspension.

As with gravitational methods the data may be cumulative or incremental, homogeneous or two layer. Calculations of size distributions from centrifugal data are more difficult than calculations from gravitational data since particle velocities increase as they move away from the axis of rotation. That is, the velocity of a particle depends on its position in the sedimenting suspension as well as its size, whereas for gravity sedimentation the settling velocity is dependent solely on size. One method of overcoming this difficulty is to use long-arm centrifuges so that the centrifugal force on all particles is approximately the same. Another solution is to use the two-layer technique, in which a thin layer of concentrated suspension is introduced on to the surface of the bulk sedimentation liquid, often referred to as the 'spin fluid'. This technique suffers problems due to 'streaming', which is discussed later, and has been extended to a three-layer or to a 'buffered line-start' in an attempt to overcome these problems. With the two-layer technique, all particles of the same size are in the same position in the centrifugal field and, hence, have the same velocity, simplifying the theoretical treatment.

With the cumulative homogeneous technique, no full solution is available relating the weight settled out, the weight undersize and time, although partial solution is possible. To overcome this problem investigators have tended to keep the time of analysis constant but varied the level of the suspension in the centrifuge.

The earliest applications of the centrifugal principle involved the modifications of existing laboratory centrifuges. There were several problems associated with these. Cylindrical tubes are unsuitable since the direction of motion of the particles is radial and this leads to deposition of particles on the walls of the tubes. This can be overcome by the use of specially-shaped tubes and minimized by the use of long-arm centrifuges. Tangential forces set up during starting and stopping cause particles to be deposited on the walls of the centrifuge tubes unless the accelerating and decelerating times are protracted, a procedure which entails the use of correction factors. Convection currents are set up which cause remixing and there are also problems in measuring the concentration gradient within the suspension. These problems have been overcome with the advent of shallow-bowl or disc centrifuges, which were first suggested in 1934 [1] but have only become popular since 1965.

12.2 Stokes' diameter determination

A particle settling in a centrifugal field is acted upon by two forces in opposition, a centrifugal force and a drag force. In the laminar-flow region this leads to the following equation:

$$\frac{\pi}{6}(\rho_s - \rho_f)D^3 \frac{d^2x}{dt^2} = \frac{\pi}{6}(\rho_s - \rho_f)D^3 \omega^2 x - 3\pi D\eta \frac{dx}{dt}$$

where x = distance from the axis to the particle.

dx/dt = outward velocity of particle,

$\rho_s; \rho_f$ = density of particle and suspension medium,

η = coefficient of viscosity of medium,

D = equivalent spherical diameter of particle,

ω = speed of rotation of centrifuge in radians per second.

At the terminal velocity this equation becomes:

$$3\pi D\eta \frac{dx}{dt} = \frac{\pi}{6}(\rho_s - \rho_f)D^3 \omega^2 x$$

$$\frac{dx}{dt} = u_c = \frac{(\rho_s - \rho_f)}{18\eta}D^2 \omega^2 x. \qquad (12.1)$$

Comparing with Stokes' equation for gravitational settling:

$$u_{st} = \frac{(\rho_s - \rho_f)}{18\eta}gD^2$$

therefore

$$u_c = \frac{\omega^2 x}{g}u_{st} = \frac{V_t}{xg} = Gu_{st}$$

where V_t is the tangential velocity at distance x from the axis and G, the separation factor, is a measure of the increased rate of settling in a centrifugal field.

12.3 Two-layer technique

12.3.1 Theory

Rewriting equation (12.1) in integral form:

$$\int_s^r \frac{dx}{x} = \int_0^t \frac{\rho_s - \rho_f}{18\eta}D^2 \omega^2 dt$$

$$\ln\frac{r}{S} = \frac{\rho_s - \rho_f}{18\eta}D_m^2 \omega^2 t \qquad (12.2)$$

$$D_m = \sqrt{\left[\frac{18\eta \ln r/S}{(\rho_s - \rho_f)\omega^2 t} \right]}$$

where t is the time for a particle of size D_m to settle from the surface of the fill liquid at distance S from the axis of the centrifuge to r, the measurement zone, which, for cumulative techniques, is equal to R, the distance from the axis to the bottom of the centrifuge. Hence at time t, all the particles at r will be of size D_m or for cumulative techniques, all particles greater than D_m will have settled out at time t.

12.3.2 Two-layer technique using a photometric method of analysis

Treasure [34] found that the simple theory for the two-layer technique was unsuitable when the concentration of the suspension was estimated by a photoextinction method, and developed the theory below.

For an injected layer of infinitesimal thickness with a light beam of thickness $2Z$ at distance R, from the axis of the centrifuge, let $D_1 > D_m > D_2$ be the diameters of the particles reaching $(R + Z), R, (R - Z)$ from the surface of radius S in time t. Then:

$$\ln \frac{R}{S} = kD^2 t$$

$$\frac{1}{D_1^2} \ln \frac{R + Z}{S} = \frac{1}{D_m^2} \ln \frac{R}{S} = \frac{1}{D_2^2} \ln \frac{R - Z}{S}.$$

Writing $D_1 = (1 + \theta)D_m$ and $D_2 = (1 - \beta)D_m$ gives

$$(1 + \theta)^2 = 1 + \frac{\ln [1 + (Z/R)]}{\ln (R/S)}$$

$$(1 - \beta)^2 = 1 + \frac{\ln [1 - (Z/R)]}{\ln (R/S)}.$$

For both θ and β both small, it may be assumed that over the range $(\theta + \beta)D_m$, n_D, the relative number of particles per unit micrometre range centred on D, may be expressed by the linear function $n_D = f + (g/D_m)D$.

Thus the total cross section in the beam:

$$\int_{D_m(1-\beta)}^{D_m(1+\theta)} n_D \times D^2 \, dD$$

is proportional to $(\theta + \beta)(f + g)D_m^3$ if high-order terms are neglected.

Now the optical density of suspension is proportional to the total scattering cross section in the beam, i.e.

$$I \alpha (f + g)(\theta + \beta)D_m \times D_m^2 \times K_m$$

where K_m is the extinction coefficient (see chapter 11) i.e:

$$I/K_m \ \alpha \ (f + g) D_m^3 \ \text{since } \theta, \beta \text{ are constant}$$

$$\alpha \ n_{D_m} \times \text{mass of one particle}$$

$$\alpha \ m_{D_m}, \text{the relative mass of particles in unit range centred on } D_m.$$

If K_m is considered constant, the plot of optical density against time represents the weight–size frequency distribution of the suspension plotted with an inverse D^2 scale.

From the experimental curve, the area:

$$(t_x - t_y) \ = \ \int_{t_x}^{t_y} I \, dt$$

$$= \ \int_{D_x}^{D_y} (n_D D^3)\left(-\frac{dD}{D^3}\right)$$

$$= \ \int_{D_y}^{D_x} n_D \cdot dD$$

the relative number of particles in the range D_x to D_y. If each ordinate is multiplied by D^3 then the area:

$$(t_x - t_y) \int_{D_y}^{D_x} n_D D^3 \, dD$$

the relative mass of particles in the range D_x to D_y.

Similarly multiplaction by D^2 gives the relative surface of particles in the range.

The same relationship holds also for an injected layer of finite thickness. For a layer thickness of about 3% of the radius of the curved liquid surface, the resultant error is about 1%.

Treasure also shows that the relationship for the gravitational case is similar:

$$I/K_m \ \alpha \ m_{D_m} \ .$$

12.3.3 Early instruments: the Marshall centrifuge and the M.S.A. particle size analyser

One method of simplifying the calculation is to float the suspension to be centrifuged on a column of denser liquid so that all particles settle essentially the same distance to reach the bottom of the centrifuge tube. This method was first used by Marshall [2]. Since all the particles commence sedimentation from the same point, the sediment will only contain particles greater than D_m (equation (12.2)). Also, the solids concentration at any point is proportional to the fraction of particles of a calculable size in the original suspension. Marshall simplified his technique further by making the settling distance $R - S$ small in comparison with the distance from

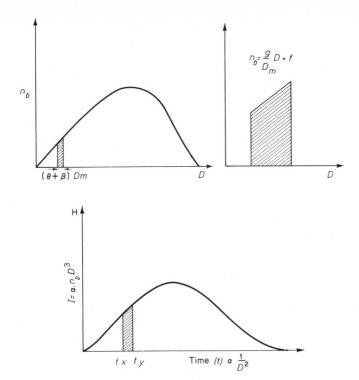

Fig. 12.1. Theory for the Kaye disc centrifuge.

the axis of rotation, thus permitting the approximation of a constant centrifugal force. It also allows the use of a cylindrical settling vessel, since the walls subtend to a smaller angle at the axis of rotation the larger their distance from this axis. Interest in the two-layer technique was re-awakened by Whitby [3], who used the special centrifuge tube shown in figure 12.2; the weight oversize is determined by the height of the sediment in the capillary.

Several papers have been published on applications of this equipment, which is available commercially as the M.S.A. particle-size analyser [4–7]. Although sediment height is proportional to sediment weight for monosize particles and only one size settles at a time, criticism has been levelled at the instrument on the ground that many particles consist of tight aggregates. In these cases, compression of the sediment column with increasing speed takes place, thus necessitating the use of correction factors [8].

Other disadvantages are: the tube is the wrong shape to eliminate wall effects; hindered settling in the neck of the capillary prevents the analysis of materials with a narrow size range, which would all settle at about the same time; the loss of sedimentation height as sediment builds up in the capillary [9]. Published results, however, are so reproducible that these are all probably unimportant. The main advantage

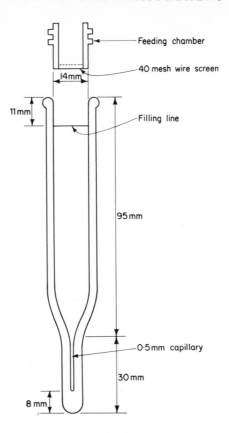

Fig. 12.2. Special centrifuge tube and feeding chamber. Sediment height is read
         with a projector type viewer (Whitby [5]).

of the method is that it is suited to both the gravitational and centrifugal range,
hence a size range from about 0·2 to 80 μm may be analysed.

12.3.4 The photocentrifuge

The first photocentrifuge was developed by Kaye [10, 11] (figure 12.3). In this
instrument, concentration changes within a suspension are followed using a light
beam (see also [48]). The instrument is usually used in the two-layer mode and
evaluated as a weight distribution using the theory developed by Treasure, but the
technique has also been used with a homogeneous suspension [20]. The original
instrument has been widely and successfully used by Burt and modifications have
been used by others [57].

In the instrument described by Bayness *et al.* [52], the light source comprises
a 12 V tungsten lamp and the receiver an ORP 12 photocell which forms part of a
balanced electrical bridge. The authors had limited success with the two- or three-
layer start method and used the homogeneous suspension in their reported results,

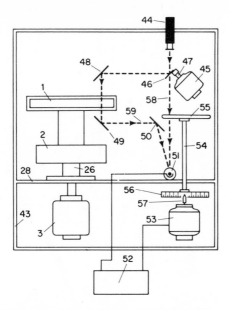

Fig. 12.3. The Kaye disc centrifuge. A hollow centrifuge tank (1) is mounted on the
flywheel (2) of a centrifuge. A source of light (44) is mounted at the top
of the container. A synchronous electric motor (45) has a mirror (46)
eccentrically mounted to its spindle (47). Mirrors (48), (49) and (50) are
arranged so as to reflect light on to a photocell (51) which has its output
connected to an a.c. amplifier (52). This amplifier can energize an a.c.
servomotor (53) whose spindle (54) carries an annular optical wedge (55),
lying between the light source (44) and the photocell (51) and a scale (56)
calibrated relative to a fixed pointer (57). Broken lines indicate the alternative paths of the light beam. When the motor (45) operates it swings
the mirror (46) round causing it to reflect light periodically along path
(59). When the intensities of the light reaching the photocell via the two
paths are equal, there is no a.c. output from the photocell. If the intensity
along path (59) is reduced due to the presence of particles in the light
beam, then the intensities are unequal, causing an energizing current to
flow from the photocell to (53) causing (54) to rotate. As the optical
wedge (55) rotates it balances out the intensities.

making no correction for the breakdown in the laws of geometric optics. This modification is now incorporated in the Joyce-Loebl disc centrifuge. Statham [53] used
a prototype instrument developed by Coulter electronics, the Photofuge. He found
streaming and distortion with the two-layer technique at concentrations above
0·01% w/w of PVC in the injection fluid, using 2 ml of fluid. At higher concentrations
the three-layer technique [54] was used, but this resulted in a coarsening of the
analysis. The use of 55 to 70% v/v of methanol in water as injection fluid with water
with 0·00075 per cent Nonidet P42 wetting agent as spin fluid improved the results.

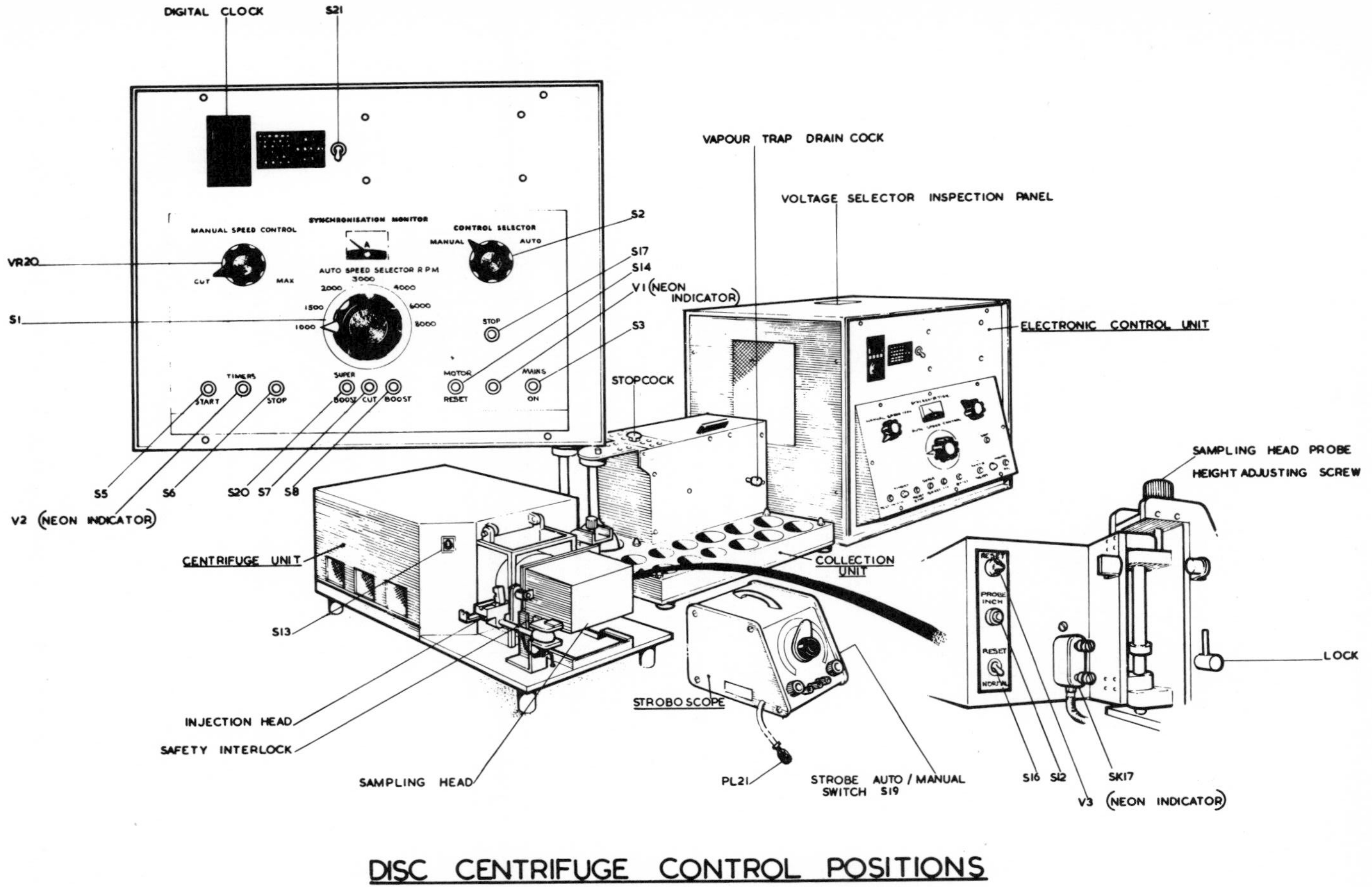

DISC CENTRIFUGE CONTROL POSITIONS

Fig. 12.4 The Joyce-Loebl disc centrifuge.

The results were corrected for the breakdown in the laws of geometric optics using Allen's method [55], which considerably altered the relative weight percentage distributions to give analyses which were in reasonable agreement with known distributions.

12.3.5 The Joyce-Loebl disc centrifuge

This instrument (figure 12.4) was developed for the determination of the size distribution of organic dyestuffs [58, 59]. It is used with a buffered line start, and the undersize fraction determined by removing the supernatant with a vacuum probe after fixed times of rotation and determining the concentration calorimetrically. Although gravimetric analyses can be made, this procedure is not recommended because of the small amount of sample used [12, 13]. Since each withdrawal gives only one point on the size analysis graph, only one or two analyses can be carried out per day. In later instruments the manufacturers have incorporated a photo-sedimentometer for quick routine comparisons and to analyse powders which the unmodified instrument could not handle. It must be stressed, however, that the curve so produced is not a size distribution as is demonstrated by Statham [53]. The instrument has been widely described [60 − 67].

It is usual with the two-layer method to disperse the solids in a liquid which is not as dense as the fill liquid in order to get stable conditions. However, it has been pointed out [16] that as soon as the particles break through the interface, the uppermost region is denser than the rest, and consequently breaks up and streamers occur. This effect can be demonstrated with the use of a stroboscope. Statham [53] and Burt [68] report a lower concentration below which streaming does not occur, but Beresford [66] found streaming at concentrations of 0·004% w/v.

Scarlett et al. [54] found the following method satisfactory: 10% aqueous sucrose spin fluid, add 1 cm^3 of distilled water to the inner surface while the disc is in uniform motion and then inject the aqueous dispersion. Jones [69, 70], in the 'buffered layer-start' technique, introduces a transient acceleration after the intro-duction of water to give a gradual density gradient instead of an interface. Beresford [66] tested the various techniques and reported that the buffered layer start was the only technique to eliminate streaming. As stated earlier, this is at variance with the results of other reserachers.

12.4 Homogeneous suspension

12.4.1 Sedimentation height small compared with distance from centrifuge axis

The simplest procedure with a homogeneous suspension is to make $R - S$ small compared with S and assume that the particles fall with constant velocity:

$$u_c = \frac{(\rho_s - \rho_f)}{18\eta} D^2 \cdot \omega^2 \left(\frac{R + S}{2} \right)$$

from equation (12.1).

This method was used by Norton and Spiel [16], who used hydrometers to follow density changes within the settling suspension; by Jacobsen and Sullivan [17] and Menis *et al.* [18], who used a cumulative method and Oden's method of tangential intercepts; by Gupta [24] who withdrew samples perpendicular to the plane of rotation and determined the concentration changes gravimetrically; by Conner *et al.* [19], who determined the sediment weight by β-back-scattering and by Hildreth and Patterson [20], who used the attenuation of a light beam in a disc centrifuge similar to Kaye's and dealt with their experimental data according to a treatment by Musgrove and Harner [21].

12.5 Cumulative sedimentation theory for a homogeneous suspension

Equation (12.2) may be written:

$$S = R \exp(-kD^2 t) \tag{12.3}$$

where

$$k = \frac{\rho_s - \rho_f}{18\eta} \omega^2.$$

At the end of t seconds, all particles greater than D_m will have reached the bottom of the tube. In addition, partial sedimentation will have taken place for all particles smaller than D_m. For each of these smaller sizes, a starting point x_0 exists, beyond which all the smaller particles will have reached R where, from equation (12.1):

$$x_0 = R \exp(-kD^2 t).$$

The volume fraction of the suspension lying between R and x_0 for a shallow bowl or flat sector-shaped tubes is equal to:

$$\frac{R^2 - x_0^2}{R^2 - S^2} = \frac{R^2}{R^2 - S^2} \{1 - \exp(-2kD^2 t)\}. \tag{12.4}$$

If the particle-size distribution is defined as $F(D)$, then $F(D) \, dD$ is the weight fraction of particles in the size range D to $D + dD$.

The weight fraction of particles with diameters greater than D_m that have completely settled is:

$$W = \int_{D_m}^{\infty} F(D) \, dD$$

The weight fraction of particles smaller than D_m that has completely settled is:

$$\int_{0}^{D_m} \frac{R^2}{R^2 - S^2} \{1 - \exp(-2kD^2 t)\} F(D) \, dD.$$

The total weight fraction deposited is:

$$P = W + \int_0^{D_m} \frac{R^2}{R^2 - S^2} \{1 - \exp(-2kD^2 t)\} F(D) \, dD. \tag{12.5}$$

The weight fraction oversize can be evaluated if the weight fraction deposited P is measured for different values of the variables S, R and t.

12.6 Variable time method (variation of P with t)

Romwalter and Vendl [25] derived a solution to the above equation by differentiating with respect to time and substituting back in the original equation. Brown [26] drew attention to an error in their derivation and stated that an exact solution for the distribution function appeared to be difficult, if not impossible, to obtain by the above method.

The following approximate solutions were derived by Robinson and Martin [27, 28], who used sector-shaped tubes. Their analyses agreed closely with those obtained by the variable-height method:

$$\int_0^{D_m} F(D) \, dD = 1 - \left[\frac{M(6 - M)}{8} p + \frac{MD_m}{8} \frac{dP}{dD} + \frac{M(M - 2)(M - 4)}{8} I(D_m) \right]$$

where

$$I(D_m) = \frac{1}{D^M} \int_0^{D_m} PD^{M-1} \, d(D)$$

$$M = \frac{4(R^2 - S^2)}{S^2 \ln R/S}.$$

12.7 Variable inner radius (variation of P with S)

Brown [26] avoided the complications arising from the differentiation of equation (12.5) with respect to time by considering the fraction sedimented in a given time interval with the centrifuge tubes filled with suspension to a series of levels. On increasing S an increasingly large fraction of suspended particles will be deposited in a given time.

Differentiating equation (12.5) with respect to S and substituting back with $\delta P/\delta S$ gives:

$$\int_{D_m}^{\infty} F(D) \, dD = P - \frac{R^2 - S^2}{2S} \frac{\delta P}{\delta S}. \tag{12.6}$$

Thus a rigorous solution is obtained by keeping t and R constant and determining the weight fraction deposited for varying heights of suspension.

Just as in gravity sedimentation, second derivatives of the fraction sedimented are required to obtain the distribution function itself. In order to obtain $F(D_m)$ in terms of the second derivatives of P, it is necessary to differentiate equations (12.3) and (12.5) with respect to S, eliminating $\delta D_m/\delta S$ from the two resulting equations:

$$\frac{\delta D_m}{\delta S} = \frac{-D_m}{2S \ln R/S} \text{ from equation (12.3)}$$

giving

$$\frac{\ln R/S}{D_m} \left[\frac{R^2 + 3S^2}{S} \frac{\delta P}{\delta S} - (R^2 - S^2) \frac{\delta^2 P}{\delta S^2} \right] = F(D_m). \tag{12.7}$$

Similarly the distribution function may be derived in terms of $\delta^2 P/\delta S \, \delta t$ and $\delta P/\delta t$ by differentiating equations (12.3) and (12.5) with respect to time:

$$\frac{2t}{D_m} \frac{\delta P}{\delta t} - \frac{R^2 - S^2}{2S} \frac{\delta^2 P}{\delta s \, dt} = F(D_m). \tag{12.8}$$

Three distinct methods are therefore available for calculating the distribution of particle sizes in a suspension, if the weight fraction sedimented is determined with sector-shaped centrifuge tubes filled to a series of levels. First, the weight fraction of particles larger than a known diameter may be calculated from equation (12.7) and the distribution function determined from the slope of the cumulative weight per cent deposited curve. Secondly, the distribution function may be calculated directly in terms of the first and second derivatives of the fraction sedimented with respect to the length of the column of suspension centrifuged by use of equation (12.7). Thirdly, from sedimentation-time curve at a series of levels, the distribution functions may be calculated by use of equation (12.8). In all cases the range of particle size covered is that of D_m as calculated from equation (12.3).

12.8 Shape of centrifuge tubes

The use of cylindrical tubes instead of sector or conoidal-shaped tubes (figure 12.5) has advantages in that they are easier to construct and may be used in ordinary laboratory centrifuges. The disadvantages of a cylindrical tube are that particles will strike the walls of the tube, agglomerate with other particles on the wall and reach the bottom more quickly than freely sedimenting particles, and convection currents will be set up due to the oblique force of the suspension on the walls of the tube.

Brown [26] states that for control tests sufficient accuracy is obtained if $S/R < 0.50$. A figure of $S/R < 0.88$ is given by Bradley [9]. However, as $R - S$ becomes smaller, it becomes more difficult to measure accurately and may produce large errors in the analysis.

The theory is modified if cylindrical tubes are used, equation (12.4) becoming:

$$\frac{R - x_0}{R - S} = \frac{R}{R - S} \{1 - \exp(-kD^2 t)\}.$$

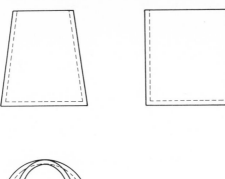

Fig. 12.5. Conoidal centrifuge tube.

This modifies equation (12.7) to:

$$\int_{D_m}^{\infty} F(D)\, dD = P - (R-S)\frac{\delta P}{\delta S}. \tag{12.9}$$

Instead of varying the quantity of suspension in the tubes S, the above equation may be used with a fixed quantity of suspension and time but with changes of R with $R - S$ constant. This is readily accomplished with cylindrical tubes, by placing blocks of known thickness under the tubes [26].

12.9 Alternative theory (variation of P with S)

An alternative approach is given by Murley [29] as follows:

If the inner radius of the centrifuging suspension is decreased by a small amount dS, then the extra weight of sample introduced into the centrifuge is $2\pi STC\, dS$, where T is the thickness of the suspension in an axial direction and C is the weight of solid per unit volume of suspension. For this extra amount of material added, all that with a particle size less than D_m will reach the collecting plane at R and all that smaller than D_m will be at a smaller radius that R at the end of the running time t. The diameter D_m is given by equation (12.3).

The extra weight of sample deposited at a place of radius R due to this change in radius dS of the top surface of the sample is therefore:

$$dP = -2\pi STC\, dS \int_{D_m}^{\infty} F(D)\, dD. \tag{12.10}$$

The negative sign occurs because the added layer causes a decrease in S. This equation applies to an apparatus where the liquid is run off and the deposited layer is retained for analysis, whereas in the type of apparatus where the overlying liquid layer is removed for estimation of the weight of solids, the following equation is applicable:

$$dP = -2\pi STC\, dS \int_{D_m}^{0} F(D)\, dD. \qquad (12.11)$$

By plotting P against S and finding the slope of the curve, $F(D)\, dD$ may be evaluated.

Equations (12.10) and (12.11) can also be derived by differentiating equation (12.5) which may be written:

$$P = \left\{1 - \int_{0}^{D_m} F(D)\, dD\right\} + \int_{0}^{D_m} \frac{R^2}{R^2 - S^2}\left\{1 - \exp(-2kD^2 t)\right\}F(D)\, dD$$

$$1 - P = \int_{0}^{D_m} \frac{1}{R^2 - S^2}\left\{R^2\,\exp(-2kD^2) - S^2\right\}F(D)\, dD$$

where $1 - P$ is the weight fraction still in suspension. The weight fraction of powder that has sedimented is P, where $P = \pi(R^2 - S^2)\, TC(1 - P)$, i.e.

$$P = \pi TC \int_{0}^{D_m} \{R^2\,\exp(-2kD^2) - S^2\}F(D)\, dD. \qquad (12.12)$$

Differentiating this with respect to S leads directly to equation (12.11).

12.10 Variable outer radius (variation of P with R)
Donoghue and Bostock [30] differentiated equation (12.5) with respect to R, giving:

$$\int_{D_m}^{\infty} F(D)\, dD = P + R\left(\frac{R^2 - S^2}{2S^2}\right)\frac{dP}{dR}. \qquad (12.13)$$

Slope measurements of the $P - R$ curve enables calculation of the weight fraction oversize.

The apparatus developed for this determination consists of a stepped centrifuge so that the suspension is contained in a space consisting of a number of annular rings, each of which has the same inner radius S, but progressively larger outer radii R from top to bottom. Particles are deposited on detachable surfaces which are removed and dried before weighing, the supernatant being removed before the centrifuge is stopped.

The advantages of this instrument are that six points on the distribution curve are determined simultaneously and the quick acceleration removes the need for correction terms for accelerating time. The main disadvantage which has prevented

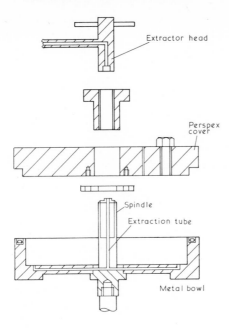

Fig. 12.6. Simcar centrifuge.

this centrifuge from becoming accepted is loss of sediment due to movement of the supernatant liquid during its withdrawal.

12.11 Incremental analysis with a homogeneous suspension

12.11.1 The Simcar centrifuge

The disc centrifuge has replaced earlier types and is now available in a variety of forms. The pipette method has long been used as a reliable method of gravity sedimentation and one of the earliest commercial disc centrifuges was a centrifugal pipette withdrawal technique [33, 56] (figure 12.6). With this instrument, concentration changes are monitored at a fixed depth below the surface. This concentration is related to the weight undersize by an integral equation for which no usable mathematical solution was known (equation (12.16)). This difficulty is avoided if the variation in centrifugal force over the settling distance is made small, i.e. $r - S \ll S$, where r is the distance from the axis of rotation to the sampling zone, but this creates design problems in the centrifugal construction. The method becomes feasible, however, with the introduction of the approximate method described below.

12.11.2 General theory

If the centrifuging time is sufficient for particles of size D to be transported from the surface S to the sampling zone r, particles in the size range D to $D + \mathrm{d}D$ will be transferred from a surface zone of thickness ΔS to the sampling zone of thickness Δr. There will be a fall in the concentration of particles of this size in the sampling zone, therefore, since the same number of particles will occupy a greater volume.

The fractional increase in volume is given by:

$$\frac{r\Delta r}{S\Delta S} = \frac{r^2}{S^2} \tag{12.14}$$

since $\Delta r/\Delta S = r/S$ from equation (12.3).

For a polydisperse system with a weight fraction in the size range D to $D + dD$ of $F(D)\,dD$, the original concentration of this weight fraction at r is given by:

$$F(D)\,dD = \frac{r^2}{S^2}\,dQ \tag{12.15}$$

where

$$dQ = \frac{C(r, t)}{C(r, 0)}$$

$$= \frac{\text{concentration of particles of size } D \text{ at } r \text{ at time } t}{\text{concentration of particles of size } D \text{ in the suspension at time } t = 0}.$$

If F_1 is the weight fraction of particles in the size range 0 to D_1

$$F_1 = \int_0^{Q_1} \frac{r^2}{S^2}\,dQ \tag{12.16}$$

which, by combining with equation (12.2), may be written:

$$Q_1 = \int_0^{D_1} \exp(-2\alpha D^2 t)\,F(D)\,dD$$

where

$$\alpha = \frac{18\eta}{(\rho_s - \rho_f)\omega^2}.$$

D_1 is the diameter of the particle that settles from radius S to radius r in time t_1, an expression developed first by Berg [31] and later by Kamak [32].

It is not possible to obtain an exact solution to this equation, since particles in the sampling zone at any particular time will have originated at points in the suspension from radius S to radius r.

An approximate solution may, however, be developed in the following manner [32]. If Q is plotted as a function of $y = (r/S)^2$ with $t' = \omega^2 t$ as parameter, a family of curves is obtained whose shape depends on the particle-size distribution function. The boundary conditions are that $Q = 1$ when $t' = 0$ for all r and $Q = 0$ for $r = S$ when $t > 0$, hence all the curves except that for $t' = 0$ will pass through the point $Q = 0, y = 1$, and they will all be asymptotic to the line $t' = 0$, which has the equation $Q = 1 \cdot 0$. Furthermore, from equation (12.16), the area under the curve is equal to $F(D_m) = F_m$.

Let Q_1 be the lowest experimentally determined concentration so that $t_1 > t_2 > \ldots$, and let Q be determined at a fixed sampling distance R_1 for various values of t'. Then one point is known on each curve in addition to the common point $y = 1$, $Q = 0$. Such a set of points is illustrated by the black circles in figure 12.7. To each such point corresponds a known value D_m obtained from equation (12.2).

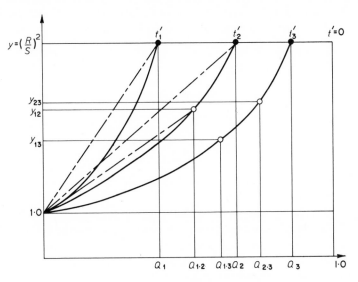

Fig. 12.7. Theoretical diagram for the Simcar centrifuge.

Further, the area included between each curve and the concentration axis and the ordinates $Q = 0$ and Q_r is equal to F_m. Thus F_m may be approximated by the trapezoidal rule, for, first of all, approximately $F_1 = \frac{1}{2}(1 + y)Q_1$. Now considering the curve for t'_2, a point can be found on it corresponding to D_1, i.e. a point such that the area under the curve up to this point is F_1, which is now known. If the ordinate at this point is called y_{12} and the abscissa Q_{12}, then by equation (12.2):

$$D_1 = \sqrt{\left[\frac{9\eta \ln y_{12}}{(Q_s - Q_f)t'_2}\right]} \quad \text{and} \quad D_2 = \sqrt{\left[\frac{9\eta \ln y}{(\rho_s - \rho_f)t'_2}\right]} \quad \text{so } y_{12} = y^{(D_1/D_2)^2}.$$

$$(12.17)$$

Also, equating areas:

$$Q_1(1 + y) = Q_{12}(1 + y_{12}) = 2F_1 \quad (12.18)$$

so both y_{12} and Q_{12} are known. Hence, by the trapezoidal rule:

$$F_2 - F_1 = \frac{1}{2}(y + y_{12})(Q_2 - Q_{12}).$$

Substituting for Q_{12} from equation (12.18):

$$F_2 = \tfrac{1}{2}(y + y_{12})Q_2 + \left[1 - \frac{y + y_{12}}{1 + y_{12}}\right] F_1$$

Proceeding in a like manner gives the general formulae:

$$F_n - F_{n-1} = \tfrac{1}{2}(y + y_{n-1, n})(Q_n - Q_{n-1, n}) \qquad (12.19)$$

$$F_{n-1} - F_{n-2} = \tfrac{1}{2}(y_{n-1, n} + y_{n-2, n})(Q_{n-1, n} - Q_{n-2, n}) \qquad (12.20)$$

and so on. By considering this series of equations with successive elimination of the Q functions, there obtains a general solution in recursive form:

$$F_i = \tfrac{1}{2}(y + y_{i-1, i})Q_i + \sum_{j=1}^{i-1} \left[\frac{y + y_{i-1, i}}{y_{j+1, i} + y_{ji}} - \frac{y + y_{i-1, i}}{y_{ji} + y_{j-1, i}}\right] F_j \qquad (12.21)$$

where

$$y_{ij} = y^{(D_i/D_j)} \qquad (12.22)$$

$$D_n = \sqrt{\frac{9\eta \ln y}{(\rho_s - \rho_f) t_n^1}} \qquad (12.23)$$

$$i = 1, 2, 3, \ldots m$$

$$y_{0, i} = 1.$$

Equations (12.21) are a set of linear equations which express the desired values of F_1 explicitly in terms of the measured values of Q_1. The coefficients of the equations depend on the value of D_i (corresponding to the values of t_i') at which the concentrations are measured; more exactly, the coefficients depend on the ratios of the values of D_i as shown by equation (12.22). Consequently, if the values of D_i are chosen in a geometric sequence when making particle-size analysis, the coefficient of equation (12.21) are considerably easier to calculate and the equations themselves are also simplified. A ratio of $\sqrt{2}$ is recommended. The coefficients in equation (12.20) depend also on the value of y, that is, on the dimension of the centrifuge bowl employed.

The modified form of equation (12.21) for experimental points in a 2:1 progression in time giving a $\sqrt{2}:1$ progression in diameter is:

$$i > 1, F_i = \tfrac{1}{2} y_B Q_i \sum_{j=1}^{i-1} \left[\frac{1}{y^{\frac{1}{2}(i-j-1)} + y^{\frac{1}{2}(i-j)}} - \frac{1}{y^{\frac{1}{2}(i-j)} + A}\right] F_j \qquad (12.24)$$

where $A = 1$ for $j = 1$, $A = y^{\frac{1}{2}(i-j-1)}$ for $j \neq 1$

$$y_B = y + y^{\frac{1}{2}}$$

when $i = 1$, $F_1 = \tfrac{1}{2}(1 + y^{\frac{1}{2}})Q_1$.

The method of using these equations to compute size distributions is as follows. The experiment data consist of a series of fractional concentrations, Q, measured at known values of ω and t, from which a value of D for each value of Q is calculated using equation (12.2). The values of Q versus D are plotted (usually on logarithmic-normal paper) and a smooth curve is drawn through the points. Values of Q are read from this curve at any convenient set of values of D in a $\sqrt{2}$ progression D_1, $D_2 = \sqrt{(2)}D_1, D_3 = 2D_1$ etc. The corresponding values of Q are called Q_1, Q_2, Q_3, etc. These values are substituted in equation (12.23) to give the values of equation (12.23) or by extrapolating the curve of Q versus D to get additional points to use in equation (12.23).

Berg solved equation (12.16) graphically by plotting r^2/S^2 against Q and determining the area under the curve, deriving the following formulae:

$$\int_0^{D_m} F(D)\,dD = C_y + \frac{y}{4a}\,5C_y - 4F\left(\frac{D}{2}\right) \text{ for } y < \frac{1}{5}a \qquad (12.25)$$

$$\int_0^{D_m} F(D)\,dD = C_y\left(1 + \frac{2y}{3S}\right) \text{ for } C_y < 0\cdot15 \qquad (12.26)$$

where $R = S + y$ and C_y is the concentration at depth y at the time required for a particle of size D_m to fall from the surface to-depth y.

Ordinarily the approximate formulae are used, the integration formula being required for nearly monodisperse powders when C_y varies greatly with y.

Equation (12.26) is used for the calculation of the smallest value of $F(D)$, that is the smallest C_y, and equation (12.27) for other values of $F(D)$. $F(D) = 0$ when $D = 0$, hence $F(D/2)$ may be estimated by joining $F(D)$ to 0 for a small value of D as most functions are linear towards the origin. The $F(D)$ curve is then built up step by step. Concentration is determined by pipette withdrawal or, alternatively, by the use of divers.

12.11.3 The LADAL X-ray centrifuge
The LADAL X-ray centrifuge [49] is an extension of the X-ray gravitational technique (figure 12.8). With X-rays, weight concentration is determined directly without disturbing the suspension. An isotope source is used which makes radial scanning possible and reduces the analysis time to a few minutes. The technique is limited to powders with components of atomic number greater than about 13 which absorb the radiation. Multimodel distributions can be evaluated in the static mode by using Kamak's equation. Scanning can be used for unimodel distributions: assuming that Harris's three-parameter distribution curve [50] describes the unknown distribution, these parameters may be found by curve-fitting [51]. Alternatively, Kamak's equation can be used in a similar manner to that illustrated in the appendix with a variable measurement radius as opposed to a variable inner radius, as in the worked example.

The disc, about 11 in in diameter, spins in an horizontal plane at speeds of 750, 1500 or 3000 rpm. An X-ray beam generated by an isotope source passes at a chosen distance from the centre of rotation through Perspex windows and a $\frac{5}{8}$ in thickness

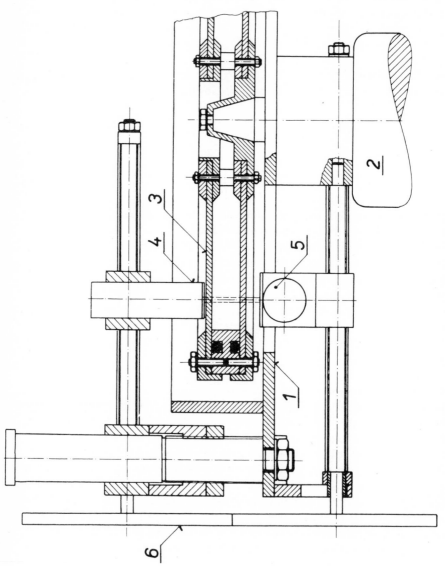

Fig. 12.8. The LADAL X-ray centrifuge: 1, casing; 2, motor; 3, disc centrifuge; 4, isotope source; 5, detector; 6, driving cogs for scanning mechanism.

of suspension. Both source and detector can be moved radially facing each other. The source, detector and counting electronics are the same as for the gravitational model.

Owing to the high initial powder concentration required (0·2 to 1·0% v/v), the homogeneous technique must be used. The emergent intensity of the X-ray beam with clear liquid in the disc is first recorded to provide a zero base line. The clear liquid is then removed and replaced with the suspension while the disc is spinning. The reading starts dropping immediately due to the continuous dilution occurring at every point due to radial settling.

The emergent intensity of the radiation is given by:

$$I = I_c \exp(-BC)$$

where B is a constant, C is the solids concentration and I_c is the emergent intensity with clear liquid in the bowl:

$$I_{max} = I_c \exp(-BC_{max})$$

hence

$$BC_{max} = \log\left(\frac{I_{max}}{I_c}\right)$$

$$BC = -\log\left(\frac{I}{I_c}\right).$$

Since the deflection of the pen-recorder is $I_c - I$, these equations are best written:

$$BC_{max} = -\log\left(1 - \frac{I_c - I_{max}}{I_c}\right).$$

$$BC = -\log\left(1 - \frac{I_c - I}{I_c}\right). \tag{12.27}$$

The approximation due to Kamak can be modified for the scanning mode of operation by replacing the constant (R/S) by the variable (R_i/S), where R_i is the position of the source and detector at time t_i, i.e. equation (12.2) becomes:

$$D_i = \sqrt{\frac{9\eta \ln y_i}{(\rho_s - \rho_f)\omega^2 t}} \tag{12.28}$$

where

$$y_i = \left(\frac{R_i}{S}\right)^2 \tag{12.29}$$

Equation (12.16) becomes:

$$F_i = \int_0^{Q_i} \left(\frac{R_i}{S}\right)^2 dQ \tag{12.30}$$

$$= \int_0^{Q_i} \exp(\alpha D^2).dQ$$

i.e.
$$\int_0^{D_i(R_i t_i)} \exp(-\alpha D^2 t) F(D) dD$$

where
$$\alpha = \frac{(\rho_s - \rho_f)\omega^2}{9}$$

$D_i(R_i t_i)$ is the largest particle present at radius R_i at time t_i and can be calculated using Stokes' law (equation (12.28)).

12.11.4 The modified pipette withdrawal centrifuge

The Simcar centrifuge was developed to conform with Kamak's theory. A major problem with this instrument is the amount of suspension required (approximately 2500 cm³ of liquid and 5 cm³ of powder), so that the liquid level does not alter appreciably during an analysis. The amount removed at each withdrawal is about 40 cm³, hence the error due to assuming a constant liquid level increases as more samples are withdrawn. It is, therefore, not advisable to withdraw more than four samples. An eight-point analysis, in the size range 5 to 0·2 μm approximately, will take up to a full day. The equation can, however, be modified to take account of this fall, so that more points can be obtained with a single run. The author was faced with the problem of analysing material of which there was only about 2 g available and, with a colleague, designed and had constructed a modified pipette withdrawal centrifuge and developed a modified theory.

12.11.5 Theory for modified pipette withdrawal technique

(a) Calculation of particle size

Let the time of the first withdrawal be t_i; the largest particle present in the withdrawn sample at this time will have fallen from the surface at radius S to the measurement zone at radius R.

Equation (12.23) will apply:

$$D_1^2 t_1 = k \log \frac{R}{S}. \tag{12.31}$$

The liquid level will then fall to R_2, where:

$$S_1^2 - S^2 = \frac{v}{\pi h} \tag{12.32}$$

v is the volume extracted (10 cm³) and h the thickness of the centrifuge disc (1 cm). The fall in the inner radius can therefore be determined:

$$\Delta S_1 = S_1 - S. \tag{12.33}$$

Let the time for the second withdrawal be t_2, then the largest particle present in the withdrawn sample will have fallen from S to x_{12} in time t_1, then a distance Δx_{12} due to the withdrawal of the first sample. Hence:

$$D_2^2 t_1 = k \log \frac{x_{12}}{S} \tag{12.34}$$

$$D_2^2(t_2 - t_1) = k \log \frac{S}{x_{12} + \Delta x_{12}} . \tag{12.35}$$

Adding these equations gives:

$$D_2^2 t_2 = k \log \frac{R}{S_1} \left(1 + \frac{\Delta x_1}{x_{12}} \right)^{-1} . \tag{12.36}$$

For the third withdrawal:
In time t_1 particles of size D_3 will fall from the surface at radius S to x_{13} hence:

$$D_3^2 t_1 = k \log \frac{x_{13}}{S} . \tag{12.37}$$

These particles will then fall a distance Δx_{21} due to the withdrawal of the first sample, where from equation (12.32):

$$(x_{13} + \Delta x_{13})^2 - x_{13}^2 = 3 \cdot 183 \tag{12.38}$$

In the next time increment particles of size D_3 will fall from radius $x_{13} + \Delta x_{13}$ to radius x_{23}, hence:

$$D_3^2(t_2 - t_1) = k \log \frac{x_{23}}{x_{13} + \Delta x_{13}} . \tag{12.39}$$

These particles will then fall a distance Δx_{23}, due to the withdrawal of the second sample, as before:

$$(x_{23} + \Delta x_{23})^2 - x_{23}^2 = 3 \cdot 183 \tag{12.40}$$

and

$$D_3^2(t_3 - t_2) = k \log \frac{R}{x_{23} + \Delta x_{23}}. \tag{12.41}$$

Adding equations (12.37), (12.39) and (12.41) gives:

$$D_3^2 t_3 = k \log \frac{R}{S} \left(1 + \frac{\Delta x_{13}}{x_{13}} \right)^{-1} \left(1 + \frac{\Delta x_{23}}{x_{23}} \right)^{-1} . \tag{12.42}$$

The bracketed terms being the correction terms for the fall in level due to each extraction.

These equations are best solved by computer using iteration techniques.

(b) Calculation of frequency undersize

Let the concentration of the final sample withdrawn be Q_1 and let the surface be at radius R_1 immediately prior to this withdrawal (figure 12.9):

Then

$$F_1 = \tfrac{1}{2}(1 + y_1)Q_1 \tag{12.43}$$

where

$$y_1 = \left(\frac{R}{R_1}\right)^2 \tag{12.44}$$

$$F_1 = \tfrac{1}{2}(1 + y_{12})Q_{12} \tag{12.45}$$

where

$$y_{12} = y_2^{(D_1/D_2)^2}. \tag{12.46}$$

Hence, by the trapezoidal rule:

$$(F_2 - F_1) = \tfrac{1}{2}(y_2 + y_{12})(Q_2 - Q_{12}); \; y_2 = \left(\frac{R}{R_2}\right)^2.$$

Substituting for Q_{12} gives:

$$F_2 = \tfrac{1}{2}(y_2 + y_{12})Q_2 + \left[1 - \frac{y_2 + y_{12}}{1 + y_{12}}\right]F_1. \tag{12.47}$$

Proceeding in a like manner gives the general formula:

$$F_n - F_{n-1} = \tfrac{1}{2}(y_n + y_{n-1, n})(Q_n - Q_{n-1, n})$$

$$F_{n-1} - F_{n-2} = \tfrac{1}{2}(y_{n-1, n} + y_{n-2, n})(Q_{n-1, n} - Q_{n-2, n}).$$

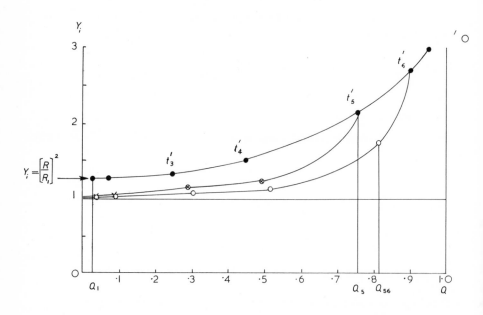

Fig. 12.9. Theoretical figure for variable inner radius centrifuge. Black circles are experimental points; open circles are derived points.

By successively eliminating the Q-functions, this gives a general equation in recursive form as before:

$$F_i = \tfrac{1}{2}(y_i + y_{i-1,\,i})Q + \sum_{j=1}^{i-1} \left[\frac{y_i + y_{i-1,\,i}}{y_{j+1,\,i} + y_{ji}} - \frac{y_i + y_{i-1,\,i}}{y_{ji} + y_{j-1,\,i}} \right] F_j \qquad (12.48)$$

where $y_i = (R/R_i)^2$ and $y_{i-1,\,i} = y_i^{(D_{i-1}/D_i)^2}$.

12.12 The supercentrifuge

The supercentrifuge rotates at several thousand revolutions per minute and may be used to determine the size distribution of particles too small to be analysed with conventional centrifuges.

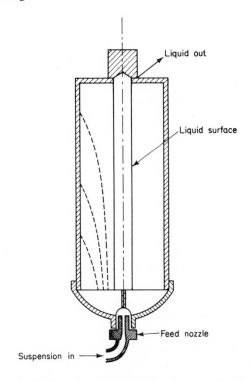

Fig. 12.10. Diagrammatic section of the Hauser-Lynn centrifuge [37].

Several ways of using Hauser's [35, 36] supercentrifuge (figure 12.10) for particle-size analysis have been described in the literature. The usual procedure involves successive fractionation of the suspension and weighing of the fractions collected on a removable liner in the bowl [38—40]. The suspension is fed into the bottom of the bowl and the particles move in a spiral path until they reach the wall. The liquid is then discharged in a annular layer over the overflow dam.

If q is the rate of flow of suspension that causes a particle of size D to be deposited at a height h above the feed inlet, it can be shown [36] that:

$$q = khD^2.$$

If the removable liner is divided into identical strips, dried and weighed, the weight deposited on each strip may be used to find the size distribution [22, p. 86]. The constant k may be evaluated from curves given by Hauser and Lynn [37], or a nomograph developed by Saunders [41] may be used.

This method of determining size distributions cannot be recommended for routine analysis and a method developed by Bradley is to be preferred [9]. This method is applicable to the Sharples supercentrifuge (figure 12.11).

If D_m is the smallest particle retained in the centrifuge, it can be shown that:

$$P = W + \int_0^{D_m} \frac{R^2 - x_0^2}{R^2 - S^2} F(D) \, dD.$$

This is identical to equation (12.5), but the relationship between x_0 and D is more complex than that for a centrifuge without flow. Bradley derives the empirical solution for the Sharples supercentrifuge as:

$$\frac{D^2 (\rho_s - \rho_f) \omega^2}{18 q} = 4 \cdot 1 \times 10^{-3} x_0^{-1 \cdot 2}.$$

This gives, for the supercentrifuge as well as for batch centrifuges:

$$W = P - \frac{R^2 - S^2}{2S} \frac{dP}{dS}$$

which is the same as equation (12.6).

Hence, the weight fraction oversize is calculable by measurement of P for different values of S at constant W and q. The quickest analytical procedure is to calculate P from gravimetric or chemical analysis of feed and overflow suspensions. Choice of flow rate and speed can be done in accordance with prior knowledge of approximate size and use of derived theoretical expressions, or by trial and error to establish the rate at which P approaches unity with maximum S.

The main disadvantages of the technique are the need for large samples and the uncertainty of end-effects in the bowl. A big advantage is the ability to use an item of standard equipment without modification for a size below the range of most of the specially-designed centrifuges, since the speeds vary between 8000 and 50 000 rev min^{-1}.

12.13 The ultracentrifuge [42–44]
The rotor of the ultracentrifuge is spun at speeds of up to 60 000 rev min^{-1} in a vacuum to minimize air drag. It may be used, therefore, to measure the size distribution of very fine particles. McCormick [45], for example, describes its use for determining the size distribution of polystyrene $0 \cdot 088 < d < 0 \cdot 511 \, \mu m$ and Brodnyan [46] uses it for determining emulsion particle size.

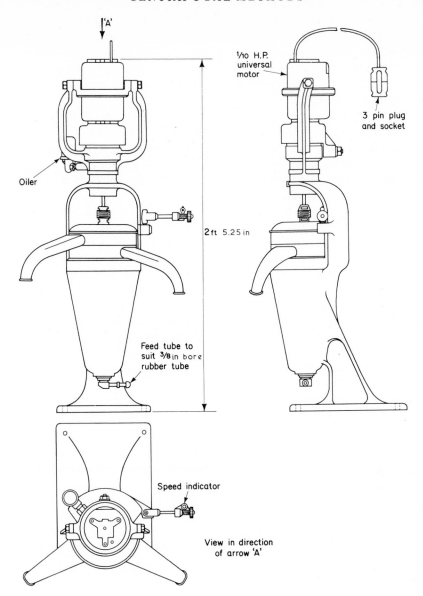

Fig. 12.11. The Sharples no. 1A open-type laboratory supercentrifuge. Motor drive.

12.14 Conclusion

Centrifugal sedimentation may be carried out by two-layer or homogeneous techniques, cumulatively or incrementally. The two-layer techniques give rise to streaming, a phenomenon most likely to affect cumulative analyses, in which the fraction sedimented against time is determined.

With ordinary centrifuge tubes, it is difficult to remove the supernatant liquid without disturbing the deposited powder; this problem is overcome with the Whitby technique, in which the height of the deposit in a capillary at the bottom of the tube is measured. However, problems arise due to non-uniform packing, and acceleration and deceleration have to be slow and controlled in order to reduce the deposit of particles on the walls of the tube.

These problems are overcome with the Joyce-Loebl centrifuge, in which there are no side walls and the fraction deposited is determined by removing the supernatant liquid, while the centrifuge is in motion, and examining it. However, it is probable that removal of the sediment occurs, due to disturbance propagated ahead of the pick-up probe and gravimetric analysis of the supernatant liquid is difficult because of the small weights involved.

The Kaye disc centrifuge is the only instrument in which the two-layer technique is used incrementally, so that the presence of streaming is unimportant, provided the streams are representative of the bulk. The concentration is determined by the attenuation of a light beam passing through the suspension, a perfect sampling device, since it does not disturb the suspension. However, the laws of geometric optics break down as the size of the particles approaches the wavelength of light, thus making it very difficult to interpret correctly the analysis results. An improvement is to use X-rays, a technique that has been used to lead glass, a $M_0 k\alpha$ source and a proportional counter for the size range 2 to $0 \cdot 1$ μm [47]. More solids may be used with homogeneous suspensions and the problem of streaming is removed. This technique may be applied to both the Kaye and Joyce-Loebl centrifuge and may probably be the best way of operating the latter.

An incremental pipette withdrawal while the centrifuge is in motion is used in the Simcar disc centrifuge, the analysis being effected gravimetrically by the use of Kamak's formula, although Berg's graphical method may be used. Cylindrical sector and conoidal centrifuge tubes have also been used, the concentration being determined by pipette withdrawal after the centrifuge had stopped. Berg has also used small spherical divers to determine concentration.

The modified pipette withdrawal technique is an improvement on the Simcar instrument, allowing a full analysis to be carried out in about an hour and a half as opposed to a full day. The amount of powder required is about one-tenth of the requirement for the Simcar, and a side effect of the increasing inner radius when samples are extracted is a speeding up of the analysis. The equipment is relatively cheap and easy to operate.

The LADAL X-ray centrifuge is more expensive than the modified pipette centrifuge, but it can be easily automated to give size distributions with the minimum of operator involvement. Using the scanning system, the time for a full-size analysis may be reduced to 15 min — far more rapid than any other technique available. It is limited in its need for powders that are opaque to X-rays.

Determination of the amount sedimented against time has found favour only with Robinson and Martin, who derived a partial solution to the equation for this case, earlier work by Martin being based on an incorrect solution of Romwalter and

Vendl. Since Robinson and Martin found good agreement between their anaylses and analyses carried out by other techniques, it is possible that this method may become more popular.

Because of the difficulty of finding a solution with respect to time of the general equation for centrifugal settling, experimenters have found solutions with respect to the outer and inner radius and based techniques on them. The apparatus for the former, the Gallenkamp stepped-disc centrifuge was not a success, since there was a tendency for the sediment to be removed with the supernatant liquid, whereas the latter technique is so laborious, one run providing only one point on the graph, that it has not found commercial favour.

Some of these techniques have been used in conjunction with a low height of settling compared to the distance of the suspension from the axis of the centrifuge, so that the centrifugal force could be considered constant. This has usually been done with cylindrical or sector-shaped centrifuge tubes, although Hildreth and Patterson used a disc and determined concentration changes photometrically.

The ranges of sizes measurable using the above techniques vary from 80 to 0·1 μm, using the M.S.A. particle-size analyser, gravitational sedimentation being used for the coarse particles; 30 to 0·3 μm with the Kaye disc centrifuge; 5 to 0·1 μm with the Simcar centrifuge and 10 to 0·01 μm with the Joyce–Loebl centrifuge. The modified pipette centrifuge operates in the range 5 to 0·05 μm, the full range covered by this technique and the gravitational pipette method is of the order of 4 decades using essentially the same technique. The LADAL X-ray gravitational and centrifugal techniques cover a similar range. The Simcar and LADAL centrifuges require about 10 to 20 g of powder, the modified pipette about 2 g and the other techniques a few milligrams.

12.15 Appendix: Worked examples

12.15.1 Simcar centrifuge

(a) Determination of F factors
These factors are constant, provided a constant volume of suspension is used, and samples are extracted in a two-to-one progression in time.

Let volume of suspension $V = 2410 \text{ cm}^3$, so that:

$$y = \left(\frac{R}{S}\right)^2 = 2.$$

Applying equation (12.18):

$$F_1 = \tfrac{1}{2}(1 + 2)Q_1$$
$$F_1 = 1 \cdot 5 Q_1.$$

Applying equation (12.24):

$$F_1 = \tfrac{1}{2}(2 + \sqrt{2})Q_2 + (2 + \sqrt{2})\left[\left(\frac{1}{2 + \sqrt{2}}\right) - \left(\frac{1}{\sqrt{2} + 1}\right)\right] F_1$$

$$F_2 = 1\cdot71Q_2 - 0\cdot62Q_1$$

$$F_3 = \tfrac{1}{2}(2+\sqrt{2})Q_3 + (2+\sqrt{2})\left[\left(\frac{1}{2+2^{\frac{1}{2}}}\right) - \left(\frac{1}{2^{\frac{1}{2}}+2^{\frac{1}{4}}}\right)\right]F_2$$

$$+ \left[\left(\frac{1}{2^{\frac{1}{4}}+2^{\frac{1}{4}}}\right) - \left(\frac{1}{2^{\frac{1}{4}}+1}\right)\right]F_1$$

$$F_3 = 1\cdot71Q_3 - 0\cdot31F_2 - 0\cdot25F_1$$

$$F_3 = 1\cdot71Q_3 - 0\cdot53Q_2 - 0\cdot18Q_3.$$

Proceeding in a like manner gives:

$$F_4 = 1\cdot71Q_4 - 0\cdot53Q_3 - 0\cdot15Q_2 - 0\cdot03Q_1$$

$$F_i = 1\cdot71Q_i - 0\cdot53Q_{i-1} - 0\cdot15Q_{i-2} - 0\cdot03Q_{i-3}.$$

Experimental results
Material: zinc oxide
Dispersant: 0·1% Calgon in distilled water
Weight of powder: 10 g
Powder density: 5·61 g cm^{-3}
Liquid viscosity: 0·01 poise
Liquid density: 1 g cm^{-3}
Centrifuge speed: $N = 480$ rev min^{-1}, $w = 16\,\pi$ rad s^{-1}.

Applying equation (12.2):

$$D^2t = 5\cdot34 \times 10^{-6} \text{ cm}^2 \text{ s}^{-1}$$

$$D = \frac{2\cdot98}{\sqrt{T}} \,\mu m \; (T \text{ in min}).$$

Time (T) (min)	Particle size (D) (μm)	Sample weight in 25 cm³ (g)	Concentration Q (%)	Percentage undersize (F)
0		0·0830*	100	—
2	2·11	0·0822	99·1	—
4	1·49	0·0800	96·5	—
8	1·05	0·0713	86·0	99·9
16	0·75	0·0610	73·5	95·4
32	0·53	0·0407	49·0	67·8
64	0·37	0·0227	27·4	42·2
128	0·26	0·0078	9·4	14·8
256	0·18	0·0027	3·2	4·8

*Determined from original concentration

Column 3 is the sample weight after drying and cooling in a desiccator, due allowance being made for the weight of dispersant.

The experiment is carried out twice, with four extractions per run. Alternatively, an allowance can be made for the fall in height of the interface, as in section 12.14.3.

12.15.2 X-ray centrifuge

Determination of F *factors.* Applying equation (12.24), gives for $R = 10$ cm, $S = 5.65$ cm:

$$F_1 = 2.06Q_1$$
$$F_2 = 2.445Q_2 - 1.6Q_1$$
$$F_3 = 2.445Q_3 - 1.438Q_2 - 0.139Q_1$$
$$F_4 = 2.445Q_4 - 0.10Q_2 + 0.055Q_1$$
$$F_5 = 2.445Q_5 - 1.438Q_4 - 0.122Q_3 + 0.052Q_2$$
$$F_i = 2.445Q_i - 1.438Q_{i-1} - 0.122Q_{i-2} + 0.052Q_{i-3}.$$

Experimental results

Material: zinc oxide
Dispersant: 0.1% Calgon in distilled water
Volume: 500 cm^3
Weight of powder: 12 g

$$R = 10 \text{ cm}$$
$$S = 5.65 \text{ cm}$$
$$w = 50\,\pi \text{ rad s}^{-1}.$$

Applying equation (12.2):

$$D^2t = 0.904 \times 10^{-6}.$$

Deflection for zero intensity $= 3 \times 20$ cm.
Deflection at zero time $\theta_{\max} = 14.1$ cm.
From equation (12.7)

$$BQ_{\max} = -\log\left(\frac{60 - 14.1}{60}\right)$$
$$BQ = -\log\left(1 - \frac{\theta}{60}\right).$$

Time $(t \div 60)$ (min)	Deflection (cm) (θ)	(BQ)	Concentration (Q) (%)	Percentage undersize $(F)(\%)$	Particle size (μm)
0	14·1	1·164	100	–	–
2	12·2	0·990	84·9	–	0·87
4	10·7	0·860	73·8	99·8	0·62
8	8·4	0·635	54·6	89·7	0·44
16	4·7	0·350	30·0	56·9	0·31
32	1·8	0·130	11·2	22·0	0·22
64	0·5	0·039	3·4	6·9	0·15

12.15.3 Modified pipette centrifuge

Experimental data
Material: zinc oxide
Dispersant: 0·1% Calgon in distilled water
Volume of suspension: 150 cm^3
Weight of powder: 1·5 g
Powder density: 5·6 g cm^{-3}
Liquid viscosity: 0·01 poise
Liquid density: 1 g cm^{-3}
Centrifuge speed: $N = 500$ rev min^{-1}.
Measurement radius: $R = 7$ cm
Bowl radius: $R_0 = 8$ cm
hence initial internal radius $S = 4·03$ cm.

Calculation of particle diameters
Provided the extraction times are in a two-to-one progression, it is only necessary to carry out this calculation once. For subsequent analyses it is only necessary to calculate D_1; the ratios of sizes will be the same as in this worked example.
1st extraction: $t = 120$ s; from equation (12.31):

$$120 D_1^2 = 3·28 \times 10^{-5} \log 1·74 \qquad \underline{D_1 = 2·52 \, \mu m} \, .$$

2nd extraction: $t = 240$ s:

equation (12.34) gives: $120 D_2^2 = 3·28 \times 10^{-5} \log \dfrac{x_{12}}{4·08}$

equation (12.35) gives: $120 D_2^2 = 3·28 \times 10^{-5} \log \dfrac{7}{x_{12} + \Delta x_{12}}$

equation (12.32) gives: $(x_{12} + \Delta x_{12})^2 - x_{12}^2 = 3·83$

Solving these equations simultaneously gives:

$$x_{12}^2 + x_{12}\Delta x_{12} = 28·56$$

$$2 x_{12} \Delta x_{12} + \Delta x_{12}^2 = 3·84$$

Assuming Δx_{12} is negligible compared with x_{12}^2, then $x_{12} = 5\cdot2$, this makes $\Delta x_{12} = 0\cdot31$.

Substituting back $x_{12} = 5\cdot20 + \alpha$, $\Delta x_{12} = 0\cdot31 + \delta$ and neglecting second and higher-order terms in α and δ gives:

$$x_{12} = 5\cdot20$$

$$\Delta x_{12} = 0\cdot297, \quad \text{hence} \quad \underline{D_2 = 1\cdot67 \ \mu m.}$$

3rd extraction: $t = 480$ s.

Assuming this progression of sizes continues:

$$D_3 \doteqdot \frac{1\cdot67^2}{2\cdot52}$$

$$D_3 \doteqdot 1\cdot10.$$

Substituting this value into equations (12.37) gives:

$$\log \frac{x_{13}}{4\cdot08} = 0\cdot0433, \quad \text{hence } x_{13} = 4\cdot58.$$

From equation (12.38):

$$\Delta x_{13} = 0\cdot34.$$

From equation (12.39):

$$\log \frac{x_{23}}{x_{13} + \Delta x_{13}} = 0\cdot0443, \quad \text{hence } x_{23} = 5\cdot45.$$

Substituting these values into equation (12.42), gives a more accurate value for D_3:

$$D_3^2 = \frac{3\cdot28 \times 10^{-5}}{480} \log 1\cdot71 \left(1 + \frac{34}{446}\right)^{-1} \left(1 + \frac{28}{531}\right)^{-1}$$

$$\underline{D_3 = 1\cdot105 \ \mu m.}$$

This process is best completed by computer which gives the diameters tabulated below:

Time (T) (min)	Diameter (μm) (D)	i	Q (%)	R_i	$y_i = \left(\dfrac{R}{R_i}\right)^2$	(F) (%)
2	2·52	7	98·1	4·03	3·02	—
4	1·69	6	89·6	4·02	2·51	0·100
8	1·108	5	77	4·76	2·17	98
16	0·716	4	50·2	5·08	1·90	66·1
32	0·457	3	23	5·39	1·69	30·4
64	0·289	2	6·2	5·68	1·53	7·9
128	0·180	1	1·2	5·95	1·38	1·4

Calculation of y *values*

Equation (12.44) gives $y_1 = 1\cdot38$, $y_2 = 1\cdot51$, and so on.

Equation (12.46) gives:

$$\log y_{12} = \left(\frac{180}{289}\right)^2 \log 1\cdot38$$

$$y_{12} = 1\cdot132, \text{ and so on.}$$

Tabulated y *values*

$y_{12} = 1\cdot132$ $y_{23} = 1\cdot180$ $y_{34} = 1\cdot226$ $y_{45} = 1\cdot326$ $y_{56} = 1\cdot326$ $y_{67} = 1\cdot4$

$y_{13} = 1\cdot051$ $y_{24} = 1\cdot072$ $y_{35} = 1\cdot094$ $y_{46} = 1\cdot123$ $y_{57} = 1\cdot162$

$y_{14} = 1\cdot021$ $y_{25} = 1\cdot029$ $y_{36} = 1\cdot040$ $y_{47} = 1\cdot056$

$y_{15} = 1\cdot009$ $y_{26} = 1\cdot013$ $y_{37} = 1\cdot017$

$y_{16} = 1\cdot003$ $y_{27} = 1\cdot006$

$y_{17} = 1\cdot002$

Calculation of F *values*

Equation (12.43) gives: $F_1 = \frac{1}{2}(1 + 1\cdot38)Q_1$ $\underline{F_1 = 1\cdot19\,Q_1}$.

Equation (12.47) gives: $F_2 = \frac{1}{2}(1\cdot53 + 1\cdot132)Q_2 + \left(1 - \dfrac{2\cdot662}{2\cdot132}\right)F_1$

$$F_2 = 1\cdot331Q_2 - 0\cdot296Q_1.$$

Equation (12.48) gives:

$$F_3 = \frac{1}{2}(1\cdot69 + 1\cdot180)Q_3 + \left[\frac{2\cdot87}{2\cdot87} - \frac{2\cdot87}{2\cdot232}\right]F_2 + \left[\frac{2\cdot87}{2\cdot232} - \frac{2\cdot87}{2\cdot052}\right]F_1$$

and so on, giving the general equations for the conditions $i_{max} = 7$, $V = 150 \text{ cm}^3$.

$$F_1 = 1\cdot19Q_1$$

$$F_2 = 1\cdot331Q_2 - 0\cdot296Q_1$$

$$F_3 = 1\cdot435Q_3 - 0\cdot426Q_2 - 0\cdot008Q_1$$

$$F_4 = 1\cdot563Q_4 - 0\cdot524Q_3 - 0\cdot051Q_2 - 0\cdot0025Q_1$$

$$F_5 = 1\cdot748Q_5 - 0\cdot704Q_4 - 0\cdot044Q_3 + 0\cdot006Q_2 + 0\cdot003Q_1$$

$$F_6 = 1\cdot962Q_6 - 0\cdot980Q_5 - 0\cdot008Q_4 + 0\cdot018Q_3$$

$$F_7 = 2\cdot257Q_7 - 1\cdot364Q_6 + 0\cdot056Q_5 + 0\cdot051Q_4 + 0\cdot004Q_3 + 0\cdot002Q_2$$

References

[1] Steel, J.G., and Bradfield, R. (1934), *Am. Soil Survey Assoc. Report, 14th Ann. Meeting Bull.*, no. 15, 88.

[2] Marshall, C.E. (1930), *Proc. R. Soc.*, **A 126**, 427.

[3] Whitby, K.T. (1955), *Heating, Piping Air Conditioning*, **61**, 449.

[4] Whitby, K.T. (1955), *J. Air Pollution Control Assoc.*, **5**, 120.

[5] Whitby, K.T., Algren, A.B., and Annis, J.C. (1958), A.S.T.M. Sp. Publ. No. 234, 117.

[6] Cartwright, L.M., and Gregg, R.Q. (1958), *Ibid.*, 127.

[7] Dewell, P. (Sept., 1966), Soc. Analyt. Chem., Particle Size Analysis Conference, Loughborough, 1966.

[8] Irani, R.R., and Fong, W.S. (1961), *Cereal Chem.*, **38**, 67.

[9] Bradley, D. (1962), *Chem. Proc. Engng*, **43**, 591, *et seq.*, 634, *et seq.*

[10] Groves, M.J., Kaye, B.H., and Scarlet, B. (1964), *B. Chem. Eng.*, **9**, 11, 742.

[11] Kaye, B.H. (1962), British Patent No. 895222.

[12] Atherton, E., and Tough, D. (1965), *J. Soc. Dyers Colourists*, 624.

[13] Tough, D. (1965), *Am. Dyestuffs Report*, **54**, 17, 34.

[14] Treasure, C.R.G., private communication.

[15] Marshall, C.E., Keen, B.A., and Schofield, R.K. (1930), *Nature*, **126**, 94.

[16] Norton, F.H., and Spiel, S.J. (1938), *J. Am. Ceram. Soc.*, **21**, 89.

[17] Jacobson, A.E., and Sullivan, W.F. (1946), *Ind. Eng. Chem., analyt ed.*, **18**, 360.

[18] Menis, O., House, H.P., and Boyd, C.M. (1957), *Oak Ridge National Laboratory Report 2345*, **22**, 86; and (1958), **23**, 87.

[19] Conner, P., Hardwick, W.M., and Laundy, B.J. (1958), *U.K.A.E.A. Report*, A.E.R.E., CE/R2465.

[20] Hildreth, J.D., and Patterson, D. (1964), *J. Soc. Dyers Colourists*, **80**, 474.

[21] Musgrove, J.R., and Harner, H.R. (1947), *Turbimetric Particle Size Analysis*, Eagle Pilcher Co., Cincinnati, Ohio, U.S.A.

[22] Irani, R.R., and Callis, C.E. (1963), *Particle Size Measurement*, Wiley, N.Y.

[23] Orr, C., and Dallavalle, J.M. (1960), *Fine Particle Measurement*, MacMillan, N.Y.

[24] Gupta, A.K. (1959), *J. Appl. Chem.*, **9**, 487.

[25] Romwalter, A., and Vendl, M. (1935), *Kolloid Z.*, **72**, 1.

[26] Brown, C. (1944), *J. Phys. Chem.*, **48**, 246.

[27] Martin, S.W. (1939), *Ind. Eng. Chem., analyt. ed.*, **11**, 471.

[28] Martin, S.W., and Robinson, H.E. (1948), *J. Phys. Colloid Chem.*, **42**, 854; (1949) *ibid.*, **53**, 860.

[29] Murley, R.D. (1965), *Nature*, 207, 1089.

[30] Donoghue, J.K., and Bostock, W. (1955), *Trans. Inst. Chem. Engrs*, **33**, 72.

[31] Berg, S. (1940), *Ingen. Vidensk. Skr. B.*, no. 2.

[32] Kamak, H.J. (1951), *Analyt. Chem.*, **23**, 6, 844.

[33] Slater, C., and Cohen, L. (1962), *J. Sci. Instrum.*, **39**, 614.

[34] Treasure, C.R.G. (1964), Whiting and Industrial Powders Research Council, Welwyn, Tech. Paper No. 50.

[35] Hauser, E.A., and Read, C.E. (1936), *J. Phys. Chem.*, **40**, 1169.

[36] Hauser, E.A., and Schachman, H.K. (1940), *ibid.*, **44**, 584.

[37] Hauser, E.A., and Lynn, J.E. (1940), *Ind. Eng. Chem.*, **32**, 660.

[38] Fancher, G., Oliphant, S.C., and Houssiere, C.R. (1942), *Ind. Eng. Chem., analyt ed.*, **14**, 552.

[39] McIntosh, J., and Seibie, F.E. (1940), *B. J. Exp. Path.*, **21**, 143.

[40] Schachman, H.K. (1948), *J. Phys*; also (1948), *Colloid Chem.*, **52**, 1035.

[41] Saunders, E. (1948), *Analyt. Chem.*, **20**, 379.

[42] Svedberg. T. (1938), *Ind. Eng. Chem., analyt ed.*, **10**, 113.

[43] Svedberg, T., and Peterson, K.O. (1940), *The Ultracentrifuge,* Oxford Univ. Press.

[44] Alexander, J. (1926), (ed.), *Colloid Chemistry,* Chemical Catalogue Co., N.Y., chapter 6.

[45] McCormick, H.W. (1964), *J. Colloid Sci.,* **19,** 173.

[46] Brodnyan, J.G. (1960), *J. Colloid Sci.,* **15,** 563.

[47] Martin, J.J., Brown, J.H., and de Bruyn, P.L. (1963) (ed., L Kuhn), *Ultrafine Particles,* Wiley, N.Y.

[48] Moser, H., and Schmidt, W. (1957), *Das Papier,* II, **189;** (1963), *ibid.,* 377.

[49] Allen, T., and Svarovsky, L. (1972), *Proc. Soc Analyt. Chem.* **9,** 2, 38−40.

[50] Harris, C.C. (1969), *A.M.I.E. Trans.,* **244,** 187.

[51] Svarovsky, L., and Friedova, J. (1972), *Powder Technol.,* **5,** 5, 273−7.

[52] Bayness, J.E., Attaway, A.V., and Young, B.W. (1972), *Proc. Soc. Analyt. Chem.,* **9,** 4, 83−6.

[53] Statham, B.R. (1972), *Proc. Soc. Analyt. Chem.,* **9,** 2, 40−3.

[54] Scarlett, B., Rippon, M., and Lloyd, P.J. (1967), 'Particle size analysis', *Soc. Analyt. Chem.* 242.

[55] Allen, T. (1968), *Powder Technol.,* **2,** 133.

[56] Vaughan, G.N., Ford, R.W., and West, H.W.H. (1969), *Proc. B. Ceram. Soc.,* **13,** 47−56.

[57] Naumann, D., and Seydel, K.J. (1969), *Plaste Kaut,* **15,** 2, 136−8.

[58] Atherton, E., and Cooper, A.C. (1962), British Patent 983, 760.

[59] Atherton, E., Cooper, A.C., and Fox, M.R. (1964), *J. Soc. Dyers Colourists,* **26,** 62.

[60] McDonald, D.P. (1969), *Chem. Proc.,* **15,** 3, 22−3.

[61] Carr, W. (1970), *Paint Oil Colour J.,* **157,** (37, 34), 8, 82−3.

[62] Carr, W. (1970), *J. Oil Colour Chem. Assoc.,* **53,** 1, 81.

[63] Carr, W. (1971), *J. Oil Colour Chem. Assoc.,* **54,** 155−73.

[64] Carr, W. (1971), *Paint Tech.,* **35,** 1, 16−23.

[65] Carr, W. (1972), 'Symposium on Particle size analysis', Bradford, publ. *Soc. Analyt. Chem.*

[66] Beresford, J. (1967), *J. Oil Colour Chemists Assoc.,* **50,** 7, 594−614.

[67] Toyoshima, Y. (1970), *J. Jap. Soc. Col. Mat.,* **43,** 7, 325−32, 364−9.

[68] Burt, M.W.F. (1964), *A.W.R.E. Report 0-76/64.*

[69] Jones, M.H. (1966), *Proc. Soc. Analyt. Chem.,* **3,**116.

[70] Jones, M.H. (1969), U.S. Patent 3, 475, 968.

13 *The Electrical Sensing Zone Method of Particle - Size Distribution Determination (The Coulter Principle)*

13.1 Introduction

The Coulter technique is a method of determining the number and size of particles suspended in an electrolyte by causing them to pass through a small orifice on either side of which is immersed an electrode. The changes in resistance as particles pass through the orifice generate voltage pulses whose amplitudes are proportional to the volumes of the particles. The pulses are amplified, sized and counted and from the derived data the size distribution of the suspended phase may be determined. The technique was originally applied to blood-cell counting [1, 2]. Kubitschek [3, 4] introduced modifications which permitted counting of bacterial cells, and pointed out that this principle could be applied to the measurement of cell-volume distributions as well as number counting. Modified instruments were soon developed with which particles could be sized as well as counted.

Since analyses may be carried out rapidly with good reproducibility using semi-skilled operators, the method has become popular in a very wide range of industries [6].

13.2 Operation

The operating principle of the instrument may be followed by referring to figure 13.1. A controlled vacuum initiates flow through a sapphire orifice let into a glass tube and unblances a mercury siphon. The system is then isolated from the vacuum source by closing tap A and flow continues due to the balancing action of the mercury siphon. The advancing column of mercury activates the counter by means of start and stop probes, so placed that a count is carried out while a known volume of electrolyte passes through the orifice (0·05 ml, 0·5 ml or 2·0 ml). The resistance across the orifice is monitored by means of immersed electrodes on either side. As each particle passes through the orifice it changes this resistance, thus generating a voltage pulse which is amplified, sized and counted, and from the derived data the size distribution of the suspended phase is determined.

The amplified voltage pulses are fed to a threshold circuit having an adjustable threshold level. The threshold level is indicated on a oscilloscope screen by a brightening of the pulse segment above the threshold setting and the pulse pattern also serves as a monitor. All pulses above the threshold level are counted and this count represents the number of particles larger than some determinable volume proportional to the appropriate threshold setting. Some instruments have upper and lower threshold circuits which permit sizing between two determinable volumes, i.e. a relative-frequency distribution. By taking a series of counts at various amplifications and threshold settings, data are directly obtained for determining number frequency against volume.

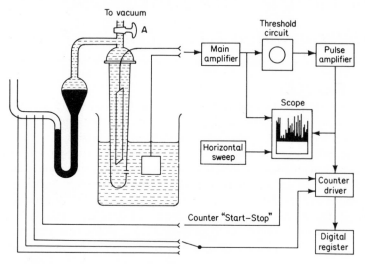

Fig. 13.1. Diagram of the Coulter counter.

13.3 Calibration

Although the detailed calibration technique varies with the type of instrument, the basic procedure is unaltered. Calibration is carried out for each electrolyte and tube with narrowly classified powders of known diameter.

If t_c is the threshold level for the average of the pulses generated by the calibration powder of known number-volume diameter d_c, then:

$$d_c = k \sqrt[3]{(t_c)} \tag{13.1}$$

where k is the calibration factor, hence d may be found for any value of t.

The counter may also be calibrated using the powder under analysis if the whole size range of the sample is covered. The volume of particles in a metered volume of suspension will be:

$$v_\rho = \frac{v}{V_s} \cdot \frac{w}{\rho_s} \tag{13.2}$$

where:

    v = volume of suspension metered for each count,
    w = total weight of powder used,
    V_s = total volume of suspension,
    ρ_s = density of particles.

Table 13.1. Coulter counter data and weight conversion.

Sample silica
Aperture diameter = 280 μm
Aperture resistance = 6350 Ω

Manometer volume = 2·0 ml
Calibration and zero data 26·4 pollen
t′ = 64 at 16, 127 at 17

Source –
Coincidence factor (F) = 13·72
Notes
conc = 0·0168 gm in 200 ml
ρ_s = 2·62 g/ml

Calibration factor (k) = 20·6

Electrolyte 0·9% w/v NaCl
Dispersant 1% Calgon
Operator –
Date –

Gain index	t′	I	F	n′ (raw counts)		$\bar{n}'$	$n'' = P\left(\dfrac{\bar{n}'}{1000}\right)^2$ −√	$n = \bar{n}' + n''$	$t = t'(F)$	$d = k\sqrt{t}$	Δn	$\bar{t}$	$(\Delta n)\bar{t}$	Progress $\Sigma(\Delta n)\bar{t}$	Cum. Weight %
3	132	1	1·00	1.1.1	0.0.0.0	0·5	—	0·5	132	105	0·5	105	53	53	0·4
	48·5	1	1·00	2.2.1.2	0.1.0.0	1·0	—	1·0	48·5	75	0·5	90	45	98	0·7
	136·5	4	0·126	35	38	36·5	—	36·5	17·2	53	35·5	32·8	1165	1263	9·0
	46	4	0·126	255	213	234	8	242	5·8	37	205·5	11·5	2370	3633	25·8
	135	7	0·0167	1004	1047	1026	14	1038	2·25	27	796	4·02	3200	6833	48·5
	47·6	7	0·0167	2629	2690	2660	97	2755	0·796	19	1717	1·52	2610	9443	66·8
	28·5	8	0·00891	6086	6135	6111	512	6545	0·252	13	3790	0·524	1988	11 431	81·2
	30·5	10	0·00311	11 569	11 591	11 580	1840	13 216	0·095	9·4	6671	0·173	1150	12 581	89·2
													14 100	100	100

A size analysis consists of decreasing number of pulses against increasing threshold settings. If $\bar{t}$ is the average theshold setting as the pulse count changes by Δn, then:

$$v_p = \frac{\pi}{6} k^3 \Sigma \, \Delta n \bar{t}$$

(13.3)

$$v_p = \frac{\pi}{6} \Sigma \, \Delta n d^3.$$

(13.4)

Hence:

$$k^3 = \frac{6}{\pi} \frac{w}{\rho_s} \frac{v}{V_s} \frac{1}{\Sigma \, \Delta n \bar{t}}.$$

(13.5)

If the calibration constant as determined by equation (13.5) differs from that determined by equation (13.1), it is likely that the whole range of powder has not been examined. That is, there are some particles present in suspension which are too small to be detected by the system. In this case, equation (13.5) may be used to determine the fraction undersize by comparing the experimental value of $\Sigma \, \Delta n \bar{t}$ with the expected value.

For the example in table 13.1, applying equation (13.5):

$$\sum_{\bar{t}=0}^{\bar{t}=max^m} \Delta n \bar{t} = \frac{6}{\pi} \frac{0 \cdot 0168}{200} \frac{2}{2 \cdot 62} \frac{1}{(20 \cdot 6)^3}$$

$$= 14\ 100\ (\mu m)^3$$

which agrees with the experimental value (column 15).

In a series of papers, Brotherton examined calibration procedures with Coulter counters models A, B, F and C [7–9], and found wide variations in k. It is interesting to note that while Brotherton found an increase of calibration constant with particle size, the converse was found by Matthews [10].

13.4 Evaluation of results

Table 13.1 shows a Coulter analysis using a model A Coulter counter.

The amplification of the pulses is controlled by a gain selector switch G, numbered from 1 to 6 (col. 1), each step being an amplification of $\sqrt{2}$. The pulse-height is further controlled by a current selector switch I (col. 3) numbered from 1 to 10 which puts known resistances in series with a 300 V d.c. supply and the electrodes. This causes the current roughly to double with each step, so that the voltage pulse is a maximum to I10, G6; these settings are used for counting the smallest particles present in the suspension. The usual procedure is to leave the gain-setting at 3; then with the current selector switch at I1, the threshold control numbered from 0 to 300, is read directly. At I2, the threshold readings t' have to be halved approximately since the current flow has been doubled; at I3 the factor is approximately one-quarter. These factors, which are known as dial expansion factors F, are given in tabular form in the Coulter handbook. Then $t' = Ft$.

The use of these two controls permits the sizing of a wide range of volumes (8000:1), a range which may be extended where necessary by using the gain control.

A range of orifice diameters is available (10 to 1000 μm). The upper particle volume diameter, which may be measured with any orifice, is limited to about 40% of the orifice diameter, since frequent blocking of the orifice occurs if larger particles are present in the suspension. Hence, with a 100 μm orifice, a size range $40 > D > 2\mu$m may be measured since $40^3 : 2^3 = 8000:1$.

The raw count is corrected for background, that is, particles which are present in the electrolyte before the addition of the powder sample, and coincidence. The latter factor has been derived empirically by the manufacturers to compensate for loss of count when two particles go through the orifice together and are counted as one, and for the gain in count due to two particles below threshold size being in such close proximity in the orifice that the pulse generated is above threshold.

Since the corrected count $\bar{n}$ of particles greater than theshold t, where particle size $d = k^3\sqrt{t}$, is known, the size distribution may be determined on a number or weight basis.

13.5 Theory

The basic assumption underlying the operation of the Coulter counter is that the response, i.e. the voltage pulse generated when a particle passes through the orifice, is directly proportional to particle volume. The reliability of the instrument depends upon the accuracy of this assumption.

The relationship between response and particle size may be determined in the following manner:

Figure 13.2(a) shows a particle passing through the orifice.
Figure 13.2(b) shows an element of the particle and orifice.
Resistance of element without a particle, $\delta R_0 = (\rho_f \delta 1)A$.

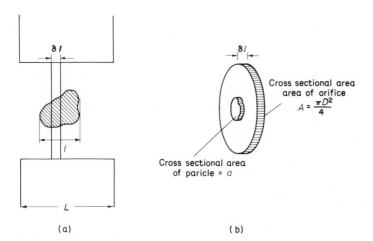

(a)   (b)

Fig. 13.2.(a), (b) The passage of a particle through the orifice of a Coulter counter.

Resistance of element with a particle included is that of two resistors in parallel:

$$\delta R = 1 \left/ \left[\frac{A-a}{\rho_f \delta l} + \frac{a}{\rho_s \delta l} \right] \right.$$

ρ_f, ρ_s are the resistivities of the particle and fluid respectively. Thus the change in the resistance of the element due to the presence of the particle $\delta(\Delta R)$ is given by:

$$\delta(\Delta R) = \delta R_0 - \delta R$$

$$= \frac{-\rho_f a \delta l}{A^2} \left(1 - \frac{\rho_f}{\rho_s} \right) \frac{1}{\left\{ 1 - \left(1 - \frac{\rho_f}{\rho_s} \right) \frac{a}{A} \right\}}. \tag{13.6}$$

The external resistance in the circuit is sufficiently high to ensure that the small change ΔR in the resistance of the orifice due to the presence of a particle will not affect the current I; the voltage pulse generated is therefore $I\Delta R$.

In practice it is found that the response is independent of the resistivity of the particle. In fact, if this were not so the whole technique would break down, since a different calibration factor would be required for each electrolyte – solid suspension. Berg [5] suggested that this may be due to oxide surface films and ionic inertia of the Helmholtz electrical double layer and associated solvent molecules at the surface of the particles, their electrical resistivity becoming infinite. The terms involving ρ_f/ρ_s may therefore be neglected.

Thus, equation (13.6) becomes:

$$\delta(\Delta R) = \frac{\rho_s a \delta l}{A^2} \left/ \left(1 - \frac{a}{A} \right) \right. . \tag{13.7}$$

The response, therefore, is not proportional to the volume of the particle, but is modified due to the term a/A.

With rod-shaped particles, this leads to an oversizing of about 6% in terms of diameter at the top size with distortion of the distribution [11]. This error decreases as a/A decreases.

Several equations relating response and particle volume have been proposed for spherical particles and these are discussed in detail by Allen and Marshall [12]. The error involved in assuming a linear relationship is about 5·5% at the top size for the technique, i.e. particle diameter equalling 0·4 times aperture diameter. Using the correction equations, the technique may be extended above this value, provided that aperture blocking does not become too troublesome.

13.6 Effect of particle shape and orientation

The total volume of particles passing through the aperture may be determined from the weight concentration of particles in the electrolyte and by the total number of particles counted (section 13.3). Discrepancies sometimes occur and the situation arises where the weight of particles counted exceeds the weight in suspension. This is usually explained as being due to the envelope of the particle being measured, as opposed to the true volume.

Model experiments have been carried out by Marshall [13], Lloyd [14] and Eckoff [15], but no firm conclusions may be drawn from them since the models used differed widely from the commercial instruments.

13.7 Coincidence correction

If it is assumed that perfect data results if particles traverse the orifice singly, two types of error result due to deviations from this ideal situation.

(a) 'Primary coincidence' or 'horizontal interaction'. Two particles in the sensitive zone about the orifice at the same instant in time will give rise to two overlapping pulses. There must be, therefore, some limit of separation at which the pulses cannot be resolved giving rise to a loss in count. This coincidence loss is minimised by using extremely dilute suspension and by using correction formulae.

(b) 'Secondary coincidence' or 'vertical interaction'. Two particles which individually give rise to pulses below threshold level collectively give rise to a single pulse above threshold level. For this to arise the particles must be of similar size (which must be close to the threshold limit) and also in close proximity.

Coincidence losses may be ascertained experimentally by counting on increasingly dilute suspension until losses become highly unlikely. By drawing a straight line through these points and extrapolating to the higher concentration regions, the loss of counts at high concentrations may be determined. This gives rise to an expression for the true count N in terms of the observed count n [2]:

$$N = n + p\left(\frac{n}{1000}\right)^2 \qquad (13.8)$$

where

$$p = 2.5\left(\frac{D}{100}\right)^3 \cdot \left(\frac{500}{v}\right) \qquad (13.9)$$

where D is the aperture diameter in micrometers and v the volume of suspension in microlitres monitored for each count.

The factor 2.5 was determined experimentally by the manufacturers using a $100\ \mu$m aperture and $v = 500\ \mu$l. The equations are stated to be accurate to within 1%.

Attempts have been made to obtain theoretical expressions which accord with practice [17, 18] and these are discussed in [12]. Pisani and Thomson [19] arrive at the following equation for primary coincidence loss:

$$N = n + \frac{S}{V}N^2 \qquad (13.10)$$

where S is the volume of the sensing zone.

According to Allen [16] the sensing zone volume equals the aperture volume plus the volume of the hemisphere about each end. Since the average length of a $100\ \mu$m aperture is $75\ \mu$m, this yields a value $p = 2.22$ which agrees well with the experimental value [equation (13.9)]. The substitution of n^2 for N^2 in this expression facilitates calculation and leads to a very small error in the derived value for n.

The experimental equation is of limited applicability since it is independent of aperture length. It was derived for a length-to-diameter ratio of 0·75 which agrees reasonably well with all but the smaller apertures, where ratios of up to 1·00 and 1·66 are more usual for 50 and 30 μm apertures respectively.

Since the number of particles N in the metered volume is proportional to solids concentration C, by the substitution $N = KC$ equation (13.10) may be written:

$$\frac{n}{C} = k - \frac{SK^2 C}{V}. \qquad (13.11)$$

Hence a plot of n/C against C will be a straight line of negative slope $- SK^2/v$. Denoting a dilute concentration as 1, double this concentration as 2, etc., the straight line will intercept the n/C axis at the value $n/C = N$, the coincidence-corrected number count for the initial concentration. Also the slope divided by the intercept squared gives S/v.

Edmundson [20] found that the slope of the line was positive for high values of n and negative for low values. Since none of the equations admit of a positive slope, the coincidence effect must be swamped by other effects. Other writers do not obtain a straight-line relationship. A possible cause may be 'shadowing', i.e. pulses which merge so that the peaks are distinct and are resolved at high threshold settings and lost at low threshold settings. This effect can be demonstrated if a full count is available since this falls as the threshold is further reduced, e.g. the counter may give $n = 19\,000$ at t equivalent to 8 μm but only 18 000 for t equivalent to 6 μm [16, 30].

Harvey [21] in an article comparing the Coulter counter model B, the Celloscope 101, the Nuclear Chicago particle-measurement system (Nuclear Chicago Corp. Des. Plaines Ill) and an instrument described by Harvey and Marr [22], examined coincidence errors in detail, comparing their analysis of Dow-latices with electron microscopy and X-ray analysis. With a 30 μm aperture, the mean transit times of particles through the sensing zone is of the order of 20 μs. The overall pulse duration will be of this order of magnitude. The Coulter counter Model B employs simple amplification of pulses by a vacuum-tube amplifier having a time constant of about 30 μs, and this increases the duration of the pulses about tenfold. Under conditions where coincidence in the sensing zone is eliminated, coincidence in the amplifier can still occur. Its effect on pulse amplitude differs from that of physical coincidence. The greater part of the 200 to 300 μs pulse duration is due to a long decay from peak to zero voltage. If a second pulse occurs within this period, its apparent peak amplitude will increase by an amount equal to the residual amplitude of the first pulse. As counting rate increases the apparent frequency of large particles will also increase. Pisani and Thomson found that size distributions with a total pulse duration of about 30 μs was still skewed and this they attributed to a distribution of transit times through the aperture due to the velocity profile across it.

Harvey stated that in order to prevent distortion of the size distribution the transit time should be four or five times the amplifier rise time. In order to examine this effect, Priem [23] constructed 50 μm apertures of length 50 to 250 μm. These were tested by Glover and the results supported Harvey's statement.

An alternative explanation [25] is that particles passing near the walls of the tube generate a trimodal pulse because of the disposition of the electric field. This abnormality is reduced with increasing length to diameter ratio apertures. The problems with these long apertures are that they degrade the signal-to-noise ratio and increase coincidence problems [24].

13.8 Pulse shape

It is claimed that many of the problems associated with the Coulter technique may be eliminated by hydrodynamic focusing [25, 26], which is incorporated in the Telefunken particle detector MS PD1 1105/1.

The shape of the pulses generated as particles pass through an aperture are shown in figure 13.3. Particles passing along the axis give well-shaped pulses, whereas particles passing near the walls give bimodal pulses. In Thom's apparatus particles are fed into the axis of the aperture (figure 13.4), thus eliminating the bimodal pulses. A secondary benefit is that the transit time is approximately the same for all particles. Size distributions using this system are found to be less skewed than those determined using the Coulter system.

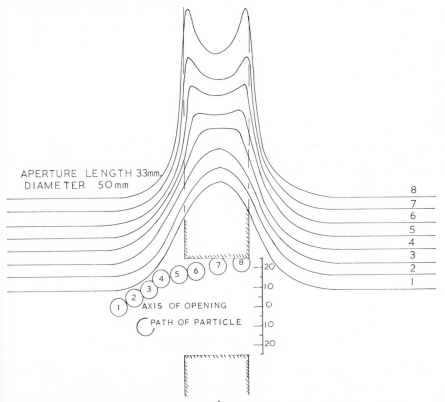

Fig. 13.3. Shape of pulses generated.

Coulter's answer to this is found with the Coulter channelysers which edit the already produced Counter pulses and reject the worst-shaped ones as opposed to producing 'clean' pulses. The edit circuit is fitted in the channelysers C.1000, P64 and P128 which fit to models B, Z_B, Z_{BI} and Z_I; mainly for medical and biological applications where precision is very important. It is probably that the edit circuit will also edit out real pulses generated by particles, but this may have a negligible effect. To date little information is available on their performance.

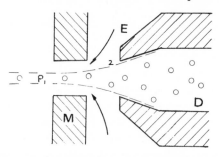

Fig. 13.4. Schematic diagram. Focusing of suspension on the axis of the measurement opening M with a probe D. The suspension streams through the axis after dilution with particle free electrolyte E.

13.9 End-point determination

At the coarse end of the size spectrum it is necessary to continue counting to zero count. At the fine end it is often found that the final value $\Delta n\bar{t}$ does not represent the 100% volume level, i.e. the counts are still increasing at the lowest threshold level. Several proposals have been made for assessing total volume in these cases [11, 27, 28]. All are essentially extrapolation techniques.

  (a) The simplest method is the purly arbitrary addition of half the last value of $\Delta n\bar{t}$, i.e. 100% volume = $\Delta n\bar{t} + \Delta n\bar{t}$ (last)/2.

  (b) Plotting of cumulative corrected number n against t or d on log-log axes with extrapolation of the curve until it becomes asymptotic with the size axis. The t or d value corresponding to this is incorporated into the calculation.

  (c) For expected normal or log-normal distributions, then plotting the weight percentage against size should give a straight line. In these cases the 100% value may be arrived at by trial and error by the addition of an estimated percentage smaller than the smallest measured size.

  (d) Plot $\Sigma \Delta n\bar{t}$ against d on log-linear paper [29]. A straight line is drawn through the last two points on the graph to intercept the $\Sigma \Delta n\bar{t}$ axis. A horizontal line is drawn through the final experimental point to intercept the axis. The 100% value is then taken as one-third the distance between the lower and upper intercept.

  (e) More sophisticated extrapolation techniques have been proposed by Harris and Jowett [27] based on the Gates-Gaudin-Schumann or the Rosin-Rammler distribution. The uncertain validity in this assumption was emphasized by Eckhoff [28], who suggested the following expression:

$$100\% \text{ volume} = \Delta n\bar{t} + \Delta n\bar{t} \text{ (last)} \Big/ \left[\left(\frac{\text{penult. } d}{\text{final } d} \right)^2 - 1 \right]$$

(f) Where there is a considerable amount of material unmeasured, equations (13.2) and (13.3) may be equated to give an estimate of 100% volume.

13.10 Commercial equipment

Coulter counter

Model A (medical)	
Model A (industrial)	Obsolete.
Model D	A simplified version of model A (medical) with facility for red and white cell-counting and rudimentary sizing.
Model D_1	Transistorized version of model D.
Model D_3	Model D_1 extended to include platelet-counting.
Model C	Twelve-channel model designed for fast analysis and computor print out. Obsolete.
Model B	Has facility for both cumulative and differential counts.
Model M converter	Facilitates easier weight conversion.
Model J. plotter	Plots directly the frequency histogram.
Model H plotter	A more sophisticated version of the J.
Model F_N	A fully transistorized version of the Model A (medical).
Model Z_B	Solid-state version of the model B.
Model S	A fully automatic medical model, giving red cell and white cell, count, haemoglobin, haemotecrit, mean-cell haemotecrit and mean-cell haemoglobin in 20 s.
Model T	A solid-state version of model C with 15 sizing channels with automatic number-to-weight conversion.
Channelysers − C.100	Accumulates data from the counter and separates it into 100 size channels.
Channelysers P64 and P120	Accumulates and separates in 64 size channels.

Celloscope

Model 30	Basic industrial model with twin simultaneously operated discriminators.
Model 401	Blood-cell counter.

Electrozone

Model 110	Fixed count-level settings for red and white cells and platelets.
Model 111	Single threshold instrument.

Model 112	Dual fixed ratio (2:1) threshold with 15 channels.
Model 112C	A second register included recording count above upper level.
Model 111L, 112L	Logarithmic conversion of particle amplitudes with mode selector for linear or log output.

Granulometer

TUR ZG1	Eastern European equivalent of Model A.
TUR ZG2	Eastern European equivalent of Model B.
TOA Microcell counter	Japanese instrument with a polypropylene apperture tube at the bottom of a cylindrical tube, i.e. facing downwards.

Telefunken particle detector

| MS PD1 1105/1 | An improved version of the Coulter principle with hydrodynamic focusing. |

13.11 Conclusion

The foregoing remarks comprise a basic statement of the Coulter principle. This technique is eminently suitable for powders in the subsieve range down to about 1μm in size and a size range in the ratio of 20:1. The size limits for the technique may be extended with care, and an element of luck, from 400 to 0.6μm. The size range may also be extended, using a multiple-tube technique or the Coulter technique in conjunction with some other sizing method. In this case, however, the analysis may become tiresome due to blocking of the aperture which occurs frequently if large particles are present in the electrolyte.

The technique has the unique capability of rapidly differentiating between two distributions with very similar peaks. With the basic counters, a single analysis can be completed in an hour or so, multiple analyses may be carried out more rapidly.

Problems can arise due to the 'black box' nature of the system, which is no more intelligent than the operator. For example, if the sample is made up of submicrometre powder, an analysis in the micrometre range will result due to the instrument counting multiple pulses as single particles.

The associated equipment, available with the basic glassware, is many and varied and enables the time for a single count to be reduced to 20 s. A more detailed description of the technique is given in [12].

References

[1]   Coulter, W.H. (1956), *Proc. of the National Electronic Conf.* **12**, 1034.
[2]   Morgan, B.B. (1957), *Research, Lond.* **10**, 271.
[3]   Kubitschek, H.E. (1958), *Nature*, **182**, 234−5.
[4]   Kubitschek, H.E. (1960), *Research*, **13**, 128.
[5]   Berg, R.H. (1958), A.S.T.M. publication No. 234.
[6]   *Coulter Industrial Bibliography*, Coulter Electronics Ltd.
[7]   Brotherton, J. (1969), *Cytobios*, **1B**, 95.

[8] Brotherton, J. (1969), *Cytobios*, **3**, 307.

[9] Brotherton, J. (1971), *Proc. Soc. Analyt. Chem.* 264–71.

[10] Matthews, B.A., and Rhodes, C.T. (1969), Paper presented at the 7th Users Conference, London; available from Coulter Electronics Ltd.

[11] Batch, B.A. (1964), *J. Inst. Fuel*, 455.

[12] Allen, T., and Marshall, K. (1972), 'The electrical sensing zone method of p.s.a.', available from the author.

[13] Mehta, R.G. (1969), Bradford Univ. M.Sc. thesis.

[14] Lloyd, P.J., Scarlett, B., and Sinclair, I. (1972), *Proc. 1970 Conference on Particle Size Analysis, Bradford*, Soc. Analyt. Chem.

[15] Eckhoff, R.K. (1969), *J. Sci. Instrum.*, ser. 2, **2**, 973–7.

[16] Allen, T. (1967), *Particle Size Analysis, Proc. Conference, Loughborough, 1966*, Soc. Analyt. Chem.

[17] Wales, M., and Wilson, J.N. (1961), *Rev. Sci. Instrum.*, **32**, 1132.

[18] Princen, L.H., and Kwolek, W.F. (1965), *Rev. Sci. Instrum.*, **36**, 646.

[19] Pisani, J.F., and Thomson, G.M. (1971), *J. Phys. E: (Sci. Instrum.)*, **4**, 5 359–61.

[20] Edmundson, I.C. (1966), *Nature*, **212**, 1450.

[21] Harvey, R.J. (1972), 'Methods in Colloidal Phys.' (*cit.* [12]).

[22] Harvey, R.J., and Marr, A.G. (1966), *J. Bact.*, **92**, 805.

[23] Priem, M. (1970), *J. Sci. Instrum. (J. Phys. E.)*, **43(6)**, 402–3.

[24] Lines, R. (1967), *Particle Size Analysis, Proc. Conference, Loughborough, 1966*, Soc. Analyt. Chem. London, 135.

[25] Thom, von R. (1971), Available from A.E.G. Telefunken 79 Ulm (Donau), Elisabethstrasse 3, Postfach 830, W. Germany.

[26] Thom, von R. (1971), German Patent No. 1 955, 094.

[27] Harris, C.C., and Jowett, A. (1965), *Nature*, **208**, 175.

[28] Eckhoff, R.K. (1966), *Proc. Coulter Counter Conference Cardiff*, pp. 80–94; available from Coulter Electronics Ltd.

[29] Samyn, J.C., and McGee, J.P. (1965), *J. Pharm. Sci.*, **54**, 12, 1794–9.

14 Radiation Scattering Methods of Particle Size Determination

14.1 Introduction

The interaction of a beam of radiation with an assembly of particles may only be used for determining the size distribution when some size separation process, such as sedimentation, is incorporated into the system. The mean size of a closely graded powder made up of very small particles may, however, be determined and the sizes of individual particles may be found and collated to give size distributions.

When a beam of radiation strikes an assembly of particles, some of it is transmitted, some absorbed and some scattered. The scattered radiation includes the diffracted, refracted and reflected parts of the original beam and the absorbed radiation is retransmitted at a longer wavelength and this is usually not picked up by the detecting device.

The mean particle size of the assembly may be found by measuring the variation in the intensity of the scattered radiation with scattering angle or, more frequently, the ratio of the intensities of the scattered radiation at fixed angles to the direction of the incident beam:

$$D = \frac{I(90 + \beta)^\circ}{I(90 - \beta)^\circ} \tag{14.1}$$

with β usually equal to 30, 45 or 60 (dissymmetry methods) [2, 3, 4].

Alternatively, the flux per unit angle at 90° to the incident beam may be measured [5]. Since the vertically polarized component of the scattered light is more sensitive to size changes, it is usual to accept only this component in the detector. The angular positions of maxima and minima in the scattered light have also been used to determine particle size, as well as the state of polarization of the scattered light, usually defined by the ratio of the horizontal and vertical components. Theoretical expressions for the attenuation of a beam of light when it traverses an assembly of particles are also available when the light is monochromatic [1]. A practical method of applying these equations is to determine the attenuation for two wavelengths. It is then possible to read off the size from theoretically based diagrams [5, 6].

The intensity of the scattered radiation is a function of $x = \pi D / \lambda_m$, where D is the diameter of the particles, λ_m the wavelength of the radiation in the medium and m the refractive index ratio of scattering particles to medium. Rigorous solutions to the various phenomena are found with the electromagnetic theory of light

314

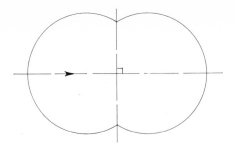

Fig. 14.1. Polar light-scattering diagram for the Rayleigh region.

scattering (the Mie theory), but since these are in a form difficult to interpret, partial solutions are more favoured. These are found by using boundary conditions and
the theory of physical optics.

The boundary conditions limit the use of scattering phenomena to molecular
weight determinations and spherical monosize colloids and aerosols in the range
$0.1 < D < 4.00 \, \mu m$, the refractive index m of the particles relative to that of the
surrounding medium lying between 1 and 2, although size information about non-
spherical particles and heterogeneous distribution may also be evaluated. Outside
the boundary regions, some solutions to the exact theory are available in the form
of tables of scattering functions prepared by the National Bureau of Standards [7].

Van de Hulst [1] discusses these boundary conditions, deriving or reproducing
the appropriate equations in terms of the m, x domain as m varies from 1 to ∞ and
x varies from 0 to ∞. Applications of these equations are reviewed in [1, 8, 9].

When white light is incident on a dilute suspension of sufficiently large, monodisperse, spherical particles, vivid colours appear at various angles to the primary
beam and the angular positions of the spectra may be used to determine particle
size.

Light-scattering methods are most effective for particles of the same order of
size as the incident radiation. Very small particles (e.g. air molecules) exhibit
Rayleigh scattering, and the scattered field is proportional to the polarizability of
the particles, i.e. to the number of electrons or essentially to the volume of the
particles. Therefore, the scattered-light intensity is proportional to the square of
the particle volume. The scattering pattern for such a particle is easily recognizable
since it is symmetrical about a scattering angle of $90°$. Figure 14.1, the Rayleigh
approximation is valid for particles of diameter less than about a twentieth of the
wavelength of light.

For somewhat larger particles (e.g. macromolecules) the Rayleigh-Gans approximation applies. The boundary conditions for this approximation to hold require the
radiation to undergo only a small phase shift in passing through a particle; hence
it applies to small particles or particles with a similar refractive index to their sur-
roundings. The scattered field is, as in the Rayleigh approximation, the sum of

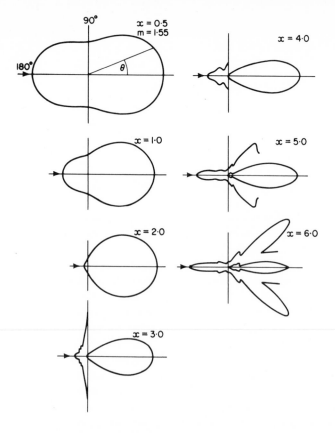

Fig. 14.2. Polar light-scattering diagrams (Vouk [39]).

contributions from each point within the particle; however, in this case the phase shift from point to point must be taken into account. The Rayleigh-Gans equation reduces to the Rayleigh equation when this is negligible. The addition of the phase shift term modifies the scattering pattern, making it asymmetric about 90°. Since the phase shift between contributing points is a minimum in the forward direction, the scattered intensity is greater towards this direction and increases with increasing particle size (figure 14.2).

Particle size may be determined by finding the position of maxima or minima in the polar-scattering pattern, dissymmetry methods (figure 14.3) or forward-angle scattering.

For Rayleigh scattering ($m - 1 \to 0$, $x < 0.3$) the vertical component of scattered intensity (I_θ) is constant. As D increases, the Rayleigh-Gans region is entered in which I_θ is inversely proportional to θ and passes through a minimum; this condition also holds for $m > 1.0$, provided x is small. However, for large x, several maxima and minima occur. Particle size may be determined using these properties for $0.18 < D < 4.0\,\mu m$ using visible light.

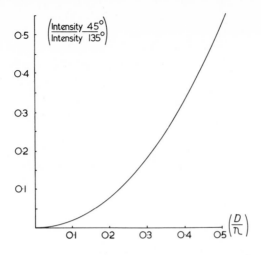

Fig. 14.3. Dependence of dissymmetry ratio D on particle size.

For particles of size comparable to the wavelength of the incident radiation, the complex Mie scattering theory is required to describe the scattering pattern. Interaction between the particle and the radiation is very strong (resonance), leading to pronounced maxima and minima (figure 14.2). The angular positions of these maxima and minima can be used for size determination.

For particles larger than the wavelength of the incident radiation, the contribution of the radiation refracted within the particle diminishes in comparison to the radiation diffracted external to the particle. For particle size to wavelength ratios of the order of four or five, the latter becomes dominant and chiefly in the forward direction. For this regime, the Mie theory reduces to the Fraunhoffer theory for geometric optics and the expression for the scattered intensity is the one for diffraction by a circular disc:

$$\left[\frac{J_1 (x \sin \theta)}{x \sin \theta} \right]^2 \tag{14.2}$$

where $x = \pi D / \lambda_m$ and J_1 is the Bessel function of order unity. The function has its first zero at $\sin \theta_{min} = 1 \cdot 22 \, \lambda / D$.

Particles whose diameter is greater than the wavelength of light are probably best examined by some other method. Light-scattering methods are, however, frequently used when the particles are not readily accessible, as in the fields of astronomy and meterology. They are also attractive for determining the size of particles suspended in a gas, e.g. effluent from chimneys, atmospheric pollution and aerosol sprays, since other methods involve collecting the particles and this may alter their state of aggregation. Optical methods have the advantages that the measurements can be made accurately, suspensions are not disturbed by the insertion of an external sampling device, the sample required is small, tests can be carried out rapidly and experimental measurements are obtained in a form which lends itself to automatic recording and remote-control techniques. A comprehensive review of light scattering, with 519 references is given by Kratohvil [37]. Light scattering is also reviewed by Kerker [30], who gives over a thousand references.

14.2 Scattered radiation

14.2.1 The Rayleigh region ($D \ll \lambda$).
In the Rayleigh region, the intensity of the scattered radiation in a direction making an angle θ with an incident beam of unit intensity is given in [1]:

$$I_\theta = |\alpha|^2 \left(\frac{2\pi}{\lambda_m}\right)^4 \frac{(1 + \cos^2 \theta)}{2r^2} \qquad (14.3)$$

where α is the particle polarizibility, r is the distance from the particle to the point of observation and λ_m the wavelength of the incident radiation in the medium surrounding the particle.

The intensity is the sum of two terms:

$$|\alpha|^2 \left(\frac{2\pi}{\lambda_m}\right)^4 \frac{1}{2r^2} \quad \text{and} \quad |\alpha|^2 \left(\frac{2\pi}{\lambda_m}\right)^4 \frac{\cos^2 \theta}{2r^2}$$

which refer respectively to the intensities of the vertically and horizontally polarized components.

For spheres:

$$\alpha = \frac{3(m^2 - 1)}{(m^2 + 2)} \frac{V}{4} . \qquad (14.4)$$

Equation (14.4) has been applied to very small particles, but is more relevant to the size determination of molecules. For:

$$m - 1 \to 0, \alpha = (m^2 - 1)\frac{V}{4}$$

$$\triangleq 2(m - 1)\frac{V}{4} \qquad (14.5)$$

where m is the index of refraction of the particle relative to that of the surrounding medium and V is the particle volume.

14.2.2 The Rayleigh-Gans region ($D < \lambda$)
The Rayleigh-Gans equation for the angular dependence of the intensity of the scattered light I_θ is given for spherical particles by the equation in [1, p. 89]:

$$I_\theta = I_0 \left[\frac{k^4 V^2 (m - 1)^2}{8\pi^2 r^2}\right] \left[\frac{3}{u^3}(\sin u - u \cos u)\right]^2 (1 + \cos^2\theta) . \qquad (14.6)$$

Again, I and $\cos^2\theta$ in the final term refer respectively to the intensities of the vertically and horizontally polarized components, and the incident beam is of intensity I_0:

$$u = \frac{2\pi D}{\lambda_m} \sin\frac{\theta}{2} \tag{14.7}$$

$$k = 2\pi/\lambda_m \tag{14.8}$$

and D is the particle diameter.

Equation (14.6) reduces to equation (14.3) when the middle term is equal to one. The scattering pattern is however modified by this second term, thus enabling size determination to be carried out in the Rayleigh-Gans region.

Differentiating equation (14.6) with respect to u and putting $dI_0/du = 0$; for minimum intensity:

$$\sin u - u \cos u = 0 \tag{14.9}$$

for maximum intensity:

$$3u \cos u - u^2 \sin u - 3 \sin u = 0 . \tag{14.10}$$

The first minimum is at $u = 4.4934$ rad, corresponding to:

$$\frac{D}{\lambda_m} \sin\left(\frac{\theta_1}{2}\right) = \frac{4.4934}{2\pi}$$

$$= 0.715. \tag{14.11}$$

Similarly, the first maximum occurs at:

$$\frac{D}{\lambda_m} \sin\left(\frac{\theta}{2}\right) = 0.916. \tag{14.12}$$

A graphical solution for all maxima and minima has been determined by Pierce and Maron [10], who, together with Elder [11, 12], extended equations (14.11) and (14.12) beyond the Rayleigh-Gans region ($m - 1 \to 0$) to $1.0 < m < 1.55$, deriving the following formulae:

$$\frac{D}{\lambda_m} \sin\left(\frac{\theta_1}{2}\right) = 1.062 - 0.347\, m \tag{14.13}$$

$$\frac{D}{\lambda_m} \sin\left(\frac{\phi_1}{2}\right) = 1.379 - 0.463\, m. \tag{14.14}$$

These equations give the positions of the first intensity minimum and maximum respectively. Tabulated data allow the calculation of various maxima and minima, provided m is known. These tables are particularly useful for determining the order of the maxima and minima, since the ratio of the sines of the half-angles are 1.72, 1.41, 1.29, etc., for the angles $\theta_1/\theta_2, \theta_2/\theta_3, \theta_3/\theta_4$, etc., and 1.58, 1.35, 1.26 for the angles ϕ_1/ϕ_2, ϕ_2/ϕ_3, ϕ_3/ϕ_4 for $m = 1$; ratios for other m are derivable from equations (14.12) and (14.13). The range of validity of this method has been investigated further by Kerker *et al.* [13], who present their results in the form of 2 % and 10 % error contour charts. The required apparatus consists of a lamp-house, a lens compartment and a phototube compartment, with the optical parts mounted on an optical bench. The light source may be a 100-W mercury vapour lamp with associated filters. The suspension is placed in a cylindrical cell at the centre of the phototube compartment. The phototube is mounted on a turntable and its output is fed to a micrometer. The observed intensities require correction because of the variation with θ of the volume of scattering suspension scanned by the phototube. This correction is made by multiplying the observed readings by $\sin \theta/2$. A plot of I/I_0 against $\sin \theta/2$ converts the minima into maxima, θ being found from the position of the first peak. The θ's so obtained vary with concentration and, since the value required is for infinite dilution, when multiple scattering is absent, θ's have to be found for several concentrations and extrapolated to zero. This concentration dependence on scattering has also been noticed with depolarization and dissymmetry methods and becomes negligible only when particle separation exceeds 200 radii [14].

14.3 State of polarization of the scattered radiation

When a system containing isotropic and monosize spherical particles is irradiated with unpolarized incident radiation, the horizontal and vertical components of the scattered light are in general functions of the three parameters, relative refractive index m, angle of observation θ and $x = \pi D/\lambda_m$. If H is the intensity of the horizontal component of the scattered light, V the vertical component and $R = H/V$, then R is also a function of m, x and θ. For given m and θ, R depends only on x; hence polarization measurements can be used to determine particle size. Again, if m and x are fixed, then R depends only on θ, hence particle size can be determined from the position of maxima and minima in the angular dependence of R on θ.

For Rayleigh scattering $R = 0$ at $\theta = 90°$. As x increases, this theory shows that R is a periodic function of diameter for monosize particles. Sinclair and La Mer [15] used this theory for plots prior to the first maximum to measure the particle sizes of aerosols ranging in size from 0·1 to 0·4 μm. La Mer, Inn and Wilson [16] used the same procedure at angles of 50° to 120° to obtain particle sizes of sulphur solutions. In this work, transmission and polarization methods yield results in accord with higher-order Tyndall spectra for sizes in the range 0·35 to 0·62 μm. Graessley and Zufall [17] have shown that in a limited region ($0·45 < D \ll 2·8\,\mu$m, $1·06 < m < 1·12$) the fluctuations in R at 90° are smoothed out and the identity:

$$\bar{R} = 1·89\,(m-1)^2\,\pi\bar{D}/\lambda_m \tag{14.15}$$

results where:

$$\bar{D} = \frac{\int_0^\infty D^{7/2} N(D)\,\mathrm{d}D}{\int_0^\infty D^{5/2} N(D)\,\mathrm{d}D} \tag{14.16}$$

and there are $N(D)$ particles in the light beam in the size range D to $D + dD$. Maron, Elder and Pierce [18] review and extend earlier work on R-measurements at 90° on monodisperse polystyrene lattices and find appreciable differences between theoretical and experimental values. They show that the discrepancy is due to inherent anistropy of the latex particles believed to be due to non-random orientation of the polymer chains in the colloidal latex particle. The size range of applicability they give to this technique is 0·135 to 1·117 μm.

Takahashi and Iwai [34] also use the monotonious variation in R at 90°.

14.4 Turbidity measurement

If a light beam falls upon an assembly of macroscopic particles the attenuation is given by:

$$I = I_0 \exp[- aNL] \tag{14.17}$$

where I is the transmitted intensity when a light beam of intensity I_0 falls on a suspension of particles of projected area a and number concentration N and traverses it by a path of length L. In the general equation relating attenuation and concentration aN is replaced by TC where T is the turbidity and C the weight concentration per unit volume. For dilute suspensions of particles smaller than 0·04 μm in diameter, the turbidity can be calculated from the equation:

$$T = \frac{32\pi^3 (m - 1)^2}{3N\lambda_m C^2} f \tag{14.18}$$

where $m = \lambda_m/\lambda_f$ is the ratio of the refractive indices of the particles and fluid; $\lambda_m = \lambda_0/\lambda_f$ is the wavelength of the light in the fluid and λ_0 is the wavelength in vacuum; N is Avogadro's number and f is very nearly equal to one [1, p. 396].

For particles larger than this:

$$T = Ka \tag{14.19}$$

where K is the extinction coefficient defined as the effective particle cross section divided by its geometric cross section. This may be evaluated theoretically, thus permitting the determination of particle size. If C is the volume concentration:

$$c = \frac{\pi}{6} Nd_v^3 \tag{14.20}$$

and the projected area for particles in random orientation is:

$$a = \frac{\pi}{4} d_s^2 . \tag{14.21}$$

Hence:

$$I = I_0 \exp\left[-\frac{3Kc}{2d_{sv}} \right] \tag{14.22}$$

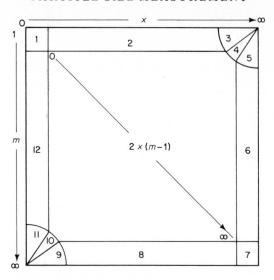

Fig. 14.4. Particle size-refractive index domain [1].

$$I = I_0 \exp\left[-\frac{1}{4} Kc S_v\right].$$ (14.23)

K has been given by van de Hulst [1, p. 132] in terms of particle size refractive index domain (figure 14.4).

Mie theory applies to the whole domain. In the boundary region, simpler equations have been derived. These equations are even simpler in the corner regions (odd numbers), which are all for a limited range of m and x. Thus, for small spheres (regions 9, 10, 11, 12, 1) K is proportional to x^4, hence turbidity is proportional to $x^4(c/d_{sv})$, i.e. T is proportional to $cD^3/4$. Similarly for very large spheres T is proportional to $4c/3D$. In the intermediate region, the approximate size must be known and the extinction coefficient determined experimentally over a sufficiently wide range of wavelengths to give a recognizable portion of the extinction curve. The difficulties are overcome with non-adsorbing (dielectric) spheres with m approximate equal to one, since the equation:

$$K = 2 - \frac{4}{\rho} \sin\rho + \frac{4}{\rho^2}(1 - \cos\rho)$$ (14.24)

is found to hold where $\rho = 2x(m-1)$ and the first maximum occurs at $d = (4\cdot09/2\pi\delta n)$, λ_{max} is the wavelength *in vacuo* of maximum turbidity and δn the difference in refractive indices of the particle and medium (figure 14.5) [1, p. 176].

Variations of this technique are also possible (Hawksley, [8, p. 200]).

An essential requirement for the detector is that it should subtend an angle smaller than $D/20$ rad at the suspension to avoid the collection of scattered light.

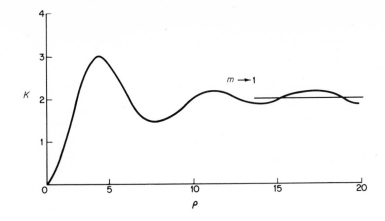

Fig. 14.5. Extinction curve for m tending to unity [1].

This requirement becomes of increasing importance with increasing values of D [19], but a simple formula may be applied to correct for acceptance of scattered light.

14.5 High-order Tyndall spectra (HOTS)

When a dilute suspension of sufficiently large, monodisperse, spherical particles is irradiated with white light, vivid colours appear at various angles to the primary beam. The angular positions of the spectra depend on m and D, hence they may be used to determine particle size in colloidal suspensions.

Since the red and green bands predominate, it is usual to observe as a function of angle θ, the ratios of the intensities of the vertical components of the red and green light in the scattered radiation. When these ratios, $R = I_{red}/I_{green}$, are plotted against θ, curves showing maxima and minima occur, the maxima being the red order, the minima green. The smaller diameters yield only one order but the number of orders increases with increasing particle size.

High-order Tyndall spectra have been studied extensively in monodisperse sulphur solutions by la Mer et al. [21–25], by Kenyon [26], in aerosols by Sinclair and La Mer [15], in polystyrene latices by La Mer and Plesner [27] and in butadiene latices by Maron and Elder [28]. Equations derived by Maron and Elder for the angular positions of the first red and green order r_1 and g_1,

$$D \sin(r_1/2) = 2300 \qquad (14.25)$$

and

$$D \sin(g_1/2) = 3120 \qquad (14.26)$$

are particular examples of equations (14.11) to (14.13).

Pierce and Maron [10] show that the angular positions of the red orders are identical with the angles at which minima occur in the intensity of the scattered light when the incident light (20) has a wavelength λ_g^{1}. Similarly, the angular positions of the

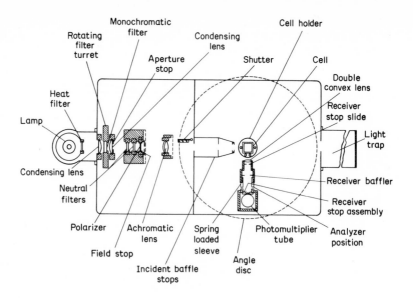

Fig. 14.6. The Absolute light-scattering photometer.

green orders coincide with the angles at which minima occur with incident light of wavelength λ_r^1 . Consequently for the same effective incident wavelengths, minimum intensity and high-order Tyndall spectra represent equivalent measurements.

For equations (14.25) and (14.26) respectively, solving with equation (14.13) gives:

$$1\cdot062 - 0\cdot347\,(1\cdot17) = 2300\,\lambda_g^1 \therefore \lambda_g^1 = 3506\ \text{Å}\ (4673\ \text{Å}\ \textit{in vacuo})$$

$$1\cdot062 - 0\cdot347\,(1\cdot17) = 3120\,\lambda_r^1 \therefore \lambda_r^1 = 4756\ \text{Å}\ (6340\ \text{Å}\ \textit{in vacuo})$$

It is pointed out that this method is qualitative unless λ_g' and λ_r' are known, e.g. La Mer's results yield a value $\lambda_g' = 3930$ Å compared with 3506 Å above.

The above equations yield weight average diameters. With increasing m the valuation of D becomes more difficult due to reduction in the intensity of the maximum and broadening of the peak. The method has been used for the size range 0·26 to 1·01 μm with apparatus similar to that described in section 14.2, the mercury vapour lamp being replaced with a 6 V tungsten lamp and Wratten filters to isolate the red and green radiation and a polarizer in front of the phototube (29).

14.6 Light-scattering equipment
Most of the equipment described in the preceding sections has been individually designed, but some commercial equipment is available. The Sinclair-Phoenix aerosol photometer brings the light to a focus at the sample cell, with a diaphragm stop placed in the optical path so that a diverging cone of darkness encompasses the

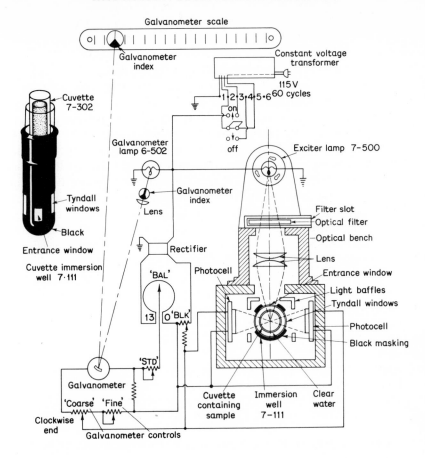

Fig. 14.7. Schematic diagram of model 7 photonephelometer. Optical and electrical systems.

light-collecting lens of the photomultiplier housing. Hence the only light reaching the detector is that which is scattered in the forward direction by particles in the aerosol under test. Solids concentration as low as $10^{-3} \mu g \, l^{-1}$ may be detected, the mass concentration at any instant being displayed on a meter or plotted on a recorder.

The Brice-Phoenix light-scattering photometer and the Absolute light-scattering photometer (figure 14.6) are designed for the determination of attenuation, dissymmetry and depolarization. The former has also been adapted to determine the particle-size distribution of an aerosol at various levels in a system flowing through a column [33].

The Model 7 photonephelometer has two photocells which receive light at $90°$ to the incident beam, the combined output being fed to a galvanometer (figure 14.7).

The Model 9 nepho-colorimeter has a third photocell in line with the transmitted beam so that the transmitted light may also be measured. Other instruments which are used for aerosol sizing are discussed in chapter 3, section 3.6.

The Differential I [31] light-scattering photometer is designed for the study of monosize particles in suspension. A cuvette containing the suspension is illuminated by an argon–ion laser beam and a scanning detector system records the intensity of the scattered light as a function of the scattering angle θ. The light-scattering patterns are matched against computer-generated curves which are available in an *Atlas of Light Scattering Curves* [38]. The analytical approach is described in [35, 36].

Where the particle size is large or the size distribution is broad, very low angle measurement of scattering provides useful information. When the size distribution is so broad that no identifiable maxima remain in the scattering curve, particles may still be measured, one at a time, in the Differential II single-particle light-scattering photometer. This instrument is designed to measure the light scattered from individual particles suspended in air to determine particle size. Particles are injected into the instrument in an air stream and introduced pneumatically into the scattering cell. Selected particles are then brought to the centre of the laser beam by means of plates and point electrodes by manual control and held in position by an automatic servomechanism which permits time-variation monitoring [32]. The compilation of sizes determined for a sample will yield the size distribution.

References

[1]   van de Hulst, H.C. (1957), *Light Scattering by Small Particles*, Wiley, N.Y.

[2]   Jennings, B.R., and Jerrard, H.G. (1965), *J. Colloid. Sci.*, **20**, 448.

[3]   Jerrard, H.G., and Sellen, D.B. (1962), *Applied Optics*, **1**, 243.

[4]   Nakagaki, M., and Shimoyama, T. (1964), *Bull. Chem. Soc., Japan*, **37**, 11, 1634.

[5]   Sakurada, I., Hosono, M., and Tamamura, S. (1964), *Bull. Inst. Chem. Res., Kyoto Univ.*, **42**, 23, 145.

[6]   Goulden, D. (1960), *Spectroturbidity of Emulsions*, National Institute for Research in Dairying, Reading University.

[7]   Lowan, A.N. (1949), National Bureau of Standards (U.S.A.), Applied Maths., Series No. 4.

[8]   Hawksley, P.G.W. (1952), *British Coal Utilisation Research Assoc. Bulletin*, **16**, (5, 6).

[9]   Orr, C., and Dallavalle, J.M. (1960), *Fine Particle Measurement*, Macmillan, N.Y.

[10] Pierce, P.E., and Maron, S.H. (1964), *J. Colloid Sci.*, **19**, 658.

[11] Maron, S.H., and Elder, M.E. (1963), *J. Colloid Sci.*, **18**, 107.

[12] Maron, S.H., Pierce, P.E., and Elder, M.E. (1963), *J. Colloid Sci.*, **18**, 391.

[13] Kerker, M., *et al.* (1964), *J. Colloid Sci.*, **19**, 193.

[14] Napper, D.H., and Ottewell, R.H. (1964), *J. Colloid Sci.*, **19**, 72.

[15] Sinclair, D., and La Mer, V.K. (1949), *Chem. Rev.*, **44**, 245.

[16] La Mer, V.K., Inn, E.C.Y., and Wilson, J.B. (1950), *J. Colloid Sci.*, **5**, 471.

[17] Graessley, W.W., and Zufall, J.H. (1964), *J. Colloid Sci.*, **19**, 516.

[18] Maron, S.H., Elder, M.E., and Pierce, P.E. (1964), *J. Colloid Sci.*, **19**, 213.

[19] Heirwegh, K.P.M. (1966), *J. Colloid Sci.*, **21**, 1–8.

[20] Walstra, P. (1965), *B. J. Appl. Phys.*, **16**.

[21] Kerker, M., and La Mer, V.K. (1950), *J. Am. Chem. Soc.*, **72**, 3516.

[22] Johnson, I., and La Mer, V.K. (1947), *J. Am. Chem. Soc.*, **69**, 1184.

[23] Barnes, M.D., *et al.* (1947), *J. Colloid Sci.*, **2**, 349.

[24] La Mer, V.K. (1948), *J. Phys. Coll. Chem.*, **52**, 65.

[25] Kenyon, A.S., and La Mer, V.K. (1949), *J. Colloid Sci.*, **4**, 163.

[26] Kenyon, A.S. (1947), *Trans. N.Y., Acad. Sci.*, **9**, 234.

[27] Plessner, I.V., and La Mer, V.K. (1957), *J. Polymer Sci.*, **24**, 147.

[28] Maron, S.H., and Elder, M.E. (1963), *J. Colloid Sci.*, **18**, 199.

[29] Bricaud, J., *et al.* (1964), *Staub*, **24**, 8, 287.

[30] Kerker, M. (1969), *The Scattering of Light and other Electromagnetic Radiation*, Academic Press, N.Y.

[31] Farone, W.A., and Kerker, M. (1966), *J. Opt. Soc. Am.*, **56**, 481.

[32] Cooke, D.D., and Kerker, M. (1973), *J. Colloid Interf. Sci.*, **42**, 1, 150–5.

[33] Cooke, D.D., Nicolson, G., and Kerker, M. (1973), *J. Colloid Interf. Sci.*, **42**, 3, 535–8.

[34] Takahashi, K., and Iwai, S. (1967), *J. Polymer Sci.*, **23**, 113.

[35] Wallace, T.P., and Kratohvil, J.P. (1970), *J. Polymer Sci.*, **A2**, 8, 1425.

[36] Wallace, T.P., and Kratohvil, J.P. (1968), *J. Polymer Sci.*, **C25**, 89.

[37] Krahtovil, J.P. (1964), *Ann. Chem.*, **36**, 5, 485R.

[38] *Atlas of Light Scattering Curves* : see List of Manufacturers and Suppliers.

[39] Vouk, V. (1948), Ph.D. thesis, London University.

15 Permeametry and Gas Diffusion

15.1 Flow of a viscous fluid through a packed bed of powder

The original work on the flow of fluids through packed beds of powders was carried out by Darcy[1], who examined the rate of flow of water from the local fountains through beds of sand of various thickness. He showed that the average velocity, as measured over the whole area of the bed, was directly proportional to the driving pressure and inversely proportional to the thickness of the bed, i.e.

$$u = K \frac{\Delta p}{L}. \tag{15.1}$$

Equation (15.1) may be compared with the expression for the mean velocity u_m of a fluid viscosity η, flowing in a pipe of circular cross section and of diameter d:

$$u_m = \frac{d^2}{32\eta} \frac{\Delta p}{L}. \tag{15.2}$$

This expression was derived by Hagen [2] and independently by Poiseuille [3].

Blake [4], and later Kozeny [5], found it necessary to use an equivalent diameter to relate flow rate with particle surface area for flow through a packed bed of powder, where:

$$\text{equivalent diameter } (d_E) = 4 \times \frac{\text{cross-sectional area normal to flow}}{\text{wetted perimeter}}. \tag{15.3}$$

For a circular pipe, $d_E = \dfrac{4\pi d^2/4}{\pi d} = d.$

Hence d_E may be regarded as a mean pipe diameter. Kozeny assumed that the pore space of a packed bed of powder could be regarded as equivalent to a bundle of parallel capillaries with a common equivalent radius, and with a cross-sectional shape representative of the average shape of the pore cross section. For a packed bed, equation (15.3) may be written:

$$\text{mean equivalent diameter} = 4 \times \frac{\text{volume of voids}}{\text{surface area of voids}}$$

$$d_E = \frac{4V_v}{S}. \tag{15.4}$$

The surface of the capillary walls is assumed to be the same as the surface of the powder S. By definition:

$$\text{porosity} = \frac{\text{volume of voids}}{\text{volume of bed}}$$

$$e = \frac{V_v}{V_v + V_s}$$

giving

$$V_v = \left(\frac{e}{1-e}\right) V_s \tag{15.5}$$

where V_s is the volume of solids.

From equations (15.3), (15.4) and (15.5):

$$d_E = 4\left(\frac{e}{1-e}\right) \frac{V_s}{S} = d.$$

Substituting in equation (15.2):

$$u_m = \frac{e^2}{(1-e)^2} \frac{V_s^2}{S^2} \frac{\Delta p}{2\eta L}. \tag{15.6}$$

The measured velocity is the approach velocity, that is, the volume flow rate divided by the whole cross-sectional area of the bed: $u = Q/A$. Knowing this, it is necessary to estimate the fluid velocity in the pore spaces. It can be shown [6, p. 392] that, in a bed of randomly distributed particles of voidage e, the average free cross-sectional area in any plane is the total cross-sectional area multiplied by e. The velocity in the pore spaces is greater than the approach velocity since the area available for flow is smaller, $u_1 = Q/eA$, therefore:

$$u = eu_1. \tag{15.7}$$

Further, the path of a capillary through the bed is tortuous with an average length L_e, which is greater than the bed thickness L, but it is to be expected that L_e is proportional to L. Thus the velocity of the fluid in the capillary u_m will be greater than u_1 due to the increase in path length:

$$u_m = \left(\frac{L_e}{L}\right) u_1. \tag{15.8}$$

From equations (15.7) and (15.8):

$$u = e\left(\frac{L}{L_e}\right) u_m. \tag{15.9}$$

Noting also that the pressure drop occurs in a length L_e giving, from equations (15.6) and (15.9):

$$u = e\left(\frac{L}{L_e}\right) \frac{e^2}{(1-e)^2} \frac{V_s^2}{2\eta S^2} \frac{\Delta p}{L_e}$$

$$S_w^2 = \frac{1}{k\eta\rho_s^2 u} \frac{e^3}{(1-e)^2} \frac{\Delta p}{L} \tag{15.10}$$

where $S = \rho_s V_s S_w$; S_w is the weight specific surface of the powder and ρ_s is the powder density. In general $k = k_0 k_1$ where $k_1 = (L_e/L)^2$, for circular capillaries, $k_0 = 2$.

k is called the aspect factor

k_1 is called the tortuousity factor

k_0 is a factor which depends on the shape and size distribution of the cross-sectional areas of the capillaries hence of the particles which make up the bed.

15.2 The aspect factor k

Carman [13] carried out numerous experiments and found that k was equal to 5 for a wide range of particles. In the derivation above k_0 for uniform circular capillaries is found to equal 2. Carman suggested [8, p. 13] that capillaries in random orientation arranged themselves at a mean angle of $45°$ to the direction of flow, thus making L_e/L equal to $\sqrt{2}$ and k_1 equal to 2.

Fowler and Hertel [32] found theoretically and Sullivan and Hertel [31] found experimentally, that for spheres $k = 4\cdot5$, for cylinders arranged parallel to flow $k = 3\cdot0$, and for cylinders arranged perpendicular to flow, $k = 6\cdot0$. Muskat and Botsel [51] obtained a value of $4\cdot5$ to $5\cdot1$ for spherical particles and Schriever [52] obtained a value of $5\cdot06$.

‡ Essenhigh [7] replaced the set of uniform capillaries by a set with a distribution of radii given by:

$$dN = k \exp(-r/r_0) dr$$

where dN is the number of capillaries of radii between r and $(r + dr)$, k and r_0 are constants. The value of S_w derived was greater than that obtained from equation (15.9) by a factor of $\sqrt{3}$, i.e. $k_0 = \frac{2}{3}$.

Carman [8, p. 35] points out that the permeability equation is not valid if the pore space is made up of widely varying radii, since the mean equivalent radius is not the correct mean value for permeability calculation. Large capillaries give disproportionately high rates of flow which swamp the effect of the small capillaries. However, if the pore size range is not too great, say less than 2:1, the results should be acceptable. It is, nevertheless, advisable to grade samples by sieving as a preliminary to surface area determinations by permeability, and to determine the surface of each of the gradings independently in order to find the specific surface of the sample. Even if the range of void size is wide, the same type of distribution will always lead to the same ratio between two average values and results are acceptable for comparative purposes. An extreme case is found with bimodal distributions. For spheres with a size ratio of 4:1 or more, small spheres may be added to large ones by occupying voids. The porosity of the bed decreases and the pore texture is non-uniform since filled voids give smaller channels than unfilled voids. Initially the rate of fall of the porosity function is greater than the decrease in flow rate, which leads to an apparent fall in specific surface, as the powder becomes finer. When all the voids are filled, the value of k falls to its correct value. Fine dust clinging to larger particles takes no part in the flow and may lead to enormous errors. When aggregation of particles occurs, the surface measured is the envelope of the aggregates leading to a low value of surface area. As the porosity decreases, the bed becomes more uniform, leading to the correct value. It is usually recommended, therefore, to reduce high porosities by compression to values between 0·4 and 0·5 to reduce this error. In practice this may cause particle fracture which results in high experimental values for surface area.

The value of k_0 also depends on the shape of the pores [30, p. 138] lying between 2·0 and 2·5 for most annular and elliptical shapes.

It can also be argued that k depends on the porosity since the specific surface determined at different porosities tends not to be constant. Alternatively, it may be argued that the Carman-Kozeny equation only holds for a limited range of porosities and this range depends upon the system under examination. In order to compensate for this various modifications of the basic equation have been proposed. Although the difficulty of determining a correct value for k limits the usefulness of perme-ametry as an absolute technique, its reproducibility and the ease with which the determination is carried out makes it a useful technique for routine analysis.

15.3 Alternative derivation of Kozeny's equation using equivalent capillaries

Replacing the packed bed of thickness L and cross section A with N uniform capil-laries of radius r gives:

$$\text{volume specific surface } S_v = \frac{2N\pi r}{(A - N\pi r^2)}$$

$$\text{porosity } e = \frac{N\pi r^2}{A}$$

hence

$$r = \frac{2}{S_v} \frac{e}{(1-e)}.$$

Substituting in equation (15.2):

$$u_m = \frac{1}{2\eta S_v^2} \frac{e^2}{(1-e)^2} \frac{\Delta p}{L}. \qquad (15.11)$$

As before, the measured velocity is the approach velocity which is less than the velocity in the capillaries, since the cross-sectional area available for flow is greater. The actual velocity in the capillaries is greater than the apparent velocity due to the tortuous path of the capillaries. Combining equation (15.11) with equation (15.9) to include these factors gives:

$$u = e\left(\frac{L}{L_e}\right) \frac{1}{2\eta S_v^2} \frac{e^2}{(1-e)^2} \cdot \frac{\Delta p}{L} \left(\frac{L}{L_e}\right)$$

which reduces to equation (15.10).

For compressible fluids, equation (15.10) is modified to:

$$u = \frac{\bar{p}}{p_1} \cdot \frac{1}{k} \frac{e^3}{(1-e)^2} \cdot \frac{\Delta p}{L} \cdot \frac{1}{\eta \rho^2 S_w^2} \tag{15.12}$$

where $\bar{p}$ is the mean pressure of the gas in the porous bed and p_1 is the inlet pressure.

This correction becomes negligible if Δp is small and p/p_1 is near to unity [8, p. 2].

15.4 Other flow equations

At low fluid velocities through packed beds of powders the viscosity term predominates, whereas at higher velocities both viscous and kinetic effects are important. Ergun and Orning [28] found that, in the transitional region, the equation relating pressure gradient and superficial fluid velocity u_f was:

$$\frac{\Delta p}{L} = 150 \frac{(1-e)^2}{e^3} \frac{\eta u_f}{d_{sv}^2} + 1 \cdot 75 \left(\frac{1-e}{e^3}\right) \frac{\rho_f u_f^2}{d_{sv}}. \tag{15.13}$$

For Reynolds' number less than 2, the second term becomes negligible compared with the first. This is the Carman-Kozeny equation with an aspect factor of $4\frac{1}{6}$. Above a Reynolds number of 2000, the first term predominates and the ratio between pressure gradient and superficial fluid velocity is a linear function of fluid mass flow rate G, where $G = u_f \rho_f$. The constant, $1 \cdot 75$, was determined experimentally by plotting $\Delta p/Lu_f$ against G since, at high Reynolds' number:

$$\frac{\Delta p}{Lu_f} = \frac{1 \cdot 71}{d_{sv}} \left(\frac{1-e}{e^3}\right) G$$

It has been found that some variation between specific surface and porosity occurs. Carman [15] suggested a correction to the porosity function, to eliminate this variation. The correction may be written:

$$\frac{(e-e'')^3}{(1-e)^2} \quad \text{for} \quad \frac{e^3}{(1-e)^2}$$

where e'' represents the absorbed fluid that does not take part in the flow. Later, Keyes [29] suggested the replacement of e'' by $a(1-e)$. The constant a may be easily determined by substituting the above expression in equation (15.17) and plotting $(h_1/h_2)^{1/3} (1-e)^{2/3}$ against e. Neither of these corrections, however, is fully satisfactory.

Rose [54] proposed that an empirical factor be introduced into the porosity function to eliminate this variation:

$$S_t^2 = S_c^2 \left\{ \frac{1 \cdot 1}{X} + 140 \frac{e^3}{(1-e)^2} S_t \frac{0 \cdot 2 e^2}{(1-e)^2} \cdot e^{10} \right\} \tag{15.14}$$

where S_t and S_c are respectively the true surface area and the surface as determined with equation (15.10) and X the ratio of porosity function proposed by Carman [13].

15.5 Experimental applications

The determination of specific surface by permeability methods was suggested independently by Carman [13] and Dallavalle [14] and elaborated experimentally by Carman [15]. The method has been the subject of a British Standard [56].

The simple Carman-Kozeny equation gives a linear relationship between flow rate and pressure drop. A non-linear relationship indicates the need for a more complex equation. For low flow rates and an indicated particle size greater than about 5 μm, the equation should hold. For industrial control purposes, the simpler equation can still be used for finer powders provided the flow rate is maintained constant and recorded, together with the derived specific surface.

Apparatus may be divided into constant flow and constant volume. In the former the pressure drop across the bed, hence the flow rate through the bed, is maintained constant. In the latter a fixed volume of air is passed through the bed by creating a pressure difference across it and allowing the air to permeate through until a predetermined decrease in pressure is attained.

Constant flow-rate methods have some advantage for research purposes if provision is made for varying the flow rate, since the effect of flow-rate variation on bed permeability can be studied. Constant- volume methods are simpler and more robust, but less versatile.

15.6 Preparation of powder bed

Various methods of packing the powder bed have been recommended. Constant-volume cells and the cell of the Fisher sub-sieve sizer should be filled in one increment only. It is often advantageous to tap or vibrate such cells before compaction, but if this is overdone size segregation may occur.

With other cells, the powder should be added in four or five increments, each increment being compacted with a plunger before adding the next, so that the bed is made up in steps. This procedure largely avoids non-uniformity of compaction down the bed which is liable to occur if the whole of the powder required is compacted in one operation.

In some laboratories a standard pressure is applied (1 MN m^{-2}) to eliminate operator bias. In order to test bed uniformity, the specific surface should be determined with two different amounts of powder packed to the same porosity.

15.7 Constant pressure permeameters

The earliest equipment designed for routine service is that of Lea and Nurse [10, 16] figure 15.1. The powder is first compressed to a known porosity in a special permeability cell of cross-sectional area A. Air flows through the bed, for which the pressure drop is measured on a manometer as h_1 and then through a capillary flowmeter, for which another pressure drop, given by h_2, is recorded.

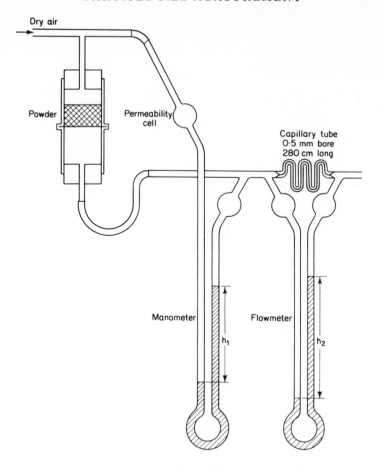

Fig. 15.1. The Lea and Nurse permeability apparatus with manometer and flowmeter [10].

The liquid in both manometers is the same and has a density ρ'. The capillary is designed to ensure that both pressure drops are small compared with atmospheric pressure, so that compressibility effects are negligible.

The volume rate of flow of air through the flowmeter is given by:

$$Q = \frac{ch_2\rho'}{\eta} \tag{15.15}$$

where c is a constant for a given capillary.

The pressure drop across the bed as measured on the manometer is:

$$p = hp'g. \tag{15.16}$$

Substituting equations (15.15) and (15.16) in equation (15.10) gives:

$$S_w = \frac{\sqrt{(g/k)}}{\rho_s(1-e)} \sqrt{\left(\frac{e^3 A h_1}{cLh_2}\right)}.$$

Taking Carman's value of 5·0 for k, this becomes:

$$S_w = \frac{14}{\rho_s(1-e)} \sqrt{\left(\frac{e^3 A h_1}{cLh_2}\right)}. \tag{15.7}$$

Since the terms on the right-hand side of the equation are known, S_w may be determined.

Gooden and Smith [17] modified the Lea and Nurse apparatus by incorporating a self-calculating chart which enabled specific surface to be read off directly. This is incorporated into the Fisher sub-sieve sizer (figure 15.2). The Gooden and Smith equation is a simple transform of the permeametry equation and is developed as follows. The porosity of the powder bed may be written:

$$e = \frac{V - M/\rho_s}{V}$$

The volume specific surface may be replaced by the surface-volume mean diameter:

$$\frac{S}{V_s} = \frac{d_s^2}{(\pi/6)d_v^3}$$

$$= \frac{6}{d_{sv}}.$$

Also:

$$\Delta p = (P - F)g$$

$$u = Fc/A$$

and

$$AL = V.$$

Applying these transformations to equation (15.10) gives:

$$d_{sv} = \frac{60\,000}{14} \sqrt{\left[\frac{\eta cF\rho_s L^2 M^2}{(V\rho_s - M)^3 (P - F)}\right]} \tag{15.18}$$

where d_{sv} = surface-weight mean diameter in micrometres,
    c = flowmeter conductance in ml s^{-1} per unit pressure (g force cm^{-2}),
    F = pressure difference across flowmeter resistance (g force cm^{-2}),
    M = mass of sample in grams,
    ρ_s = density of sample in g cm^{-3},
    V = apparent volume of compacted sample in ml,
    P = overall pressure head in g force cm^{-2}.

The instrument chart is calibrated to be used with a standard sample volume of 1 cm^3. It is therefore calibrated according to the equation:

$$d_{sv} = \frac{CL}{(AL - 1)^{3/2}} \sqrt{\left(\frac{F}{P - F}\right)} \tag{15.19}$$

where C is a constant.

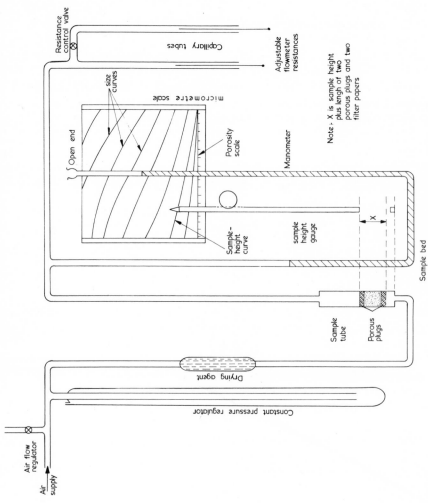

Fig. 15.2. The Fisher sub-sieve sizer.

The chart also indicates the bed porosity e in accordance with the equation:

$$e = 1 - 1/AL \tag{15.20}$$

If a different sample is used so that $M/\rho_s = X$ is not unity, the average particle diameter can nevertheless be calculated from the diameter indicated on the chart [39]. Since the chart only extends to a porosity of 0·40, this is necessary for powders that pack to a lower porosity.

Many authors [18, 19, 22, 29, 39] have observed that the average particle diameter varies with porosity and usually passes through a minimum. Since this minimum value is more reproducible than the value at a fixed porosity, some authors prefer this value. For this purpose the Fisher sub-sieve sizer is more convenient than other types of apparatus since it incorporates a device for compressing the powders to successively lower porosities.

If X cm^3 of powder is used instead of 1 cm^3, comparison of equations (15.18) and (15.19) shows that the average particle diameter d_{sv} will be related to the indicated particle diameter by:

$$d_{sv} = X\left\{\frac{1 - 1/AL}{1 - X/AL}\right\} d_{sv} \tag{15.21}$$

Similarly the bed porosity e can be calculated from the indicated porosity e':

$$e = 1 - X(1 - e'). \tag{15.22}$$

A recommended volume to use in order to extend the range to the minimal attainable porosity is $X = 1·25$ cm^3 [39].

The A.S.T.M. method for cement [40] standardizes operating conditions by stipulating a porosity of 0·5. This is satisfactory since cement is flowing and non-cohesive; the range of porosities achievable with cement is limited.

Some values obtained with griseofulvin are shown in table 15.1. The low initial values are probably due to the tendency of fine powders to form lumpy aggregates. Until the bed is packed uniformly air will pass more readily round them than through them. Thus the experimental values will be too low. Most workers accept the maximum value due to its higher reproducibility [39].

Porosity	0·6	0·55	0·5	0·45	0·4	0·35	0·30	0·25
Specific cm^2 g^{-1} surface	4500	4820	5150	5460	7300	9080	9080	7760

15.8 Constant-volume permeameters

In the apparatus devised by Blaine [53; 30, p. 142] the inlet end of the bed is open to atmosphere (figure 15.3).

Since, in this type of apparatus, the pressure drop varies as the experiment proceeds, equation (15.12) is modified in the following manner. Let the time for the oil level to fall from start to A be t, and let the time for the oil level to fall a distance δh when the inbalance is h be δt. Then: $\Delta p = h\rho' g$ where ρ' is the density of the oil and:

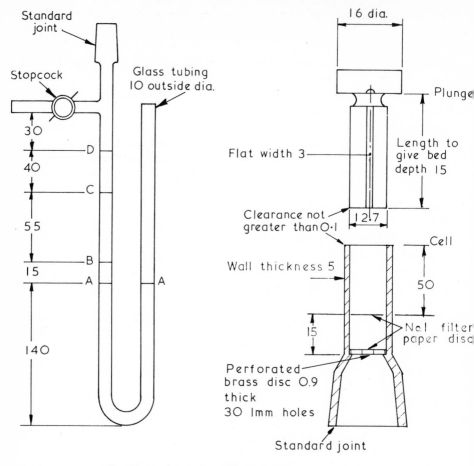

All dimensions in millimetres

Fig. 15.3. (*a*) Blaine apparatus. (*b*) Cell and plunger for Blaine apparatus.

$$u = \frac{1}{A}\frac{dV}{dt} = \frac{1}{A}\frac{adh}{dt}$$

where dV is the volume of air displaced by the oil as it falls.

Substituting in equation (15.12) and putting $k = 5$:

$$S_w^2 \frac{a}{A}\cdot\frac{dh}{dt} = \frac{1}{5\eta\rho_s^2}\frac{e^3}{(1-e)^2}\cdot\frac{h\rho'g}{L}$$

$$S_w^2 \int_{h_1}^{h_2}\frac{dh}{h} = \frac{A}{5a\eta\rho_s^2}\frac{e^3}{(1-e)^2}\cdot\frac{\rho'g}{L}\int_0^t dt$$

$$S_w = \sqrt{\left[\frac{kte^3}{\rho_s^2 L (1-e)^2}\right]} \qquad (15.23)$$

where k, an instrument constant, is equal to

$$\frac{A\rho^1 g}{5a\,\eta\,\ln(h_2/h_1)}.$$

The specific surface measured, using the Blaine method, is found to decrease with the porosity of the powder bed. This effect can be eliminated by writing equation (15.23) as:

$$S_w = \sqrt{\left(\frac{k}{\rho^2 L}\right)} \cdot \frac{e^{3/2}}{(1-e)}\, t^{1/2}$$

i.e.

$$S_w = Z\,\frac{e^{3/2}}{(1-e)}\,t^{1/2}$$

$$\log t = 2\log S_w - 2\log Z - \log \frac{e^{3/2}}{(1-e)}. \qquad (15.24)$$

Usui [20] replaced the last term with $C + De$ and showed that the relationship between $\log t$ and e was linear, proving that C and D were constants independent of e. A plot of $\log t$ against e therefore yields a value for surface area, the calculation being simplified if comparison is made with a standard powder.

A simplified form of the air permeameter was developed by Rigden [19]. In his apparatus, air was caused to flow through a bed of powder by the pressure of oil displaced from equilibrium in two chambers which were connected to the permeability cell and to each other in U-tube fashion. An instrument working on this principle is available in England as the Griffin surface area of powder apparatus (figure 15.4).

Another variation of the variable flow technique is the Reynolds' and Branson auto-permeameter, in which air is pumped into the inlet side to unbalance a mercury manometer. The tap is then closed and air flows through the packed bed to atmosphere. On rebalancing, the mercury contacts start–stop probes attached to a timing device. The pressure difference (Δp) between these probes and the mean pressure $\bar{p}$ are instrument constants. The flow rate is given by:

$$\frac{dv}{dt} = \frac{1}{\bar{p}}\frac{\Delta p}{t}.$$

Substituting this in the Carman-Kozeny equation, yields a similar equation to the Rigden equation. The automatic timing device on this instrument makes it preferable to the Rigden.

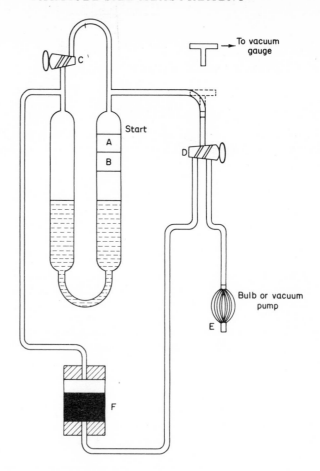

Fig. 15.4. The Griffin surface area of powder apparatus.

15.9 Fine particles

Pechukas and Gage [21] designed an apparatus for fine particle measurement. This was modified and automated by Carman and Malherbe [22]. The plug of material is formed in the brass sample tube A (figure 15.5). Clamp E controls the mercury flow into the graduated cylinder C, the pressure being controlled at atmospheric by the manometer F. The side arm T_1 is used for gases other than air. Calculations are carried out according to section 15.6. The plug is formed in a special press by compression between hardened steel plunders. By taking known weights of powder the measurements may be carried out at a known and predetermined porosity, e.g. 0·45. Carman and Malherbe recommended that the final stages of compression be carried out in small increments and that the plungers be removed frequently to prevent jamming.

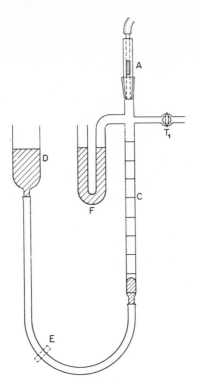

Fig. 15.5. Modified Pechukas and Gage apparatus for fine powders [22].

15.10 Types of flow

With compacted beds of very fine powders and gases near atmospheric pressure or with coarse powders and gases at reduced pressure, the mean free path of the gas molecules is of the same order as the capillary diameter. This results in slippage at the capillary walls so that the rate of flow is higher than that calculated from Poiseuille's law. If the pressure is further reduced until the mean free path is much greater than capillary diameter, viscosity takes no part in flow, since molecules collide only with capillary walls and not with each other. Such free molecular flow is really a process of diffusion and takes place for each constituent of a mixture against its own partial pressure gradient even if the total pressure at each end of the capillary is the same.

There are, therefore, three types of flow to consider. In the first, the flow is viscous and equation (15.10) may be applied; in the transitional regional in which the mean free path λ of the gas molecules is of the same order as the capillary diameter, the slip term is of the same order as the viscous term and both have to be evaluated; in the molecular region, the slip term predominates.

15.11 Transitional region between viscous and molecular flow

Poiseuille's equation was developed by assuming that the velocity at the capillary walls was zero. If it is assumed that the velocity does not reach zero until a distance $x\lambda$ beyond the capillary walls, the modified equation for the average velocity becomes:

$$U_m = \frac{\Delta p}{k\eta LS_v^2}\frac{e^3}{(1-e)^2} + \frac{\Delta p}{k\eta LS_v}\frac{e^2}{(1-e)}Z\lambda \tag{15.25}$$

where $Z = 2x$.

Rigden [9] assumed a value for x of:

$$x = \frac{2-f}{f} \tag{15.26}$$

where f is the fraction of molecules undergoing diffuse reflection from the capillary walls. If the capillary walls are smooth, molecules striking them at any angle rebound at the same angle with the same average velocity and the component of velocity perpendicular to the wall reversed. This is termed *specular reflection*. The surfaces of packed beds of powder are not smooth and molecules striking them rebound in any direction. This is termed *diffuse reflection* or *inelastic collision*. The maximum value of f is unity which makes $x = 1$ for molecular flow conditions.

Lea and Nurse [10] modified the Poiseuille equation (15.2) by assuming a slip velocity at the capillary walls so that:

$$U_m = \frac{d^2}{32\eta}\frac{\Delta p}{L}\left[1 - \left(\frac{8M}{d}\right)\lambda\right] \tag{15.27}$$

where M is a constant, i.e.

$$x = M. \tag{15.28}$$

Rigden [11] accepted Millikan's value of 0.874 for M, making f greater than unity; The required compensating factor to bring equation (15.27) into line with other equations is $(16M/d)$, making:

$$x = 1.748 \text{ and } f = 0.73.$$

Carman [8] added an extra term to Poisieuille's equation to take account of slip:

$$U_m = \frac{d^2}{32\eta}\cdot\frac{\Delta p}{L} + \frac{d}{4\xi}\frac{\Delta p}{L} \tag{15.29}$$

where, the coefficient of external friction is defined by Millikan as:

$$\xi = \tfrac{1}{2}\rho g\bar{v}\left(\frac{f}{2-f}\right) \tag{15.30}$$

where $\bar{v}$ is the mean thermal velocity and ρ_g is the density of the gas.

Substituting for viscosity from equation (15.31) reduces the equation to 15.25, but quoted values of the constant in equation (15.31) vary ($0.5, 0.31, 0.35, \pi/10$, $1/3$) (see [8, 34–37]). Alternative forms of equation (15.25) have been used and may be derived by substituting from the equations below:

$$\bar{v} = \left(\frac{8RT}{\pi M}\right); \quad \rho_g = \frac{M}{RT}p; \quad \eta = \tfrac{1}{2}\rho_g\bar{v}\lambda. \tag{15.31}$$

15.12 Experimental techniques for determining Z

Carman and Arnell [12] used the following form of equation (15.25):

$$\frac{P_1}{P}\bar{v} = \frac{1}{k\eta S_v^2}\frac{e^3}{(1-e)^2}\frac{\Delta p}{L} + \frac{1}{kpS_v}\frac{e^2}{1-e}\frac{\Delta p}{L}\sqrt{\left(\frac{2RT}{\pi M}\right)} \cdot \delta k_0 \cdot \frac{8}{3}. \tag{15.32}$$

They found $\delta k_0/k \longrightarrow 0.45$ by plotting $(\bar{p}_1/\Delta p)(V/At)$ against $\bar{p}$, where $V/At = v$. At the intercept $\bar{p} = 0$, $\delta k_0/k$ can be found. Using the identities (15.31), this yields a value $Z = 3.82$.

Rigden [9] measured the flow rate and the pressure drop across a packed bed of powder using oil manometers.

The volume rate of flow $Q = ACh_2\rho'$ is given by the oil manometer flowmeter with a flow meter constant C and oil of density ρ'. Also the pressure drop across the bed is given by $\Delta p = h_1\rho'$.

Substituting these values into equation (15.25) gives:

$$\frac{h_2}{h_1} = \frac{A}{k\eta LCS_v^2}\frac{e^3}{(1-e)^2} + \frac{A}{k\eta LCS_v}\frac{e^2}{(1-e)}2\left(\frac{2-f}{f_1}\right)\lambda. \tag{15.33}$$

Rigden plotted h_2/h_1 against $100/\bar{p}$. At the intercept $100/\bar{p} = 0$

$$\lambda = 0 \text{ since } \lambda\alpha(1/\bar{p}).$$

Denoting the intercept value as $(h_2/h_1)_1$ gives:

$$S_K = \frac{Ae^3}{k\eta LC(1-e)^2}\left(\frac{h_1}{h_2}\right)_1 \tag{15.34}$$

where S_K is the surface area independent of 'slip'. The slope of the graph is:

$$\frac{A}{k\eta LCS_v}\frac{e^2}{(1-e)} \cdot 2\left(\frac{2-f}{f}\right)\lambda \tag{15.35}$$

Hence:

$$2\left(\frac{2-f_1}{f_1}\right)\lambda = \frac{e}{S_K(1-e)} \cdot \frac{\text{slope}}{\text{intercept}}. \tag{15.36}$$

Rigden found that S_K was approximately equal to S_v so it was in order to interchange them. However, the uncorrected value of S as derived directly from the viscous term was appreciably smaller than the intercept value from the graph. The average experimental value of Z was found to be 3.80, making $f = 0.69$, but a great deal of scatter was found, i.e. $3.0 < Z < 4.2$.

15.13 Calculation of permeability surface

Although the above graphical method may also be used to determine specific surface, a rather elaborate apparatus is needed and several experiments are required for one value of specific surface. For practical purposes it is preferable to make a single measurement with the simplest form of apparatus.

If the viscous term predominates, the specific surface is determined using equation (15.12) taking the aspect factor k to be equal to 5. If the compressibility factor is negligible, this equation takes the form of equation (15.10).

When the molecular term predominates the specific surface is obtained from the second term in equation (15.25) with $Z = 3.4$.

When the two terms are comparable the specific surface is obtained as follows. The specific surface using the viscous flow term (equation (15.10)) is:

$$S_K^2 = \frac{\Delta p}{5\eta Lu} \frac{e^3}{(1-e)^2}.$$

(15.37)

The specific surface using the molecular flow term is:

$$S_M = \frac{\Delta p}{5\eta Lu} \frac{e^2}{(1-e)} 3.4 \lambda.$$

(15.38)

Substituting these equations in equation (15.25) gives:

$$\frac{S_K^2}{S_v^2} + \frac{S_M}{S_v} = 1.$$

(15.39)

This is a quadratic in S_v having the following solution:

$$S_v = \frac{S_M}{2} + \sqrt{\left(\frac{S_M^2}{4} + S_K^2\right)}.$$

(15.40)

Crowl [38] carried out a series of experiments using pigments comparing Carman and Malherbe's equations ((15.25) with $Z = 3.4$), Rose's equation (15.14) and nitrogen adsorption. He found good agreement between the Carman and Malherbe figures and nitrogen adsorption, a ratio of 0.6 to 0.8 being obtained with a range of surface areas from 1 to 100 m^2 g^{-1}. The Rose figures were considerably lower, ranging from 0.2 to 0.5, and being particularly poor with pigments of high surface area. With fine pigments, surface area above about 10 to 12 m^2 g^{-1} by nitrogen adsorption, the agreement was less satisfactory but the order of fineness agreed with nitrogen adsorption results.

15.14 Diffusional flow for surface-area measurement

Consider a large container of gas at a concentration C_2; let the gas diffuse through a packed bed of powder of length L, cross-sectional area A and porosity e; into a container of volume V where the gas concentration C_1 is much smaller than C_2.

The flow rate through the bed (g mol cm^{-3} for c.g.s. system) can be derived from Fick's laws of diffusion [41] and is given by:

$$C_1 = \frac{eAD_s}{LV} C_2 \left(t - \frac{L^2}{6D_t}\right).$$ (15.41)

Rewriting in terms of pressure, after Babbit [42]:

$$p_1 = \frac{eAD_s}{LV} p_2 \left(t - \frac{L^2}{6D_t}\right)$$ (15.42)

where p_1 is the pressure in the outlet container,
D_t is the time-lag diffusion constant,
D_s is the steady-state diffusion constant.

A graph of outlet pressure p_1 against time can be obtained at one inlet pressure p_2. This graph will be asymptotic to a line of slope:

$$\frac{dp_1}{dt} = \frac{eAD_s}{LV} p_2.$$ (15.43)

This line will intersect the line through the initial value of p_1 and parallel to the abscissa at a time

$$t_L = \frac{L_e^2}{6D_t} = \frac{k_1^2 L^2}{6D_t}$$ (15.44)

The diffusion coefficients obtained from steady state (D_s) and time lag (D_t) are not always the same. This can be explained by adsorption into pores during the transient period. Thus the pore volume in the transient state can be different to that in the steady state.

15.15 The relationship between diffusion constant and specific surface

Knudsen [43, 44] deduced that the energy flow rate G through a capillary with a pressure drop across its ends of Δp as:

$$G = \frac{4}{3} r \sqrt{\frac{2RT}{\pi M}} \cdot \frac{A \Delta p}{L} \left(\frac{2-f}{f}\right)$$ (15.45)

where RT and M are the molar gas constant, the absolute temperature and the gas molecular weight.

Knudsen's equation can be expressed in terms of the diffusion constant since:

$$G = \frac{eA \Delta p}{L} D = V \frac{dp}{dt}$$ (15.46)

and

$$r = \frac{2}{S_v} \left(\frac{e}{1-e}\right).$$

Hence, inserting in equation (15.43) gives for steady-state molecular flow:

$$V \frac{dp}{dt} = \frac{8}{3} \frac{eA \Delta p}{LS_v} \left(\frac{e}{1-e}\right) \sqrt{\frac{2RT}{\pi M}} \left(\frac{2-f}{f}\right).$$ (15.47)

Inserting in equation (15.44) gives for transient state molecular flow:

$$S_v = 16\left(\frac{e}{1-e}\right)\sqrt{\frac{2RT}{M}}\frac{t_L}{k_1^2 L^2}\left(\frac{2-f}{f}\right)$$ (15.48)

Comparing equation (15.47) with equation (15.38) using the transforms in equation (15.31) and replacing $V(dp/dt)$ by $p(dV/dt)$ gives:

$$\frac{Z}{k} = 3{\cdot}4\frac{2-f_0}{f_0}.$$

Assuming a value of unity for k_0 and $\sqrt{2}$ for k_1 makes $f_0 = 1$ when $Z = 3{\cdot}4$, which is in agreement with the experimental value for the transitional region.

Deryagin [33] showed that the numerical constant 4/3 in equation (15.45) should be replaced by 12/13 for inelastic collisions, and Pollard and Present [45] use a constant of $\pi/2$.

A similar equation was derived by Kraus and Ross [24] who neglected the tortuosity factor on the grounds that it was already accounted for in the derivation of the diffusion equation.

The general form of equation (15.47) is:

$$\frac{1}{A}\frac{dv}{dt} = \beta\left(\frac{e^2}{1-e}\right)\frac{1}{LS_v}\sqrt{\frac{2RT}{\pi M}}.$$ (15.49)

The values for β derived by the various authors are:

Barrer and Grove	8/3 =	2·66
Pollard and Present	π =	3·14
Kraus and Ross	48/13 =	3·70
Derjaguin	8/3 =	2·66.

Using the slip-term value $(Z = 3{\cdot}4)$ and assuming $k = 1$, gives $\beta = 8/13$. However, assuming $f = 1$ in deriving the slip term would give a value $Z = 2$ and $\beta = 1{\cdot}57$. However, this comparison cannot be carried too far due to the effect of the aspect factor. If this is assumed equal to 2 when $f = 1$, this makes $Z = 5$ and $\beta = 3{\cdot}92$.

15.16 Transient state diffusional flow

Barrer and Groves [23] applied equation (15.48) to obtain:

$$S_v = 8\left(\frac{e}{1-e}\right)\sqrt{\frac{2RT}{\pi M}}\frac{t_L}{L_2}$$ (15.50)

assuming $k_1 = \sqrt{2}$ after Carman.

Equation (15.50) has been applied experimentally by Kraus and Ross [24] and Krishnamoorthy [46].

The apparatus of Kraus and Ross (figure 15.6) consists essentially of two 4 litre reservoirs connected through the cell holding the powder. A mercury manometer

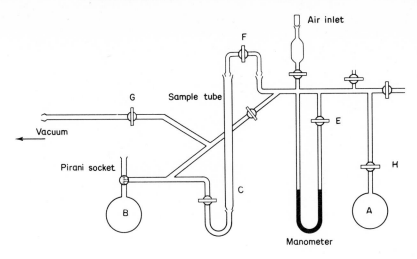

Fig. 15.6. Transient flow apparatus (Kraus and Ross).

was used to measure the pressure on the high-pressure side and a calibrated thermo-couple vacuum gauge was used to measure the pressure on the discharge side. Before an experiment, the whole system was evacuated and flushed with the gas being used. The system was then pumped down to 1 or 2 μ of mercury and shut off from the pumps with stopcock G. Stopcocks E and F were closed and the desired inlet pressure established by bleeding gas into reservoir A through H. At zero time, stopcock F was opened and the gas was allowed to diffuse through the cell C into reservoir B. Figure 15.7 shows a typical flow-rate curve. The time lag t_L is determined by extra-polation of the straight line, steady-state portion of the curve to the initial pressure in the cell and discharge reservoir.

Krishnamoorthy [46, 47] found that the time lag remained constant at 1;48 min for rutile titanium dioxide over a range of inlet pressures (54 to 103 mm Hg) with $L = 15\cdot3$ cm, $e = 0\cdot726$, $\rho_s = 4\cdot26$ g cm^{-3}, $T = 20°$ C, $R = 8\cdot314 \times 10^7$ erg deg^{-1} mol^{-1} and $M = 29\cdot37$ (air), equation (15.44) using Krauss and Ross's constant (144/13) gave $S_w = 6\cdot05$ m^2 g^{-1} compared with the BET nitrogen gas-adsorption value of $14\cdot5$ m^2 g^{-1}. Kraus and Ross [24] reported that in all five samples they used comparable results with the BET method were obtained. Krishnamoorthy attributed his low values to specular reflection.

With zinc oxide, Krishnamoorthy found that the time lag increased with de-creasing inlet pressures. Extrapolation to zero inlet pressure after Barrer [48] and Barrer and Grove [23] gave a value which produced a surface area in agreement with BET. Since there is no theoretical justification for such an extrapolation and since there is some difficulty in determining t_L accurately, this method is not recommended for routine analyses.

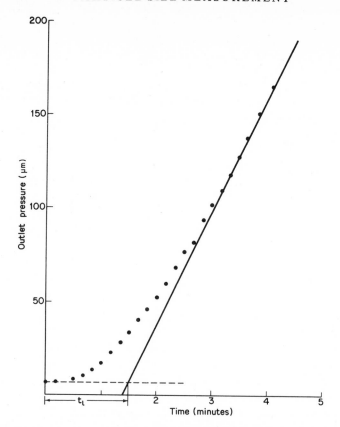

Fig. 15.7. Flow-rate curve for the transient flow apparatus.

15.17 Steady-state flow

Early work [49] was carried out using the apparatus shown in figure 15.6. The slope of figure 15.7 is given by equation (15.43) which, in conjunction with equations (15.45) and (15.46), gives:

$$G = V\frac{dp_1}{dt} = \frac{8}{3}\frac{Ap_2}{LS_v}\left(\frac{e^2}{1-e}\right)\sqrt{\frac{2RT}{\pi M}}. \tag{15.51}$$

A graph of energy flow rate $V(dp_1)/dt$ against p_2 gives a straight line from which S_v can be determined (figure 15.8). These results were found to be in good agreement with BET gas-adsorption values. On the basis of this work the simplified apparatus shown in figure 15.9 was constructed [50]. The system is first evacuated with tap 4 closed. Taps 1, 2 and 3 are then closed and gas is allowed in on the inlet size by opening tap 4, thus unbalancing the mercury manometer. Opening tap 1 allows the gas to flow through the powder plug, the flow rate being monitored by the changing inlet pressure which is recorded as a deflection θ on a pen-recorder graph

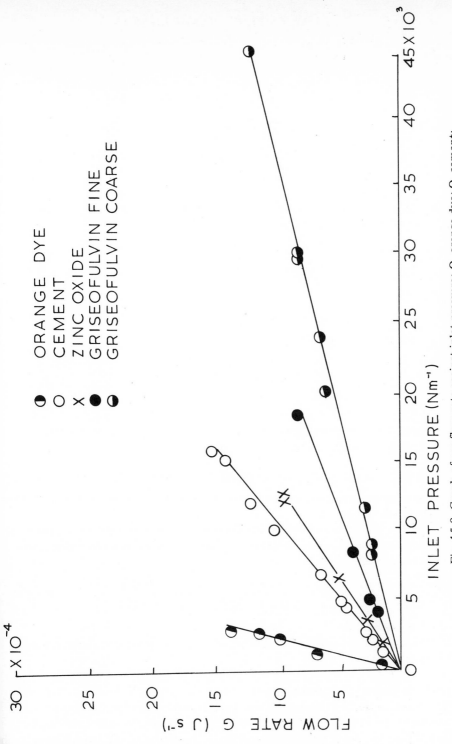

Fig. 15.8. Graph of gas-flow rate against inlet pressure: O, orange dye; O, cement; X. zinc oxide; O, griseofulvin fine; O, griseofulvin coarse.

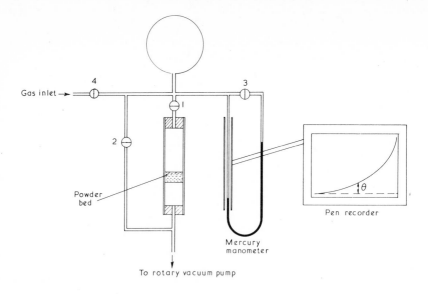

Fig. 15.9. Simple gas-diffusion apparatus.

Then:
$$\frac{1}{\theta}\frac{d\theta}{dt} = \frac{8}{3}\frac{A}{LS_v}\left(\frac{e^2}{1-e}\right)\sqrt{\frac{2R\overline{T}}{\pi M}}.$$
(15.52)

This instrument gives highly reproducible results which are similar to BET values.

Orr [55] developed an apparatus, the Knudsen-Flow permeameter, which is based on the following form of Deryagin's equation:

$$S_v = \frac{24}{13}\left(\frac{2}{\pi}\right)^{1/2}\frac{Ae^2\Delta p}{Q(MRT)^{1/2}L}$$
(15.53)

where Q is in mol cm^{-2} s^{-1}.

The flow rate of helium [9] passing through a packed bed of powder is measured together with the upstream pressure p and pressure drop across the bed which gives, on rearrangement:

$$S_v = 0.481\frac{Ae}{q[M(273+\theta)]^{1/2}}\frac{\Delta p}{L}\left[\frac{760}{p}\left(\frac{273+\theta}{273}\right)\right]$$
(15.54)

where q is in cm^2 sec^{-1}.

The relationship found by Orr between specific surface and pressure drop was semilogarithmic.

15.18 The liquid phase permeameter

In the early stages of development, liquid permeameters were favoured. As long as there is no appreciable size fraction below 5 μm, this is still the easiest technique. Below 5 μm, the use of liquids becomes unsatisfactory, due to settling and segregation

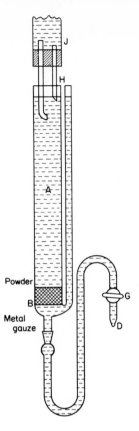

Fig. 15.10. Liquid phase permeameter [13].

the difficulty of removing air bubbles and aggregation. Gas permeametry was also
more attractive due to the higher permeabilities of air and other gases. However,
the surface areas determined by air permeametry were less than those determined
by liquid permeametry and the difference increased with decreasing size. Though
gas permeameters were introduced, they were not placed on a satisfactory footing
until the difference between liquid and gas permeabilities was shown to be due to
slip in gases and corrections to the Kozeny equation were derived.

The apparatus used by Carman [13], Walther [25], Wiggins *et al.* [26] is shown
in figure 15.10. The powder is formed into a bed in a uniform tube A, and rests on
the metal gauze B. The gauze is supported horizontally by a loosely-wound spiral.
The flow of liquid is adjusted to a steady rate with stopcock G, and the difference
in level between D and the constant level in A gives the pressure drop causing flow.
Air bubbles enter the tube H, causing a constant level to be maintained in A and
the volume of liquid supplied in known time is given by the graduated reservoir J.
The bed is formed by washing a known weight of powder into A, using small

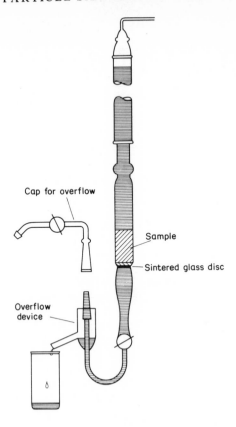

Cap for overflow

Sample

Sintered glass disc

Overflow
device

Fig. 15.11. The variable head permeameter [27].

quantities at a time and allowing each to settle into place with the assistance of gentle
suction. The thickness is measured with acathetometer.

Dodd, Davis and Pidgeon [27] used the apparatus shown in figure 15.11, in
which the head decreased during an experiment and the surface was determined
using equation (15.32).

15.19 Application to hindered settling
The settling of particles, constrained to fixed positions, in a stagnant liquid is ana-
logous to the permeametry situation where the liquid is moving and the bed is fixed.
For a sedimenting suspension, the pressure head may be replaced by the gravitational
minus the buoyant force on the particles:

$$\frac{\Delta p}{L} = (\rho_s - \rho_f)e.$$

Replacing also the volume specific surface by $6/d_{sv}$ modifies equation (15.10) to:

$$u = u_{st}\left(\frac{e}{1-e}\right)^2.$$

This equation is very similar to the ones derived for particles settling in a concentrated suspension (equations (15.49) and (15.50)).

References

[1] Darcy, H.P.G. (1856), *Les Fontaines Publiques de la Ville de Dijon*, Victor Dalamont.

[2] Hagen, G. (1839), *Ann. Phys. (Pogg. Ann.)*, **46**, 423.

[3] Poiseuille, J. (1846), *Inst. de France Acad. Des Sci., 9, 433.*

[4] Blake, F.C. (1922), *Trans. Am. Inst. Chem. Engrs*, **14**, 415.

[5] Kozeny, J. (1927), *Ber. Wien. Akad.*, **136A**, 271.

[6] Coulson, J.M., and Richardson, J.F. (1955), *Chemical Engineering*, Pergamon Press.

[7] Essenhigh, R.H. (Nov., 1955), *Safety in Mines Res. Est.*, Report No. 120.

[8] Carman, P.C. (1956), *Flow of Gases through Porous Media*, Butterworths.

[9] Ridgen, P.J. (1954), *Road Res. Tech., Paper No. 28*, (H.M.S.O.).

[10] Lea, F.M., and Nurse, R.W. (1947), Symposium on Particle Size Analysis, *Trans. Inst. Chem. Engrs*, **25**, 47.

[11] Rigden, P.J. (1956), *Nature*, **157**, 268, 694.

[12] Carman, P.C., and Arnell, J.C. (1948), *Canad. J. Res.*, **26**, 128.

[13] Carman, P.C. (1938), *J. Soc. Chem. Ind., Lond. (Trans.)*, **57**, 225.

[14] Dallavalle, J.M. (1938), *Chem. Met. Eng.*, **45**, 688.

[15] Carman, P.C. (1941), *A.S.T.M., Symposium on New Methods for Particle Size Determination in the Sub-sieve Range*, 24.

[16] Lea, F.M., and Nurse, R.W. (1939), *J. Soc. Chem. Ind.*, **58**, 277.

[17] Gooden, E.L., and Smith, C.M. (1940), *Ind. Eng. Chem., analyt. ed.*, **12**, 479.

[18] Pendleton, A.G. (1960), *Chem. Process Eng.*, **41**, 147–8.

[19] Rigden, R.J. (1947), *J. Soc. Chem. Ind., Lond. (Trans,)*, **66**, 191.

[20] Usui, K. (1964), *J. Soc. Mat. Sci., Japan*, **13**, 828.

[21] Pechukas, A., and Gage, F.W. (1946), *Ind. Eng. Chem, Analyt. ed.*, **18**, 370.

[22] Carman, P.C., and Malherbe, P. le R. (1950), *J. Soc. Chem. Ind.*, **69**, 134.

[23] Barrer, R.M., and Grove, D.M. (1951), *Trans. Farad. Soc.*, **47**, 826, 837.

[24] Kraus, G., Ross, R.W., and Girifalco, L.A. (1953), *J. Phys. Chem.*, **57**, 330.

[25] Walther, H. (1943), *Kolloid-Z.*, **103**, 233.

[26] Wiggins, E.J., Campbell, W.B., and Maas, O. (1948), *Canad. J. Res.*, **26A**, 128.

[27] Dodd, C.G., Davis, J.W., and Pidgeon, F.D. (1951), *Ind. Eng. Chem.*, **55**, 684.

[28] Ergun, S., and Orning, A.A. (1949), *Ind. Eng. Chem*, **41**, 1179.

[29] Keyes, W.F. (1946), *Ind. Eng. Chem.*, **18**, 33.

[30] Orr, C., and Dallavalle, J.M. (1959), *Fine Particle Measurement*, Macmillan, N.Y.

[31] Sullivan, R.R., and Hertel, K.L. (1940), *J. Appl. Phys.*, **11**, 761.

[32] Fowler, J.L., and Hertel, K.L. (1940), *J. Appl. Phys.*, **11**, 496.

[33] Deryagin, B. (1946), *Compte. Rendu Acad. Sci., U.S.S.R.*, **53**, 623; and (1956) *J. Appl. Chem., U.S.S.R.*, **29**, 49.

[34] Kaye, G.W.C. and Laby, T.H. (1966), 13th ed., Physical and Chemical Constants, Longmans, London.

[35] Millikan, *loc. cit.* [16].

[36] Partington (1958), *General and Organic Chemistry,*

[37] *Encyclopaedia of Science and Technology* (1960), McGraw-Hill.

[38] Crowl, V.T. (1959), *Research Mem., No. 274,* **12,** 7, Paint Research Station, Teddington, Middlesex.

[39] Edmondson, I.C., and Toothill, J.P.R. (1963), *Analyst,* October, 805–8.

[40] A.S.T.M. Standard: (1961), Part 4, p. 149.

[41] Crank, J. (1946), *Mathematics of Diffusion,* Clarendon Press, Oxford.

[42] Babbit, J.D. (1951), *Can. J. Physics,* **29,** 427,.437.

[43] Knudsen, M. (1909), *Ann. Physik,* **4,** 28, 75, 999.

[44] Knudsen, M. (1911), *Ann. Physik,* **4,** 34, 593–656.

[45] Pollard, W.G., and Present, R.D. (1948), *Phys. Rev.,* **73,** 762.

[46] Krishnamoorthy, T.S. (1966), Univ. of Bradford, M.Sc. thesis.

[47] Allen, T., Standley-Wood, N.G., and Krishnamoorthy, T.S. (1966), *Particle Size Analysis Conference, Loughborough,* 1966, Soc. Analyt. Chem., London.

[48] Barrer, R.M. (1954), *B. J. Applied. Phys.,* suppl. 3.

[49] Allen, T. (1971), *Silicates Industrials,* **36,** 718, 173–85.

[50] Stanley-Wood, N.G. (1969), Univ. of Bradford, Ph.D. thesis.

[51] Muskat and Botsel (*cit.* [8]).

[52] Schriever (*cit.* [8]).

[53] Blaine, R.L. (1943), *A.S.T.M., Bull. No.* 12B.

[54] Rose, H.E. (1952), *J. Appl. Chem.,* **2,** 511.

[55] Orr, C. (1967), *Anal. Chem.,* **39,** 834.

[56] British Standard 4359: (1971), Part 2, *Determination of Specific Surface of Powders.*

16 *Gas Adsorption*

16.1 Introduction

A commonly used method of determining the specific surface of solids is by the physical adsorption of a gas on the solid and the determination of the monolayer capacity V_m. This is defined as the quantity of adsorbate required to cover the adsorbent with a monolayer. Usually a second layer may be forming before the monolayer is complete, but V_m is determined from the isotherm equations irrespective of this. There are also other gas-adsorption methods in which the surface area is determined without determining the monolayer capacity. The fact that gases are adsorbed on solid surfaces was known as early as the late eighteenth century, but systematic studies of this phenomenon have been carried out only in the past fifty years.

Adsorption processes may be classified as physical or chemical, depending on the nature of the forces involved. Physical adsorption, also termed van der Waals adsorption, is caused by molecular interaction forces; the formation of a physically adsorbed layer may be likened to the condensation of a vapour to form a liquid. This type of adsorption is therefore of importance only at temperatures below the critical temperature for the gas. Not only is the heat of physical adsorption of the same order of magnitude as that of liquefaction, but physically adsorbed layers behave in many respects like two-dimensional liquids. On the other hand, chemical adsorption (chemisorption) involves some degree of specific chemical interaction between the adsorbate and the adsorbent and, correspondingly, the energies of adsorption may be quite large and comparable to those of chemical bond formation.

Since physical adsorption is the result of relatively weak interaction between solids and gases, almost all the gas adsorbed can be removed by evacuation at the same temperature at which it was adsorbed. The quantity of physically adsorbed gas at a given pressure increases with decreasing temperature. Consequently, most adsorption measurements for the purpose of determining surface areas are made at low temperatures. Gas that is chemisorbed may be difficult to remove merely by reducing the pressure, and when it does occur, it may be accompanied by chemical changes.

Experimental results of adsorption are most commonly plotted in terms of the volume of gas adsorbed as a function of the equilibrium pressure. Plots involving the volume adsorbed and the pressure at which the adsorption takes place are called isotherms.

16.2 Theories of adsorption

16.2.1 Langmuir's isotherm for ideal localized monolayers

The first theoretical equation relating the quantity of adsorbed gas to the equilibrium pressure of the gas was proposed by Langmuir [4]. In his model, adsorption is limited to a monolayer and his equation has limited applicability to physical adsorption with wider application to chemical adsorption and the adsorption of solute, including dye molecules, from solution.

His method was to equate the number of molecules evaporating from the surface with the number condensing on the surface. Since surface forces are short range, only molecules striking a bare surface are adsorbed; molecules striking a previously adsorbed molecule are elastically reflected back into the gas phase.

From kinetic theory, the number of molecules striking unit area in unit time is given by:

$$Z = \frac{P}{\sqrt{2\pi m k T}}$$

where k is Boltzman's constant, m is the mass of a molecule, P is the pressure and T is the absolute temperature.

The number evaporating n depends upon the energy binding the molecules to the surface. If Q is the energy evolved when a molecule is adsorbed and τ_0 the molecular vibration time, residence time is given by:

$$\tau = \tau_0 \exp\left(+\frac{Q}{RT}\right)$$

where τ_0 is of the order of 10^{-13} s and, for physical adsorption, Q has a value between about 1·5 and 9·0 k cal mol^{-1}; this gives τ_0 value between 10^{-12} and 4×10^{-7} s [3, p.463].

Hence the number of molecules evaporating in unit time is:

$$n = n_0 \exp\left(-\frac{Q}{RT}\right).$$

Defining α_0 as the ratio of inelastic to total collisions with the bare surface (α_0 tends to unity under conditions of dynamic equilibrium):

$$\text{rate of adsorption} = \text{rate of desorption}$$

$$\frac{P}{\sqrt{2\pi m k T}} \alpha_0 (1 - \theta) = n_0 \left[\exp\left(-\frac{Q}{RT}\right)\right] \theta.$$

If the volume of gas adsorbed at pressure p is V, and the volume required to form a monolayer is V_m, then:

$$\theta = \frac{V}{V_m} = \frac{bP}{1 + bp}$$

where
$$b = \frac{\alpha_0}{\sqrt{2\pi m k T n_0}} \exp\left(-\frac{Q}{RT}\right). \tag{16.1}$$

The equation is usually written in the form:

$$\frac{p}{V} = \frac{1}{bV_m} + \frac{P}{V_m}. \tag{16.2}$$

A plot of P/V against P yields the monolayer capacity V_m. To relate this to surface area it is necessary to know the area occupied by one molecule, σ. Surface area from the monolayer capacity can be calculated by:

$$S_w = \frac{N\sigma V_m}{M_v} \tag{16.3}$$

where S_w = specific surface area in $m^2 g^{-1}$.

N = Avagadro number, $6 \cdot 023 \times 10^{23} \dfrac{\text{molecules}}{\text{gram molecule}}$,

σ = area occupied by one adsorbate molecule, usually taken as $16 \cdot 2 \times 10^{-20} m^2$, for nitrogen,

V_m = monolayer capacity ml,

M_v = gram molecular volume = 22410 ml,

$$S_w = \frac{(6 \cdot 023 \times 10^{23})(16 \cdot 2 \times 16^{-20})}{(22\,410)} V_m$$

$= 4 \cdot 35 V_m$ for nitrogen at liquid nitrogen temperature. $\tag{16.4}$

It is usually assumed that molecules are adsorbed as wholes (discrete entities) on to definite points of attachment on the surface and each point can accomodate only one adsorbed molecule. If adsorption takes place first on high energy-level sites, this must be compensated for by lateral interaction increasing the energy of adsorption of the molecules adsorbed later. Alternatively, if there are no high energy-level sites, the energies of the adsorbed molecules are independent of the presence or absence of other adsorbed molecules on neighbouring points of attachment.

From equation (16.2), at low pressures $(1 + bP)$ tends to unity, bp may be neglected and Henry's law [13, p.104] is obeyed:

$$V = bP V_m.$$

At high pressures bP is large compared with unity and $V = V_m$, therefore the isotherm approaches saturation.

If these requirements break down and Q is a linear function of θ, the following equation develops [102].

$$mRT \ln P/P_0 = 1 - V/V_m \tag{16.5}$$

V is plotted against $\log P$ intersecting the ordinate at $V = V_m$. This equation has been applied to the adsorption of carbon dioxide on to alumina at $22°C$; $(80 < P < 400)$mm Hg and $P_0 = 4500$ mm Hg. V was found to equal V_m when $x = 0.10$, the same relative pressure as found for adsorption of carbon dioxide at $-78°C$ and the same value for V_m [103].

If Q is a logarithmic function of θ the Freundlich equation develops:

$$mRT \ln P/P_0 = \ln \theta. \tag{16.6a}$$

This has been applied to the adsorption of hydrogen on metallic tungsten [102]. Sips [104] considered a combination of the Langmuir and Freundlich isotherm:

$$\theta = \frac{AP^{1/n}}{1 + AP^{1/n}} \tag{16.6b}$$

which has the proper limits for monolayer adsorption but reduces to equation (16.6) at low pressures.

In a later paper, Sips [105] revised his theory and arrived at:

$$\theta = \left(\frac{P}{a + P}\right)^c \quad \text{where } a \text{ is a constant.}$$

The Langmuir equation has also been derived from a thermodynamic (5) and statistical (6) basis.

16.2.2 BET isotherm for multilayer adsorption

The most important step in the study of adsorption came with a derivation by Brunauer, Emmett and Teller [9], for the multilayer adsorption of gases on solid surfaces. This multilayer adsorption theory known generally as the BET theory has occupied a central position in gas adsorption studies and surface-area measurements ever since.

On the assumption that the forces that produce condensation are chiefly responsible for the binding energy of multimolecular adsorption, they proceeded to derive the isotherm equation for multimolecular adsorption by a method that was a generalization of Langmuir's treatment of the unimolecular layer. The generalization of the ideal localized monolayer treatment is effected by assuming that each first layer adsorbed molecule serves as a site for the adsorption of a molecule into the second layer and so on. Hence, the concept of localization prevails at all layers and the forces of mutual interaction are neglected.

$S_0, S_1, S_2, \ldots S_i$ represent the areas covered by $0, 1, 2, \ldots i$ layers of adsorbate molecules. At equilibrium, the rate of condensation on S_0 is equal to the rate of evaporation from S_1 giving:

$$a_1 PS_0 = b_1 S_1 \exp(-Q_1/RT). \tag{16.7}$$

where P = pressure,
      Q_1 = heat of adsorption of the first layer,
      a_1, b_1 = constants.

This is essentially Langmuir's equation, involving the assumption that a_1, b_1, E are independent of the number of adsorbed molecules already present in the first layer.

Similarly, at the first layer in equilibrium:

$$a_2 PS_1 = b_2 S_2 \exp(-Q_2/RT). \tag{16.8}$$

and so on.

In general for equilibrium between the $(i-1)$th and ith layer

$$a_i PS_{i-1} = b_i S_i \exp(-Q_i/RT). \tag{16.9}$$

The total surface area of the solid is given by:

$$A = \sum_{i=0}^{i=\infty} S_i \tag{16.10}$$

and the total volume of the adsorbate by:

$$V = V_0 \sum_{i=0}^{i=\infty} iS_i \tag{16.11}$$

where V_0 = the volume of gas adsorbed on unit surface to form a complete monolayer.

Dividing equation (16.11) by equation (16.10) gives:

$$\frac{V}{A V_0} = \frac{V}{V_m} = \frac{\sum\limits_{i=0}^{i=\infty} iS_i}{\sum\limits_{i=0}^{i=\infty} S_i} \tag{16.12}$$

An essentially similar equation has been arrived at earlier by Baly [10], who could proceed further only by empirical means. Brunauer et al. [9], proceeded to solve this summation by two simplifying assumptions, that:

$$Q_2 = Q_3 = \cdots = Q_i = Q_L \tag{16.13}$$

where Q_L is the heat of liquefaction of the bulk liquid, and:

$$\frac{b_2}{a_2} = \frac{b_3}{a_3} = \cdots = \frac{b_1}{a_1} = g, \text{ a constant.} \tag{16.14}$$

In other words, the evaporation and concentration properties of the molecules in the second and higher adsorbed layers are the same as those of the liquid state. Rewriting:

$$S_1 = yS_0, \text{ where } y = \frac{a_1}{b_1} P \exp(Q_1/RT) \tag{16.15}$$

$$S_2 = S_1 x, \text{ where } x = (P/g) \exp(Q_L/RT) \tag{16.16}$$

$$S_3 = xS_2 = x^2 S_1 \tag{16.17}$$

and in the general case:

$$S_i = xS_{i-1} = x^{i-1} S_i = yx^{i-1} S_0 = cx^i S_0 \tag{16.18}$$

where

$$c = \frac{y}{x} = \frac{a_1 g}{b_1} \exp\left[(Q_1 - Q_L)/RT\right].$$

where $a_1 g/b_1$ approximates to unity.

Substituting equation (16.18) in equation (16.12):

$$\frac{V}{V_m} = \frac{c \sum_{i=1}^{i=\infty} ix^i}{1 + c \sum_{1=1}^{1=\infty} x^i}. \tag{16.19}$$

The summation in the denominator is merely the sum of an infinite geometric progression:

$$\sum_{i=1}^{i=\infty} x^i = \frac{x}{1-x} \tag{16.20}$$

while that in the numerator is:

$$\sum_{i=1}^{i=\infty} ix^i = x \frac{d}{dx} \sum_{i=0}^{i=\infty} x^i = \frac{x}{(1-x)^2}. \tag{16.21}$$

Therefore

$$\frac{V}{V_m} = \frac{cx}{(1-x)(1-x+cx)}. \tag{16.22}$$

On a free surface the amount adsorbed is infinite. Thus at $P = P_0$, the saturation vapour pressure of the adsorbate at the temperature of adsorption, x must be 1, in order to make $V = \infty$. Therefore:

$$\frac{a_2}{b_2} P \exp(Q_L/RT) = 1, \text{ when } x = \frac{P}{P_0}. \tag{16.23}$$

Substituting in equation (16.22):

$$V = \frac{V_m cP}{(P_0 - P)[1 + (c-1)P/P_0]} \tag{16.24}$$

which transforms to:

$$\frac{P}{V(P_0 - P)} = \frac{1}{V_m c} + \frac{c-1}{V_m c} \frac{P}{P_0} \tag{16.25}$$

which is the commonly known form of the BET equation. A plot of $P/V(P_0 - P)$ against P/P_0 should yield a straight line having a slope $(c - 1)/V_m c$ and an intercept $1/V_m c$.

This equation is capable of describing type 1, type 2 and type 3 isotherms, depending upon the constant c. In general it has been found that only type 2 isotherms (i.e. those with high values of c) have well defined 'Knee-bends', which are essential for accurate V_m values. The preference for using nitrogen at liquid nitrogen temperature is due to the fact that at liquid nitrogen temperatures with all solids so far reported, this gas exhibits high c values.

For type 2 isotherms, the BET equation has been found to be valid generally between 0·05 and 0·3 relative pressure, but examples have also been reported where this range has been extended or shortened [21].

The internal consistency of the BET method has been demonstrated by many [2, 13], by their measurements on several solids. The degree of correspondence between the specific surfaces obtained with several adsorbates allows confidence to be placed in the method.

The intercepts obtained are usually very small. Negative values of intercepts in the BET plot have also been reported [22]. MacIver and Emmett [23] find that this can be accounted for by the BET equation not fitting the results at $P/P_0 > 0·2$.

Young and Crowell [13] have listed the molecular areas of many adsorbates. In practice, to get consistency, the molecular areas are corrected on the basis of the area of nitrogen molecules $\sigma = 16·2$ Å^2 for nitrogen at liquid-nitrogen temperature. In extreme cases it has been found that where the area of the molecule depends also on the surface of the solid, calibration for that particular solid may be necessary [24].

When $c \gg 1$ equation (16.25) takes the form:

$$(P_0 - P)V = P_0 V_m \tag{16.25b}$$

Hence, it may be assumed that for high c-values the BET plot passes through the origin and the slope is inversely proportional to the monolayer capacity. Thus only one experimental point is required. This simplification is frequently applied for routine analyses.

16.2.3 The three-parameter BET equation

If , owing to special considerations, the number of layers cannot exceed n, the equation becomes:

$$V = \frac{V_m c x}{(1-x)} \frac{1 - (n+1)x^n + n x^{n+1}}{1 + (c-1)x - c x^{n+1}} \tag{16.26}$$

which is referred to as the n layers BET equation; this applies to adsorption in limited space such as a capillary.

When $n = 1$, it reduces, at all values of c (unlike the simple BET equation which only reduces when $x \ll 1$ and $c \gg 1$) to the Langmuir equation. The n-layer equation also reduces to the same form as the Langmuir equation when $n = 2$ and

$c = 4$ [11], and if $n \gg 3$ it is analytically capable of reproducing the shapes of all five isotherm types provided c lies within certain narrow ranges of values [12], or x lies between 0·05 and 0·35 [98].

Brunauer, Emmett and Teller successfully applied this isotherm equation to a variety of experimental isotherms obtained by themselves and others.

This BET equation for adsorption of gases includes isotherms of types 1, 2 and 3 but not 4 and 5. However, Brunauer *et al.*, derived a new isotherm equation to cover all five types [1].

The BET equation has also been derived by statistical reasonings by several authors [13];

The three-parameter BET equation may be written:

$$\frac{V}{V_m} = \frac{c\phi(n, x)}{1 + c\theta(n, x)}$$

where

$$\phi(n, x) = \frac{x(1-x) - nx^n(1-x)}{(1-x)^2}$$

$$\theta(n, x) = \frac{x(1-x)^2}{(1-x)}.$$

Joyner *et al.* [106] compiled tables of ϕ and θ for increasing x. Using these tables the best straight line is selected for ϕ against θ since the linear form of the equation is:

$$\frac{\phi}{V} = \frac{1}{cV_m} + \frac{\theta}{V_m}. \tag{16.27}$$

This procedure is best carried out with a computer.

Pickett [99] derives a simpler equation for adsorption in a parallel plate pore. This also reduces to the BET equation in the BET region.

16.2.4 Discussion of the BET theory

The adsorption constant c is similar to b in the Langmuir equation. If a plot of the left-hand side of equation (16.22) against x is to be linear, c must be constant. There are no isotherms where c remains constant for all x, the limits for the equation suually being taken as $0·05 < x < 0·35$.

The monolayer capacity of an isotherm occurs at the so-called point B on the V, P isotherm where the slope of the isotherm changes at the completion of the monolayer. This is normally situated between x equal to 0·05 and 0·15. At relative pressures above about 0·35 the BET equation predicts adsorption greater than observed.

Cassell [14, 15] showed, using Gibb's adsorption isotherm, that the surface tension of the adsorbed film at $P = P_0$ is negative, arising from the total disregard of the interaction forces. Since the BET model assumes the existence of localized adsorption at all layers, the molecules being located on top of one another, and since the adsorption can take place in the nth layer before the $(n-1)$th layer is filled, the adsorbed phase is built up not as a series of continuous layers, but as a random system

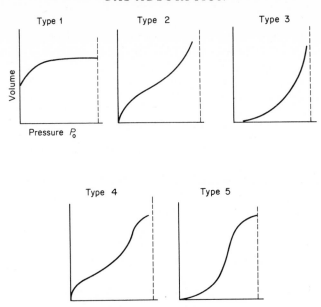

Fig. 16.1. Types of adsorption isotherms (volume adsorbed against pressure).

of vertical molecular columns. Halsey [16] has pointed out that the combinational entropy term associated with these random molecular piles is responsible for the stability of the BET adsorbed layers at pressures below the saturation vapour pressure. This large entropy term is the cause of too large adsorptions observed when $P/P_0 > 0.35$.

Gregg and Jacobs [17] doubted the validity of the assumption that the adsorbed phase is liquid-like, and found that the integration constants of the Clausius-Clapeyron equation as applied to adsorption and vapour pressure do not show the interrelationship demanded by BET theory. They conclude that any constant can be used in the place of P_0 and that the correspondence between the adsorbed and the liquid phase is a loose one, arising out of the fact that the same type of forces is involved.

Halsey [18] pointed out that the hypothesis that an isolated adsorbed molecule can adsorb a second molecule on top, yielding the full energy of liquefaction, and that in turn the second molecule can adsorb a third, and so on, is untenable. If the molecules are hexagonally packed, one would be much more likely to find a second-layer molecule adsorbed above the centre of a triangular array of first-layer molecules. Applying this modification, the BET model results in very little second-layer adsorption when the first layer is one-third full and virtually no adsorption in the third layer except at high relative pressures. Values of V_m given by this modified theory, however, do not differ appreciably from that given by the simple BET theory.

16.2.5 Shapes of isotherms

Five shapes of adsorption isotherms are known [1] and are shown in figure 16.1.
Type 1 is associated with systems where adsorption does not proceed beyond a monolayer. All the others involve multilayer formation.

For high c-values, type 2 isotherm occurs, while for c less than 2, type 3 occurs:
Since c approximates to:

$$\exp\left[(E_1 - E_L)/RT\right]$$

type 3 isotherms are characterized by a heat of adsorption equal to or less than the
heat of liquefaction of the pure adsorbates.

Types 4 and 5 are characteristic of multilayer adsorption on highly porous adsorbents, the flattening of the isotherms at the highest pressures being considered to be
due to capillary phenomena. In general, these isotherms are reversible, but in some
porous solids the adsorption and desorption curves form a hysteresis loop. The
hysteresis has been explained [2, 3] as being due to the curvature of the meniscus.
As the pressure of the adsorbate is decreased from the saturation point, the gas
molecules condensed int he capillary cracks of adsorbent do not evaporate as
readily as they would from the bulk liquid, owing to the lowering of the vapour
pressure over the concave meniscus formed by the condensed liquid in the pores.

Although layers at different levels of coverage exist simultaneously, monolayer
completion occurs at the point of inflection of the V, P isotherm. This is known as
point B and this 'knee' becomes more pronounced as c increases.

16.2.6 Modification of the BET equation

Several modifications have been derived to extend the scope of the BET equation.
Hüttig [19, 20] derived a formulation of the localized multilayer adsorption on a
uniform surface. The difference between the BET and the Hüttig theories is in the
assumption by the latter than the evaporation of the ith layer molecule is entirely
unimpeded by the presence of molecules in the $(i + 1)$th layer, whereas the BET
contention is that $(i + 1)$ th layer molecules are completely effective in preventing
the evaporation of underlying molecules. Hüttig's final equation is:

$$\frac{V}{V_m} = \frac{(cP/P_0)}{(1 + cP/P_0)}(1 + P/P_0) \tag{16.28}$$

i.e.

$$\frac{P}{V}(1 + P/P_0) = \frac{P_0}{cV_m} + \frac{P}{V_m} \tag{16.29}$$

so that a plot of $(P/V)(1 + (P/P_0))$ against P (or more conventionally P/P_0) should
be linear with a slope of $1/V_m$ and intercept of P_0/cV_m. Theory and experiment
agree up to $P/P_0 = 0.7$, but, at higher pressures, Hüttig's equation predicts too low
an amount adsorbed whereas that the BET is larger than the amount observed. For
the majority of gas-solid systems the V_m values calculated from Hüttig's equation
exceed the BET values by 2 to 20% depending upon the value of c [13]. Compromise
equations between Hüttig and BET have also been attempted [13].

16.2.7 The relative method of Harkins and Jura

Harkins and Jura [25] derived an isotherm, by analogy with condensed liquid layers, independent of V_m, hence avoiding any explicit assumption of the value of the molecular area of the adsorbate int he calculation of the surface area.

Condensed monolayers on water are characterized by the fact that they exhibit a linear $PV -$ area relationship.

$$\pi = b - a\sigma \tag{16.30}$$

where π and σ are the pressure and mean area per molecule, while a and b are constants. This linear-pressure relationship persists up to high pressures where the film is several molecules thick. They transformed this equation into an equivalent equation

$$\ln P = B^1 - A^1/V^2 \tag{16.31}$$

$$\ln\left(\frac{P}{P_0}\right) = B - A/V^2 \tag{16.32}$$

where B is a constant of integration and:

$$A = \frac{10^{20} a S^2 M^2}{2RTN} \tag{16.33}$$

where a is a constant, S the surface area of the solid, M the molar-gas volume, R the gas constant, T the absolute temperature and N Avagadro's number.

Equation (16.32) involves only the quantities P and V which are measured directly in the experimental determination of adsorption. Harkins and Jura reported that this simple isotherm was valid over more than twice the pressure range of any other two-constant adsorption isotherms.

A plot of $\log P/P_0$ against $1/V^2$ should give a straight line of slope $- A$. From equation (16.33), it is evident that the surface area of the solid is related to the slope of the line by the relation:

$$S = k\sqrt{A} \tag{16.34}$$

where k is a constant for a given gas at a constant temperature. For convenience, the values of k are so determined that when V is in ml g^{-1} at standard conditions, S is in m^2 g^{-1}.

The constant k had to be determined by calibration, using an independent surface area method. For this reason, the method is usually referred to as HJ relative or HJr method. The original determinations were carried out using anatase whose area had been evaluated from heat of wetting measurements.

Orr and Dallavalle [2] have listed the value of k for some gases (table 16.1):

It was tacitly assumed that k was a function solely of the temperature and the nature of the adsorbate and independent of the nature of the solid. Fundamentally the HJr method is empirical.

If the relation between $\log P/P_0$ and $1/V^2$ is expressed by two or more segments with different slopes then, according to Harkins and Jura, the slope for the

Table 16.1. The value of HJr constants

Gas	Temp (°C)	k
Nitrogen	−195·8	4·06
Argon	−195·8	3·56
Water vapour	25	3·83
n-Butane	0	13·6
n-Heptane	25	16·9
Pentene	20	12·7
Pentene-1	20	12·2

lower-pressure region is always to be taken, since this is the one in which the transition from a monolayer to a polylayer always occurs. The result of more than one straight line is attributed to the existence of more than one condensed phase.

It may be noted that the BET method yields a value for V_m from which the surface area is to be calculated whereas the HJr method yields the surface area directly without giving the value of V_m.

16.2.8 Comparison between BET and HJr methods

Livingstone [26, 27] and Emmett [28] have found that in the linear BET region (∞ form, $P/P_0 = 0.05$ to 0.3) a linear HJr plot is obtained only when $50 < c < 250$. For $c = 10$, 5 or 2, and $P/P_0 < 0.4$, there is no linear relationship, while for $c = 100$ the range of mutual validity of the two equations is limited to the region 0.01 to about 0.13 relative pressure. Smith and Bell [29] extended this inquiry to the n-layers BET equation.

Both the BET and HJr methods are open to criticism in that they involve the arbitrary selection of constants (k and σ) which undoubtedly depend on the nature of the solid surface.

Of the two, the HJr method is relatively inferior for the following reasons [13]:

(i)   The quantity $1/V^2$ is sensitive to slight errors in V.
(ii)   The range of relative pressure over which a linear HJr plot obtains is variable, depending upon the value of c in the BET equation. For each new solid, a large number of experimental points may be needed in order to locate this linear region.
(iii) Some system yield HJr plots with more than one linear section.

However, the adsorption of nitrogen at $-195°C$ on the majority of solids is characterized by c values in the range 50–240, so that the surface areas obtained from the two equations are in agreement.

16.2.9 The t-curve method

It was found by de Boer et al. [84] that the amount of nitrogen adsorbed per unit of surface area of non-porous adsorbents is a unique function of the relative pressure for a large number of inorganic oxides and hydroxides as well as for graphitized carbon blocks. If it is assumed that the adsorbed nitrogen multilayer has the same molar volume as the bulk liquid at the same temperature, then the common isotherm may be represented in the form of a t-curve representing the thickness of the adsorbed layer (in Å) as a function of x.

The common t-curve cannot be used for all substances. When one plots t-curves for a great variety of nonporous substances, and one tries to draw an average line through all the points, this average curve may well show deviations of 10% or more from the experimental points. When the t-value is only used for pore size analysis, these errors are small enough to be neglected. For surface area evaluation, however, t-curves with smaller deviations are required, and these should be common for groups of materials such as halides, metals, graphite. Lecloux [92], however, suggests a dependancy on c rather than on type of material. The statistical thickness of the adsorbed layer is given by:

$$ t = \frac{MV_{sp}}{M_v} \frac{V}{S_w} $$

$$ = 15\cdot47 \frac{V}{S_w} \times 10^4 \text{ Å} \tag{16.35} $$

where M is the molecular weight of the gas,

    V_{sp} is the specific volume of the adsorbate (cm^3 g^{-1}),

    S_w is the BET weight specific surface (m^2 g^{-1}),

    M_v is the molar volume 22 140 cm^3,

    V is the volume of nitrogen adsorbed in cm^3 N.T.P. per gram of adsorbent.

     This is practically independent of the nature of the sample.

The constant, 0·001 547, is the required factor to convert V from cm^3 vapour to cm^3 liquid.

When the area occupied by a nitrogen molecule is taken as 16·27 Å^2, $S_w = 4\cdot37$ V_m m^2 g^{-1} and the statistical thickness can be expressed as:

$$ t = 3\cdot54 \frac{V}{V_m} \text{ Å.} \tag{16.36} $$

Schull [85] and Barrett et al. [86], using different reasoning, arrived at a constant of 4·3 as compared with 3·54.

de Boer's t-curve is shown in figure 16.2. Experimentally, values of V measured as a function of relative pressure are transformed to functions of t. This gives a straight line passing through the origin and the specific surface may be obtained from the slope [87] (equation (16.35)). For the construction of this $V - t$ plot, Lippens et al. [88] published tables of t against x from $t = 3\cdot51$ Å at $x = 0\cdot08$ to $t = 9\cdot96$ Å at $x = 0\cdot76$.

The t-method is based on the BET conception, but yields additional information.

For non-porous solids a graph of V against t yields a straight line (figure 16.3). Deviations from the straight line are interpreted as (a) decrease in accessible surface area due to blocking of macropores, and (b) onset of capillary condensation in intermediate pores. A second linear portion gives the surface area of what is left, that is, the surface area of the wider capillaries or of the outside area of the granules.

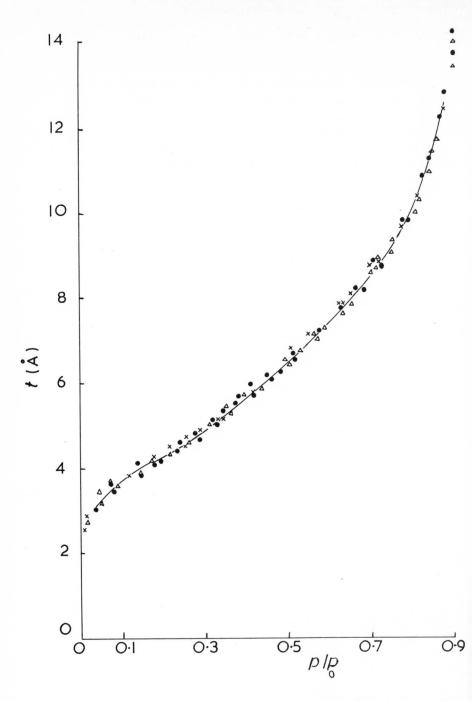

Fig. 16.2. The common *t*-curve of multi-molecular nitorgen adsorption on oxidic and hydroxidic adsorbents [84].

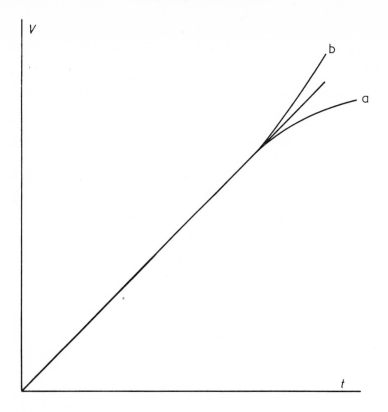

Fig. 16.3. The $V - t$ curve.

There are two equations which describe the experimental t-curve [89], those of Anderson [90]:

$$V = \frac{V_m\, ckx}{(1 - kx)\{1 + (c - 1)\, kx\}} \tag{16.37}$$

with $c = 53$ and $k = 76$, and Harkins and Jura, which may be written as:

$$\log x = 0{\cdot}034 - \frac{13{\cdot}99}{t^2}. \tag{16.38}$$

Brockhoff [91] extended the t-curve to a relative pressure of $0{\cdot}92$.

The surface area obtained using this technique will not be exactly the same as the surface area using the BET equation, since c varies in this equation and an average value is used in the t-curve.

16.2.10 Kiselev's equation

Dubinin classified pores into three groups: micropores, having widths of 15 to 20 Å;

macropores, having widths or radii greater than 200 to 1000 Å; and transition pores, in the intermediate size range. It is generally agreed that the BET equation gives the correct surface area with nitrogen as adsorbate, provided no micropores are present [98, 100].

A criterion as to the correctness of the BET equation is its agreement with other models, such as those derived from the Kelvin equation. This has been applied as follows:

$$RT \ln x = \frac{-2\gamma V_m}{r_k} \tag{16.39}$$

which is the Kelvin equation for pressure lowering over a concave meniscus. If a_H is the number of moles adsorbed at the beginning of the hysteresis loop when the relative pressure is x_H, a small increase of pressure will lead to Δa moles of adsorbate being adsorbed, where:

$$\Delta a = \frac{\Delta V}{V_m}.$$

ΔV is the liquid volume of adsorbate adsorbed. This volume will fill the core of pores of surface area ΔS and core radius r_k. For cylindrical pores:

$$r_k \Delta S = 2\Delta V \tag{16.40}$$

hence

$$\Delta S = -\frac{RT}{\gamma} \ln x \, \Delta a.$$

This may be written:

$$S = \frac{RT}{\gamma} \int_{a_H}^{a_S} \ln x \, da \tag{16.41}$$

where a_S is the number of moles adsorbed at saturation pressure. This is known as Kiselev's equation [101].

Brunauer [98] uses the following form of equation (16.40), which he claims reduces the equation to a model-less equation as opposed to the adoption of cylindrical pores:

$$r_H \Delta S = \Delta V \tag{16.42}$$

where r_H is the hydraulic radius.

16.3 Experimental techniques–factors affecting adsorption

16.3.1 Degassing
A most important preliminary to the accurate measurement of an adsorption isotherm is the preparation of the adsorbent surface. In their usual state all solid surfaces are covered with a physically adsorbed film which must be removed or 'degassed' before any quantitative measurements are made. As the binding energy in

physical adsorption is due to weak van der Waal's forces, this film should be readily removed if the solid is maintained at a high temperature while under vacuum.

The degree of degassing attained is dependent therefore on three variables: pressure, temperature and time. In test and control work, the degassing conditions may be chosen empirically and maintained identical in all estimations since only reproducibility is required. For more accurate measurements, conditions have to be chosen more carefully.

16.3.2 Pressure
Although it is advisable to degas at as low a pressure as possible, due to considerations of time and equipment, the degassing pressure is kept as high as is consistent with accurate results. The pressures usually recommended are easily attainable with a diffusion pump. Emmett [30], for example, recommends 10^{-5} mm Hg, while Joy [31] recommends 10^{-4} mm Hg, since under this condition the rate of degassing is controlled largely by diffusion from the interior of the particle.

For routine analysis, Bugge and Kerlogue [32] found that a vacuum of 10^{-2} to 10^{-3} mm Hg is sufficient and the difference in surface areas so obtained was smaller by less that 3 % from those obtained at pressures of 10^{-5} mm.

16.3.3 Temperature and time
Recommended temperatures and times for degassing vary considerably in the literature, and it is difficult to establish any single degassing condition acceptable for all solids. However, Orr and Dallavalle [2] give an empirical relationship which they suggest is acceptable as a safe limit for ordinary degassing at pressure of less than 5×10^{-6} mm Hg.

$$\theta = 14 \cdot 4 \times 10^{-4} \, t^{-1 \cdot 77} \qquad (16.43)$$

where θ is in hours and t in °C (applicable between 100 and 400°C). This can only be taken as a general safe limit as many others have found that the necessary time is much less [2].

McBain [33] has recommended an adsorption—desorption cycle to reduce the time of degassing. He flushes the surface with adsorbate at the temperature of the forthcoming measurements, followed by heating in vacuum.

16.3.4 Adsorbate gas and surface area
The most commonly used gas for the measurement of reasonably high surface areas is nitrogen at liquid temperature. Since the volumes of the gas adsorbed are high, the consequent changes in the pressure can be measured accurately with a manometer in the constant-volume methods.

However, for powders of low surface areas the fraction of the nitrogen gas in the system that is adsorbed is so low, resulting in negligible pressure changes, that manometric pressure measurements cannot be used. In such cases ethylene at liquid-oxygen temperature [34, 35] and krypton at liquid-nitrogen temperature [36] have been used as the adsorbate gas. Since krypton has a saturation vapour pressure, at this temperature of about 2 mm Hg, the BET range of relative pressure is about 0·1 to about 0·6 mm Hg. Small changes in pressure in this pressure region can be measured accurately by the use of gauges which measure low pressure.

16.4 Experimental techniques – volumetric methods

16.4.1 Principle

A great variety of volumetric apparatus has been described in the literature, the earlier ones of which have been reviewed by Joy [31]. In all the volumetric methods, the principle underlying the determinations is the same. The pressure, volume and the temperature of a quantity of adsorbate is measured and the amount of gas present is calculated. The material is then brought into contact with the adsorbate, and when the constant pressure, volume, temperature conditions show the system to have attained equilibrium, the amount of gas is again calculated. The difference between the amount of gas present initially and finally represents the adsorbate 'lost' from the gas phase to the adsorbed phase. The accurate determination of the amount of gas unadsorbed at equilibrium depends upon a precise knowledge of the 'dead-space' or the space surrounding the adsorbent particles. The dead-space volume is usually determined by expansion measurements using helium, whose adsorption can be assumed to be negligible. Estimation of the quantity of unadsorbed gas is often complicated by the fact that part of the dead-space is at room temperature and part at the temperature of the adsorbent.

Since the amount adsorbed represents the difference between the amount admitted to the dead-space and the amount remaining in the dead-space at equilibrium, it can only be evaluated with confidence if these two quantities are of unlike magnitude. To achieve this , the apparatus is so designed as to minimize the dead-space volume. In practice, it is convenient to fix the volume and temperature and measure the changes in pressure.

Regardless of the particular design, the basic apparatus must provide means for removing gases and vapours which all materials pick up when exposed to the atmosphere. The apparatus must also provide means for permitting readsorption of known quantities of the gas on to the material. It should also have evacuating systems, gauges to measure the vacuum, a gas storage part, and the analytical part.

16.4.2 Volumetric apparatus for high surface areas

Conventional types of nitrogen adsorption apparatus invariably follow the assembly originally described by Emmett [37], shown in figure 16.4. Adsorbate gas is taken into the burette and its pressure measured on the manometer. The stopcock between the sample and the burette is then opened and the new pressure, after allowing time for the equilibrium to be established, is read on the manometer. The volume of the gas admitted to the sample bulb is proportional to the difference in the pressures before and after opening the stopcock. This later pressure is also the equilibrium adsorption pressure. The volume adsorbed is equal to the volume admitted less the volume of gas required to fill the dead-space in the sample bulb and the burette connections. To obtain more adsorption points, the mercury level is raised

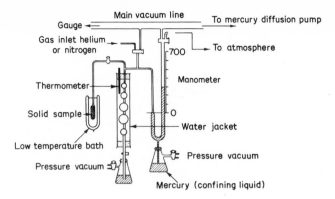

Fig. 16.4. Emmett's apparatus for surface-area determination by gas adsorption.

to the next volume mark and a new pressure established. Helium is used to calibrate the dead-space. In all adsorption calculations a correction for the non-ideal behaviour of nitrogen at liquid nitrogen temperature is included. In a method like this, the total volume admitted is found by summing the separate doses.

The main disadvantage of the original design is that the sample tube is not connected directly to the vacuum line and hence any powder flying from the tube is likely to contaminate the whole apparatus. Elaborations of the same apparatus have also been described [39—41]. Vance and Pattison [42] have also described a similar apparatus in detail.

A number of refinements have been suggested either to increase the accuracy or reduce the tedium of measurements. For example, Vance and Pattison [42] used a magic-eye electrical zero-point device for the manometer. Harkins and Jura [43] used a narrow-bore mercury cut-off to serve as a null-point instrument, the absolute pressure being measured on a wide-bore manometer. Several authors have shown [45, 46] how the functions of a manometer and burette can be combined in a single device. Cathetometers have also been used to improve the accuracy [43].

Bugge and Kerlogue [32] simplified the apparatus by using only one bulb instead of several, but with a loss of versatility. They also gave a simplified method of calculation to eliminate the dead-space determination. It appears that this procedure is satisfactory only when the produce $V_m c$ is large enough to cause the BET plot to pass through the origin [31]. Several authors have tried to use oxygen or nitrogen thermometers for the accurate measurements of the saturation vapour pressure of nitrogen [32, 42]. Loebenstein and Deitz [46] developed an apparatus not requiring a vacuum system by adsorbing nitrogen from a mixture of nitrogen and helium. They degassed the sample in a current of helium.

16.4.3 Volumetric apparatus for low surface areas

For the measurement of low surface areas, adsorptions are carried out at very low pressures readily measured by means of low-pressure measuring techniques. Krypton gas with a saturated vapour pressure of about 2 mm Hg and ethylene gas with 0·1 mm Hg saturated vapour pressure at liquid air temperatures lend themselves readily for low-pressure measurement.

Wooten and Brown [34] used this low-pressure method to measure the surface areas of oxide-coated cathodes, about 100 cm^2, by adsorption of ethylene and butane at $-183°C$ and $-116°C$ respectively. Because of the very low pressures involved in the technique, no leaks can be tolerated in the system. The apparatus was, therefore, made entirely of glass and used mercury cut-offs instead of stopcocks. The sample chamber was welded on to the system to eliminate any possibility of leaks due to a ground glassjoint. A dry-ice trap between the sample and the mercury cut-offs served to prevent mercury vapour from reaching the sample. Equilibrium pressure measurements were made with a highly sensitive McLeod gauge. Lister and McDonald [35] have described in detail the construction and calibration of low-temperature ethylene adsorption apparatus.

In measurements of such low pressures, two obvious risks must be considered, namely, the desorption of water and other vapours from the glass walls of the apparatus and thermal transpiration [13]. By heating the entire system for a short while or by permanently keeping the system under vacuum, most of the adsorbed vapours from the glass walls should be removed. Otherwise, the slowly desorbing vapours will increase the pressure in the system during adsorption measurements leading to erroneous results.

When low-pressure measurements are made on a gauge held at a different temperature from that part of the apparatus where the adsorption takes place, correction for thermal molecular flow should be considered. To obtain accurate results, Lister and MacDonald [35] prepared and used correction data.

In most low-pressure measurements, the correction for unadsorbed gas is very small, even negligible, so that no effort need be made to minimize the volume of the dead-space.

Krypton at liquid-air temperatures has a vapour pressure of about 2 mm Hg, intermediate between those of ethane and nitrogen. Krypton is thus suited for the measurements of a much smaller surface area than is possible with nitrogen, adsorption of ethane or ethylene. In addition, the pressures encountered in krypton adsorption at the temperature of liquid nitrogen are low enough for the deviations from perfect gas relations to be neglected.

The adsorption equipments are similar to those already described, the only difference being the pressure range of the gauge. Several types of apparatus have been described in the literature [47–49].

Krypton has the additional advantage that the pressure within the range related to krypton adsorption can be detected precisely with thermisters, hence avoiding the use of McLeod gauges. Rosenberg [50], Dollimore [51], Leipziger and Altamari [52] have used thermister gauges successfully. Leipziger [52] has discussed the design, construction and precision of thermisters.

Aylmore and Jepson [80] used a novel method of krypton adsorption. They used labelled krypton (Kr^{85}) as adsorbate and from the measurement of the activity they calculated pressures.

Among the various gases used for the adsorption measurements on low surface areas, krypton at liquid nitrogen temperature appears to be the popular choice.

16.5 Experimental techniques – gravimetric methods

16.5.1 Principle

The gravimetric techniques have the great advantage over the volumetric methods in that the volume of the adsorption system is quite immaterial and the amount of gas adsorbed is observed directly by measuring the increase in the weight of the solid sample upon exposure to a gas or vapour. The tedious volume calibration and dead-space determinations are thus eliminated.

The main disadvantages of the method are:

  (i)   The apparatus is much less robust and correspondingly more difficult to construct and maintain than volumetric apparatus.

 (ii)   The apparatus has to be calibrated by placing known weights in the adsorbent-pan, and the method is hence subject to the errors always attached to determination which are dependent on the constancy of calibrations of easily fatigued and strained mechanical systems.

(iii)   Buoyancy corrections have to be made.

16.5.2 Single-spring balances

McBain and Bakr [33] introduced a sorption balance, the essential features of which are a quartz helical spring supporting a small gold or platinum bucket in which the sample is placed. The spring is calibrated by adding small known weights to the bucket and measuring the increase in length of the spring with a reading microscope. These calibrations must be done over the entire range of temperatures at which adsorption measurements are made. The liquid adsorbate, free from dissolved gases, is sealed in a small glass bulb and placed with a magnetic hammer in a glass or quartz envelope ('balance case'). The balance is heated in vacuum for outgassing. Finally the case is sealed off, the lower end cooled and the bulb broken. Adsorption measurements are carried out with the lower end in one thermostat bath to control the temperature of the liquid and the upper end in another to control that of the solid. The equilibrium pressure can be calculated from the temperature of the liquid, provided vapour pressure data are available. The amount adsorbed is proportional to the spring extension and the correction for buoyancy is significant at higher pressures.

This type of balance is restricted in use to condensible adsorbates and is especially useful at higher pressures. Morris and Maass [53], Dunn and Pomeroy [54], McBain and Sessions [55, 56] have used a similar apparatus.

Several others have used similar apparatus with improvements and modifications to suit their applications. Boyd and Livingston [57] used mercury cut-offs in the vapour-handling and compressing system. The pressure was controlled by compressing the gas in the dosing bulb, and it was read on a mercury manometer or a McLeod gauge depending upon the range. Seborg, Simmons and Baird [58] dried the sample in a current of dry air, and obtained the adsorption points subsequently by passing the air through saturators filled with solutions of known vapour pressure. Dubinin and Timofeev [59] used a magnetically-operated greaseless doser for the precise admission of adsorbate increments. Automatic recording techniques have also been attempted [60].

16.5.3 Multiple – spring balances

Gravimetric methods have the additional advantage that several determinations can be carried out simultaneously by connecting several balance cases to the same gas or vapour manifold and observing the individual spring extensions.

Seborg and Stamm [61] connected five or six simple spring units in series. Pidgeon and Maass [62], Mulligan et al. [63], Stamm and Woodruff [64] have all described similar multiple-spring balances. Mulligan et al. connected as many as fifteen springs to the same apparatus.

16.5.4 Beam balances

Beam-type vacuum balances have greater sensitivity than the helical-spring balances and also the troublesome buoyancy correction at higher pressures is eliminated, at least partially if not completely.

Beam balances can be of either high sensitivity at very low total loads or of medium sensitivity at large total loads, which are in contrast to the normal short-spring balances which have a medium sensitivity at low total loads.

The majority of the high sensitivity low-load balances are based on those originally designed by Barrett, Birnie and Cohen [65] and by Gulbransen [66]. Barrett et al. used a glass beam 40 cm long supported on a tungsten torsion wire and enclosed the whole assembly in a tubular glass casing connected to the vapour and vacuum manifolds. Calibration was effected by moving a small soft-iron rider along the beam by means of a magnet outside the case. Gulbransen's balance was constructed from glass rod, quartz fibres and metal wires on the same principles as an ordinary chemical balance.

Rhodin's microbalance [67–69] is essentially a modification of these, in which some stability is sacrificed for increased sensitivity by the use of thinner and lighter wires. This balance has been adopted by Bowers and Long [70] for adsorption at liquid-helium temperatures. Rhodin's balance was made as symmetrical as possible, in order to eliminate buoyancy corrections and to minimize thermal eddy currents. The adsorbent and counter weights were matched to within 10^{-5} g and immersed to the same depth in identical thermostatic baths and the outgassing was done at 400°C in a vacuum of 10^{-7} mm. With this balance, it was possible to observe a vertical displacement of 10 mm to better than 0·01 mm and with loads up to 1 g, it was possible to observe weight changes of 10^{-7} g ± 20 % in a reproducible manner.

Beam balances have also been operated as null-point instruments. The beam is acted upon by a solenoid outside the balance housing, the current through the solenoid being adjusted to restore the beam to its horizontal position. One such

balance by Gregg [71] uses two concentric solenoids, the inner one suspended
from the beam and the outer one fixed to the envelope. The original balance had a
sensitivity of 0·3 mg, the range of load being as high as 10 to 20 mg. In an automatic
version of this instrument described by Gregg and Wintle [72] , a photoelectrically-
operated relay adjusts a potentiometer slide-wire contact which is connected to the
solenoids on the balance.

Although so many different types of gravimetric apparatus have been reported,
they have not become popular due to their delicate nature and the difficulty of
accurately compensating for buoyancy effects.

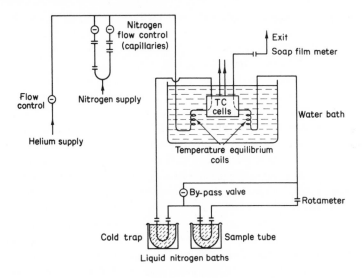

Fig. 16.5. Schematic diagram of Nelsen and Eggertsen's apparatus.

16.6 Continuous-flow gas-chromatographic methods

In recent years, a continuous-flow method, based on the gas-chromatographic technique, has been introduced for the measurement of surface area of fine powders by
gas adsorption. A scheme was first proposed by Loebenstein and Deitz [46] for
reducing the vacuum requirements by using a flowing mixture of the adsorbate and
an inert gas, such as helium. in order to obtain the low adsorbate gas pressure required.

The method, a modification of gas-adsorption chromatography in which the
column packing is the sample itself and the mobile gas phase is a mixture of a
suitable adsorbate and an inert gas, was developed by Nelsen and Eggertsen [73].
They used nitrogen as the adsorbate and helium as the carrier gas in the following
manner.

A known mixture of nitrogen and helium is passed through the sample and then
through a thermal conductivity cell connected to a recording potentiometer. When
the sample is cooled in liquid nitrogen, the sample adsorbs the nitrogen from the

mobile phase; this is indicated by a peak on the recorder chart, and after equilibrium is established, the recorder pen resumes its original position. Removing the coolant gives a desorption peak equal in area and in the opposite direction to the adsorption peak and either peak may be used to measure the nitrogen adsorbed.

Calibration for such a system may be either absolute (by injecting a known amount of nitrogen into the mobile phase at the point normally occupied by the sample and obtaining a factor for the amount of nitrogen per unit peak area on the resulting recorded curve), or by comparison with a sample of known surface area.

A schematic diagram of their apparatus is shown in figure 16.5. Nitrogen flow control was achieved by two capillary tubes in parallel, 0·25 mm inner diameter and 150 and 300 mm long. The capillaries were used independently or together to give three nitrogen flow-rates in the range of 5–20 ml min^{-1} with a pressure head of 2 lb in^{-2} g. The helium flow was controlled by needle valves. The flow measurements were made by rotameter and soap-film meter.

The mobile phase was first passed through the reference arm of the thermal conductivity cell, on to the sample and then, again, to the thermal conductivity cell, which was immersed in a temperature-controlled bath.

Nelsen and Eggertsen measured adsorption at three flow rates, i.e. at three partial pressures. The sample was outgassed at desired temperature (up to 500°C), while being purged with He at 20 ml min^{-1} for 1 h. Nitrogen relative pressures in the range of 0·05–0·3 and a total nitrogen and helium flow of 50 ml min^{-1} were used. The desorption peaks were used for measurement because they were relatively free from tailing effects.

Calculation is essentially the same as for the pressure-volume method but is much simpler since no free-space corrections are needed. The authors assumed complete linearity of the thermal conductivity cell over the concentration range employed. They analysed samples ranging in surface area from 3 to 450 m^{2}g^{-1} and the results obtained on continuous flow and pressure volume methods were in good agreement.

The main advantages of the continuous-flow method over the conventional BET method are:

   (i)   elimination of fragile and complicated glassware;
  (ii)   elimination of a high vacuum system;
 (iii)   permanent records obtained automatically;
 (iv)   speed and simplicity;
  (v)   elimination of dead-space correction.

Ellis, Forest and Howe [74] made some modification and improvements to the original technique for their specific applications. The schematic diagram of their apparatus is shown in figure 16.6. All flow controls were done by needle valves and all flow measurements were made by rotameters. They used a helium flow rate of 50 ml min^{-1} and a nitrogen flow rate of 3, 5 or 10 ml min^{-1}.

By taking more care (when chilling the sample to avoid shock effects in the gas stream),tthey could extend the method to surface areas in the region of 0·01 m^{2}g^{-1}. They obtained good linearity in the BET plot, even with surface areas as low as 0·02 m^{2}g^{-1}. They analysed samples with surface areas of 14·2 to 0·005 m^{2}g^{-1}.

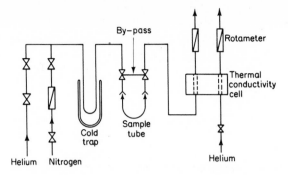

Fig. 16.6. Schematic diagram of Ellis, Forrest and Howe's apparatus.

Below $0.01 \, m^2 g^{-1}$ conventional adsorption methods with nitrogen are not practical and hence no results using the PVT methods were given by them. Above that range agreement between the continuous flow and PVT methods was good, but in their results the surface-area value by the new method was slightly higher than that given by the PVT method.

Ellis *et al.* [74] also developed a shortened method using only one flow rate, i.e. a single-point method. Since, usually, the BET intercept is very small, the intercept term can be ignored and $S_w \, \alpha \, V(P_0 - P)/P$. For constant P values, i.e. N_2/He flow-rate ratio constant in the flow stream, $S_w \, \alpha \, V$. Since $V \alpha$ area of recorder chart, a plot of S_w against area for fixed sample weight and fixed N_2/He ratio should be linear. They analysed a number of samples (300 mg each) and determined the adsorption peak areas for 10 ml min^{-1} flow of nitrogen and 50 ml min^{-1} helium and obtained a linear graph from which the surface areas of subsequent samples were obtained. Results by this method were also comparable to those obtained by the normal BET method based on PVT measurements. This method was especially good compared with multipoint methods for routine measurements, as one sample can be analysed per hour.

Atkins [75] developed a precision instrument for use in the carbon black industry. For precision measurements he stated that it is necessary to consider the effect of changes in ambient temperature, barometric pressure, liquid-nitrogen temperature and nitrogen concentration in the gas mixture. Correction for the non-linearity of the katharometer was also necessary, and was achieved either by adjusting the sample size so that the desorption and calibration peaks were of the same height, or by using a correction factor; this was determined as a function of relative peak areas, i.e. desorption peak area divided by the calibration peak area. Atkins used heat exchanger coils in the detector circuit in addition to the temperature control of the detector. Two different premixed gases were connected to the apparatus so that either of them could be used or both together. The apparatus also had special calibration valves and calibration loops to select the volume of gas nearest to the desorption volume for calibration so that similarly shaped calibration peaks and heights of similar magnitude were obtained. He has also tabulated the variables like

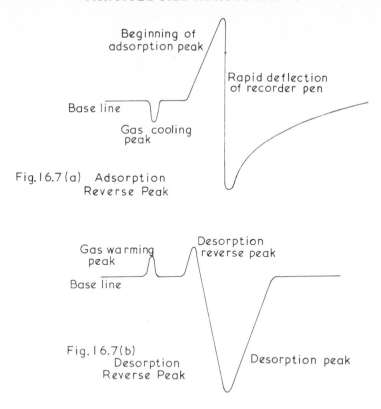

Beginning of
adsorption peak

Rapid deflection
of recorder pen

Base line

Gas cooling
peak

Fig. 16.7 (a)   Adsorption
Reverse Peak

Gas warming
peak

Desorption
reverse peak

Base line

Fig. 16.7 (b)
Desorption
Reverse Peak

Desorption peak

Fig. 16.7. Shape of peaks obtained with Nelsen and Eggertsen-type equipment with
powder of low surface area.

percentage nitrogen in the mixture, calibration loop temperature, barometric and
saturated vapour pressure of the nitrogen and the corresponding percentage changes
in calculated surface area due to their variation and has discussed the errors due to
the non-linearity of the katharometer.

Haley [76] extended the continuous-flow measurement to include the size distribution in pores in the 10 to 300 Å radius range. He used 10 % nitrogen in helium
(as mobile phase) at various pressures up to 150 lb in^{-2}a, causing the nitrogen
partial pressure to reach its liquefaction point, consequently varying the nitrogen
relative pressure in the sample tube in the range 0·16 to 1. Nitrogen adsorbed or
desorbed, by increasing or decreasing the pressure in the tube, was measured continuously. He also measured surface areas and obtained a variation of approximately
± 2·5 % in the range of 40 to 1250 m^{2}g^{-1}.

Since helium is extremely expensive, it may be replaced by other gases which are
not adsorbed under the experimental conditions, e.g. hydrogen. Whitehead [77]
used hydrogen as a carrier gas at a flow rate of 50 ml min^{-1} and found it was very
satisfactory.

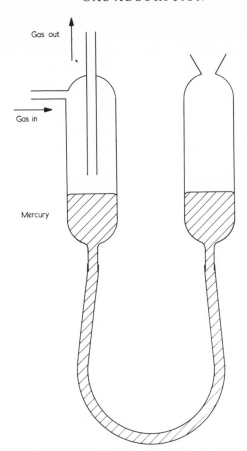

Gas out

Gas in

Mercury

Fig. 16.8. The expansion chamber.

Several problems arise when the Nelsen and Eggertsen-type apparatus is used for measuring surface areas less than $500 \text{ cm}^2\text{g}^{-1}$, the adsorption and desorption peaks having the shapes shown in figure 16.7.

During adsorption a peak is produced when the sample tube is immersed in liquid nitrogen. This immersion causes a contraction of the gas inside the sample tube and a reduction in the gas flow through the katharometer; the thermistor on the measurement side warms up causing a change in its resistance and a peak on the recorder chart. The adsorption peak results from a cooling of the thermistor due to removal of nitrogen from the stream which causes an increase in the thermal conductivity of the gas mixture.

A reverse peak occurs midway through the adsorption. During desorption a gas-warming peak occurs and, immediately prior to desorption, a desorption-reverse peak. Since the desorption peak is used for measurement purposes, effort has been

mainly directed at finding an explanation for the desorption reverse peak and correcting for it.

Lovell [81] considered that the reverse peak on desorption was due to transverse
thermal diffusion. When the sample tube is removed from the coolant, pre-cooling
of the gas stream in the inlet section quickly ceases and gas enters the sample-catch-
ing section at very nearly room temperature. Since the sample is still cold, partial
separation of the gases takes place due to transverse thermal diffusion, nitrogen
moving to the walls of the container and helium to the centre. Gas flow is more
rapid at the centre and helium-rich gas is carried to the katharometer, giving rise to
a thermistor cooling peak. Immediately afterwards, when the temperature of the
sample tube has risen considerably, the separated nitrogen diffuses into the gas
stream and produces a peak in the opposite direction and necessarily of the same
area. It can be seen that, when a sample is present in the container, the area of the
desorption peak will be increased by the area of the reverse peak. Thus, the true
area of the desorption trace may be obtained by subtracting the area of the reverse
peak from that of the observed peak.

Lovell's experimental refinement was to allow the desorbed gases to expand into
a vessel whose volume could be adjusted by altering the amount of mercury in it
(figure 16.8).

As the gas expands, the mercury level is forced down and the pressure is equalized
by lowering the mercury level in a second container. When the desorption and
expansion process is complete and enough time has elapsed for mixing to take place,
the adsorbed gas is swept through the thermal-conductivity cell and the area of the
desorption peak measured with no interference from a reverse peak.

16.6.1 Commercially available continuous-flow-type apparatus

Perkin-Elmer Ltd. manufacture a continuous-flow apparatus called the Perkin Elmer
shell sorptometer, model 212C. The manufacturers claim that surface areas can be
determined from approximately 0·1 to 1000 $m^2 g^{-1}$. A typical three-point surface-
area determination can be carried out in 20 to 30 min using pre-mixed gases. Degassing is carried out by heating samples with a gas purge [96].

Atkins [75], using the above apparatus, obtained a relative standard deviation,
varying from 1·76 % to 2·99 % according to sample material, with ten single-point
determinations, each with a new sample. With his own equipment, the comparable
deviation varied from 0·25 % to 1·35 %.

Similar instruments for one-point or multipoint evaluations are available from
Quantachrome. Calibration is accomplished with precision gas syringes to inject
known amounts of adsorbate into the gas flow. These instruments are claimed to be
particularly useful for low surface-area powders.

Although elaborate precautions and the use of more complicated apparatus
improved the precision of the technique, the accuracy of the commercial equipment
should suffice for most normal applications.

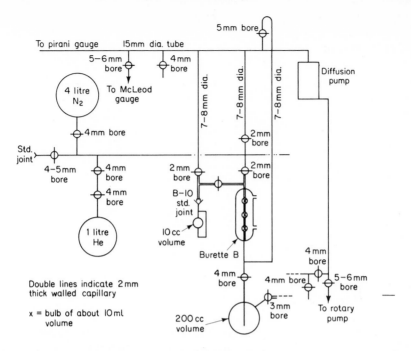

Fig. 16.9. Gas adsorption apparatus, schematic diagram.

16.7 Standard volumetric gas-adsorption apparatus

Nitrogen gas-adsorption apparatus is fully described in B.S.4359:1969, Part 1. The standard apparatus is rather time-consuming in operation and several commercial versions are available. With these equipments, operator involvement and operating time are reduced, usually with a reduction in accuracy and versatility, and it is recommended that these should always be calibrated against the standard equipment.

In the apparatus illustrated (figure 16.9), the main vacuum line consists of a 15-mm bore glass tube to which are attached the adsorption unit, a McLeod gauge and a Pirani gauge. A 4 l flask containing nitrogen and a 1 l flask containing helium are connected to a secondary line which is joined to a gas burette, a sample tube and a mercury manometer. The gas burette consists of three carefully calibrated bulbs enclosed in a water jacket. The volume in the burette can be adjusted by raising the level of the mercury to any one of three calibration marks and the pressure may be read on the manometer. The sample tube is connected to the gas burette through a ground-glass joint. The glass tube connection between the water-jacketed burette and the liquid-nitrogen thermostated sample tube is made of a short length of 2 mm capillary to keep the volume of dead-space not thermostated to a minimum. The sample tube, of about 10 ml volume, is specially designed to prevent loss of powder by 'spitting' during degassing (figure 16.10).

A third vacuum line controls the vacuum in the mercury reservoirs of the gas burettes and the McLeod gauge which may also be opened to the atmosphere to

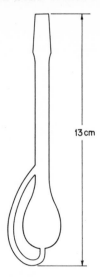

13 cm

Fig. 16.10. The sample tube for the static BET method.

raise or lower the level of the mercury. The entire system is evacuated by a mercury diffusion pump backed by a rotary pump capable of an ultimate vacuum of 10^{-6} mm Hg. A small electrical furnace is used to heat the sample tube while the sample is degassed.

16.7.1 Worked example
The predetermined cumulative volumes of the gas burettes by filling with mercury and weighing are:

$$V_1 = 9 \cdot 19 \text{ ml}; \quad V_2 = 17 \cdot 56 \text{ ml}; \quad V_3 = 26 \cdot 85 \text{ ml}.$$

The sample is weighed in the sample tube and fitted to the apparatus, and the system is then evacuated. The heating furnace is then placed round the sample tube and degassing proceeds under vacuum. The tube is then immersed in liquid nitrogen and helium is drawn into the burette, and the pressure noted. The helium is then allowed to expand into the sample tube and the pressure again noted. The volume of gas in the burette at S.T.P. is calculated as follows, using the experimental data presented in table 16.2:

$$V_0 = \frac{P}{P_0} \frac{T_0}{T} V = \frac{163 \cdot 5}{760} \frac{273}{285} \, 9 \cdot 19 = 1 \cdot 892 \text{ ml}.$$

After expansion: ·

$$V_0 = \frac{46 \cdot 0}{760} \frac{273}{285} \, 9 \cdot 19 = 0 \cdot 533 \text{ ml}.$$

Thus, the sample tube contains $(1 \cdot 892 - 0 \cdot 533)$ ml of gas under a pressure of 46·0 mm Hg.

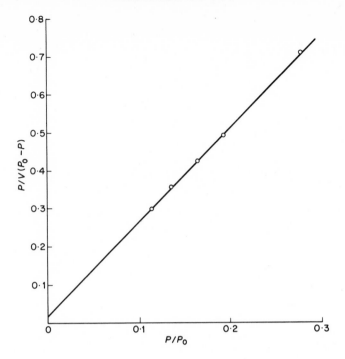

Fig. 16.11. BET plot.

$$\text{The free-space factor} = \frac{1 \cdot 892 - 0 \cdot 533}{46 \cdot 0} \text{ ml mm}^{-1} \text{ pressure}$$

$$= 0 \cdot 029\ 56 \text{ ml mm}^{-1}.$$

After the free-space factor determination the helium is pumped out of the system and nitrogen admitted into the burette. Time is allowed for the gas to reach equilibrium temperature and the pressure is then noted. The gas is then admitted to the sample tube and the pressure again noted. All volumes are reduced to S.T.P.

(i) Volume of nitrogen admitted $= \dfrac{142 \cdot 5}{760} \cdot \dfrac{273}{285} \cdot 26 \cdot 85 = 4 \cdot 830$ ml.

Volume remaining in burette after expansion =

$\dfrac{27 \cdot 0}{760} \cdot \dfrac{273}{285} \cdot 9 \cdot 19$ $= 0 \cdot 312$ ml

Volume in free space $= 0 \cdot 02956 \times 27 \cdot 0$ $= 0 \cdot 789$ ml

Volume adsorbed $4 \cdot 830 - (0 \cdot 312 + 0 \cdot 798)$ $= 3 \cdot 720$ ml.

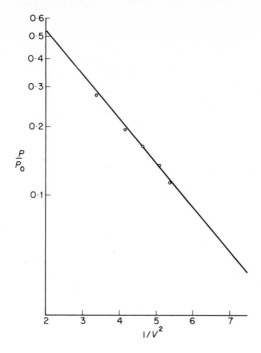

Fig. 16.12. HJr plot.

(ii)	More nitrogen admitted to the burette	= 5·380 ml
	Nitrogen already in the sample tube	= 4·518 ml
	Total nitrogen in the system	= 9·898 ml.

The calculations are carried out cumulatively in steps in the same manner. The observed and calculated data are given in table 16.2.

A BET plot of $P/V(P_0 - P)$ against P/P_0 gives a value of V_m from which the surface is determined from the equation:

$$S_w = 4 \cdot 35\, V_m \, \text{m}^2 \, \text{g}^{-1}.$$

A Harkins and Jura plot of P/P_0 against $1/V^2$ on semi-log paper has a negative slope A from which the surface area is determined using:

$$S_w = 4 \cdot 06\, A \, \text{m}^2 \, \text{g}^{-1}$$

16.8 Commercially available volumetric and gravimetric-type apparatus

There is available a wide range of commercial equipment. These generally offer rapid surface-area evaluation with some loss of accuracy. Glass equipment can be produced cheaply and is capable of providing results at a similar rate to commercial equipment (6 analyses per day), but skilled, careful operators are required and an analysis rate of 1 or 2 per day is more usual.

Table 16.2. Observed and calculated data for a sample

Sample: Cement, Hoogovern cement (cerny) **Klasse – B** *Weight:* 10·2028 gm *Degassing:* 300°C, 3 h *Temperature of the water jacket:* 12°C *Burette used:* B

Sample	Gas	Burette volume	Pressure mm	Volume of the gas in the burette ml	Volume of the gas in the sample tube ml	Volume of the gas in the free space ml	Volume o the total gas ml	V_{ad}	V_{ad}/s
Off	He	1	163·5	1·892		1·359	Free space factor		
On	He	1	46·0	0·533		1·359	$\dfrac{1\cdot359}{46} = 0.02956\ \dfrac{ml}{mm}$		
Off	N$_2$	3	142·5	4·830			4·830		
On	N$_2$	1	27·0	0·312	4·518				
Off	N$_2$	3	159·0	5·380			9·898		
On	N$_2$	3	86·5	2·930	6·968	2·575		4·393	0·431
On	N$_2$	2	103·5	2·290	7·608	3·090		4·518	0·443
On	N$_2$	1	125·0	1·448	8·450	3·722		4·728	0·464
Off	N$_2$	3	174·5	5·920			14·370		
On	N$_2$	3	147·0	4·980	9·390	4·390		5·000	0·490
On	N$_2$	1	211·5	2·445	11·925	6·350		5·575	0·546

BET and HJr data are given in table 16.3. BET and HJr plots are shown in figures 16.11 nad 16.12 respectively.

Table 16.3. BET and HJr data

P	$V\mathrm{ml\,g^{-1}}$	P/P_0	$P/V(P_0 - P)$	$1/V^2 p$ per g
86·5	0·431	0·114	0·298	5·38
103·5	0·443	0·136	0·356	5·09
125·0	0·464	0·165	0·424	4·63
137·0	0·490	0·489	0·194	4·15
211·5	0·546	0·278	0·706	3·36

BET plot

Slope = 2·47
Intercept = 0·02
$1/V_m$ = 2·49
V_m = 0·405 ml
S_w = 1·76 m² g⁻¹

HJr plot

Slope = 0·196
S_w = 1·79 m² g⁻¹

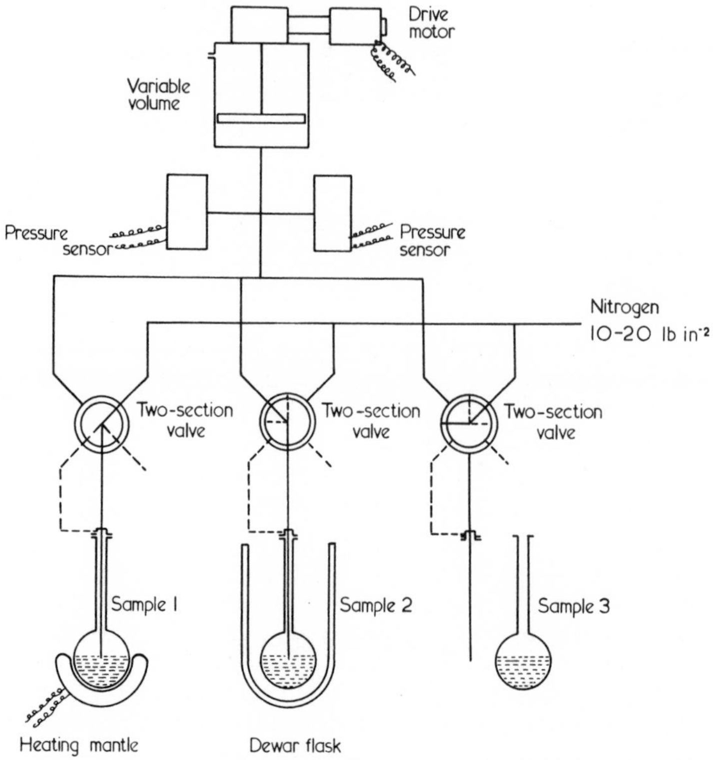

Fig. 16.13. Schematic diagram of model 2200.

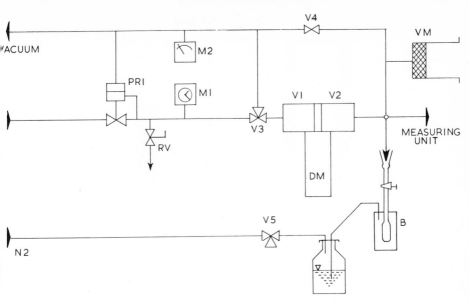

Fig. 16.14. Schematic diagram of Carlo Erba sorptomatic.

Micromeritics, for example, manufacture several instruments, one of the simplest of which is the model 2200 (figure 16.13). This is designed for single-point BET, using fixed pressures and variable volume.

A known volume of gas is introduced into the sample tube at a fixed higher pressure. The bulb is then immersed in liquid nitrogen and the pressure drops to a second fixed point. The volume reading is indicative of amount of gas adsorbed. An empirical correction is added to compensate for using the origin for the BET line instead of determining an intercept.

The technique used by the Carlo Erba Sorptomatic (figure 16.14) is as follows. A special metering pump allows the injection into a previously outgassed cuvette kept at constant temperature of known and reproducible volumes of gas $V1$, $V2$, $V3$ etc. the cuvette pressure will reach pressures P, $2P$, $3P$, etc. accordingly. The maximum pressure reachable by the system will be equal to the saturation pressure (gas in equilibrium with the liquid phase). By repeating the test with a cuvette containing a solid adsorbent, after each injection a part of the gas introduced will be adsorbed and the equilibrium pressure will result $P'P$, $2P'2P$, $3P'3P$. Knowing the volumes of the injected gas, it is possible to calculate the volumes of gas adsorbed at the various equilibrium pressures and then plot the adsorption isotherm.

Numinco market the Orr surface-area pore-volume analyser with a claimed precision of 1 % surfaces from 0·1 to 1000 + $m^2 g^{-1}$ using the conventional BET volumetric method. A less accurate, but simpler and more versatile, apparatus is available as the Numinco surface-area and density apparatus with which density may be determined to better than 1 % and surface may be determined by multiple-point and single-point BET, and by a single-point flow method due to Innes [78].

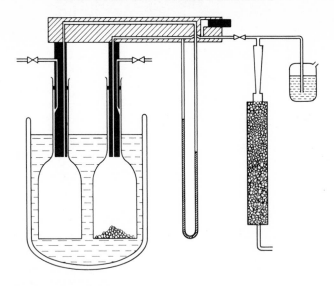

Fig. 16.15. The Ströhline areameter.

The Ströhline areameter (figure 16.15) consists of an adsorption vessel with the sample and a reference vessel on either side of a mercury manometer [79, 83]. Degassing is carried out by purging with dry measuring gas with the sample tube in a heating block. Both vessels are then filled with nitrogen at ambient temperature and atmospheric pressure, after which they are immersed in a liquid-nitrogen bath. Adsorption of nitrogen on to the sample creates a pressure difference across the manometer from which the surface area of the sample may be determined, correction being applied for the sample volume and the effect of the change in height of the manometer level. The surface may be determined by a simple nomogram of by calculation. This is essentially a one-point method of determining specific surface and may be used for surfaces in the range 0·2 to $1000\,\mathrm{m}^2\,\mathrm{g}^{-1}$. The reproducibility is of the order of 1 % and the error introduced by assuming that the BET-plot passes through the origin produces specific surfaces about 10 % lower than those obtained using the conventional multipoint method. Using one-point determinations, up to 16 analses per day may be performed. Alternatively, the nitrogen may be fed in under pressure and a full isotherm determined [95].

The Gravimat is a beam-balance for surface-area and pore-size distribution measurement. A full description of this instrument is given in [93] and a description of the measuring technique for nitrogen adsorption in [94, 97]. It is possible to measure and control pressures from atmospheric down to $10^{-3}\,\mathrm{mm}$ Hg, hence the instrument can be used with a range of adsorbates.

The balance has a sensitivity of $0\cdot1\,\mu g$, but thermal effects and buoyancy reduce the measuring accuracy; a monolayer of $34\cdot8\,\mathrm{cm}^2$ of nitrogen weighs $1\cdot0\,\mu g$ giving a lower limit of surface-area measurement of $100\,\mathrm{cm}^2$. Conditions are more favourable with krypton with which $18\cdot7\,\mathrm{cm}^2$ weighs $1\cdot0\,\mu g$.

References

[1] Brunauer, S., Deming, L.S., Deming, W.E., and Teller, E. (1940), *J. Am. Chem. Soc.*, **62**, 1723.

[2] Orr, C., and Dallavalle, J.M. (1959), *Fine Particle Measurement*, Macmillan, N.Y.

[3] Adamson, A.W. (1960), *Physical Chemistry of Surfaces*, Interscience, N.Y.

[4] Langmuir, I. (1918), *J. Am. Chem. Soc.*, **40**, 1361.

[5] Volmer, M. (1925), *Z. Physik, Chem.*, **115**, 253.

[6] Fowler, R.H. (1935), *Proc. Camb. Phil. Soc.*, **31**, 260.

[7] Brunauer, S., and Emmett, P.H. (1937), *J. Am. Chem. Soc.*, **59**, 2682.

[8] Emmett, P.H., and Dewitt, T.W. (1937), *J. Am. Chem. Soc.*, **59**, 2682.

[9] Brunauer, S., Emmett, P.H., and Teller, E. (1938), *J. Am. Chem. Soc.*, **60**, 309.

[10] Baly, E.G.G. (1937), *Proc. R. Soc.*, **A160**, 465.

[11] Jones, D.C., and Birks, E.W. (1950), *J. Chem. Soc.*, 1127.

[12] Jones, D.C. (1951), *J. Chem. Soc.*, 1461.

[13] Young, D.M., and Crowell, A.D. (1962), *Physical Adsorption of Gases*, Butterworths.

[14] Cassel, H.M. (1944), *J. Chem. Phys.*, **12**, 115.

[15] Cassel, H.M. (1944), *J. Phys. Chem.*, **48**, 195.

[16] Halsey, G.D. (1952), *Adv. Catalysis*, **4**, 259.

[17] Gregg, S.J., and Jacobs, J. (1948), *Trans. Faraday Soc.*, **44**, 574.

[18] Halsey, G.D. (1948), *J. Chem. Phys.*, **16**, 931.

[19] Hüttig, G.F. (1948), *Monatsh. Chem.*, **78**, 177.

[20] Ross, S. (1953), *J. Phys. Chem.*, **53**, 383.'

[21] Corrin, M.L. (1953), *J. Am. Chem. Soc.*, **75**, 4623.

[22] Loeser, E.H., Harkins, W.D., and Twiss, S.B. (1953), *J. Phys. Chem.*, **57**, 591.

[23] MacIver, D.S., and Emmett, P.H. (1956), *J. Phys. Chem.*, **60**, 824.

[24] Dzisko, V.A., and Krasnopolskaya, V.N. (1952), *Zhur. Fiz. Khim.*, **26**, 1841.

[25] Harkins, W.D., and Jura, G. (1943), *J. Chem. Phys.*, **11**, 430, 431.

[26] Livingstone, H.K. (1947), *J. Chem. Phys.*, **15**, 617.

[27] Livingstone, H.K. (1944), *J. Chem. Phys.*, **12**, 466.

[28] Emmett, P.H. (1946), *J. Am. Chem. Soc.*, **68**, 1784.

[29] Smith, T.D., and Bell, R. (1948), *Nature*, **162**, 109.

[30] Emmett, P.H. (1941), *A.S.T.M. Symposium on New Methods for Particle Size Determinations in the Sub sieve Range*, pp. 95–105.

[31] Joy, A.S. (1953), *Vacuum*, **3**, 254.

[32] Bugge, P.E., and Kerlogue, R.H. (1947), *J. Soc. Chem. Ind., Lond.*, **66**, 377.

[33] McBain, J.W., and Bakr, A.M. (1926), *J. Am. Chem. Soc.*, **48**, 690.

[34] Wooten, L.A., and Brown, C. (1943), *J. Am. Chem. Soc.*, **65**, 113.

[35] Lister, B.A.J., and MacDonald, L.A. (1952), U.K. A.E.R.E. Report C/R 915.

[36] Beebe, R.A., Beckwith, J.B., and Honig, J.M. (1945), *J. Am. Chem. Soc.*, **67**, 1554.

[37] Emmett, P.H. (1940), 12th Report of the Committee on Catalysis, chapter 4, *Physical Adsorption in the Study of the Catalysis Surface*, Wiley, N.Y.

[38] Joyner, L.G. (1949), *Scientific and Industrial Glass Blowing and Laboratory Techniques*, Instruments Publ. Co., Pittsburgh, Pennsylvania, U.S.A.

[39] Emmett, P.H. (1944), *Colloid Chem.*, vol. V, Reinhold, N.Y.

[40] Harvey, E.N. (1947), *A.S.T.M. Symposium on Paint and Paint Material.*

[41] Schubert, Y., and Kopelman, B. (1952), *Powder Metall. Bull.*, **6**, 105.
[42] Vance, R.F., and Pattison, J.N. (1954), 'Special Report on Apparatus for Surface Area Determination and Other Adsorption Studies on Solids', Battelle Memorial Institute, Ohio, U.S.A.
[43] Harkins, W.D., and Jura, G. (1944), *J. Am. Chem. Soc.*, **66**, 1366.
[44] Thompson, J.B., Washburn, E.R., and Guildner, L.A. (1952), *J. Phys. Chem.*, **56**, 979.
[45] Bensen, S.W., and Ellis, D.A. (1948), *J. Am. Chem. Soc.*, **70**, 3563.
[46] Loebenstein, W.V., and Deitz, V.R. (1951), *J. Res. Nat. Bur. Stand.*, **46**, 51.
[47] Pickering, H.L., and Eckstrom, H.C. (1952), *J. Am. Chem. Soc.*, **74**, 4775.
[48] Tomlinson, L., U.K.A.E.A. Report 1, G.R. – TN/S – 1032.
[49] Haul, R.A.W. (1956), *Angew. Chem.*, **68**, 238.
[50] Rosenberg, A.J. (1956), *J. Am. Soc.*, **78**, 2929.
[51] Dollimore, J. (1963), *Chem. Ind.*, no. 18, 742.
[52] Leipziger, F.D., and Altamari, L.A. (1960), *Nuclear Sci., Eng.*, **8**, 312.
[53] Morris, H.E., and Maass, P. (1933), *Canad. J. Res.*, **9**, 240.
[54] Dunn, R.C., and Pomeroy, H.H. (1947), *J. Phys. Colloid Chem.*, **51**, 981.
[55] McBain, J.W., and Britton, H.T.S. (1930), *J. Am. Chem.Soc.*, **52**, 2198.
[56] McBain, J.W., and Sessions, R.F. (1948), *J. Colloid Sci.*, **3**, 213.
[57] Boyd, G.E., and Livingstone, H.K. (1942), *J. Am. Chem. Soc.*, **64**, 2838.
[58] Seborg, C.O., Simmons, F.A., and Baird, P.K. (1936), *Ind. Eng. Chem. (Industr.)*, **28**, 1245.
[59] Dubinin, M.M., and Timofeev, D.P. (1947), *Zhur. Fiz. Khim.*, **21**, 1213.
[60] Lemcke, W., and Hofmann, U. (1934), *Angew. Chem.*, **47**, 37.
[61] Seborg, C.O., and Stamm, A.J. (1931), *Ind. Eng. Chem. (Industr.)*, **23**, 1271.
[62] Pidgeon, L.M., and Maass, O. (1950), *J. Am. Chem. Soc.*, **52**, 1053.
[63] Mulligan, W.O., Simpson, W.C., Bushey, G.L., Richford, H.H., and Draper, A.L. (1951), *Analyt. Chem.*, **23**, 739.
[64] Stamm, A.J., and Woodruff, S.A. (1941), *Ind. Eng. Chem. Analyt. ed.*, **13**, 386.
[65] Barrett, H.M., Birnie, A.W., and Cohen, M. (1940), *J. Am. Chem. Soc.*, **62**, 2839.
[66] Gulbransen, E.A. (1944), *Rev. Sci. Instrum.*, **15**, 201.
[67] Rhodin, T.N. (1950), *J. Am. Chem. Soc.*, **72**, 4343.
[68] Rhodin, T.N. (1950), *J. Am. Chem. Soc.*, **72**, 5691.
[69] Rhodin, T.N. (1953), *Adv. Catalysis*, **5**, 39.
[70] Bowers, R., and Long, E.A. (1955), *Rev. Sci. Instrum.*, **26**, 337.
[71] Gregg, S.J. (1946), *J. Chem. Soc.*, **561**, 564.
[72] Gregg, S.J., and Wintle, M.F. (1946), *J. Sci. Instrum.*, **23**, 259.
[73] Nelsen, F.M., and Eggertsen, F.T. (1958), *Analyt. Chem.*, **30**, 1387.
[74] Ellis, J.F., Forrest, C.W., and Howe, D.D. (1960), U.K.A.E.R.E. Report D–E, G.R. 229 (CA).
[75] Atkins, J.H. (1964), *Analyt. Chem.*, **36**, 579.
[76] Haley, A.J. (1963), *J. Appl. Chem.*, **13**, 392.
[77] Whitehead, R.C. (1966), private communication.
[78] Innes, W.B. (1951), *Analyt. Chem.*, **23**, 759.
[79] Haul, R., and Dümbgen, G. (1960), *Chem. Ing. Techn., Part 1*, **32**, 349; (1963) *Part 2*, **35**, 586.
[80] Aylmore, D.W., and Jepson, W.B. (1961), *J. Sci. Instrum.*, **38**, 4, 156.

[81]   Lovell, G.H.B. (1970), 'Surface area determination', *Proc. Soc. Chem. Ind. Conference, Bristol, 1969,* Butterworths.

[82]   Hardman, J.S. (1971), Leeds Univ., Ph.D. thesis.

[83]   Gall, L. (1964), *Angewandte Mess., Regeltechnik,* **4**, 12, 107–11.

[84]   de Boer, J.H., Linsen, B.G., and Osinga, J. (1965), *J. Catalysis,* **4**, 643.

[85]   Schull, C.G., Elkin, P.B., and Roess, L.C. (1948), *J. Am. Chem. Soc.,* **70**, 1405.

[86]   Barret, E.P., Joyner, L.G., and Halenda, P.P. (1951), *J. Am. Chem. Soc.,* **73**, 373.

[87]   Lippens, B.C., and de Boer, J.H. (1965), *J. Catalysis,* **4**, 319.

[88]   Lippens, B.C., Linsen, B.G., and de Boer, J.H. (1964), *J. Catalysis,* **3**, 32.

[89]   de Boer, J.H. (1970), 'Surface area determination', *Proc. Soc. Chem. Ind. Conference, Bristol, 1969,* Butterworths.

[90]   Anderson, R.B. (1946), *J. Am. Chem. Soc.,* **68**, 686.

[91]   Brockhoff, J.C.P. (1969), Delft Univ., thesis (*cit.* [89]).

[92]   Lecloux, A. (1970), *J. Catalysis,* **81**, 22.

[93]   Robens, E. (1969), *Laboratory Practice,* **18**, 3, 292.

[94]   Robens, E., and Sandstede, G. (1967), *Z. Instrum.,* **75**, 167–78.

[95]   Roth, R. (1971), *Staub-Reinhalt Luft,* **31**, 8, 320–2.

[96]   Lapointe, C.M. (1970), *Can. Mines Br. Tech. Bull.,* TB119, 27.

[97]   Robens, E., and Sandstede, G. (1969), *J. Sci. Instrum.,* series 2, **2**, 4, 365–8.

[98]   Brunauer, S. (1970), 'Surface area determination', *Proc. Soc. Chem. Ind. Conference, Bristol, 1969,* Butterworths.

[99]   Pickett, G. (1945), *J. Am. Chem. Soc.,* **67**, 1958.

[100]   Gregg, S.J., and Sing, K.S.W. (1967), *Adsorption, Surface Area and Porosity,* Academic Press, N.Y.

[101]   Kiselev, A.V. (1945), *USP Khim,* **14**, 367.

[102]   Halsey, G., and Taylor, H.S. (1947), *J. Chem. Phys.,* **15**, 9, 624–30.

[103]   Burevski, D. (1975), Univ. of Bradford, Ph.D. thesis, to be published.

[104]   Sips, R. (1948), *J. Chem. Phys.,* **16**, 490.

[105]   Sips, R. (1950), *ibid.,* **18**, 1024.

[106]   Joyner, L.G., Weinberger, E.B., and Montgomery, C.W. (1945), *J. Am. Chem. Soc.,* **67**, 2182–8.

17 Other Methods for Determining Surface Area

17.1 Introduction

The most widely used method for surface-area determination is low-temperature gas adsorption, particularly nitrogen and krypton at liquid-nitrogen temperature. Most gases can and have been used, and these include water vapour at room temperature and carbon-dioxide at room temperature and at $-78°C$. The problems that arise when one deviates from the standard conditions are; what is the applicable molecular area and what is the correct theoretical model to use? The first question is usually resolved by accepting published values or carrying out experiments to determine molecular area by comparison with nitrogen adsorption at liquid-nitrogen temperature. Since there is no unanimity in published data, the second procedure is probably preferable. The second question is usually resolved from an examination of the isotherm, the BET or the Langmuir equation being then used. When coverage is very low, as with carbon dioxide at room temperature, the Freundlich equation may be applicable.

Permeametry, and to a lesser extent, gas diffusion are used for comparison purposes due to their ease of operation and simplicity. Surface areas may also be calculated from size distribution data and this transformation is the subject of a British Standard (B.S. 4359: 1971, Part 3).

Other adsorption techniques include adsorption from solution, and here the problem is one of determining the amount adsorbed since this is usually very small. Adsorption studies have been described with fatty acids, polymers, ions, dyestuffs and electrolytes using a range of analytical techniques. The most usual experimental method of determining a single point on the adsorption isotherm of a binary solution is to bring a known amount of solution of known composition into contact with a known weight of adsorbent in a vessel at the required temperature and stir for several hours. After equilibrium an aliquot part of the bulk liquid is separated and the concentration change determined by some suitable method. The amount adsorbed will then be some function of the final concentration.

Surface areas may also be determined from heats of adsorption and this technique has been greatly simplified with the introduction of the flow microcalorimeter. This instrument can be used with gas or liquid mixtures to determine heats of adsorption and amount adsorbed; it thus provides information on molecular areas as well as energies of adsorption.

17.2 Calculation from size distribution data

If the fractional weight of powder of measured mean size d_r is x_r, then:

$$x_r W = \alpha_v \rho_s n_r d_r^3 \tag{17.1}$$

where W is the total weight of powder, ρ_s the powder density, α_v the volume-shape factor and n_r the number of particles of size d_r.

The surface of this fraction is:

$$\Delta S = \alpha_s n_r d_r^2 \tag{17.2}$$

where α_s is the surface shape factor.

The specific surface is equal to S/W which, for a weight distribution, is:

$$S_w = \sum \frac{\alpha_s}{\rho_s \alpha_v} \frac{x_r}{d_r}$$

$$= \sum \frac{\alpha_{sv}}{\rho_s} \frac{x_r}{d_r} \tag{17.3}$$

α_{sv} and ρ_s are usually considered to be constant over a limited size range making:

$$S_w = \frac{\alpha_{sv}}{\rho_s} \sum \frac{x_r}{d_r}. \tag{17.4}$$

For a number distribution:

$$S_w = \frac{\alpha_{sv}}{\rho_s} \frac{\sum n_r d_r^2}{\sum n_r d_r^3}. \tag{17.5}$$

It is usual to use an additional suffix to denote the method of measurement. Thus, for a sieve analysis, equation (17.4) becomes;

$$S_w = \frac{\alpha_{sv,A}}{\rho_s} \sum \frac{x_r}{d_{r,A}}. \tag{17.6}$$

Alternatively:

$$S_{w,A} = \frac{6}{\rho_s} \sum \frac{x_r}{d_{r,A}}. \tag{17.7}$$

S_w is the weight specific surface determined using a previously obtained value for the surface volume shape coefficient. $S_{w,A}$ is the weight specific surface by sieving assuming spherical particles. The former is suitable for comparison with other techniques such as permeametry; the latter, for comparison between powders using the same technique. This type of conversion is dealt with in B.S. 4359: 1972, Part 3.

Surface area may be obtained more readily if the distributions are log-normal or Rosin-Rammler, since the equations developed in chapter 4 may be used. Surface area may also be determined by turbidity using equation (9.14).

17.3 Adsorption from solution

The accumulation of one molecular species at the interface between a solid and a solution is governed by complex phenomena. The molecules may accumulate at the interface as a result of interfacial tension, may attach on to the solid surface through strong chemical valency forces or may attach on to the solid surface through relatively weak physical, Van der Waal's, attractive forces. In physical adsorption, the desorption isotherm is essentially the same as the adsorption isotherm, whereas for chemisorption the molecules are not easily removed by merely lowering the equilibrium concentration of the solution.

Molecules are adsorbed on solid surfaces by interaction of the unsatisfied force fields of the surface atoms of the solid with the force fields of the molecules striking the surface. In this way the free energy of the solid surface is diminished [1]. The type of interaction, if any, that occurs between the solute molecules and the solid will be dependent on the nature of the surface and of the solute molecules.

In adsorption from solution a complicating factor arises, that of the possibility of competition between the solvent and solute molecules for the sites on the surface. The competition between the components of a solution depends mostly on the difference in the strength of interaction between adsorbent and the adsorbates.

17.3.1 Orientation of molecules at the solid–liquid interface

The idea of molecular orientation at interfaces was conceived by Benjamin Franklin who in 1765 spread olive oil on a water surface and estimated the thickness of the resulting film at one ten-millionth of an inch. In subsequent work with films of oil on water, Lord Rayleigh [2] in England and Miss Pockels [3] in Germany established that the films were only one molecule thick. Langmuir [4] introduced new experimental methods of great importance which resulted in new conceptions concerning these films.

Instead of working with oils, Langmuir used pure substances of known constitution and observed the effect of varying this constitution. He measured the outward pressure of the films directly by use of a floating barrier with a device to measure the force on it. The clearest results were obtained with normal saturated fatty acids and alcohols. Langmuir found that as the area on which the film was spread was reduced, no appreciable surface pressure developed until the area per molecule had been reduced to approximately 22 $Å^2$, at which point the pressure increased very rapidly with further decrease in area. One of the most striking facts illustrated by Langmuir's work is that the area is independent of the number of carbon atoms in the molecules. This would indicate that the molecules are orientated vertically to the surface of liquid and are orientated in the same manner in all the films regardless of chain lengths. According to Adam [1] each molecule occupies an area of 20·5 $Å^2$ on the surface of the substrate.

Some investigators suggest that the effective area occupied by fatty acid molecules at solid–liquid interfaces is the same as the occupied by these molecules in films on water. The area for stearic acid for example ranges from 20·5 to 25·1 $Å^2$, the former being the area for closest packing of ellipses and the latter the area for free rotation [5, 6].

However, a greater variation than this is expected for an immobile interface since the adsorbate is not constrained to take up any definite orientation. In adsorption on carbon blacks, Kipling and Wright [7] suggest that stearic acid is adsorbed with the hydrocarbon chain parallel to the surface, the effective areas of each stearic acid molecule being calculated as 114 Å^2. Kipling and Wright [8] also suggest that this is true of other acids in homologous series and adsorption of these acids by non-polar adsorbents indicates that the major axis of the hydrocarbon chain is parallel to the surface. McBain and Dunn's [9] results for adsorption of cetyl alcohol by magnesium oxide are also probably best interpreted in terms of orientation parallel to the surface. Smith and Hurley [37] determined the surface area of fatty acid molecules adsorbed on to carbon block from cyclohexane and arrived at a value of 20·5 Å^2, which suggested a perpendicular orientation.

Ward [11] suggested a coiling into a hemispherical shape, and Allen and Patel [12, 13] found that the surface increased from 19·2 Å^2 to 70·2 Å^2 with chain length irrespective of the adsorbent, while for alcohols the increase for long-chain alcohols was 20·1 Å^2 to 60·5 Å^2 [14]. These values were explained in terms of coiling of the chains.

In early work on oxides, it was suggested by Harkins and Gans [15, 16], that oleic acid and butyric acids adopted the perpendicular orientation on titania, as did stearic acid on aluminium hydroxide [17]. In these experiments it was not clear whether adsorption was physical or chemical in nature. This now seems an important distinction to draw, especially with basic solids. In chemisorption, the orientation of the solute generally presents no problem, as the functional group determines the point of attachment. Thus the long-chain fatty acids are attached to the surface by carhoxyl group, -COOH, with the hydrocarbon chain perpendicular to the surface.

Harkins and Jura [18] have shown that the mean molecular area of nitrogen when adsorbed is not a constant value, but varies with the nature of the substrate. The molecular area of the adsorbed molecule was reported to vary from 13·6 to 16·9 Å^2 per molecule. While this may introduce some uncertainty into the values for areas of some very polar solids, it does not seriously reduce the utility of adsorption for determining surface-area value.

17.3.2 Polarity of organic liquids and adsorbents

Generally the organic liquids and solid adsorbents are classified according to their polarity, i.e. as to whether they are essentially polar or non-polar in character.

Polar molecules are defined as uncharged molecules in which the centre of gravity of positive and negative charges do not coincide, and these therefore show dipole moments. The larger the dipole-moment, the more polar the molecule. The term *polar group* is applied to a portion of a molecule with polar characteristics, such as -OH, -COOH, -COON$_a$, -COOR and similar groups.

Non-polar molecules have an equal number of positive and negative charges with coinciding centres of gravity. Dipole-moment is zero for non-polar molecules. The term *non-polar* may be applied to a portion of a large molecule with non-polar characteristics such as, benzene, *n*-heptane, hexane and other hydrocarbons.

The general rule is that a polar adsorbate will tend to prefer that phase which is the more polar, i.e. it will be strongly adsorbed by a polar adsorbent from a non-polar solution. Similarly, non-polar adsorbate will be adsorbed strongly on non-polar adsorbent from a polar solution.

Freundlich [19] found the order of increasing adsorption of normal fatty acids from aqueous solution on to a blood charcoal to be formic, acetic, propionic, butyric in increasing order. The same order of adsorption isotherm for homologous series of fatty acid, formic through caproic acids, from water on to Noril charcoal was reported by Linner and Gortner [20]. These results agree well with Traube's rule [21]. Holmes and McKelvey [22] made a logical extension of Freundlich's statement by noting that the situation was really a relative one and that a reversal order should occur if a polar adsorbent and a non-polar solvent were used. They indeed observed the reverse sequence for fatty acids adsorbed on silicagel from toluene solution. This agrees with the general observation that silica gel and charcoal, water and toluene are opposite in their polarity. Langmuir [24] gave an instructive interpretation to this rule. The work W to transfer one mole of solute from solution to surface is: (see [25], p. 95)

$$W = RT \ln \frac{C_s}{C} = RT \ln \frac{\Gamma}{\tau C} \tag{17.8}$$

where C_s is the surface concentration and is given by Γ/τ, where Γ denotes the moles of solute adsorbed per unit area and τ is the film thickness. For solutes of chain length n and $(n-1)$ the difference in work is then:

$$W_n - W_{n-1} = RT \ln \left(\frac{\Gamma_n}{\Gamma_{n-1}} \frac{C_{n-1}}{C_n} \right). \tag{17.9}$$

Traube found that for each additional CH_2 group the concentration required to give a certain surface tension was reduced by a factor of 3, i.e.

$$\text{If } C_{n-1} = 3C_n \text{ then } \gamma_n = \gamma_{n-1}$$

and

$$W_n - W_{n-1} = RT \ln 3$$

$$= 640 \text{ cal mol}^{-1}.$$

The figure of 640 cal mol^{-1} may be regarded as the work to bring one CH_2 group from the body of the solution to the surface region. Adamson [25, p. 95] assumed this to imply that the chains were lying flat on the surface, but suggested that this was undoubtedly an oversimplification.

Harkins and Dahlstrom [23] have shown that the oxides of titanium, tin and zinc act like water in attracting polar rather than non-polar groups. Thus in oils any -COOH, -OH, -COOR, -CN and other similar groups orient toward the particle of oxide powder and the hydrocarbon groups towards the oil.

17.3.3 Drying of organic liquids and adsorbents

In adsorption by solids from liquid phase, substances present in low concentration are often adsorbed preferentially. The presence of water and other impurities in the solution may therefore have an effect on the adsorption. The purification and drying procedure usually employed consists of a fractionation, after which the recovered solution is stored over metallic sodium or other drying agents such as silicagel, calcium sulphate, alumina, etc. A very useful method of purification of solvents is given by Weissberger and associates [26].

It has been reported by Harkins and Dahlstrom [23] that extremely small quantities of water in benzene increase the energy of immersion of the used oxides to about three times the value for pure benzene.

Most solid adsorbents are capable of adsorbing water vapour from the atmosphere and should therefore be dried. The drying of adsorbent is usually done by heating for 2 or 3 hours at 120 to 130°C. Many workers claim [27, 28] that his temperature is sometimes not high enough to drive away previously adsorbed vapours by the solids. If a higher temperature is used, then care should be taken that the solid is not altered by being heated, e.g. that sintering or alteration of the nature of the surface does not take place. The temperature of drying must therefore be carefully chosen for each adsorbent.

Some authors consider that adsorbents should be outgassed before use and then be introduced to the solution in the absence of air. But others claim that such outgassing treatment does not affect the extent of adsorption. Thus, it was reported by Greenhill [29] and by Russell and Cochran [17] that adsorption was essentially the same on metals, metal-oxides, and non-porous alumina, whether the samples were degassed or not prior to exposure to the solutions; gases adsorbed on the solids being apparently displaced by the liquid phase [30]. No systematic effect was found in adsorption by charcoal from mixtures of carbon tetrachloride and methanol [31]. Hirst and Lancaster [32] examined the effect of very small quantities of water on the interaction of stearic acid with finely divided solids. For adsorbents such as TiO_2, SiO_2, TiC and SiC, the presence of water was found to reduce the amount of acid adsorbed to form a monolayer, and with reactive materials such as Cu, Cu2O, CuO, Zn and ZnO, water was found to initiate chemical reaction.

17.4 Methods of analysis of amount of solute adsorbed on to the solid surfaces

In almost all studies of adsorption by solids from solution, it is necessary to measure the concentration of the solution before and after adsorption. A variety of analytical methods of analysis may be used to measure such changes in concentration; including the Langmuir trough, Gravimetric, Titrimetric, Interferometry and Precolumn method.

17.4.1 Langmuir trough [4]

This technique can be useful where the adsorptive can easily be spread on an aqueous substrate to give a coherent film. The area occupied by the adsorptive film, after evaporation of the solvent, is proportional to the weight present. This method has been successfully applied to analysis of solutions of long-chain fatty acids by Hutchinson [33], Gregg [34], Greenhill [29] and of alcohols and phenols by Crisp [35] in organic solvents such as benzene. Equal volumes of solution before and after adsorption were spread on aqueous substrate.

17.4.2 Gravimetric method

If an involatile solute is dissolved in a volatile solvent, analysis can be effected by evaporating off the solvent from a sample of known weight and weighing the residual solute. This simple technique was adopted by Smith and Fuzek [36] and thereafter widely used in many laboratories. In their procedure, an estimated 0·5 to 1 g of adsorbent was placed in a glass sorption tube to which a vacuum source could be attached. Then 40 ml solution of fatty acid (0·15 g) in benzene was introduced in to the sorption tube. The tube was then stoppered tightly and shaken for a definite period of time. The tube was then centrifuged in order to settle the adsorbent and 5 ml of clear liquid withdrawn. This liquid was delivered into a weighed container which was placed in an oven at a temperature just below the boiling point of the solvent. Evaporation of the solvent was speeded by means of a slow stream of filtered air, and the fatty acid which remained after the evaporation was determined by weighing. Blank runs established the dependability of this analytical procedure. The adsorption tube was restoppered, shaken again for a definite interval of time, and some of the liquid removed and analysed as just described. At the end of the experiment the adsorbent was filtered out, dried and weighed under CO_2. The weight of the adsorbent was corrected for the weight of adsorbed fatty acid.

17.4.3 Volumetric method

Many standard procedures are available for studying adsorption by volumetric or titrimetric method. Adsorption of fatty acids [37] has frequently been examined by titration with aqueous alkali; even if the fatty acid was originally dissolved in an organic solvent. The extraction of the acid from the solvent seems to cause no difficulty, especially if warm ethyl alcohol is added [38], but the validity of the method should be checked by titration of a known sample for each time.

Conductimetry [39] and potentiometry [40] titrations have been used as alternatives to those carried out with a coloured indicator.

17.4.4 The Rayleigh interferometer

This instrument is used to measure the differences in refractive index or in optical path-length between two liquids being compared; this is obtained by a 'null' method. The drum reading is converted into a difference in composition by means of a calibration curve. This curve is drawn by successive comparisons of a set of mixtures of accurately known composition, covering the relevant range of concentration value plotted as successive points are cumulative, so considerable care is required in constructing the calibration ourve. The use of the interferometer is restricted to systems with a small difference in refractive index, otherwise a large number of standard mixtures have to be made up for calibration.

Bartell and Sloan [41], Ewing and Rhoda [42] have made successful use of the interferometer in measuring the change in concentration due to adsorption from non-aqueous solutions. Further details of the instrument are given by Candler [43].

17.4.5 The Precolumn method
This was suggested by Groszek [44] for measuring the amount of solute adsorbed on to a solid surface using the flow microcalorimeter. This is described in detail later.

17.5 Theory for adsorption from a solution
Liquid-phase adsorption methods depend on the establishment of an equilibrium between adsorbed and unadsorbed solute molecules. Adsorption of solute on to the surface of solid will continue till it reaches a saturation point giving a clear plateau in the isotherm. As the isotherm usually tends towards a limiting value, the limit has often been taken to correspond to the coverage of the surface with a complete monolayer of the solute. The equation derived for monolayer coverage is:

$$\frac{x_1 x_2}{\Gamma_1^{(n)}} = \frac{1}{K x_m} + \frac{K-1}{K} \cdot \frac{x_1}{x_m} \tag{17.10}$$

where $\Gamma_1^{(n)}$ is the Gibbs adsorption value, x_1 and x_2 are the mole fractions of the two components of a completely miscible colution and K is a constant.

For K much greater than unity and for low concentrations of component one, this reduces to Langmuir's equation. Alternatively, the Langmuir equation replacing pressure p with concentration of solution C, has been used to determine the limiting value [12–14].

$$\frac{C}{x} = \frac{1}{K x_m} + \frac{C}{x_m}; \quad S_w = \frac{N_\sigma x_m}{M_v} \tag{17.11}$$

where x = amount of solute adsorbed per gram of adsorbent,
   x_m = solute monolayer capacity,
   K = constant,
   N = Avogradro's number,
   σ = area occupied per molecule,
   M_v = molar volume.

Thus a plot of C/x versus C should give a straight line of slope $1/x_m$ and intercept $1/K x_m$.

For the determination of specific surface of the adsorbent, three things are required, namely:

   (1) The area σ occupied by one molecule of the solute in a close-packed film on the surface of the adsorbent must be known.
   (2) It must be possible to clearly locate a point on the isotherm which corresponds to a complete monolayer adsorbed.

(3) Any competitive adsorption on the adsorbent surface of solvent molecules must be compensated for.

17.6 Quantitative methods for adsorption from a solution

17.6.1 Adsorption of non-electrolytes

This is usually considered to be essentially monolayer adsorption with competition between solvent and solute. The non-electrolytes that have been studied are mainly fatty acids, aromatic acids, esters, and other single functionless group compounds plus a great variety of more complex species such as porphyrins, bile pigments, carotenoids, lipoids and dyestuffs.

17.6.2 Fatty-acid adsorption

It has been known for a long time that when fatty-acid molecules are closely packed on the surface of distilled water, each molecule occupies an area of $20 \cdot 5$ $Å^2$ irrespective of the length of the hydrocarbon chain [25].

This property was used by Harkins and Gans [15] for the determination of the surface area of titanium dioxide, using oleic acid; their results were in general agreement with microscopy. Since then the method has been used extensively and a detailed review is to be found in Orr and Dallavalle [10 (p. 21)].

Smith and Fusek employed the procedure described in section 17.4.2.

Another procedure of Smith and Fusek was to place 20 ml of solvent containing $0 \cdot 2$ to $0 \cdot 4$ g of fatty acid in a tube and mix for 24 h. After this time the tube was centrifuged, 10 ml of the liquid withdrawn and 10 ml of pure solvent added. The procedure was then repeated. The fatty-acid content of the liquid samples withdrawn was determined as before [36].

Gregg [34] used the same solvent but determined the number of gram molecules adsorbed with a surface-tension balance. Smith and Hurley [37] however, recommended the use of cyclohexene as solvent, and stated that with some solvents multilayer adsorption takes place. Hirst and Lancaster [32], instead of adding more fatty acid to the solvent, increased C/C_s by decreasing the temperature of the solution.

The specific surface area determined by liquid-phase adsorptions will usually be low due to adsorption of the solvent. It is thus preferable that determinations should be carried out with a variety of solvents and comparisons made with a standard technique such as gas adsorption.

17.6.3 Adsorption of polymers

Adsorption isotherms of linear polymer molecules are found to be of the Langmuir type [47, 48]. Many workers assume the molecules are adsorbed in the shape of a random coil and [45, 46] have developed equations to give the area occupied by a molecule. Some workers assume a modified Langmuir equation to be necessary since polymers may occupy more than one site [49]. Others adopt a more empirical approach [50]. An estimate of the inner and outer surface areas of porous solids

has also been obtained by using a set of polystyrene fractions having a narrow range
of molecular weights [51].

17.6.4 Adsorption of dyes

Dyes have been used by many investigators for specific surface determination, but
their use has not been widely accepted because of the inconsistency of the reported
results both between different dyes and with other methods [52, 53]. Giles [54]
attributes these inconsistencies mainly to injudicious choice of dyes. He recommends
the use of methylene blue BP, brilliant basic red B, crystal violet BP, victoria pure
lake blue BO, orange II or solway ultra-blue. The two BP dyes can be used as
bought, the rest need some pre-treatment.

The experimental technique is to tumble gently 0·05 to 0·50 g of sample with
10 ml aqueous solutions of dye at room temperature; 10 to 30 minutes is a sufficient
time for non-porous solids, but 12 to 48 hours may be required for porous powders.
The tubes are then centrifuged and the solutions analysed spectrophotometrically.
With porous powders, a rate curve develops; extrapolating this back to zero gives the
surface concentration of dye, the saturated value represents total coverage. The isotherms usually have a long plateau, and this value is accepted as monolayer coverage;
this feature makes the method attractive as a one-point technique. A review of the
use of dyestuffs for surface area determination has been presented by Padday [55].

17.6.5 Adsorption of electrolytes

There are several variations of this technique. The negative adsorption method is
based on the exclusion of co-ions from the electrical double layer surrounding
charged particles [56]. The ion exchange method is based on the replacing of
loosely held ions by others of the same sign [25, p. 593]. A large amount of work
has been done on the adsorption of electrolytes by ionic crystals and the adsorption
of ions from solution on to metals. Since the adsorption tends to be very small and
the measurements rather tedious, these are not suitable as routine methods.

17.7 Theory for heat of adsorption from a liquid phase

17.7.1 Surface free-energy of a fluid

A fluid has a surface energy only when it exists in a sufficiently condensed state. A
gas has no surface energy. Because of the uniform energy distribution in a gas, no
difference exists between an internal molecule in the centre of the gas volume and a
molecule located near to a wall.

The theory for the forces acting between molecules was put forward by
Lennard-Jones and Devonshire [57]. The liquid molecule is assumed located in a
cage formed by the neighbouring molecules, and is constantly under the influences
of their fields yet being sufficiently free to execute translatory and rotary move-
ments.

Each molecule in a liquid volume is surrounded by other molecules on all sides,
and hence is subjected to attractive forces acting in all directions. Generally speaking

a uniform attraction in all directions is exerted by every molecule for a period of time which is relatively long compared with periods of vibration.

Very different conditions obtain at the surface. The molecules are attracted back towards the liquid and also from all sides by their neighbours, yet no attraction acts outward to compensate for the attraction towards the centre. Each surface molecule is subjected to a powerful attraction towards the centre acting, for symmetrical reasons, in a direction normal to the surface.

The work required to increase the area of the surface by an infinitesimal amount dA, at constant temperature, pressure and composition, is done against a tension γ, generally known as the surface tension. The surface tension can be defined from the point of view of energy involved as shown by Brillouin [58] and Michand [59]. The free-energy change dF is equal to the reversible work done:

$$dF = \gamma dA$$

$$\gamma = \frac{(dF)}{(dA)_{T,P,n}} = F_s \qquad (17.12)$$

where F_s is surface free-energy per unit area.

Surface tension and free energy, are in effect, two different aspects of the same matter. In the c.g.s. system, the number which, in dynes per centimetre, indicates the surface tension will, in ergs per square centimetre, express the surface free-energy of the liquid. The two equations above express a fundamental relationship in surface chemistry.

17.7.2 Surface entropy and energy

The entropy of a system at constant pressure, surface area and composition is:

$$-S = \frac{(dF)}{(dT)_{P,A,n}}. \qquad (17.13)$$

For a pure liquid, the surface entropy per square centimeter S_s is:

$$-S_s = \frac{d\gamma}{dT} \qquad (17.14)$$

The total surface energy per square centimetre E_s for a pure liquid is:

$$E_s = F_s + TS_s \qquad (17.15)$$

or as usually expressed:

$$E_s = \gamma - T\frac{d\gamma}{dT}. \qquad (17.16)$$

It is the work which must be done in order to remove from the bulk of the liquid and bring to the surface, a sufficient number of molecules to form a surface unit. Conversely, energy is liberated when a liquid surface disappears due to the return of the molecules from the surface to the centre of the liquid. The total surface energy of a pure liquid is generally larger than the surface free energy.

17.7.3 Heat of immersion

The present accepted theory of the heat of immersion is due to Bangham [60, 61] Razouk [62], Harkins [63] and their associates.

When a clean solid surface is immersed in or wetted by a liquid, it leads to the disappearance of the solid surface and the formation of a solid–liquid interface. As a result of the disappearance of the solid surface, the total energy of the sblid surface is liberated. The formation of the solid–liquid interface leads to an absorption of energy equal to the energy of the interface. Thus from thermodynamic consideration the heat of immersion (E_{imm}) is equal to the surface energy of the solid–gas E_{sv}, minus the interfacial energy E_{sL} between the solid and the liquid, so:

$$E_{imm} = (E_{sv} - E_{sL})S$$

$$-q_0 = \frac{E_{imm}}{W} = S_w (E_{sv} - E_{sL}) \qquad (17.17)$$

where q_0 is the heat evolved per gram of solid, S_w is the weight specific surface area of solid, and E the energy per unit area.

By analogy with equation (17.16), the surface energy when solid–liquid and solid vapour are in contact is written as:

$$E_{sL} = \gamma_{sL} - T \frac{d\gamma_{sL}}{dT}$$

$$E_{sv} = \gamma_{sv} - T \frac{d\gamma_{sv}}{dT}.$$

Which on combination gives:

$$(E_{sv} - E_{sL}) = \left(\gamma_{sv} - T \frac{d\gamma_{sv}}{dT} \right) - \left(\gamma_{sL} - T \frac{d\gamma_{sL}}{dT} \right)$$

$$= (\gamma_{sv} - \gamma_{sL}) - T \frac{d(\gamma_{sv} - \gamma_{sL})}{dT} . \qquad (17.18)$$

This may be simplified by the use of the adhesion tension of relationship of Young and Dupre ([64], cit [25]).

$$\gamma_{sv} = \gamma_{sL} + \gamma_{vL} \cos \theta$$

or

$$\gamma_{vL} \cos \theta = \gamma_{sv} - \gamma_{sL} \qquad (17.19)$$

where θ is the contact angle between the solid and liquid.

If equation (17.19) is substituted in (17.18), it is found that upon simplification:

$$E_{sv} - E_{sL} = \gamma_L - T \frac{d\gamma_L}{dT} \cos \theta. \qquad (17.20)$$

Finally substituting equation (17.20) into (17.17) and considering that a liquid that wets a solid has zero contact angle, $\cos \theta = 1$.

$$-q_0 = S_w \ \gamma_L - T \frac{d\gamma_L}{dT} \tag{17.21}$$

or

$$S_w = \frac{-q_0}{\gamma_L - T \frac{d\gamma_L}{dT}} . \tag{17.22}$$

17.8 Static calorimetry

The calorimetric method may be used in two ways: immersion of the bare out-gassed solid in pure liquid [65], and immersion of the solid precoated with the vapour phase [66]. The first approach is the most difficult due to the problem of determining E_s, hence the second approach is more widely used.

If the solid is first equilibrated with saturated vapour then immersed in pure liquid adsorbate, the solid vapour interface is destroyed and the heat liberated per unit area should correspond simply to E_L, the surface energy of the pure liquid. The above assumption is made in what is termed the absolute method of Harkin and Jura who obtained a heat of immersion of 0·409 cal g^{-1} for titanium dioxide which, divided by the surface energy of the adsorbent, water (2·83 × 10^{-6} cal cm^{-2}) gave a surface area of 14·4 m^2 g^{-1}. For a comprehensive bibliography and des-cription of the calorimeters used, readers are referred to Adamson [25].

The same technique was used by Clint et al. [67] for the determination of the surface of carbon blocks by the adsorption of n-alkanes. Equation (17.22) was used with the following correction for small particles where the thickness of the adsorbed layer t was not negligible in comparison with the particle radius r:

$$S_w^1 = \left(\frac{r}{r + t}\right)^2 S_w . \tag{17.23}$$

For low surface areas this method gave reasonable agreement with other techniques, but the surfaces for smaller particles were too low. The method was essentially comparative since the entropy is obtained using a reference sample. The method was considered unsuitable for powders having a surface area smaller than 20 m^{2}g^{-1}.

17.9 Flow microcalorimetry

A variation of this technique is employed with the flow microcalorimeter (figure 17.1). The calorimeter consists of a metal block [1] surrounding a cylindrical cavity in which the calorimeter cell [2] is situated. The cell forms a continuation of the inlet tube for the carrier liquid and is joined to the outlet [4]. The outlet tube is fitted with a 200-mesh stainless-steel gauze [3] on which the powdered solids [5] are placed.

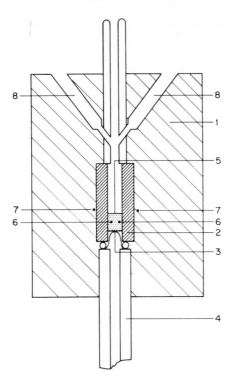

Fig. 17.1. Schematic diagram of the flow microcalorimeter: 1, metal block; 2, P.T.
F.E. calorimeter cell; 3, fine stainless-steel gauze; 4, metal outlet tube;
5, powder bed; 6, two thermisters; 7, reference thermisters; 8, cavities
to hold containers of carrier liquid or solution for analyses at elevated
temperatures.

17.9.1 Experimental procedures – liquids

There are three main experimental methods of studying the heat of adsorption at
solid–liquid interface by using the flow microcalorimeter. These are generally
referred as:

(a) Pulse or injection adsorption;
(b) Equilibrium adsorption;
(c) Successive of incremental adsorption.

(a) Pulse adsorption

In the pulse method a micrometer syringe may be used to introduce small quantities
of surface active substances (e.g. 1–100 μg as 0·1 to 1% solutions). These should be
introduced into the stream of carrier liquid against the wall of the inlet tube below
the point at which the liquid leaves the flow-control capillary.

(a) Pulse adsorption

(b) Equilibrium adsorption

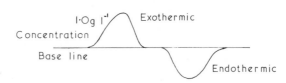

(c) Succesive adsorption

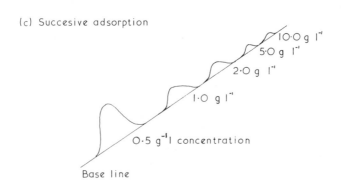

Fig. 17.2. Typical pulses. Heat of adsorption of n-butanol in n-heptone on to Fe_2O_3 adsorbent. (*a*) Pulse adsorption. (*b*) Equilibrium adsorption (*c*) Successive adsorption.

Any change in the calorimeter cell will be registered by the recorder due to adsorption of active agent from a solution on the solid surfaces. Normally adsorption is accompanied by the evolution of heat in the bed with a corresponding recorder deflection. In the case of an irreversible (chemical) change, the recorder pen will return to the base-line, but if the change is reversible (physical) the pen will cross the base-line to describe a negative heat of desorption. A typical pulse adsorption is shown in figure 17.2 (*a*).

(b) Equilibrium adsorption
In this method two reservoirs are prepared, one of which contains the pure carrier liquid (solvent) and the second the solution of active agent. Initially a steady flow of carrier liquid is allowed to flow through the adsorbent bed. When the calorimeter comes to thermal equilibrium, giving a stable base-line on the recorder chart, the flow of carrier liquid may be interchanged for the flow of active solution. Care should be taken that the flow-rate of this solution should not differ from that of

the carrier liquid by more than 0.01 ml min^{-1}.

Adsorption of solute, which is accompanied by a heat, hence temperature, change is measured by the thermistors which are connected via a Wheatstone bridge network to a potentiometric recorder. The result for an exothermic reaction (heat evolution typical of adsorption) is a positive pulse on the pen-recorder trace which then returns to the base line when the adsorption of solute is complete. Desorption may be carried out by returning to a flow of the carrier liquid. The result for an endothermic reaction (heat of adsorption typical of desorption) is a negative pulse on the recorder trace, see figure 17.2 (b).

For physical desorption, the area under the pulse is the same as the area under the adsorption peak. The rate of desorption, which controls the shape of the desorption pulse, depends on the relative strengths of adsorption of the solute and solvent. In some instances a long time elapses before all the solute molecules are removed, and this results in the desorption pulse having a long trailing tail, making it difficult to determine when desorption is complete.

In chemical adsorption the heat generated will be greater than for physical adsorption (greater than, compared with less than, 10 K cal mol^{-1}). Further, the desorption peak is much smaller thant he adsorption peak.

Adsorption—desorption of various solute concentrations may be studied on the same plug or different plugs of the same adsorbents. This way the form of adsorption isotherm can be determined.

In practice it is found that using the same plug of adsorbent and different concentration of solution is not a good method to adopt for the adsorption process, due to the difficulty of determining when desorption is complete. It is therefore necessary to use a different plug for each point on the isotherm.

(c) Successive adsorption

In this method of using increasing concentrations of the solution for adsorption on to the adsorbent a series of heat effects occur (pulses), and these generally decrease for equal increments in solute concentration. When the surface of an adsorbent is completely saturated with the solute, further runs with increasing concentration do not give any heat effects. Adding the pulse areas gives the same results as using the technique described in the above section. This method is however simpler than the previous one, although errors in measuring pulse areas are compounded.

This method is therefore the preferred one. An example of the the type of results obtained is shown in figure 17.2 (c).

17.9.2 Calibration

Calibration is effected by replacing the standard outlet tube with one containing a heating coil. With a powder bed in position and the carrier liquid flowing known quantities of heat are injected into the system. A calibration line is then produced of area under the pulses against heat injected.

17.9.3 Determination of the amount of solute adsorbed
The precolumn method

In constructing adsorption isotherms, it is necessary to measure the amount of solute adsorbed at a range of concentrations. This is usually done by determining changes in the concentrations of solute before and after contact with a given mass of adsorbent. For the following however a variation of this technique known as the precolumn method is used.

The adsorbent is placed in a precolumn constructed from a glass tube with the same internal diameter as the cell in the calorimeter. The carrier liquid is then percolated through the adsorbent in the precolumn before it entered the adsorbent in the calorimeter. To determine the amount of solute adsorbed from a given solution, the flow of carrier liquid is stopped at time t_1 and at the same time the flow of solution is started. If the precolumn contained an inert solid, the solution would emerge at time t_0 and would then contact the adsorbent in the calorimeter, but when the precolumn contains an adsorbent, the solute is retained, so that solvent only emerges at time t_0, the solution emerging at a later time t_2. The difference between t_2 and t_0 is a measure of the amount of solute adsorbed.

In the above method the critical steps are the accurate determination of the time at which the solution emerges from the precolumn and an accurate knowledge of the constant flow-rate of solution through the precolumn. It is also necessary to ensure, for all adsorbates, that the flow-rates used are sufficiently low to enable full saturation of the adsorbate in the precolumn. If the flow-rate of the solution is too high, solution may emerge from the precolumn before the adsorbent is fully saturated. In such a case the estimate for the amount of solute adsorbed would be lower that the equilibrium value.

However, if the retention time and constant flow rate are known, the amount of the solute adsorbed can be calculated from the equations:

$$x = \frac{t \cdot C \cdot f}{w}. \tag{17.24}$$

Where x = amount of solute adsorbed (mg/g),
$\quad\; t$ = retention time ($t_2 - t_0$),
$\quad C$ = concentration of solute (mg ml^{-1}),
$\quad\; f$ = flow rate of solution (ml min^{-1}),
and w = weight of adosrbent in the precolumn (gram).

17.9.4 Gases

A similar procedure can be carried out with gases using the mark 2V flow microcalorimeter. This technique has been used with carbon dioxide, with nitrogen as the carrier gas at 298°C, and results compared with static adsorption using standard gas-adsorption techniques.

17.9.5 Application to the determination of surface area

Using liquid-flow microcalorimetry, it is possible to determine the area occupied per molecule and the energy of adsorption per molecule. Allen and Patel [12, 13] investigated a range of long-chain fatty acids and long–chain alcohols and obtained information on molecular orientation at solid–solution interfaces. Surface areas may be evaluated using the following form of equation (17.22):

$$S_w = K_0 q_m \tag{17.25}$$

where q_m is the Langmuir monolayer value. For the adsorption of n-octoic acid from n-heptane, $K_0 = 16 \cdot 7 \text{ m}^2 \text{ J}^{-1}$, and two-thirds of the determined surface areas agreed with BET nitrogen adsorption values to within 10%. Full details of experimental procedures and results are given in [68].

For the adsorption of gases Burevski [69] found the energy of adsorption was not constant but varied with coverage. The manner in which it varied depended on the system under examination, rendering the method unsuitable for surface-area determination.

References

[1] Adam, N.K. (1941), *The Physics and Chemistry of Surfaces*, Oxford University Press.
[2] Rayleigh, Lord (1899), *Phil. Mag.*, **48**, 321.
[3] Pockels, A. (1891), *Nature*, **43**, 437.
[4] Langmuir, I. (1917), *J. Am. Chem. Soc.*, **39**, 1848.
[5] Linnar, E.R., and Williams, A.P. (1950), *J. Phys. Colloid Chem.*, **54**, 605.
[6] Vold, M.J. (1952), *J. Colloid Sci.*, 7, 196.
[7] Kipling, J.J., and Wright, E.H.M. (1963), *J. Chem. Soc.*, 3382.
[8] Kipling, J.J., and Wright, E.H.M. *ibid.*; (1964) *ibid.*, 3535.
[9] McBain, J.D., and Dunn, R.C. (1948), *J. Colloid Sci.*, 3, 308.
[10] Orr, C., and Dallevalle, J.M., (1959), *Fine Particle Measurement*, MacMillan, New York.
[11] Ward, A.F.H. (1946), *Trans. Faraday Soc.*, **42**, 399.
[12] Allen, T., and Patel, R.M. (1971), *J. Colloid Interface Sci.*, **35**, 4, 647–55.
[13] Allen, T., and Patel, R.M. (1971), *Particle Size Analysis*, Soc. Analyt. Chem., London.
[14] Allen, T., and Patel, R.M. (1970), *J. Appl. Chem.*, **20**, 165–71.
[15] Harkins, W.D., and Gans, D.M. (1931), *J. Am. Chem. Soc.*, **53**, 2804.
[16] Harkins, W.D., and Gans, D.M. (1932), *J. Phys. Chem.*, **36**, 86.
[17] Russel, A.S., and Cochran, C.N. (1950), *Ind. Eng. Chem.*, **42**, 1332.
[18] Harkins, W.D., and Jura, G. (1944), *Chem. Phys.*, **66**, 1366.
[19] Freundlich, H. (1907), *Z. Physik Chem.*, **57**, 385.
[20] Linner, E.R., and Gortner, R.A. (1935), *J. Phys. Chem.*, **39**, 35–67.
[21] Traube, I. (1891), *Ann. Liepzig*, **265**, 27.
[22] Holmes, H.N., and McKelvey, J.B. (1928), *J. Phys. Chem.*, **32**, 1522.
[23] Harkins, W.D., and Dahlstrom, R. (1930), *Ind. Eng. Chem.*, **22**, 897.
[24] Langmuir, I. (1917), *Trans. Faraday Soc.*, **42**, 399.
[25] Adamson, A.W. (1963), *Physical Chemistry of Surfaces*, Interscience, N.Y.
[26] Weissberger, A., Proskauer, E.S., Riddick, J.A., and Troops, E.E. (1955), *Organic Solvents*, Interscience, N.Y.

[27] de Boer, J.H. (1953), *The Dynamical Characteristics of Adsorption*, Princeton University Press.

[28] Berthier, P., Kerlan, L., and Courty, C. (1958), *Compte Rendu.*, **246**, 1851.

[29] Greenhill, E.B. (1949), *Trans. Faraday Soc.*, **45**, 625.

[30] Krasnovskii, A.A., and Gurevich, T.N. (1949), *Chem. Abstr.*, **43**, 728.

[31] Innes, W.B., and Rowley, H.H. (1947), *J. Phys. Chem.*, **51**, 1172.

[32] Hirst, W., and Lancaster, J.K. (1951), *Trans Faraday Soc.*, **47**, 315.

[33] Hutchinson, E. (1947), *Trans. Faraday Soc.*, **43**, 439.

[34] Gregg, S.J. (1947), *Symposium on particle size analysis, Trans. Inst. Chem. Eng. (London)*, **25**, 40–6.

[35] Crisp, D.J. (1956), *J. Colloid Sci.*, **11**, 356.

[36] Smith, H.A., and Fusek, J.F. (1946), *J. Am. Chem. Soc.*, **68**, 229.

[37] Smith, H.A., and Hurley, R.B. (1949), *J. Phys. Colloid Chem.*, **53**, 1409.

[38] Kipling, J.J., and Wright, E.H.M. (1962), *J. Chem. Soc.*, **855**, 3382–9.

[39] Maron, S.H., Ulevith, I.N., and Elder, M.E. (1949), *Anal. Chem.*, **21**, 691.

[40] Hanson, R.S., and Clampitt, B.H. (1954), *J. Phys. Chem.*, **58**, 908.

[41] Bartell, F.E., and Sloan, C.K. (1929), *J. Am. Chem. Soc.*, **51**, 1637.

[42] Ewing, W.W., and Rhoda, R.N. (1951), *Anal. Chem.*, **22**, 1453.

[43] Candler, C. (1951), *Modern Interferometers*, Hilger, London.

[44] Groszek, A.J. (1968), *S.C.I. Monograph, No. 28*, 174.

[45] Flory, P.J. (1953), *Principles of Polymer Chemistry*, Cornhill University Press, Ithica, p. 579.

[46] Morawetz, H. (1965), *Macromolecules in Solution*, Interscience, N.Y.

[47] Jenkel, E., and Rumbach, B. (1951), *Z. Electrochem.*, **55**, 612.

[48] Habden, J.F., and Jellinek, H.H.G. (1953), *J. Polymer Sci.*, **11**, 365.

[49] Frisch, H.C., and Simha, R., (1954), *J. Phys. Chem.*, **58**, 507.

[50] Jellinek, H.H.G., and Northey, H.L. (1954), *J. Polymer Sci.*, **14**, 583.

[51] Eltekov, Yu, A. (1970), *Surface Area Determination*, Butterworths, pp. 295–8.

[52] Kolthoff, I.M., and MacNevin, W.N. (1937), *J. Amer. Soc.*, **59**, 1639.

[53] Japling, D.W. (1952), *J. Appl. Chem.*, **2**, 642.

[54] Giles, G.H., Silva, A.P.D., and Trivedi, A.S. (1970), *Surface Area Determination.* Butterworths.

[55] Padday, J.F. (1970), *ibid.*, pp. 331–7.

[56] Lyklema, J., and Van der Hul, H.J. (1970), *ibid.*, pp. 341–54.

[57] Lennard-Jones, J.E., and Devonshire. (1937), *Proc. R. Soc.*, **163A**, 53.

[58] Brillouin, Leon. (1938), *J. Phys.*, **9**, 7, 462.

[59] Michand, F. (1939), *J. de Chim. Phys.*, **36**, 23.

[60] Bangram, D.H., and Razouk, R.I. (1937), *Trans. Faraday Soc.*, **33**, 1459.

[61] Bangram, D.H., and Razouk, R.I. (1938), *Proc. R. Soc.*, **166**, 572.

[62] Razouk, R.I. (1941), *J. Phys. Chem.*, **45**, 179.

[63] Harkins, W.D. (1919), *Proc. Nat. Acad. Sci.*, **5**, 562.

[64] Dupre, A. (1869), *Mechanical Theory of Heat*, Paris, p. 368.

[65] Gregg, S.J., and Sing, K.S.W. (1967), *Adsorption Surface Area and Porosity*, Academic Press, London.

[66] Harkins, W.D., and Jura, G. (1944), *J. Am. Chem. Soc.*, **66**, 1362.

[67] Clint, J.H., Clunie, J.S., Goodman, J.F., and Tate, J.R. (1970), *Surface Area Determination Proc. Int. Symposium, Bristol, 1969*, Butterworths.

[68] Patel, R.M. (1971), 'Physical adsorption at solid—liquid interface', Univ. of Bradford, Ph. D. thesis.

[69] Burevski, D., private communications, Ph. D. project, Univ. of Bradford.

18 *Determination of Pore Size Distribution*

18.1 Miscellaneous techniques

Pore size and size distribution have significant effect over a wide range of phenomena from the adsorbancy of fine powders in chemical catalysis to the frost resistance of bricks. Due to this, pore-size measurements have been described using a wide range of techniques and apparatus. Pore surface area is generally accepted as being the difference between the area of the surface envelope of the particle and its total surface area. The pores may be made up of fissures and cavities in the particle: they may be V-shaped, i.e. wide-necked; or 'ink-bottle' pores, i.e. narrow-necked. In order that their volume distribution may be determined, it is necessary that they are not totally enclosed and that the molecules used for measurement purposes may enter through the neck. The presence and extent of small open pores may be determined by finding the volume of a powder by immersing it in mercury and finding the volume displacement, then finding the volume in a gas pyknometer, using helium as the gas [1]. Since mercury does not wet most solids it leaves the pores unfilled, and the difference between the two volumes is the pore volume. Closed pores may be evaluated by grinding the powder which opens out some of the pores, thus decreasing the apparent solid volume [2].

Total pore volume may be determined by boiling the powder in a liquid, decanting the liquid and determining the volume of liquid taken up by the solid after it has been superficially dried. Pore-size distribution may be found by using a range of liquids of different molecular sizes [2]. Direct visual examination of particle sections under the optical and electron microscopes has also been used with a range of powders [3–6].

18.2 Gas-adsorption methods

Total pore volume and pore-size distribution may be determined from gas-adsorption isotherms. If the amount of gas adsorbed on the external surface is small compared with the amount adsorbed in the pores, the pore volume is the volume of gas adsorbed at the saturation pressure. With many adsorbants a hysteresis loop occurs between the adsorption and desorption curves after a monolayer has been completed. This has been explained as being due to capillary condensation in the pores of the adsorbent. As the pressure is reduced, the adsorbate does not evaporate as readily from the capillaries as it does from a flat surface due to a lowering of the vapour pressure over the concave meniscus formed by the condensed vapour in the pores. The lowering of the vapour pressure for a cylindrical capillary of radius r is given by

414

the Kelvin equation:

$$RT \ln \frac{p}{p_0} = \frac{-2\gamma V_L}{r} \cos \theta. \qquad (18.1)$$

Here p_0 is the saturated vapour pressure of the system at the temperature $T^\circ K$, γ and V_L are the surface tension and the molar volume of the adsorbate in liquid form, R is the molar gas constant and θ the angle of contact between the liquid and the walls of the pore.

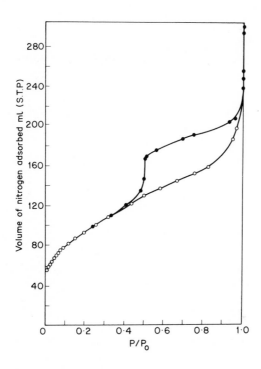

Fig. 18.1. Adsorption of nitrogen on activated clay catalyst. Open circles indicate adsorption; solid circles, desorption [9]. Total (BET) area, $S_w = 339 \text{ m}^2 \text{ g}^{-1}$ monomolecular volume $v_m = 78\cdot 0$ ml.

For nitrogen at liquid-nitrogen temperature, $\gamma = 8\cdot72$ dyne cm^{-1}, $V_L = 34\cdot68$ cm^3 mol^{-1}, $R = 8\cdot314 \times 10^7$ erg mol^{-1}, $T = -195^\circ C$, $\theta = 90^\circ$:

$$r_k = \frac{-4.1}{\log x}.$$

This equation may be developed from thermodynamic considerations [1, p. 137] or by using the method of Young and Laplace [1, p. 141]. The two equations that develop are respectively:

$$\frac{S}{V_v} = -\frac{RT \ln x}{\gamma V_L \cos \theta} \tag{18.2}$$

$$RT \ln x = -\gamma V_L \left[\frac{1}{r_1} + \frac{1}{r_2} \right] \cos \theta \tag{18.3}$$

where $x = p/p_0$, S and V_v are the surface area and the volume of the pores respectively, r_1 and r_2 are the radii of curvature of the curved surface of the meniscus in mutually perpendicular planes.

18.3 The hysteresis loop

Consider a cylindrical pore of radius r_p. The effective radius is the core or Kelvin radius r_k where:

$$r_k = r_p - t \tag{18.4}$$

and t is the thickness of condensed vapour in the pores. During adsorption the radii to be inserted in equation (18.3) are $r_1 = r_k$ and $r_2 = \infty$. During desorption the radii are $r_1 = r_2 = r_k$. Inserting in equation (18.3) gives:

$$x_A^2 = x_D. \tag{18.5}$$

(A = adsorption, D = desorption.)
Hence, for a given volume v adsorbed $x_A > x_D$.

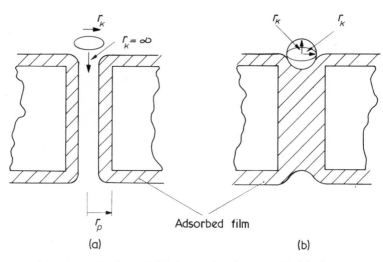

Fig. 18.2. (*a*) Adsorption in, and (*b*) desorption from a cylindrical pore.

Fifteen shape groups of capillaries were analysed by de Boer [2] from a consideration of five types of hysteresis loop (figure 18.3).

Type A Both adsorption and desorption branches are steep at intermediate relative pressures.

Type B The adsorption branch is steep at saturation pressure, the desorption branch at intermediate relative pressures.

Type C The adsorption branch is steep, at intermediate relative pressures the desorption branch is sloping.

Type D The adsorption branch is steep at saturation pressure, the desorption branch is sloping.

Type E The adsorption branch has a sloping character, the desorption branch is steep at intermediate relative pressures.

Type A includes tubular capillaries open at both ends; tubular capillaries with slightly widened parts; tubular capillaries of two different main dimensions, wide-necked 'ink-bottle' pores provided $r_n <$ to $r_w < 2r_n$; tubular capillaries with one narrowed part, narrow-necked 'ink-bottle' pores; capillaries with wide parts and narrow short necks open at both ends, trough shaped capillaries (r_n, r_w are the radii of the narrow and wide part respectively).

Type B includes open slit-shaped capillaries with parallel walls, capillaries with very wide bodies and narrow short necks.

Type C typifies a heterogeneous distribution of pores of some of the following shape groups, tapered or doubly tapered capillaries and wedge-formed capillaries with closed sides and open ends.

Type D loops occur for a heterogeneous assembly of capillaries with wide bodies of sufficiently wide dimension r_w and having a greatly varying range of narrow necks; wedge-shaped capillaries open at both ends.

Type E loops can be formed by assemblies of capillaries of one of the shape groups for type A when the dimensions responsible for the adsorption branch are heterogeneously distributed and the dimensions responsible for the desorption branch are of equal size.

The theoretical treatment for open-ended cylindrical pores has already been covered, and results in equations (18.5). For tubular capillaries with narrow necks and wide bodies where $r_w \leqslant 2r_n$, the necks will fill when the relative pressure corresponds to r_n; this will produce a spherical meniscus in the wider parts and increase the pressure there to $RTr_n \ln x = -2\gamma V \cos \theta$, which is greater than the pressure required to fill the wider parts ($RTr_w \ln x = -\gamma V \cos \theta$). The whole capillary will therefore fill at the adsorption pressure for the small capillary. On desorption it is emptied when the pressure is given by $RT \ln x_D = 2\gamma V/r_n \cos \theta$. Hence $x_D = x_A^2$, as before.

For parallel plates or open slit-shaped capillaries, a meniscus cannot be formed during adsorption, but during desorption a cylindrical meniscus is already present, hence desorption is delayed to produce hysteresis.

With 'ink-bottle' pores with wide closed bodies and open short necks, the necks are filled at a relative pressure corresponding to r_n, but it is only at a relative pressure corresponding to $\frac{1}{2}r_w$ that the whole capillary is filled. Emptying takes place at a relative pressure corresponding to $\frac{1}{2}r_n$. Hence $x_D = x_A^2$.

For a full discussion, readers are referred to the original paper [2].

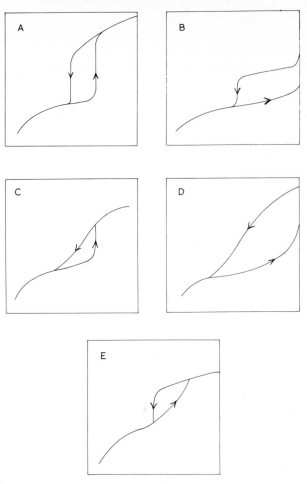

Fig. 18.3. de Boer's five types of hysteresis loop.

18.4 Pore-size distribution by gas adsorption

From the Kelvin equation one can valculate the value of r, say r_1, corresponding to any given point on the isotherm, i.e. for any given value of the relative pressure, x_1 and volume adsorbed v_1. If one were to neglect the amount adsorbed on the walls, then v_1 would be equal to the volume of all the pores which have radii up to and including r_1. One could then plot a graph of v against r and the pore-size distribution would result.

If allowance is made for the thickness of the adsorbed film t, the relevant radius would be $r_1 - t_1$ and the volume adsorbed would be made up of two parts, the volume-filling capillary cores and the volume which increases the thickness of the adsorbed layer on pores with radii greater than r_1. In order to determine the pore-size distribution, it is therefore necessary to know t.

Oulton [3] assumed the thickness of the adsorbed layer remained constant over the whole pressure region. Wheeler [4] considered the thickness to be equal to the monolayer capacity as calculated from the BET theory and suggested a mathematical model for pore-size distribution. Shull [5] pointed out that this gave too high a value for t in the high-pressure region and used the multilayer thickness from experimental data with non-porous solids. He then developed a simplified model for fitting experimental data to theoretical size distributions. Barrett *et al.* [6] used a computation which is in effect a tabular integration of Wheeler's equation, but they introduce a constant C in a manner criticized by Pierce [8]. Their distributions do, however, tend to agree with those obtained by high-pressure mercury-intrusion methods [9].

Cranston and Inkley [7] derived a curve of thickness of adsorbed layer t against relative pressure x from published isotherms on fifteen non-porous materials by dividing the volume of nitrogen adsorbed by the BET surface area. They state that their method may be applied either to the adsorption or desorption branch of the isotherm and that the indications were that the adsorption branch should be used, a proposal which was at variance with current practice. They assumed cylindrical pores with one end closed but stated that this assumption was unnecessary.

Pierce [8] begins with the sample saturated with vapour at p_0 and derived a pore-size distribution by considering incremental desorption as the pressure drops. He uses a cylindrical pore model and applies the Kelvin equation, assuming the residual layers to be the same as on a non-porous surface at the same relative pressure. Attempts to improve and simplify the earlier models have been carried out by Dollimore and Heal [10], who used a cylindrical model; Innes [11], who used a parallel plate model; and Roberts [12], whose method is applicable to both the above models.

Other recent contributions include a series of sixteen papers on studies on pore systems in catalysts by de Boer and associates [13], a book by Gregg and Sing [1] and an international symposium [14]. Brunauer [16] introduces a method of sizing micropores (radii less than 15 Å) which are not amenable to t-curve-type analysis and de Boer [13] discusses the t-curve method for sizing intermediate pores (20 to 2000 Å). It is generally agreed that the shape of the t-curve depends upon the energy of adsorption t increasing in thickness at the same relative pressure with increasing energy, i.e. increasing C-value. This is relatively unimportant in the intermediate pore region where t is only part of the adsorption, but in the micropore (MP) region it is essential that the correct t-curve be employed.

18.5 The t-curve method for intermediate pores

If V_m is the monolayer capacity of the reference non-porous solid, the adsorption V at any pressure can be converted into film thickness:

$$t = y\left(\frac{V}{V_m}\right) \qquad (18.6)$$

where y is the thickness of one molecule.

de Boer [13.1] assumed hexagonal packing for nitrogen, this gives:

$$y = \frac{28}{16 \cdot 2 \times 0 \cdot 0^{-16} \times 6 \times 10^{23}} \frac{1}{0 \cdot 81} \text{ cm}$$

$$= 3 \cdot 54 \times 10^{-8} \text{ cm} \tag{18.7}$$

If a cubical packing is assumed $y = \sqrt{16 \cdot 2} = 4 \cdot 02$ Å. Schull [5] and Wheeler [4] assumed a more open packing and arrived at a value of $4 \cdot 3$ Å for y.

Wheeler [4] suggested that the adsorption on the walls of fine pores is probably greater than on an open surface at low relative pressures and proposed the use of Halsey's equation [15].

$$t^3 \ln \frac{p_0}{p} = 5y. \tag{18.8}$$

This equation was also used by Dollimore and Heal [10].

The theoretical approach is to consider a system of open-ended cylindrical pores completely filled with liquid at saturation vapour pressure. A slight lowering of the pressure will result in the desorption of a measureable quantity of gas. Let this volume by Δv_1, for a fall in pressure from p_1 to p_2, and assume that this empties all pores with radii greater than r_2, leaving a residual film of thickness t_2. Equation (18.1) may be written:

$$\ln p_1/p_0 = \frac{2\gamma V_2}{RT(r_1 - t_1)} \tag{18.9}$$

$$\ln p_2/p_0 = \frac{2\gamma V_L}{RT(r_2 - t_2)} \tag{18.10}$$

and the average pore size $\qquad r_{1 \cdot 2} = \frac{1}{2}(r_1 + r_2)$

$$\tag{18.11}$$

and $\qquad t_{1 \cdot 2} = \frac{1}{2}(t_1 + t_2)$

If the volume of gas desorbed is reduced to millilitres per gram of adsorbate at S.T.P. (Δv_a), then the condensed volume of the desorbed gas is:

$$\Delta v_c = \frac{\Delta v_a M}{\rho V} \tag{18.12}$$

where M is the molecular weight of the adsorbate, ρ the density of the liquefied gas at its saturated vapour pressure and V the gas molar volume at S.T.P. For nitrogen:

$$\Delta v_c = \frac{28}{22\,400 \times 0 \cdot 808} \Delta v_a$$

$$= 1 \cdot 547 \times 10^{-3} \Delta v_a. \tag{18.13}$$

The condensed volume of the gas desorbed as the pressure falls from p_1 to p_2 may be written:

$$\Delta v_c = (r_{1 \cdot 2} - t)^2 L_{1 \cdot 2}(r) \tag{18.14}$$

where $L_{1.2}(r)$ is the frequency (i.e. total length) or pores in the size range t_2 to r_1. The total volume desorbed is:

$$v_s - v_K = v_c = \int_{r_K}^{\infty} \pi(r-t)^2 L(r)\,dr \tag{18.15}$$

where v_s is the volume of gas adsorbed at saturation pressure and v_K is the volume adsorbed at a pressure p corresponding to a pore size $r = r_K + t$ as given by equation (18.1).

Consider the increment of gas desorbed at a mean relative pressure $p_{1.2}/p_0$ corresponding to a mean pore size $r_{1.2}$ given by equations (18.9) to (18.11). The volume of the pores in the size range is related to the volume of gas desorbed by the equation:

$$\Delta v_p = \left(\frac{r_{1.2}}{r_{1.2} - t_{1.2}}\right)^2 \Delta v_c \tag{18.16}$$

The pore surface is given by:

$$\Delta S = 2\pi r_{1.2} \Delta L_{1.2} \tag{18.17}$$

where $\Delta L_{1.2}$ is the length of pores of mean size $r_{1.2}$. The pore volume in this size range may also be written:

$$\Delta v_p = \pi r_{1.2}^2 \Delta L_{1.2} \tag{18.18}$$

From equations (18.17) and (18.18):

$$\Delta S = \frac{2\Delta v_p}{r_{1.2}}. \tag{18.19}$$

Combining with equations (18.16) and (18.13) gives, for nitrogen:

$$\Delta S = 30 \cdot 9 \frac{r_{1.2}}{(r_{1.2} - t_{1.2})^2} \Delta v_a \tag{18.20}$$

with Δv_a in ml g^{-1} at S.T.P. and r and t in Ångströms to give ΔS in m^2 g^{-1}.

Table 18.1 gives experimental data from reference [5]; the t-values are given by Wheeler [4] and $r - t$ is calculated using equation (18.1). The pore-surface area in the size range r_1 to r_2 is given by equation (18.20) and so the frequency distribution may be determined. The total pore area is of the same order as the BET surface area, and, if the external surface is small compared with the pore surface, it may be assumed that the difference represents the surface of pores smaller than $16 \cdot 3$ Å in radius, since it can be seen that the surface area of pores with radii greater than $203 \cdot 8$ Å is negligible. This permits the cummulative frequency curve to be calculated. The length and surface pore-size distributions may be determined by using equations (18.17) and (18.18) respectively. The relative percentage pore-size distribution $(100/S)(dS/dr)$ is plotted in figure 18.4. An alternative procedure is to plot r against v_a, using the data from Table 18.1 to smooth out experimental errors and data from the graph for the size-distribution calculation. There is no significant

Table 18.1. Calculation of pore-size distribution for activated clay

P/P_0	v_a ml g^{-1} (S.T.P.)	t Å	$r-t$ Å	r Å	Δv_a ml g^{-1} (S.T.P.)	$r_{1.2}$ Å	$r_{1.2}-t_{1.2}$ Å	ΔS m^2 g^{-1}	Δr Å	$\Delta S/\Delta r$ m^2 g^{-1} Å	$100\Delta S/S\Delta r$ %/Å	Cumulative frequency undersize m^2 m^{-1}	%
0·35	110·3	7·3	9·0	16·3								39·2	11·6
0·385	114·4	7·5	9·89	17·39	4·1	16·85	9·45	24·3	1·09	22·3	6·60	63·5	18·8
0·42	120·1	7·8	10·88	18·68	5·7	18·04	10·39	29·6	1·29	24·9	7·34	93·1	27·5
0·46	127·0	8·1	12·16	20·26	6·9	19·47	11·52	31·5	1·58	19·7	5·80	124·6	36·8
0·48	133·2	8·2	12·86	21·06	6·2	20·66	12·51	25·3	0·80	31·6	9·30	149·9	44·0
0·51	167·0	8·4	14·02	22·42	33·8	21·74	13·44	126·0	1·36	92·7	27·30	275·9	81·5
0·56	173·6	8·9	16·29	25·19	6·3	23·81	15·15	23·0	2·77	7·3	2·15	296·2	87·5
0·59	176·5	9·25	17·89	27·14	3·2	26·17	17·09	8·8	1·95	4·5	1·32	305·0	89·4
0·62	179·3	9·5	19·75	29·25	2·8	28·20	18·82	6·8	2·11	3·2	0·93	311·8	92·0
0·65	181·9	9·8	20·80	30·60	2·6	29·93	20·28	5·0	1·35	4·3	1·26	317·6	93·8
0·68	184·2	10·2	24·48	34·68	2·3	32·64	22·64	4·5	4·08	1·1	0·32	322·1	94·8
0·71	186·2	10·6	27·56	38·16	2·0	36·42	26·42	3·3	3·48	0·96	0·28	325·4	96·0
0·745	188·8	11·1	32·07	43·17	2·6	40·67	29·82	3·7	5·01	0·72	0·21	329·1	97·0
0·770	190·5	11·5	36·12	47·62	1·7	45·40	34·10	2·1	4·45	0·46	0·13	331·2	97·8
0·81	193·5	12·3	44·80	57·10	3·0	52·36	40·46	3·0	9·48	0·32	0·09	334·2	98·3
0·85	196·2	14·0	58·09	72·09	2·7	64·6	51·45	2·0	15·0	0·14	0·04	336·2	99·1
0·90	199·7	15·5	89·60	105·10	3·5	88·6	73·35	1·8	33·0	0·06	0·02	338·0	100·0
0·95	205·3	19·8	184·02	203·82	5·6	104·5	136·8	1·0	98·7	0·01	—	339·0	100·0

$$S = 299·8$$

Total surface area (monolayer BET) = 339 m^2 g^{-1}.

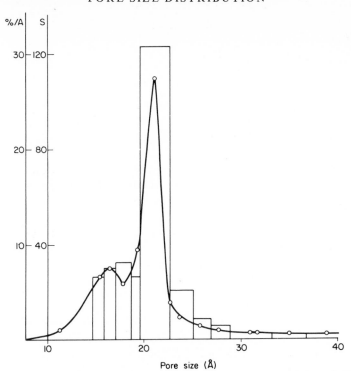

Fig. 18.4. Pore-size distribution. The histogram shows the distribution of surface
area, the height of each bar represents the area to be found in all the
capillaries whose radii lie within the limits of the bar. The curve shows the
relative percentage frequency distribution.

difference in the shape of the curve if Oulton's mean value for t or Shull's experimental values are used.

Provided the correct form of the Kelvin equation is used, this treatment may
also be applied to the adsorption branch of the isotherm. The derived pore-size
distribution will, of course, depend on the model applied, for example, the relevant
Kelvin equation for parallel slits of separation $2r$ is:

$$\ln \frac{p}{p_0} = \frac{\gamma V_L}{2RT(r-t)}.$$

Pore volume may also be determined from the hysteresis loop [14, p. 97]. Alternative equations may be built up for different models, but there is some agreement
that the t-plot method is of most use with external and slit pores [14, p. 97, 141].

18.6 The Modelless method for pore-structure analysis

The above methods are based on the Kelvin equation, in which assumptions have to
be made regarding pore shape. In 1967 Brunauer et al. [16, 17] introduced a method
of analysis which did not assume a pore shape. The method is based on the hysteresis

region of the isotherm, the pore volume and surface distribution being determined as a function of hydraulic radius defined as:

$$r_h = \frac{\text{volume of pores}}{\text{surface of pores}}.$$

For cylindrical pores r_h equals half the radius of the cylinder, for parallel plates r_h is half the distance between the plates. The analysis can be performed on either the adsorption or desorption branch of the isotherm but the latter is preferred by the authors.

When x is lowered from 1·0 to 0·95 a group of pores empty by capillary evaporation, leaving a multilayer of adsorbed film on the walls. The part of the pore space which is empty is called the core and the volume desorbed is the volume of a group of cores.

When a group of pores empty by capillary evaporation, new surfaces form in the pores. The free-energy change in this process is $\gamma \, ds$. At the same time da moles of liquid are transferred to the gas phase; the free-energy change in this process is $\Delta\mu da$.

$$\Delta\mu da = \gamma ds. \tag{18.21}$$

This equation was developed by Kiselev [18] who integrated to obtain:

$$S = \frac{1}{\gamma} \int_{a_s}^{a_H} RT \ln x \, da. \tag{18.22}$$

This equation was used for total surface-area determination and for such purposes has only limited applicability. However, it has no such limitations for determining the pore surface area. When x is lowered from 1·0 to 0·95, 'a' moles is desorbed; this, multiplied by the molar volume of the liquid adsorbate (34·65 ml mol^{-1} for N_2 at 77·3 K), gives the volume of cores of the first group of pores V_1. The core volume divided by the core surface gives the hydraulic radius of the group.

When x is lowered from 0·95 to 0·90, the total number of moles a_2 comprises two parts, the volume of cores of the second group V_2 plus the volume desorbed from the walls of the first group. Assuming parallel plate pores, this is $V_2^1 = S_1(t_2 - t_1)$ ml with the t-values taken from the appropriate t-curve.

If the pores are assumed cylindrical the correction is:

$$V_2^1 = S_1(t_1 - t_2) + \frac{S_1}{4r_1}(t_1 - t_2)^2. \tag{18.23}$$

The second term has a negligible effect, hence the method is approximately modelless. The process can be continued for decreasing values of x.

18.7 Analysis of micropores: the MP method
The micropore method [19] was developed for pore analysis in the sub-16 Å diameter region. The method is based on the use of the appropriate t-curve; the correct choice is far more important in the MP method than in the modelless method,

since the relative pressures are less than 0·4 whereas in the modelless method the
t-values are those obtained for higher pressures. In this region the heats of adsorption
affect the film thickness strongly in the first adsorbed layer, weakly in the second
and hardly at all in subsequent layers. Far more important than this is that in the
MP method the t-values constitute the total pore volume, whereas in the modelless
method it only appears as a correction term.

Brunauer [20] shows that the micropore isotherm looks very similar to a
Langmuir isotherm (figure 18.5), but yields a straight line BET plot with $S_{BET} =$
793 m^2 g^{-1}. From the slope of the $V - t$ curve a value $S_t = 792$ m^2 g^{-1} obtains the
curve deviating downward from the straight line as t progresses from $t = 4·0$ to
$t = 45$ Å. The tangent between these two values indicates a surface area of 520
m^2 g^{-1}, indicating a pore area of 272 m^2 g^{-1} for pores in this range. The volume of
the pores in this range is given by:

$$v = \tfrac{1}{2}(S_1 - S_2)(t_1 + t_2).$$

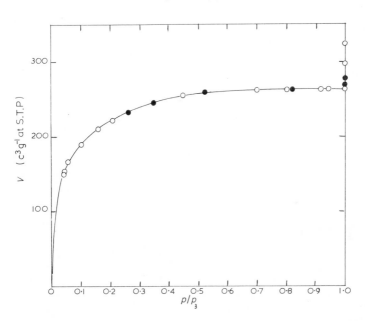

Fig. 18.5. Adsorption–desorption isotherm of nitrogen on silica gel Davidson 03 at
77·3 K. Empty circles adsorption; black circles desorption.

One proceeds in a similar manner to the second pore group and so on (figure
18.6). The analysis terminates when there is no further change in slope.

18.8. Mercury porosimetry
Mercury porosimetry has been reviewed in detail by Rappeneau [21] Scholten [22],
Spencer [23], Diamond [24] and Rootare [25].

The method is based on the fact that a minimum pressure P is required to force mercury through an entrance. This pressure is given by the Young and Laplace equation (see 25) which, for circular pores of radius r, may be written:

$$p = \frac{2\gamma\cos\theta}{r} \tag{18.25}$$

where γ is the surface tension of mercury and θ the angle of contact.

The pore volume distribution is measured by determining the cumulative volumes of mercury entering the sample as the pressure is increased in steps, the pressures being converted into pore radii using the above equation.

In almost all porosimeters, the sample is evacuated and then immersed in mercury; pressure is applied and the amount of mercury penetrating into the pores determined by the fall in level of the interface between the mercury and the hydraulic fluid, correction being applied for compression of the mercury and distortion of the inter-face. The change in the electrical resistance of a wire dipped in the mercury is often used to measure the change in volume of the mercury Δ_v. For mercury the surface tension is usually taken to be 480 dyne cm^{-1}. Normally a value of $140°$ is taken for θ making:

$$r = \frac{106}{p} \tag{18.26}$$

where p is in lb/in^2 and r is in microns.

Mercury porosimetry is not applicable where the mercury will come into contact with metals with which it forms amalgams. An interesting alternative to mercury to use in these cases is glycerine [27]. These results were later compared with a method using a sedimentation balance and showed good agreement [45].

To gain maximum information it is necessary for the initial pressure to be as low as possible and a number of low pressure porosimeters have been developed for this purpose [30]. Leppard and Spence [28] designed an apparatus for lump samples in the range $(200 > r > 3\cdot5)\,\mu m$. Reich [29] for $(500 > r > 0\cdot05)\,\mu m$.

The low pressure region is frequently the region where interparticle filling takes place (voids); pore distribution curves frequently have plateaus which form a de-marcation between voids and pores. Problems can arise due to damage to the pores under pressure, fracture can occur thus opening up previously blind pores [23].

The method was proposed by Washburn [31] and the first experimental data were published by Hendersen, Ridgeway and Ross [32] who used compressed gas to obtain pressures in the range 30 to 900 lb in^{-2}. Ritter and Drake [33] extended the pressure range to 10 000 lb in^{-2}, using a compressed oil-pumping system which they considered to be safer than compressed gas. Drake [34] later extended the pressure to 60 000 lb in^{-2}, corresponding to pore diameters greater than 35 Å. Further development was carried out by Burdine, Gournay and Reichertz [35], who used dry air at low pressures and cylinder nitrogen at high pressures. A simplified apparatus was described by Bucker, Felsenthal and Conley [36], and an instrument based on Drake's design with the mechanical pumping system replaced by a hand pump is available from the American Instrument Company. The method is now

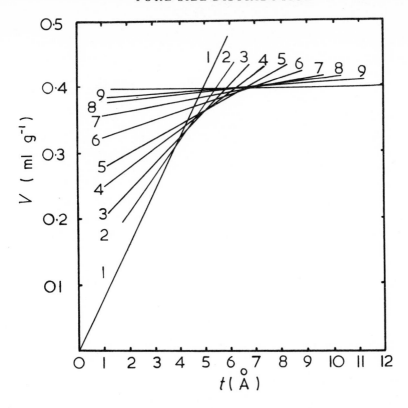

Fig. 18.6. Isotherm of figure 18.5 converted into a $v - t$ plot. The surface areas of the pore walls of the different pore groups are obtained from differences between the slopes of straight lines 1 to 9, and the pore widths are obtained from the abscissa values. The figure illustrates the MP method of analysis of micropores.

widely used and an extensive literature is available in which modified apparatus [37–40] is described and the accuracy of the technique discussed [41].

The principle of the technique may be understood by considering the apparatus used by Drake [34] shown in figure 18.7.

The dilatometer consists of a sample chamber of a sample chamber connected to a capillary tube down the length of which runs a resistance wire which can be connected to a resistance bridge. The dilatometer containing the sample is placed in the filling device, shown in figure 18.8, and heat-treated under vacuum to remove adsorbed vapour. After treatment the whole assembly is cooled and mercury is allowed to spill over the top of the dilatometer. The dilatometer is placed in a blast-proof chamber and re-evacuated and further heat treatment is carried out. The sample is next cooled to room temperature and covered with mercury while under vacuum. Electrical connections are made and the chamber closed. Nitrogen or oil pressure is cautiously applied and the heat of compression allowed to dissipate

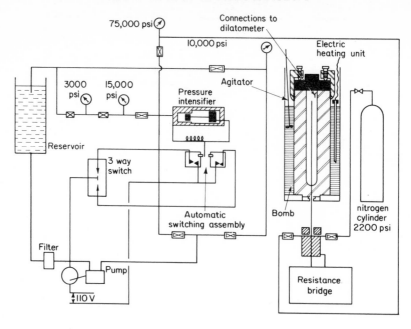

Fig. 18.7. High-pressure plant for mercury porosimeter (Drake [34]).

before readings are taken. Resistance readings are taken at intervals until constancy is obtained. A pressurizing schedule similar to that shown in table 18.2 is followed, the volume penetration of mercury being derived from the calibration constant for the resistance wire which is in millilitres per ohm.

The data in table 18.2 are from Drake [34]. The surface area was determined using a McBain-Bakr gravimetric nitrogen adsorption apparatus. The total pore volume was determined using the helium and mercury volume determination as described in section 18.1. 76·3% of the total pore volume consists of pores greater than 17·7 Å in radius and this corresponds to a pore surface of 51% of total surface. Assuming that 0·508 ml g^{-1} is the total pore volume and 223 m^2 g^{-1} the specific

Table 18.2. Table of experimental pressurising data

Pressure (lb in^{-2})	1000	10 000	25 000	50 000	60 000
$(V_0 - V)$ (ml g^{-1})	0·076	0·199	0·253	0·363	0·388
Mean pore radius (Å)	583	74	31·8	19·5	
d$(V_0 - V)$ (ml g^{-1})	0·123	0·054	0·110	0·025	
Mean pressure (lb in^{-2})	5·500	17 500	37 500	55 000	
Δs (m^2 g^{-1})	4·2	14·8	69·3	25·5	

surface area, and also that the surface area of pores above 1060 Å in radius is negligible, it can be shown that the mean volume pore diameter is 87 Å and the mean surface pore diameter is 35 Å. Mercury under a pressure p will enter all pores larger than those of radius r given by equations(18.25) and((18.26).

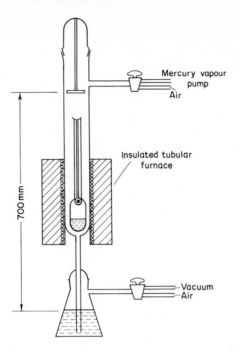

700 mm

Mercury vapour
pump

Air

Insulated tubular
furnace

Vacuum
Air

Fig. 18.8. Filling device for dilatometer.

As the pressure is increased, mercury is forced into smaller and smaller pores, the volume of pores due to any increment in pressure being given by the change in the apparent volume of mercury; the size range of the pores can be found from the pressures, by equation (18.25).

If the total volume of all pores having radii between r and $r + dr$ is dV then:

$$D_3(r) = dV/dr \qquad (18.27)$$

where $D_3(r)$ is the volume pore frequency per unit interval of size. From equation (18.25):

$$p \, dr + r \, dp = 0$$

hence

$$D_3(r) = -\frac{p}{r}\frac{dV}{dp}. \qquad (18.28)$$

Since the terms on the right-hand side are determinable, $D_3(r)$ may be found. The relation between pore surface and pore volume is (equation (18.25))

$$\frac{dS}{dV} = \frac{2}{r}. \qquad (18.29)$$

The surface pore frequency per unit interval of size is therefore given by:

$$D_2(r) = \frac{dS}{dr}$$

$$= \frac{2}{r} \cdot \frac{dV}{dr}. \tag{18.30}$$

The length pore frequency per unit interval of size is, from equation (18.17):

$$D_1(r) = \frac{2p}{\pi r^2} \cdot \frac{dV}{dr}. \tag{18.31}$$

The volume measured by the dilatometer is the volume of all pores having radii greater than r. The pressurizing curve is $V_0 - V$ as a function of p. The slope of the curve is $d(V_0 - V)/dt = -dV/dt$ and $D_3(r)$ may be found from the equation:

$$D_3(r) = \frac{p}{r} \frac{d(V_0 - V)}{dt}. \tag{18.32}$$

A plot of $D_3(r)$ against r gives the relative frequency distribution.

Cochran and Cosgrove [42] compared the analysis of aluminium using a porosimeter with a gas adsorption analysis using n-butane (table 18.3). The Kelvin equation (18.1) is used for the n-butane data, the lowest radius being calculated at the point where the adsorption branch of the hysteresis loop joins the adsorption branch. Their results are given in table 18.3.

Table 18.3. Pore volume (ml g^{-1}) between pore radius limits (Å)

Alcoa H 41 Pore										Re- main- der	Total pore volume
Radius	45 000	2000	1000	500	200	100	50	30	15		
Porosimeter		0·006	0·002	0·001	0·001	0·001	0·004	0·357			0·373
n-butane					0·008	0·004	0·021	0·161		0·258	0·458

The n-butane yields a larger volume due to the presence of pores smaller than 30 Å in radius. The remainder is the volume of gas sorbed on to the sample and in the pores to a thickness of approximately two monolayers before capillary condensation starts.

Zweitering [43] reported data on pore-size distribution in the range where mercury porosimetry and nitrogen adsorption overlap and found reasonable agreement. Other relevant comparisons have been made by Dubinin and co-workers who found good agreement particularly for benzene isotherms. Sneck [46] compared water adsorption and mercury porosimetry and found significant difference.

References

[1] Gregg, G.J., and Sing, K.S.W. (1967), *Adsorption, Surface Area and Porosity*, Academic Press, N.Y.

[2] de Boer, J.H. (1958), *The Structure and Properties of Porous Materials*, Butterworths, p. 68.

[3] Oulton, T.D. (1948), *J. Phys. Colloid. Chem.*, **52**, 1296.

[4] Wheeler, A. (1955). *Catalysis*, Vol. 2, (Emmet, D.H., *et al.*), Rheinhold, N.Y., p. 118.

[5] Schull, C.G. (1948), *J. Am. Chem. Soc.*, **70**, 1405.

[6] Barrett, E.P., Joyner, L.G., and Halenda, P.O. (1951), *J. Am. Chem. Soc.*, **73**, 373–80.

[7] Cranston, R.W., and Inkley, F.A. (1957), *Advances in Catalysis*, (ed. A. Farkas), Vol. 9, Academic Press, N.Y., pp. 143–154.

[8] Pierce, C. (1953), *J. Phys. Chem.*, **57**, 149–52.

[9] Jayner, L.G., Barrett, E.P., and Skold, R. (1951), *J. Am. Chem. Soc.*, **73**, 3155.

[10] Dollimore, D., and Heal, G.R. (1964), *J. Appl. Chem.*, **14**, 109.

[11] Innes, W.B. (1957), *Analyt. Chem.*, **29**, 7, 1069–73.

[12] Roberts, B.F. (1967), *J. Colloid Interf. Sci.*, **23**, 266–73.

[13] de Boer, J.H., *et al.*, *J. Catalysis*.

[13.1] (1964), **3**, 32–37.

[13.2] **3**, 38–43.

[13.3] **3**, 44–9.

[13.4] **3**, 268–73.

[13.5] (1965), **4**, 319–23.

[13.6] **4**, 643–8.

[13.7] **4**, 649–53.

[13.8] (1967), **7**, 135–9.

[13.9] **9**, 8–14.

[13.10] **9**, 15–27.

[13.11] (1968), **10**, 153–65.

[13.12] **10**, 368–74.

[13.13] **10**, 377–90.

[13.14] **10**, 391–400.

[13.15] **11**, 46–53.

[14] Everett, D.H., and Ottewill, R.H. (ed.) (1970), *Surface Area Determination*, Butterworths.

[15] Halsey, G.D. (1948), *J. Chem. Phys.*, **16**, 931.

[16] Brunauer, S., Mikhail, R. Sh., and Bodor, E.E. (1967), *J. Colloid Interface Sci.*, **23**, 266.

[17] Brunauer, S., Mikhail, R. Sh., and Bodor, E.E. (1967), *J. Colloid Interface Sci.*, **25**, 353.

[18] Kiselev, A.V. (1945), *Usp Khim*, **14**, 367.

[19] Brunauer, S., Mikhail, R.S., and Bodor, E.E. (1968), *J. Coloid Interface Sci.*, **26**, 45.

[20] Brunauer, S. (1970), *Chemical Engng Progress Symposium*, **96**, 65, 1–10.

[21] Rappeneau, J. (1965), *Les Carbenes*, Vol 2, 134–140, Masson, Paris, chapter 14.

[22] Scholten, J.J.F. (1967), *Porous carbon solids* (ed., R.L. Bond), Academic Press, pp. 225–49.

[23] Spencer, D.J.H. (1969), *British Coal Utilisation Research Assoc. Bull.*, **33**, 10, 228–39.

[24] Diamond, S. (1970), *Clay Min.*, **18**, 7.

[25] Rootare, H.M., and Nyce, A.C. (1971), *Int, J. Powder Metall.*, **7**, 1, 3–11.

[26] Adamson, A.W. (1963), *Physical Chemistry of Surfaces*, Interscience, N.Y.

[27] Svata, M. (1968), *Abh. sächs Akad. Wiss*, **49**, 5, 191–6.

[28] Leppard, C.J., and Spencer, D.H.T. (1968), *J. Sci. Instrum.*, ser. 2, 1, 573–5.

[29] Reich, B. (1967), *Chem. Ing. Tech.*, **39**, 22, 1275–9.

[30] Baker, D.J. (1971), *J. Phys. E: Sci. Instrum.*, **4**, 5, 388–9.

[31] Washburn, E.W. (1921), *Proc. Nat. Acad. Sci.*, **7**, 115–16.

[32] Henderson, L.M., Ridgeway, C.M., and Ross, W.B. (1940), *Refiner Natural Gasoline Mfr.*, **19**, 185.

[33] Ritter, H.L., and Drake, L.C. (1945), *Ind. Eng. Chem., analyt. ed.*, **17**, 787.

[34] Drake, L.C. (1949), *Ind. Eng. Chem.*, **41**, 780.

[35] Burdine, N.T., Gournay, L.S., and Reichertz, P.O. (1950), *Trans. Am. Inst. Mining Metal Engrs*, **189**, 196.

[36] Bucker, H.P., Felsenthal, M., and Conley, F.R. (1956), *J. Petrol Technol.*, **8**, 65.

[37] Watson, A., May, J.O., and Butterworth, B. (1957), *Trans. B. Ceram. Soc.*, **56**, 37.

[38] Plachenov, T.G. (1955), *J. Appl. Chem., USSR*, **28**, 223.

[39] Guyer, A., Boehlen, B., and Guyer, A., Jr. (1959), *Helv. Chim. Acta.*, **42**, 2103.

[40] Cameron, A., and Stacey, W.O. (1960), *Chem. Ind. (London)*, 222–3.

[41] Sarakhov, A.I. (1956), *Isvest. Akad. Nauk. SSSR, Otdel Khim Nauk*, (1956) English translation, *Bull. Acad. Sci. USSR Div. Chem. Sci.*, 3–8. 5–11 and 150–7.

[42] Cochran, C.N., and Cosgrove, L.A. (1957), *J. Phys. Chem.*, **61**, 1417.

[43] Zweitering, P. (1958), *The Structure and Properties of Porous Solids*, Butterworths, p. 287.

[44] Dubinin, M.M., Vishyakova, E.G., Zhukovskaya, E.A., Leont'ev, V.M., Lukyanovich, V.M., and Sarakhov, A.I. (1951), *Russ. J. Phys. Chem.*, **34**, 959.

[45] Svata, M., and Zabransky, Z. (1968–9), *Powder Technol.*, **2**, 159–61.

[46] Sneck, T., and Cinonen, M. (1970), *Valtion Tek Tutkimaslaitos Julk*, no. 155, 60.

Appendix 1 *Equipment and Suppliers*

The names given in brackets are those of agents. The equipment is listed in chapter order as it occurs in the text.

SAMPLING DEVICES (Chapter 1)

Spinning Riffler	Microscal
Sample Divider	Pascal
Rotary Riffler	Freeman Laboratories
Rotary Sample Divider	Glen Creston
Sample Splitter	Fritsch (Christison)

FLUE SAMPLERS (Chapter 2)

Smoke Dust Monitor	Airflow Development
BCURA Gas Flow Monitor	
Smoke Density meter (chimneys/ducts)	Bailey Meters and Controls
Stack Monitors	Research Appliance Company
In Stack Samplers	Anderson
Dust Samplers	Anderson
Smoke Density Measuring Instruments	Erwin Sick, Pearson Panke
C.E.R.L. Flue Dust Monitor	Foster Instruments
High Sensitivity Air Monitor	Photoelectronics

AEROSOL SAMPLERS (Chapter 3)

Thermal Precipitators (Standard and Long Term)	Casella
Gravimetric Dust Sampler	(U.S. Agents M.S.A.)
Cascade Impactor, Hexhlet	(U.S. Agents M.S.A.)
Wrights T.P. (Ch 3 ref 94)	Adams
Hamiltons T.P. (Ch 3 ref 98)	Adams
Konisampler T.P.	Ficklen
British Standard Deposit Gauge	Glass Developments
Continuous Oscillating and Gravimetric T.P.	American Instruments
Thermopositor	American Instruments
Dräger Dust Sampler	Drägerwerk
Thermal Precipitators, Konimeter, Dust Collectors, Gravicon, Porticon Dust Sampler (filters)	Sartorious (Howe)
Electrostatic Air Sampler kit	Bendix
Olin particle mass Monitor (Ch 3 ref 131, 132)	Thermo-Systems, Proner
Electrostatic Air Sampler	Thermo-Systems, Proner
Smoke pollution Sampler	Charles Austin

Cascade Centripeter	Bird and Tole
Membrane Filters	Nuclepore
Membrane Filters	Gelman, Millipore
Settlement Dust Counter	Casella, M.S.A.
Hexhlet Gravimetric Personal Sampler	Casella, M.S.A.
Settlement Dust Sampler	Research Appliances
Cascade Impactor	Research Appliances
Portable Dust Sampler	Rotheroe and Mitchell
Periodic Air Sampler	Rotheroe and Mitchell
Personal Sampler	Anderson
Cascade Sampler	Anderson
Aerosol Gravimetric Spectrometer	Fleming
Air Pollution Monitors	Fleming
Particle Sampling Unit	Fleming
Dust Sampling Unit	Fleming
Millipore Sampling Set	Thermal Control
Konimeter	Carl Zeiss Jena
AERA Portable Air Sampler	Addy Products
Light Scattering Counters	High Accuracy Products (Air Supply)
	Royco (Hawksley)
	Bausch and Lomb (Applied Research Laboratories)
Light Reflectance Monitor	Research Appliance
Aerosol Spectrometers	Sartorious
Sigrist Dust Measuring Equip.	(Howe)
Electricon Smoke Monitor	Ronald Trist
Coulter Contamination Counter	Coulter
LIDAR, Smoke Plume Tracking	Laser Associates
Laser light scattering particle counter	Procedyne

SIEVING EQUIPMENT (Chapter 5)

Woven wire sieves	Endecattes, Pascall, Greenings
Inclyno Sieve Shaker, Turbine Sifter	Pascall
Electroformed Sieves	Buckbee Mears (Production Sales and Services)
Electroformed Sieves	Veco
Electroformed Sieves	Endecottes
Fisher Wheeler Sieve Shaker	Fisher
Sieve Shakers	American Instruments, Pascall
Sieve Shakers	Endecottes
Allen-Bradley Sonic Sifter	ATM Corporation (Kek)
Small Portable Sieve Shaker	La Pine
Tyler Ro Tap	La Pine
Alpine Air Jet	Alpine, Lavino
Wet and Dry Sieve Shakers	Fritsch (Howe)

MICROSCOPES (Chapter 6)

Watson Image Splitting Eyepiece	Watson
Push Button counter	Casella
Vicker Image Shearing Eyepiece	Vickers
Zeiss Endter P.S.A.	Carl Zeiss (Degenhardt)
Metals Research P.S.A.	Metals Research
Quantimet	Image Analysing Computors
MC	Millipore
Spri Analyser	Sondes Place Research
Superscope Electron Microscope	JEOL (Delviljem)
(also SEMs)	
Magnifiers	Polaron
e.m. grids	Maron and Morton
Aids for e.m.	Alan Agar
The Timbrell Analyser	Coulter U.S.A.
The Q.M.S. System	Bausch and Lomb

MISCELLANEOUS DISPERSING EQUIPMENT (Chapter 8)

Ultrasonic Dispersers	Mullard, Ultrasonics
Pyknometers	Numinco
Ultrasonic Cleaner	Fritsch (Christison)
Helium Air Pyknometer	Micrometetics (Coulter UK)
Anti Static Agent M441	I.C.I.
Spraygun for electron microscopy	Aerograph

SEDIMENTATION EQUIPMENT (Chapters 9 and 10)

Pipettes and Hydrometers	Gallenkamp
Granulometer	Brezina
WASP photosedimentometer	Microscal
Wagner turbidimeter	La Pine
EEL photosedimentometer	Evans
Bound Brook photosedimentometer	Goring Kerr
Micromerograph	Franklin
Shimadzu Sedimentograph	Shimadzu
	Northgate Traders
Sartorious Sedimentation Balance	Sartorious
Micron Particle Distributometer	Bush GF
Palo-Travis Particle Size Apparatus	Pola
Fisher Dotts Apparatus	Fisher
Travis Method of Two layer Analysis	Schaar
LADAL X Ray Sedimentometer	Microscal
Sedigraph X Ray Sedimentometer	Micromeretics (Coulter UK)

CLASSIFIERS (Chapter 11)

Walther	Walther
Cascade Elutriator	American Instrument
Microsplit Separator	British Rema
Major Classifier	Donaldson
Centrifugal Classifier	Micromeretics

Andrews Kinetic Water	Griffin and George
Gonell	Chemisches Laboratorium
Haultain Infrasizer	Infrasizers
Roller	American Instrument
Bahco	Dietert (Neu)
Hexhlet Collector (Walton's Horizontal)	Casella
Microplex Classifier	Lavino
Nauta Hosokawa Classifier	Nautamix
Alanysette 8	Fritsch (Howe)
Donaldson Classifier	Donaldsons

CENTRIFUGES (Chapter 12)

Simcar	Simon Carves
Joyce Loebl Disc	Joyce Loebl
Kaye Disc	Martin Sweeny
Sharples Centrifuge	Pennwalt Appliances (U.S.A.)
Whitby Apparatus	Mines Safety
LADAL X-Ray	Microscal
Modified Pipette	Allen

STREAMING PRINCIPLE (Chapter 13)

Coulter Counter	Coulter
Celloscope	Lars
P.D. Analyser	Berg
Particle Volume Detector	Telefunken
TOA Microcellcounter	Toa
Granulometer	V.E.B.

LIGHT SCATTERING (see also Aerosol Samplers) (Chapter 14)

Shimadzu Light Scattering Photometer	Shimadzu
Sinclair Phoenix Forward	Phoenix
Scattering Light Photometer	Phoenix
Brice-Phoenix L.S.P.	Phoenix
Absolute L.S.P.	American Instruments
Photo-Nephelometers	Coleman
Recording Turbidimeter	General Electric Company
Scattermaster	Manufacturing Engineering Company
Photometers	Shimadzu, Societe Francaise, Nethreler, Polymer Consultants
Differential Light Scattering Photometers	Science Spectrum
Atlas of Light Scattering Curves	Science Spectrum

PERMEAMETRY (Chapter 15)

Fisher sub-sieve sizer	Kek
Rigden Apparatus	Gallenkamp
Knudsen Flow Permeameter	Micromeretics
The Griffin Surface Area of Powders Apparatus	Griffin and George

GAS ADSORPTION (Surface Area and Porosimetry) Chapters 16, 17 and 18)

Perkin-Elmer Shell Sorptometer	Perkin-Elmer
Ströhline Areameter	Ströhlin
Quantasorb and Monosorb	Ameresco
	Quantachrome Corporation
Gravimat	Sartorious
A range of instruments	Micromeretics (Coulters UK)
Sorptomatic	Carlo Erba (Systems and Components)
Areatron	Leybold
Air displacement porometer	Numinco
Surface area and gas adsorption equipment	Numinco
Flow Microcalorimeter	Microscal
Mercury Porosimeters	American Instrument
	Carlo Erba (Systems and Components)
	Micromeretics (Coulters UK)
	Carlo Erba.

Appendix 2 *Manufacturers' and Suppliers' Addresses*

Adams, L. Ltd, Minerva Road, London, NW10.
Addy Products Ltd, Solent Industrial Estate, Botley, Hampshire SO3 2FQ.
Aerograph Co., Lower Sydenham, London SW26.
Agar, Alan, W., 127 Rye Street, Bishop's Stortford, Hertfordshire.
Airflow Development, 31 Lancaster Road, High Wycombe, Buckinghamshire.
Airsupply International Gateway House, 302–8 High Street, Slough, Berkshire.
Alpine, Augsberg, W. Germany.
Ameresco Inc., 101 Park Street, Montclair, New Jersey 07042, U.S.A.
American Instruments Co., 8030 Georgia Avenue, Silver Springs, Maryland, U.S.A.
Anderson 2000 Inc., P.O. Box 20769, Atlanta, Georgia 30320, U.S.A.
Applied Research Laboratories, Wingate Road, Luton, Bedfordshire.
A.T.M. Corporation, Sonic Sifter Division, P.O. Box 2405, Milwaukee, Wisconsin 53214, U.S.A.

Bailey Meters and Controls, 218 Purley Way, Croydon, Surrey
Bausch & Lomb Inc., 820 Linden Avenue, 30320 Rochester, New York 14625, U.S.A.
Bendix Vacuum Ltd, Scientific Instruments and Equipment Division, Easthead Avenue, Wokingham, Berkshire RG11 2PW.
Berg, R., Particle Data Inc., P.O. Box 265, Elmhurst, Illinois 60126, U.S.A.
Brezina, J., Hauptstrasse 68, D-6901 Waldhilsbach, W. Germany.
British Rema, P.O. Box 31, Imperial Steel Works, Sheffield S9 1RA.
Buckbee Mears Co., 245 East 6th Street, St Paul 1, Minnesota, U.S.A.
Bush, G.F. & Associates, Princeton, New Jersey, U.S.A.

Carl Zeiss, 7082 Oberkochen, W. Germany.
Carl Zeiss Jena Ltd, VEB Carl Zeiss, Jena, W. Germany; also England House, 93–7 New Cavendish Street, London W1.
Carlo Erba, via Carlo Imbonati 24, 20159, Milan, Italy.
Casella, C.F. & Co., Regent House, Britannia Walk, London N1.
Charles Austin Pumps, Petersham Works, 100 Royston Road, Byfleet, Surrey.
Chemishes Laboratorium für Tonindustrie, Goslar, Harz, W. Germany.
Christison, Albany Road, East Gateshead Industrial Estate, Gateshead, Co. Durham NE8 3AT.
Coleman Instruments Inc., 42 Madison Street, Maywood, Illinois, U.S.A.

Coulter Electronics, High Street South, Dunstable, Bedfordshire.
Coulter Electronics, 590 West 20th Street, Hialeah, Florida, U.S.A.

Degenhardt & Co. Ltd, 6 Cavendish Square, London W1.
Delviljem (London) Ltd, Delviljim House, Shakespeare Road, Finchley, Middlesex.
Dietert, H. & Co., 9330 Roselawn Avenue, Detroit, Michigan, U.S.A.
Donaldson Co. Inc., 1400 West 94th Street, Minneapolis, Minnesota 55431, U.S.A.
Draeger Normalair Ltd, Kitty Brewster, Blythe, Northumberland.
Dragerwerk Lubeck, D-24 Lubeck 1, P.O. Box 1339, Moislinger Allee 53−55,
    W. Germany.

Endecottes Ltd, Lombard Road, London SW19.
Erwin Sick Optik-Elektronik, D-7808 Waldkirch, W. Germany, An der Allee 7−9,
    Postfach 310.
Evans Electroselenium Ltd, Halstead, Essex.

Ficklen, Joseph, B., 1848 East Mountain Street, Pasadena 7, California, U.S.A.
Fisher Scientific Co., Pittsburgh 19, Pennsylvania, U.S.A.
Fleming Instruments Ltd, Lever Street, Bolton, Lancashire BL3 6BJ.
Foster Instruments, Sydney Road, Muswell Hill, London N10.
Franklin Electronics Inc., Bridgeport, Pennsylvannia, U.S.A.
Freeman Labs Inc., 9290 Evenhouse Avenue, Rosemount, Illinois 60018, U.S.A.
Fritsch, Albert & Co., D6580 Idar-Oberstein 1, W. Germany.

Gallenkamp Ltd, Portrack Lane, Stockton-on-Tees, Co. Durham.
Gardner Laboratory, Bethesda, Maryland, U.S.A.
Gelman Hawksley, 12 Peter Road, Lancing, Sussex.
Gelman Instruments Co., 600 South Wagner Road, Ann Arbor, Michigan 48106,
    U.S.A.
General Electric Co., Schenectady, New York, U.S.A.
Glass Developments Ltd, Sudbourne Road, Brixton Hill, London SW2.
Glen Creston, The Red House, Broadway, Stanmore, Middlesex.
Goring Kerr Ltd, Hanover Way, Windsor, Berkshire.
Greenings, Britannia Works, Printing House Lane, Hayes, Middlesex.
Griffin & George Ltd, Wembley, Middlesex.

Hawksley & Sons Ltd, 12 Peter Road, Lancing, Sussex.
High Accuracy Products, Corp., 141 Spring Street, Claremont, California 91711,
    U.S.A.
Hird-Brown Ltd, Lever Street, Bolton, Lancashire BL3 6BJ.
Howe, V.A. & Co. Ltd, 88 Peterborough Road, London SW6.

Image Analysing Computers Ltd, Melbourne, Royston SG6 6ET, Hertfordshire;
    also 40 Robert Pitt Drive, Monsey, New York 10952, U.S.A.
Imperial Chemical Industries Ltd, Nobel Division, Stevenston, Ayrshire, Scotland.
Infrasizers Ltd, Toronto, Ontario, Canada.

Japan Electron Optics Ltd, Jealco House, Grove Park, Edgware Road, Collindale,
    London NW9; also 477, Riverside Avenue, Medford, Massachusetts 02155, U.S.A.
Joyce Loebl Ltd, Princesway, Team Valley, Gateshead 11, Co. Durham.

Kek Ltd, Hully Road, Hurdsfield Industrial Estate, Macclesfield, Cheshire SK10 2ND.

La Pine Scientific Co., Chicago 29, Illinois, U.S.A.
Lars, A.B. Ljungberg & Co., Stockholm, Sweden.
Laser Associates Ltd, Paynes Lane, Rugby, Warwickshire.
Lavino, Garrard House, 31–45 Gresham Street, London EC2.

Manufacturing Engineering and Equipment Corporation, Warrington, Pennsylvania,
    U.S.A.
Mason & Morton Ltd, 32–40 Headstone Drive, Wealdstone, Harrow, Middlesex.
Metals Research Ltd, 91 King Street, Cambridge.
Micromeretics Instrum Corporation, 800 Goshen Springs Road, Norcroft, Georgia
    30071, U.S.A.
Microscal Ltd, 20 Mattock Lane, Ealing, London.
Millipore Corp., Ashby Road, Bedford, Massachusetts 01730, U.S.A.
Mines Safety Appliances Co. Ltd, Greenford, Middlesex.
Mines Safety Appliances Co. Ltd, 201 Braddock Avenue, Pittsburgh 8, Pennsylvania,
    U.S.A.
Mullard Equipment Ltd, Manor Royal, Crawley, Sussex.

Nautamix, N.V., P.O. Box 773, Haarlem, Holland.
Nethreler & Hinz. GmbH, Hamburg, W. Germany.
NEU Engineering Ltd, 32–4 Baker Street, Weybridge, Surrey.
NEU, Etablissement, P.O. Box 28, Lille, France.
Northgate Traders Ltd, London EC2.
Nuclepore Corp., 7035 Commerce Circle, Pleasanton, California 64566, U.S.A.
Numek Instruments and Controls Corporation, Appolo, Pennsylvania, U.S.A.
Numinco, 300 Seco Road, Monroeville, Pennsylvania 15146, U.S.A.

Pascall Ltd, Gatwick Road, Crawley, Sussex.
Pearson Panke Ltd, 1–3 Halegrove Gardens, London NW7.
Pennwalt Ltd, Doman Road, Camberley, Surrey.
Perkin Elmer Ltd, Beaconsfield, Buckinghamshire.
Phoenix Precision Instrument Co., 3803 Fifth Street, Philadelphia, Pennsylvania
    19140, U.S.A.
Photoelectronics Ltd, Arcail House, Restmor Way, Hockbridge, Wallington, Surrey.
Pola Laboratory Supplies Inc., New York 7, U.S.A.
Polaron, 4 Shakespeare Road, Finchley, London N3.
Polymer Consultants Ltd, London.
Procedyne Corporation, 221 Somerset Street, New Brunswick, New Jersey, U.S.A.
Production Sales and Services Ltd, New Malden, Surrey.
Prosser Scientific Instruments Ltd, Lady Lane Industrial Estate, Hadleigh, Ipswich,
    Suffolk IP7 6DQ.

Quantachrome Corp., 337 Glen Cove Road, Greenvale, New York 11548, U.S.A.

Rao Instrument Co. Ltd, Brooklyn, New York, U.S.A.
Research Appliance Co., Route 8, Gibsonia, Pennsylvania 15044, U.S.A.
Ronald Trist Controls Ltd, Bath Road, Slough, Berkshire.
Rotheroe & Mitchell Ltd, Aintree Road, Greenford, Middlesex.
Royco Instruments, 141 Jefferson Drive, Menlo Park, California 94025, U.S.A.

Sartorious Werke, GmbH, D-34 Gottingen, W. Germany.
Schaar & Co., Chicago, Illinois, U.S.A.
Science Spectrum, 1216 State Street, P.O. Box 3003, Santa Barbara, California, U.S.A.
Sharples Centrifuges Ltd, Camberley, Surrey.
Shimadzu Seisakusho Ltd, Kanda, Mitoshirocho, Chiyodra-Ku, Tokyo, Japan.
Simon Carves Ltd, Stockport, Lancashire.
Societe Francaise d'Instruments de Controle et d'Analuses, Le Mesnil, Saint Denise, France.
Sondes Place Research Institute, Dorking, Surrey.
Ströhline, Dusseldorf, W. Germany.
Systems and Components Ltd, Broadway, Market Lavington, Devizes, Wiltshire.

Techmation Ltd, 58 Edgware Way, Edgware, Middlesex.
Telefunken, A.E.G., 79 Ulm, Elisabethstrasse 3, W. Germany.
Thermal Control Co. Ltd, 138 Old Shoreham Road, Hove, Sussex.
Thermo-Systems Inc., 2500 Cleveland Avenue, North St Pauls, Minnesota 55113, U.S.A.
TOA Electric Co., Kobe, Japan.

Ultrasonics Ltd, Otley Road, Bradford, Yorkshire.

V.E.B. Transformratoren und Rontegemwerk, 48 Overbeckstrasse 8030, Dresden, West Germany.
Veco N.V. Zeefplatenfabrick, Eerbeck (Veluive), The Netherlands.
Vickers Instruments Ltd, Haxby Road, York.

Walther & Co., Aktiengesellschaft, 5 Köln-Dellbrück, W. Germany.
Warmain International Pty Ltd, Artarman, N.S.W., Australia.
Watson, W. & Sons Ltd, Barnet, Hertfordshire.

Zimney Corporation, Monrovia, California, U.S.A.

Author Index

(references at the end of each chapter are in brackets)

Ackerman, L., 119, (126)
Adam, N.K., 396, (411)
Adamson, A.W., 184, (189), 356, (391), 398, 402, 403, (411)
Agafonova, N.I., 62, (72)
Agar, A.W., 134, (152)
Alex, W., 200, (219), 227, (245)
Alexander, J., 290, (300)
Algren, A.B., 221, (244)
Algren, A.B., 269, 270, (296)
Allen, M., 119, (126)
Allen, R.P., 130, (150)
Allen, T., 27, (30), 147, (151), 198, 203, 208, (219), 230, 236, (245), 273, 283, (300), 306, 307, 312, (313), 347, 348, (353), 397, 401, 411, (411)
Altamari, L.A., 374, (392)
Ames, D.P., 229, (245)
Amor, A.F., 148, (152)
Andersen, A.A., 44, 46, (54), 58, (71)
Andersen, J., 119, (126)
Anderson, G.W., 66, (73)
Anderson, R.B., 369, (393)
Andreasen, A.H.M., 194, 197, 198, 199, (219), 254, (263).
Andrews, L., 254, 255, (263)
Annis, J.C., 221, (244), 269, 270, (298)
Antwerp van, W.R., 58, (71)
Arakawa, M., 214, (219), 227, (244)
Arnell, J.C., 343, (353)
Aschenbrenner, B.C., 139, (151)
Atherton, E., 273, 299, (300)
Atkins, J.H., 379, 382, (392)
Attaway, A.V., 270, (300)
Aylmore, D.W., 374, (392)
Aylward, M., 58, (70)

Babbit, J.D., 345, (354)
Bachmann, D., 225, (245)
Bachmann, J.M., 58, (71)
Backus, R.C., 134, (152)
Badzioch, S., 31, 35, 45, 49, (53), 261, (264)
Bahco, A.B., 44, (53)
Bailey, G.W., 134, 135, (152)
Baird, P.K., 376, (392)

Baker, D.J., 426, (431)
Bakr, A.M., 371, 375, (391)
Balasmov, V., 64, (73)
Baldocci, R., 182, (189)
Baly, E.G.G., 359, (391)
Bangram, D.M., 405, (412)
Barker, D., 61, (70)
Barnes, M.D., 323, (327)
Barnet, M., 146, (151).
Barrer, R.M., 346, 347, (353)
Barret, E.P., 367, (393), 414, 419, (430)
Barret, H.M., 376, (392)
Barsic, N.J., 59, (71)
Bartell, F.E., 180, (189), 401, (412)
Batch, B.A., 306, (313)
Baturin, V.P., 110, (111)
Bauer, E.E., 211, (219)
Bayness, J.E., 270, (300)
Beadle, D.G., 62, 64, (72)
Becher, P., 141, (152)
Beckwith, J.B., 371, (391)
Beebe, R.A., 371, (391)
Beer, J.M., 37, (53)
Bell, H.A., 147, (151)
Bell, R., 366, (391)
Beanrie, M., 62, (72)
Bensen, S.W., 373, (391)
Beresford, J., 273, (300)
Berg, R.H., 306, (312)
Berg, S., 197, 212, (219), 280, (299)
Berner, A., 58, (70)
Berns, E.G., 258, (263)
Berthier, P., 399, (412)
Birchfield, H.P., 237, (245)
Birkhill, R.S., 225, (245)
Birnie, A.W., 376, (392)
Bishop, D.L., 224, (244)
Blackett, J.M., 35, (53)
Blaine, R.L., 337, 338, (353)
Blake, F.C., 328, (353)
Blignaut, P.J., 62, (72).
Block, M., 148, (152)
Blythe, H.N., 254, 256, (263)
Boardman, R.P., 176, (177)
Bobrowski, G.S., 123, (127)

Bochlen, B., 426, (431)
Bodin, D., 62, (72)
Bodor, E.E., 419, 423, 424, (430)
Boer, J.H. de, 366, 367, 368, 369, (393), 399, (412), 414, 416, 417, 418, (430)
Boothroyd, R.G., 162, 169, (177)
Bostock, W., 222, 223, 229, (244), 278 (299)
Bowers, R., 376, (392)
Boyd, C.M., 274, (299)
Boyd, G.E., 375, (392)
Brackett, F., 62, (72)
Bradburn, J.A., 55, (70)
Bradfield, R., 266, (298)
Bradley, D., 269, 276, 290, (299)
Bradley, D.E., 134, (152)
Bradwig, J.G., 64, (72)
Brandt, O., 67, (73)
Brenner, M., 160, 162, 168, 169, 170, 173, 176, (177)
Brezina, J., 230, (248)
Bricaud, J., 324, (327)
Brillouin, L., 404, (412)
Brink, J.A., 58, (71)
Brinkman, H.C., 174, (177)
Britton, M.T.S., 375, (392)
Brockhoff, J.C.P., 369, (393)
Brodnyan, J., 290, (300)
Brotherton, J., 304, (312), (313)
Brown, C., 275, 276, 277, (299), 371, 374, (391)
Brown, J.F., 207, (219)
Brown, J.H., 292, (300)
Brown, O.E., 123, (127)
Brunauer, S., 358, 362, 364, 370, (391), 419, 423, 424, 425 (430), (431)
Brundle, C.R., 136, (152)
Bruyn, P.L. de, 292, (300)
Bryant, A.C., 232, (245)
Bryant, D.P., 182, (190)
Bucholz, H., 58, (71)
Bucker, H.P., 426, (431)
Bugge, P.E., 371, 373, (391)
Bulba, E., 52, (53)
Burckle, J.O., 41, (53)
Burdenkin, J.T., 64, (72)
Burdine, N.T., 426, (431)
Burevski, D., 358, (393), 411, (413)
Burgers, J.M., 174, (177)
Burson, J.H., 262, (264)
Burt, M.G.W., 23, 24, 25, (30), 119, 120, 123, (127), 183, 184, (190) 273, (300)
Busmey, G.L., 376, (392)
Butterworth, B., 426, (431)
Buzagh, A. von, 182, (189)
Botsel, 330, (353)
Byers, D.H., 55, (70)

Cadle, R.D., 64, (72)
Callis, C.F., 94, (111), 121, (126), 129, 135, 149, (150), 221, 229, 232, (244), 290, (299)

Cameron, A., 426, (431)
Campbell, W.B., 351, (353)
Candler, C., 401, (412)
Carman, P.C., 330, 331, 332, 333, 337, 342, 343, 351, (353)
Carpenter, F.G., 119, (129)
Carr, W., 273, (300)
Cartwright, J., 62, (72), 81, (111), 133, 134, (152)
Cartwright, L.M., 269, (299)
Cassel, H.M., 67, (73), 362, (391)
Cauchy, A., 137, (151)
Caveney, R.J., 134, (153)
Cawood, W., 137, (151)
Cember, M., 64, (72)
Chang, C.C., 135, (152)
Charman, W.N., 128, (152)
Chatfield, E.J., 142, (152)
Chmara, P., 70, (73)
Christenson, D.L., 70, (73)
Christensen, E.B., 170 (177)
Church, T., 77, (111)
Cinonen, M., 430, (431)
Clampitt, B.H., 400, (412)
Clark, M.G., 55, (70)
Clint, J.H., 406, (412)
Clunie, J.S., 406, (412)
Cochran, C.N., 397, 399, (411), 429, (431)
Cohen, L., 229, (245), 279, (299)
Cohen, M., 376, (392)
Cole, M., 77, (111), 148, (152)
Colon, F.J., 120, 121, (126)
Conley, F.R., 426, (431)
Conlin, S.G., 207, (219)
Connor, P., 237, (245), 274, (299)
Cooke, D.D., 325, 326, (327)
Coulson, J.M., 329, (353)
Cooper, A.C., 273, (300)
Corcoran, J.F., 135, (152)
Cordell, R.E., 8, (30)
Corn, M., 58, (71)
Corrin, M.L., 361, (391)
Cosgrove, L.A., 429, (431)
Coull, J., 168, (177)
Coulter, W.H., 301, (312)
Courty, C., 399, (412)
Coutts, J., 222, 224, (244)
Cousley, D., 147, (151)
Cowan, M., 59, (71)
Crandall, W.A., 261, (264)
Crank, J., 344, (354)
Cranston, R.W., 419, (430)
Crawley, D.F.C., 121, (126)
Crisp, D.J., 400, (412)
Critchlow, A., 61, 64, (70), (72)
Crowell, A.D., 361, 362, 364, 366, 373, (391)
Crowl, V.T., 82, 83, (111), 134, 137, (151), (152), 180, 181, (190), 344, (354)
Crowthers, E.M., 222, (244)
Cunningham, 161, (177)
Cunnings, P.T., 59 (71)

Daescher, M.W., 120, 121, 122, (126), (127)
Dahlstrom, R., 398, 399, (411)
Dallavalle, J.M., 62, 64, (72), 129, 135, 139,
　　(150), 211, (219), (299), 315, (326), 333,
　　(353), 361, 364, 365, 371, (391), 402, (411)
Daniel, J., 62, (72)
Darcy, H.P.G., 328, (353)
Darlow, M.N., 62, (72)
Davies, C.N., 31, (53), 58, (70), 161, 164,
　　171, (177)
Davies, J.G., 64, (72)
Davies, R., 148, (152)
Davies, R.J., 237, (245)
Davis, J.W., 352, (353)
Deitz, V.K., 119, (126)
Deitz, V.R., 373, 377, (392).
Delly, J.G., 130, (153)
Demmrich, H., 52, (53)
Denning, L.S., 362, 364, (391)
Denning, W.E., 362, 364, (391)
Derrick, J.C., 60, (71)
Deryagin, B., 346, (353)
Devonshire, 403, (412)
Dewell, P., 269, (299)
Dewitt, T.W., (391)
Diamond, S., 425, (431)
Dodd, C.G., 130, (152), 352, (353).
Dollimore, D., 176, (177), 183, (189), 419,
　　(430)
Dollimore, J., 374, (392)
Donague, J.K., 64, (72), 223, (244), 278,
　　(299)
Donnelly, H.F.E., 237, (245)
Dorizin, V.G., 52, (53)
Dorsey, J.A., 41, (53)
Dotts, W.M., 235, (244)
Doyle, G.J., 66, (73)
Drake, L.C., 426, 427, (431)
Draper, E.L., 376, (392)
Drinker, P., 55, 56, (70)
Drummond, D.G., 133, 134, (152)
Dibinin, M.M., 376, (392)
Dubois, E., 58, (71)
Dumbgen, 390, (392)
Duncombe, C.G., 235, (245)
Dunmore, J.M., 61, (70)
Dunn, E.J., 129, (150)
Dunn, R.C., 375, (392), 397, (411)
Dupre, A., 405, (412)
Dyson, J., 144, (152)
Dzisko, V.A., 361, (391)

Eadie, F.A., 221, 230, (244)
Eckert, J.J.D., 134, (153)
Eckhoff, R.K., 307, 311, (313)
Eckstrom, H.C., 374, (391)
Edmondson, I.C., 337, (354)
Edwald, P., 223, 235, (244), (245)
Eggertsen, F.T., 377, (392)
Einbinder, M., 58, (71)

Einstein, A., 163, (177)
Elder, M.E., 319, 321, 323, (326), 400, (412)
Eldridge, A., 254, (263)
Elkin, P.B., 367, (393)
Ellis, J.F., 378, 379, (392)
Ellis, J.R., 135, (152)
Ellison, J.McK., 85, (111), 130, (150)
Eltekov, Y.U., 403, (412)
Emmett, P.H., 358, 366, 371, 372, 373, (391)
Engdahl, R.B., 52, (53)
Epstein, P.S., 62, (72)
Ergun, S., 332, (353)
Essenhigh, R.H., 330, (353)
Everett, D.H., 419, (430)
Ewing, W.W., 401, (412)

Fagerhalt, G., 116, (126)
Fahrenwald, A.W., 116, 119, (126)
Fairs, G.L., 81, (111), 137, 139, 140, (151),
　　(152)
Famularo, J., 174, (177)
Fancher, G., 289 (299)
Farone, W.A., 326, (329)
Farr, L.E., 56, (70)
Feicht, F.L., 58, (71)
Fells, I., 37, (53)
Felsenthal, M., 426, (431)
Feret, R.L., 131, (150)
Ferry, R.M., 56, (70)
Fewtrell, C.A., 23, (30)
Fisher, M.A., 66, (73)
Fite, W.L., 62, (72)
Flory, P.J., 402, (412)
Folk, R.L., 111, (112)
Fong, W.S., 269, (299)
Fooks, J.C., 21, 22, (29)
Ford, R.W., 279, (300)
Forrest, C.W., 378, 379, (392)
Fowler, J.L., 330, (353)
Fowler, R.H., 258, (391)
Fox, M.R., 273, (300)
Freeman, D.S., 232, (245)
Freund, M., 67, (73)
Freundlich, H., 398, (411)
Friedova, J., 283, (300)
Friedrich, W., 227, (245)
Frisch, H.C., 402, (412)
Fritts, S.S., 119, (126)
Fuchs, N.A., 162, (177)
Furmidge, C.G.L., 147, (151)
Fusek, J.F., 400, 402, (412)

Gage, F.W., 340, (353).
Galatchi, G.L., 183, (189)
Gale, R.H., 229, (244)
Gall, L., 390, (393)
Gans, D.M., 397, 402, (411)
Gardner, W., 194, (220)
Garman, R.J., 224, (244)
Gaudin, A.M., 222, 229, (244), (246)

Geertsma, J.C., 225, (245)
Gerstenberg, M., 225, (245)
Gessner, M., 235, (245)
Giles, G.H., 403, (412)
Gille, F., 195, (220)
Gillespie, G.R., 58, (70)
Gilmore, J., 70, (73)
Girafalco, L.A., 346, (353)
Glaess, M.E., 130, (150)
Glowiak, B., 58, (71)
Godridge, A., 261, (264)
Goetz, A., 58, 60, (71), (72)
Goldschmidt, V.W., 67, 70, (73)
Goldstein, S., 163, (177)
Gonell, H.W., 257, (263)
Gooden, E.L., 335, (353)
Goodhue, L.D., 235, (245)
Goodman, J.F., 406, (412)
Gordon, M.T., 62, (72)
Gortner, R.A., 398, (411)
Goulden, D., 314, (326)
Gournay, L.S., 426, (431)
Graessley, W.W., 320, (326)
Grandillo, A.D., 200, 227, (245)
Granville, R.A., 41, (53), (54)
Green, M., 129, 130, (150)
Green, M.L., 162, (177)
Green, H.L., 55, 58, (70), (71)
Green, R.A., 237, (245)
Greenburg, L., 56, 58, (70)
Greenhill, E.B., 399, 400, (412)
Gregg, R.Q., 269, (299)
Gregg, S.J., 363, 377, (391), 400, 402,
    (412), 414, 415, 419, (430)
Griffiths, J.C., 110, (111), (112)
Grindell, D.H., 52, (53)
Grindter, E.M., 142, (152)
Grinrod, P.S., 200, (219)
Groszek, A.J., 401, (412)
Grove, D.M., 346, (353)
Groves, M.J., 182, (190), 269, (299)
Gruszka, J., 64, (72)
Gucker, F.T., 66, 67, 70, (73)
Guildner, L.A., 377, (392)
Gulbransen, E.A., 376, (392)
Gullaston, D.K., 237, (245)
Gupta, A.K., 274, (299)
Gurevich, T.N., 399, (412)
Gurney, S.W., 59, (71)
Guruswamy, S., 139, (152)
Guyer, A., 426, (431)

Habden, J.F., 402, (412)
Hagen, G., 328, (353)
Haines, G.F., 31, (53)
Halenda, P.P., 367, (393), 414, 419, (430)
Haley, A.J., 380, (392)
Halsey, G., (393)
Halsey, G.D. 363, (391), 419, 426, (430)
Hamilton, R.J., 61, 64, (70), (73), 138, 148
    (152)

Hanel, G., 58, (71)
Haners, Y., 199, (219)
Hanson, D.N., 62, (72)
Hanson, R.S., 400,(412)
Happel, J., 160, 162, 168, 169, 170, 173,
    176, (177)
Hardman, J.S., (393)
Hardwick, W.M., 237, (245), 274, (299)
Harkins, W.D., 361, 365, 373, (391), 397,
    398, 399, 402, 406, (411)
Harner, H.R., 274, (299)
Harris, C.C., 227, (245), 283, (300), 310, (313)
Harris, G.W., 61, (70)
Harris, W.J., 64, (72)
Hartmann, M.G., 56, (70)
Harvey, E.N., 373, (391)
Harvey, R.J., 308, (313)
Harwood, M.G., 130, (150)
Hatch, L.P., 81, (111)
Hatch, T., 55, 56, 64, (70), (73)
Haul, R.A.W., 374, 390, (392)
Haultain, H.E.T., 258, (263)
Hauser, E.A., 289, 290, (299)
Hausner, M.H., 77
Hawes, R.W.M., 29, (29)
Hawksley, P.G.W., 35, (53), 147, (151), 161,
    170, 171, 174, (177), 235, (245), 261,
    (264), 315, (322)
Hayes, A.D., 62, (72)
Heal, G.R., 176, (177), 419, (430)
Heidemann, E., 70, (73)
Heirwegh, K.P.M., 323, (327)
Heiss, F., 168, (177)
Hemeon, W.C.L., 31, (53)
Henderson, L.M., 426, (431)
Hendrix, W.P., 207, 208, (220)
Heneveld, W.H., 58, (71)
Herdan, G., 59, 62, 92, 94, (111), 120, (126),
    131, 132, (150), 236, 237, (245)
Hertel, K.L., 330, (353)
Heywood, H., 77, 78, 89, (111), 119, 124,
    (126), 131, 132, 139, (150), 166, (177),
    200, 203, 213, (218), (219), 223, 235,
    (244)
Hickin, G.K., 207, (219)
Hidy, G.M., 59, (71)
Hildreth, J.D., 270, 274, 293, (299)
Hirst, W., 399, 402, (412)
Hodge, H.G., 58, (70)
Hodkinson, J.R., 64, (72), 85, (111)
Hofmann, U., 376, (392)
Holdsworth, J.F., 138, (151)
Holmes, I.N., 398, (411)
Honig, J.M., 371, (391)
Horsfall, F., 237, (245)
Hosey, A.S., 55, (70)
Hosono, M., 314, (326)
Hounam, R.F., 59, (73)
Householder, M.K., 70, (73)
House, H.P., 274, (299)

Houssiere, C.R., 289, (299)
Howe, D.D., 378, 379, (392)
Howells, T.J., 37, (53)
Howink, E.H., 62, (72)
Hughes, T.H., 257, (263)
Hulley, B.J., 6, (30)
Huna, W., 148, (152)
Hurd, F.K., 62, (73)
Husar, R.B., 59, (71)
Hurley, R.B., 397, 400, 402, (412)
Hutchinson, E., 400, (412)
Hüttig, G.F., 364, (391)

Imris, P., 222, (244)
Inn, E.C.Y., 320, (326)
Innes, W.B., 389, (391), 399, (412), 419, (430)
Irani, R.R., 94, (111), 121, (126), 129, 135, 149, (150), 221, 229, 232, (244), 269, 290, (299)
Iwai, S., 321, (327)

Jacobs, J., 363, (391)
Jacobsen, A.E., 224, (244), 273, (299)
Jacobson, M., 58, (71)
Jaffrey, W.G., 41, (53), (54)
James, G.W., 214, (219)
Japling, D.W., 403, (412)
Jarrett, B.A., 203, 213, (219), 223, 235, (244)
Jellinek, H.H.G., 402, (412)
Jenkel, E., 402, (412)
Jennings, B.R., 314, (326)
Jennings, D.S., 194, (220)
Jepson, W.B., 374, (392)
Jerrard, H.G., 314, (326)
Jesse, A., 148, (152)
Joffe, A.D., 135, (152)
Johne, R., 176, (177)
Johnson, E.I., 237, (245)
Johnson, I., 323, (327)
Johnson, R., 198, 211, 212, 213, (219)
Johnson, S.A., 59, (71)
Johnstone, H.F., 58, (70)
Jones, D.C., 361, 362, (391)
Jones, M.H., 273, (300)
Jones, T.M., 123, (127)
Joos, P., 200, (219)
Joos, E., 199, (220)
Jowett, A., 227, 237, (245), 310, (313)
Joy, A.S., 371, 372, 373, (391)
Joyner, L.G., 362, (391), 414, 419, (430)
Junge, C., 62, (72)
Jura, G., 365, 373, (391), 397, 406, (411)

Kabak, J., 232, (245)
Kaiser, F., 260, (264)
Kallai, T., 60, (72)
Kalmus, E.E., 60, 61, (72)
Kalshoven, J., 207, (219)
Kamak, H.J., 280, (299)
Kast, W., 198, (220)

Katz, S.M., 56, 66, (70), (73)
Kay, D.H., 132, 134, (152)
Kaye, B.H., 18, 23, (29), 116, 118, 119, 123, 124, (126), 147, (151), 176, (177), 214, (219), 269, 271, (299)
Kaye, G.W.C., 343, (353)
Keafer, D., 67, (73)
Keen, B.A., 273, (299)
Keith, C.M., 60, (71)
Keller, J.D., 66, (73)
Kelly, W.S., 235, (245)
Keng, E.Y.H., 183, (190), 262, (264)
Kennedy, D.A., 67, (73)
Kenyon, A.S., 323, (327)
Kerker, M., 52, (53), 318, 320, 323, (326)
Kerlan, L., 399, (412)
Kerlogue, R.H., 371, 373, (391)
Keyes, W.F., 332, 337, (353)
Khan, A.A., 27, (30)
Kiff, P.R., 125, (126)
Kiffer, C., 229, (244)
King, J., 237, (245)
Kipling, J.J., 397, 400, (411)
Kiselev, A.V., 370, (393), 424, (431)
Kitto, P.M., 62, 64, (72)
Knapp, R.T., 224, 235, (244), (245)
Knudsen, M., 345, (353)
Koettgen, P., 194, (220)
Koglin, B., 182, (188)
Kolthoff, I.M., 403, (412)
Konig, W., 52, (53)
Kovall, G.E., 123, (127)
Kovar, V., 70, (73)
Kozeny, J., 328, (353)
Kramer, E.O., 235, (245)
Krasnopolskaya, V.N., 361, (391)
Krasnovskii, A.A., 399, (412)
Kratel, R., 67, (72)
Kratomvil, J.P., 318, (327)
Kraus, G., 194, (220), 346, 347, (353)
Krishnamoorthy, T.S., 346, 347, (354)
Krumbein, W.C., 110, (111), 143, (152)
Krzyzewski, Z., 198, (220)
Kuncewicz, L., 198, (220)
Kwolek, W.F., 307, (313)
Kubitschek, 301, (312)
Kynch, C.J., 173, (177)

Laby, T.H., 343, (353)
La Mer, V.K., 52, (53), 320, 323, (326), (327)
Lancaster, J.K., 399, 402, (412)
Landsperersky, H., 222, (244)
Lane, W.R., 55, (70)
Lane, W.R., 162, (177)
Langejan, J.J.D., 41, (53)
Langer, G., 67, (73)
Langmuir, I., 356, (391), 396, 399, (411)
Lapointe, C.M., 382, (393)
Lapple, C.E., 161, (177), 262, (264)
Lark, P.D., 143, (152)

Ladkin, S., 58, (70)
Lauer, O., 123, (126), (127)
Laundy, B.J., 237, (245), 274, (299)
Lauterbach, K.E., 62, (72)
Lea, F.M., 333, 334, 342, (353)
Leary, J.A., 59, (71)
Lecloux, A., 367, (393)
Lees, G., 77, (111)
Lees, B., 37, (53)
Lehman, H., 194, (220)
Leipziger, F.D., 374, (392)
Lemcke, W., 376, (392)
Lennard-Jones, J.E., 403, (412)
Lenz, F., 130, (150)
Leont'ev, V.M., 430, (431)
Leppard, C.J., 426, (431)
Leschonski, K., 194, 195, 197, 198, 199,
    (219), 224, (244), 249, 258, 261
    (263), (264)
Levich, V.G., 168, (177)
Lewis, P.C., 203, (219)
Lieberman, A., 66, (73)
Lilierfield, P., 70, (73)
Lines, R., 309, (313)
Linnar, E.R., 396, 398, (411)
Linsen, B.G., 366, 367, 368, (393)
Lippens, B.C., 367, (393)
Lister, B.A.J., 371, 374, (391)
Littlefield, J.B., 58, (70)
Liu, B.Y.H., 59, (71)
Livingstone, H.K., 366, 375, (391), (392)
Lloyd, H.B., 203, (219)
Lloyd, P.J., 307, (313), 271, 273, (300)
Loebenstein, W.V., 373, 377, (392)
Loeser, E.H., 361, (391)
Long, E.A., 376, (392)
Lovell, G.H.B., 382, (393)
Loos, E., 227, (245)
Lorentz, H., 159, 160, 163, (177)
Lorenz, R., 194, 198, (220)
Lothian, G.F., 203, (219)
Loveridge, D.J., 232, (245)
Lowan, A.N., 315, (326)
Lundberg, J.J.V., 194, 197, 198, (219)
Ludwig, F.L., 60, (72)
Lundgren, D.A., 59, (71), (73)
Lyklema, J., 403, (412)
Lynn, J.E., 289, 290, (299)
Lynn, L.G., 44, 45, (54).

Maas, O., 351, (353), 376, (392)
Maass, P., 375, (392)
MacCalman, D., 119, (126)
Maclay, W.N., 142, (152)
MacDonald, L.A., 371, 374, (391)
MacIver, D.S., 361, (391)
MacNevin, W.N., 403, (412)
MacWaters, J.T., 62, (72)
Maguire, B.A., 61, (70)
Malherbe, P.R., 337, 340, 341, (353)
Malmetra, V.M., 123, (127)

Mandersloot, W.G.B., 225, (245)
Maron, S.M., 319, 321, 323, (326), 400, (412)
Marr, A.G., 308, (313)
Marshall, C.E., 221, (244), 268, (298), (299)
Marshall, K., 306, 307, 312, (313)
Martens, A.E., 66, (73)
Martin, G., 131, (150)
Martin, J.J., 292, 293, (300)
Martin, R.A., 64, (73)
Martin, S.W., 275, (299)
Matalyavickus, V.P., 62, (72)
Matijevic, E., 52, (53)
Matthews, B.A., 304, (313)
Maude, A.D., 174, (177)
May, J.O., 426, (431)
May, J.R., 56, 57, (70), 137, 138, (151)
McBain, J.W., 371, 375, (391), (392), 397,
    (411)
McCrone, W.C., 130, (153)
McCormick, H.W., 290, (300)
McCulley, C.R., 130, (150)
McDonald, D.P., 273, (300)
McFarland, A.R., 59, (73)
McGee, J.P., 310, (313)
McIntyre, D.D., 110, (111)
McKelvey, J.B., 398, (411)
McManus, D.A., 110, (111)
McNew, G.L., 237, (245)
McShane, W.P., 52, (53)
Memta, R.G., 307, (313)
Meigs, R.R., 59 (71)
Mengelsdorf, P.C., 227, (245)
Menis, O., 274, (299)
Mercer, T.T., 62, (72)
Michand, F., 404, (412)
Mikhail, R.S.L., 419, 423, 424, (430)
Millikan, 343, (354)
Milner, H.B., 111, (112)
Mishima, H., 214, (219)
Mitchell, R.L., 52, (53), 58, (70)
Moltini, E., 119, (126)
Molzhe, J., 52, (53)
Montgomery, C.W., 362, (393)
Montgomery, T.L., 58, (71)
Moran, P.A.P., 131, (150)
Moran, R.F., 119, (126)
Morawetz, H., 402, (412)
Morgan, B.B., 146, (151), 301, (312)
Morgan, V.T., 203, 204, (219)
Morley, M.C., 37, (53)
Morony, M.J., (111)
Moroz, W.J., 66, (73)
Morris, H.E., 375, (392)
Morris, E.J., 62, (72)
Morrow, P.E., 62, (72)
Moser, H., 270, (300)
Mulford, D.F., 139, (151)
Muller, L.D., 29, (29)
Muller, R.H., 224, (244)

Mulligan, W.O., 376, (392)
Mulling, J.C., 62, (73)
Mullin, J.W., 121, (126), (127)
Mumford, D., 225, 226, (245)
Murley, R.D., 277, (299)
Musgrove, J.R., 274, (299)
Muskat, 330, (353)

Nakagaki, M., 314, (326)
Napper, D.H., 320, (326)
Naumann, D., 270, (300)
Nauman, A.Z., 164, (177)
Nelsen, F.M., 377, (392)
Newton, H.W., 249, (264)
Newton, W.H., 249, (264)
Nicolson, G., 325, (327)
Niedick, E.A., 122, (127)
Nissan, A.H., 223, (244)
Noll, K.E., 58, (71)
Nonhebel, G., 207, (219)
Nonhebel, G., 37, 41, (53)
Northey, H.L., 402, (412)
Norton, F.H., 273, (299)
Nurse, R.W., 333, 334, 342, (353)
Nyce, A.C., 425, (431)

O'Connor, D.T., 59, (73)
Oden, S., 200, (220), 222, 224, (244)
O'Donell, H., 58, (71)
Okamoto, N., 214 (219)
O'Konski, C.T., 66, (73)
Olin, J.G., 70, (73)
Oliphant, S.C., 289, (299)
Oliver, J.P., 207, (219)
Orr, C., 62, 64, (72), (73), 129, 135, 139,
    (150), 207, 208, 211, (219), 262, (264),
    (299), 314, (326), 331, 337, 350, (353),
    361, 364, 365, 371, 402, (411)
Orning, A.A., 332, (353)
Oseen, C.W., 163, 173, (177)
Osinga, J., 366, 368, (393)
Ottewill, R.H., 320, (326), 419, (430)
Oulton, T.D., 414, 419, 423, (430)
Overbeck, F.M., 41, (54)
Owens, J.S., 56, 59, (70)

Padday, J.F., 403, (412).
Page, H.G., 110, (111)
Palik, E.S., 229, (245)
Parfitt, G., 178, (189)
Patel, R.M., 397, 401, 411, (411), (413)
Partington, 343, (354)
Patterson, D., 270, 274, 293, (299)
Patterson, H., 137, (151)
Pattison, J.N., 373, (392)
Payne, B.O., (152)
Payne, R.E., 221, 230, (244)
Pearce, M., (29)
Pearson, J.R.A., 163, (177)
Pechukas, A., 340, (353)
Peel, J.S.H., 62, (72)

Pendleton, A.G., 337, (353)
Perry, J.H., 182, (190)
Peters, E.D., 126, (126)
Peterson, K.O., 290, (299)
Pettyjohn, E.A., 170, (177)
Phelps, B.A., 148, (152)
Phillips, J.W., 147, (151)
Pickard, H.B., 66, (73)
Pickering, H.L., 374, (392)
Pickett, G., 362, (393)
Pidgeon, F.D., 130, (152), 352, (353)
Pidgeon, L.M., 376, (392)
Pierce, C., 419, (430)
Pierce, J.O., 58, (71)
Pierce, P.E., 319, 321, 323, (326)
Pilcher, J.M., 58, (70)
Pilezynski, R., 58, (71)
Pisani, J.F., 307, (313)
Pitts, J.H., 66, (73)
Plachenov, T.G., 426, (431)
Plessner, I.V., 323, (327)
Pockels, A., 396, (411)
Poiseville, J., 328, (353)
Pollard, W.G., 346, (353)
Pomeroy, H.H., 375, (391)
Powers, T.C., 175, (177)
Preinig, O., 58, (70)
Present, R.D., 346, (353)
Pretorius, S.T., 225, (245)
Prewett, W.G., 64, (72)
Priem, 308, (313)
Princen, L.H., 307, (313)
Proctor, T.D., 61, (70)
Proskauer, E.S., 399, (411)
Proudman, I., 163, (177)
Pryor, E.J., 254, (263)

Rabatin, G.J., 229, (244)
Rabson, S.R., (111)
Ramakrishnav, 176, (177)
Rammler, E., 98, (111)
Ranz, W.E., 58, (70)
Rappeneau, J., 425, (431)
Rayleigh, L., 156, (177), 396, (411)
Razouk, R.I., 405, (412)
Read, C.E., 289, (299)
Reed, L.E., 37, (53)
Reich, B., 426, (431)
Reichertz, P.O., 426, (431)
Rendall, R.E.G., 64, (73)
Renshaw, F.M., 58, (71)
Revell, R.S.M., 134, (152)
Rhoda, R.N., 401, (412)
Rhodes, C.T., 304, (313)
Rhodin, T.N., 376, (392)
Richards, J.C., 247, (254)
Richardson, J.F., 174, (177), 329, (353)
Richford, H.H., 376, (392)
Riddick, J.A., 399, (411)
Ridgeway, C.N., 426, (431)

Rigden, P.J., 339, 342, 343, 350, (353)
Rimber, G.D., 67, (73)
Rinde, H., 224, (244)
Rippon, M., 271, 273, (300)
Ritter, L.C., 426, (431)
Robens, E., 390, (393)
Roberts, B.F., 410, (430)
Roberts, F., 146, (151)
Robinson, E., 60, (72)
Robinson, G.W., 194, (218)
Robinson, H.E., 275, 293, (299)
Rock, H., 52, (53)
Roller, P.S., 251, 257, (263)
Roess, L.C., 367, (393)
Ross, S., 364, (391)
Rolwink, W., 62, (72)
Romwalter, A., 275, 292, (299)
Rootare, H.M., 425, (431)
Rose, H.E., 203, (219), 332, 344, (354)
Rosenberg, A.J., 374, (392)
Rosenberg, L.D., 121, (127)
Rosin, P., 98, (111)
Rosinski, J., 130, (150)
Rossi, C., 182, (189)
Ross, R.W., 346, 347, (353)
Ross, W.B., 426, (431)
Roth, R., 390, (393)
Rowe, S.H., 128, (152)
Rowley, H.H., 399, (412)
Rumbach, B., 402, (412)
Rumpf, H., 258, 260, 261, (263), (264)
Russel, A.S., 397, 399, (411)
Rvyssen, R., 199, (219)

Sakurada, I., 314, (326)
Samyn, J.C., 310, (313)
Sandstede, G., 390, (393)
Sansone, E.B., 31, 34, (54)
Sarakhov, A.I., 426, (431)
Saunders, E., 290, (299)
Sawyer, K.F., 59, (71)
Scarlett, B., 307, (313), 269, 271, 273, (299)
Schachman, H.K., 289, (299)
Schadt, C.F., 64, (72)
Schaller, R.E., 262, (264)
Schickertanz, W., 55, (70)
Schillar, L., 164, (177)
Schlechten, A.W., 229, (246)
Schlechter, A.M., 222, (244)
Schmidt, W., 270, (300)
Schofield, R.K., 273, (299)
Scholten, J.J.F., 425, (431)
Schöne, E., 254, (263)
Schrenk, H.H., 58, (71)
Schriever, 330, (354)
Schubert, Y., 373, (392)
Schull, C.G., 367, (393), 414, 419, 423, (430)
Schultz, M., 67, (73)
Schumann, R., 222, 229, (244), (246)
Schweyer, H.E., (111)

Scott, K.J., 225, 226, (245)
Seborg, C.O., 376, (392)
Sessions, R.F., 375, (392)
Seibert, E.E., 120, 122, (126)
Sellen, D.B., 314, (326)
Sem., G.J., 70, (73)
Seydel, K.J., 270, (300)
Shergold, F.A., 116, (126)
Sherwood, R.J., 59, (73)
Shimoyama, T., 314, (326)
Silva, A.P.D., 403, (412)
Simma, R., 402, (412)
Simmons, F.A., 376, (392)
Simpson, W.C., 376, (392)
Sinclair, D., 320, 323, (326)
Sinclair, I., 307, (313)
Sing, K.S.W., 370, (393), 406, (412), 414, 415, 419, (430)
Sips, R., 358, (393)
Skidmore, J.W., 133, 134, (152)
Skold, R., 419, (430)
Skrebowski, J.N., 207, (219)
Slater, C., 279, (299)
Sloan, C.K., 401, (412)
Soloman, W.R., 58, (71)
Sonkin, L.S., 58, (71)
Soole, B.W., 58, (71)
Soper, A.K., 235, (245)
Smith, C.M., 235, (245), 335, (353)
Smith, D.S.L.E., 61, (70)
Smith, G.W., 56, (70)
Smith, H.A., 397, 400, 402, (412)
Smith, S.E., 55, (70)
Smith, T.D., 366, (391)
Sneck, T., 430, (431)
Spencer, D.H.T., 426, (431)
Spencer, D.J.H., 425, (431)
Speil, S.J., (299)
Stacey, W.O., 426, (431)
Stairmand, C.J., 31, 37, 38, 39, (53), 124, (126), 223, 232, (245), 251, 253, 254, 258, (263)
Stamm, A.J., 235, (245), 376, (392)
Stanley, N., 64, (72)
Stanley-Wood, N.G., 348, (353), (354)
States, M.N., 193, (218)
Statham, B.R., 271, 273, (300)
Steel, J.G., 267, (298)
Steinheitz, A.R., 132, (151)
Steinour, H.H., 175, (177)
Stockdale, S.W., 116, 119, (126)
Stokes, G.G., 157, (177)
Strauss, W., 63, (72)
Stutzer, M., 148, (152)
Suhm, H.O., 124, (127)
Suito, E., 214, (219), 227, (244)
Sullivan, R.R., 330, (353)
Sullivan, W.F., 224, (244), 273, (299)
Svarovsky, L., 208, (220), 283, (300)

Svata, M., 426, (431)
Svedberg, T., 224, (244), 290, (299)
Swartz, G.A., 62, (72)
Szaboles, G., 37, 41, (53)

Tait, G.W.C., 60, (72)
Takahashi, K., 321, (327)
Tamamura, S., 314, (326)
Tate, J.R., 406, (412)
Taylor, H.S., 357, (393)
Taylor, N.J., 135, (152)
Taylor, W.K., 146, (151)
Teller, E., 358, 362, 364, (391)
Thayer, K.B., 41, (54)
Thomas, J.W., 67, (73)
Thomas, M.D., 194, (220)
Thomas, R.C., 58, (70)
Thompson, J.B., 377, (392)
Thomson, G.M., 308, (313)
Thom, von R., 309, (313)
Thring, M.W., 50, (53)
Timbrell, V., 130, 140, 143, 145, 146,
   (151), (152)
Timofeev, D.P., 376, (392)
Tomkieff, S.L., 131, 132, (150)
Tomlinson, L., 374, (392)
Toothill, J.P.R., 337, (354)
Tough, D., 273, (299)
Toyoshima, Y., 273, (300)
Taube, I., 398, (411)
Trautner, R.P., 70, (73)
Travis, P.M., 221, (244)
Treasure, C.R.G., 267, (299)
Trivedi, A.S., 403, (412)
Troops, E.E., 399, (411)
Truog, E., 237, (245)
Twiss, S.B., 361, (391)
Tye, F.L., 232, (245)

Ulevith, E.N., 400, (413)
Usui, K., 339, (353)

Vance, R.F., 373, (392)
Van de Hulst, J.C., 66, (73), 314, 315, 318,
   321, 322, 323, (326)
Van der Hull, H.J., 403, (412)
Van Tonder, J.C., 225, (245)
Vaughan, G.N., 279, (300)
Vendl, M., 275, 293, (299)
Vick, F.A., 146, (151)
Viljoen, N.J.S., (245)
Vishyakova, E.G., 430, (431)
Voegtlin, C., 58, (70)
Vold, M.J., 396, (411)
Volmer, M., 358, (391)
Vouk, V., 203, (219), 316, (327)

Wadel, H., 77, (111)
Waldmann, L., 63, (72)
Wales, M., 307, (313)
Walkenhurst, W., 64, (72)
Wallace, T.P., 326, (327)

Walstra, P., 323, (327)
Walter, E., 37, (53)
Walther, H., 351, (353)
Walton, C.W., 180, (189)
Walton, H.H., 64, (72)
Walton, W.H., 64, 84, (71), (72), 146, (151)
Walton, W.M., 134, (151)
Ward, A.F.M., 397, (411)
Warren, H., 56, (70)
Washburn, E.D., 180, (189)
Washburn, E.R., 377, (392)
Washburn, E.W., 426, (431)
Watson, A., 426, (431)
Watson, H.H., 31, (53), 58, 64, (71), (72),
   137, 139, (151)
Watson, J.A., 64, (72)
Weber, M., 119, (126)
Weigner, G., 235, (245)
Weilbacher, M., 258, 261, (263), (264)
Weinberger, E.B., 362, (393)
Weissberger, A., 399, (411)
Welford, G.A., 129, (152)
Werner, D., 221, (244)
Wessel, J., 247, (264)
West, H.W.H., 279, (300)
Wharton, R.A., 23, (30)
Wheeler, A., 414, 419, 420, 421, (430)
Whitby, K.T., 59, (71), 116, 117, 119, (126),
   221, 223, (244), 269, 270, (298)
Whitehead, R.C., 380, (392)
White, P.A.F., 55, (70)
Whiteley, A.B., 37, 49, (53)
Whitemore, R.L., 174, (177)
Wiggins, E.J., 351, (353)
Wilcox, J.D., 58, (71)
Wilkie, C.R., 62, (72)
Williams, A.P., 396, (411)
Williams, D.J., 134, 135, (152)
Williams, G., 148, (152)
Williams, R.C., 135, (152)
Williams, S.R., 59, (71)
Wilson, J.B., 320, (326)
Wilson, J.N., 307, (313)
Wintle, M;F., 377, (392)
Withrow, J.R., 235, (245)
Withstandley, V.D., 66, (73)
Wober, W.G., 52, (53)
Wolfe, E.A., 31, (54)
Wong, J.B., 58, (70)
Woodruf, F.S.A., 376, (392)
Wooldridge, W.D.S., 180, (189)
Wooten, L.A., 371, 374, (391)
Work, L.T., (111)
Wright, B.M., 55, 64, (70), (72), (73)
Wright, E.H.M., 400, (411), (412)
Wright, W.C., 62, (72)
Wyckoff, R.W.G., 135, (152)

Yaffe, C.D., 55, (70)
Yang, R.T., 59, (71)

Yano, S., 214, (219)
Yoshikawa, H.H., 62, (72)
Young, B.W., 270, (300)
Young, D.M., 361, 362, 364, 366, 374, (391)
Young, J., 147, (151)
Young, J.Z., 146, (151)

Zabransky, Z., 426, (431)

Zaki, W.N., 174, (177)
Zalderns, N.G., 123, (127)
Zenack, U., 60, (72)
Zhukovskava, E.A., 430, (431)
Zufall, J.H., 320, (326)
Zweitering, P., 430, (431)

Subject Index

Absolute light scattering photometer, 324
Acoustical sampler, 52
Acoustical counter, Langer, 67
Adsorption from solution, 396
Aerosoloscope, 66
Analysette 9 classifier, 260
Analysette 8 elutriator, 260
Anderson stack sampler, 44, 46
Andrews water elutriator, 254
Antistatic agent, 234
Arithmetic normal distributions, 93
Aspect factor, 330
Atlas of light-scattering curves, 326
Auger process, 135
Average diameters, 85

Balances, sedimentation, 223
Bausch and Lomb dust counter, 60
B.C.U.R.A. sedimentation column, 232
Beta adsorption impactor, 70
Beta-back scattering, 237
B.E.T. equation, 358
B.E.T. equation, Three parameter, 361
Blaine permeameter, 337
Blythe elutriator, 254
Boltzman's constant, 356
Bostock torsion balance, 229
Brice—Phoenix light scattering photometer, 325
Brownian motion, 162

Calorimetry, flow, 406
Calorimetry, static, 406
Carlo Erba Sorptomatic, 389
Carman—Kozeny equation, 328
Cascade impactors and impingers, 56
Casella counter, 147
Casella dust counter, 56
Celloscope, 308, 311
Chatfield particle size analyser, 142
Chute splitting, 16, 17
Centrifuge, LADAL X-ray, 283, 284, 295—296
Centrifuge, modified pipette, 288—289, 296—298
Centrifuge tubes, shape of, 277
Centrifuge, Simcar, 278—283, 293—295
Classifiers, 247

Classifiers, commercial, 263
Conifuge, 59, 60
Coning and quartering, 15
Convection currents, 200
Coulter counter, 182: technique, 301; coincidence, 307; particle shape, 306; pulse shape, 309; end point, 310
Cunningham's correction, 161
Cyclones, sampling, 40, 41

decanting, 236
density determination, 183
Differential light-scattering photometer, 326
Diffusion battery, 67
diffusion for surface area determination, 341
dispersing solutions, 185
divers, 212
Donaldson classifier, 262
dye adsorption, 403

elutriators, 254
electroformed micromesh sieves, 120
electrolyte adsorption, 403
electrostatic precipitator, 42, 61, 70
Electrozone, 311
Ellis, Forrest and Hoew's apparatus, 379
Emmett's apparatus, 373
Ergun and Orning equation, 332
extinction coefficient, 202

fatty acid adsorption, 402
felvation, 123
filtration, dust, 61
Fisher—Dotts apparatus, 235
Fisher sub-sieve sizer, 335
Freundlich equation, 358
gas adsorption, 355; degassing, 370; pressure, 371; temperature and time, 371; experimental techniques, 372; volumetric apparatus, 372; gravimetric methods, 375

Gonell elutriator, 253, 256, 258
Granulometer (Coulter principle), 312
Granulometer (sedimentation), 232
graticules, 137; Porton, 58
Gravimat, 390
Griffin permeameter, 340

Harkins and Jura, absolute method, Relative method, 365
heat of adsorption, 403
heat of immersion, 405
Henry's law, 357
Heywood's shape factors, 77
H.I.A.C. dust counter, 66
high order Tyndall spectra, 323
hindered settling, 176, 352
hot wire anenometer, 67
Humphries micrometer eyepiece, 143
hydrometers, 210
hysteresis, 416

I.C.I. sedimentation column, 232
Impingement sampler, 43
Isokinetic sampler, 45
Isokinetic sampling, 31, 45–50

Joyce Loebl disc centrifuge, 271, 273, 274

Kaye Disc Centrifuge, 269, 271
Kiselev's equation, 369
Konimeter, 58

Laminar flow, 157
Langmuir's isotherm, 356, 358, 359
Langmuir trough, 399
Lark particle counter, 143
Lea and Nurse permeameter, 333
light scattering, 66
log-normal distributions, 95

manometric methods, 235
Marshall centrifuge, 268
mercury porosimetry, 425
Metals Research Analyser, 147
Microid pipette flask shaker, 19
Micromerograph, 230
Micromeretics, 389
Micromeretics classifier, 262
micropore (MP) method, 424
Microscopy, optical, 129; Transmission electron, 132; Scanning electron, 136
Mines Safety Appliances (M.S.A.) Particle Size Analyser, 221, 268, 269, 270
modelless method, 423
Molecular orientation at solid–liquid interface, 396
Mullard film scanning analyser, 147

Nelson and Eggertsen's apparatus, 377
Non-electrolyte, adsorption of, 402
Numinco, 389

on line dust extraction, 42, 44
Orr, surface area, pore volume analyser, 389

particle size, definitions, 75
Perkin Elmer Shell Sorptometer, 382
permeameter, liquid phase, 350
permeameters, constant pressure, 333, constant volume, 337

permeametry, 328
phi-notation, 110
Photocentrifuge, 268, 270
Photofuge, 270
Photonephelometer, 325
photosedimentation, 200
photosedimentometers, EEL, 203, Bound Brooke, 204, WASP, 205, 214
pipette method, 194, 200
Poiseuille equation, 328
polarisation of light for particle sizing, 320
polymer adsorption, 402
pore size distribution determination, 414
potential energy curve, 181
precolumn method, 401, 410
pressure on walls method, 235
Pyknometers, 183

Quantachrome, 382
Quantitative image analysers, 148

Rank Cintel automatic microscope, 147
Rayleigh interferometer, 400
Rayleigh-Gans Scattering, 318
Rayleigh light scattering, 318
Reynolds and Branson auto-permeameter, 339
Rigden permeameter, 339
Roller elutriator, 257
Rosin–Rammler distribution, 98, 330
Royco, airborne dust counter, 66

sample divider, moving flap, 21
sample divider, rotary, 21
sample splitter, Fook, 21, 22
sampler for dusty gases, 41
sampler, Geco, 4, 6
sampler, impingement, 56
sampler, pneumatic probe, 14
sampler, suspension, 23, 24
sampler, table, 15, 16
sampler, tubular, 36
sampling nozzles, 37, 38, 39
sampling spears, 11
Sartorious balance, 225
scoop sampling, 19, 23
Shimadzu balance, 225
sieves, calibration of, 124
sieving errors, 115
Sinclair Phoenix Aerosol Photometer, 324
Sonic sifter, 124
Spinning riffler, 17, 18, 23
Spri particle analyser, 142
Stokes diameter, 266
Ströhline Areameter, 390
Supercentrifuge, 289
surface entropy, 404

t-curve, 366; for pore size distribution, 419
Telefunken Particle Detector, 312
thermal precipitation, 62
Thermopositor, 64, 65

TOA Microcell counter, 312
transient state diffusional flow, 347
turbidity, 321
two layer method, 222, 267

Vickers image splitting eyepiece, 145
Viscosity, 183; of a suspension, 163

Wadell's shape factor, 77
Washburn equation, 180

Watson image shearing eyepiece, 144
wet sieving, 121
wetting agents, 184; Nonidet P42, 271

X-ray sedimentation, 206; LADAL sedimentometer, 208, 218; Sedigraph, 208

Young and Laplace equation, 415

Zeiss—Endter particle sizer, 141